PERSPECTIVES
IN
COMMUNITY
MENTAL HEALTH

Modern Applications in Psychology
under the editorship of
Joseph D. Matarazzo

PERSPECTIVES IN COMMUNITY MENTAL HEALTH

ARTHUR J. BINDMAN
COMMONWEALTH OF MASSACHUSETTS
DEPARTMENT OF MENTAL HEALTH

and

ALLEN D. SPIEGEL
STATE UNIVERSITY OF NEW YORK
DOWNSTATE MEDICAL CENTER

Editors

ALDINE PUBLISHING COMPANY / *Chicago*

First published 1969
Aldine Publishing Company
529 South Wabash Avenue
Chicago, Illinois 60605

Library of Congress Catalog Card Number: 72-82132
SBN 202-26027
Designed by Bernard Schleifer
Printed in the United States of America

Acknowledgments

WITHOUT the gracious cooperation and interest of the many authors and publishers represented in this book it could not have reached fruition. In addition, our spirits were constantly lifted by the encouragement of Joseph Matarazzo. A special debt of gratitude must also be expressed to Lewis B. Klebanoff, who was instrumental in the conception of a book of this type, and to Stuart Golann, whose editorial comments helped us achieve further order and parsimony. Secretarial assistance by Irene Clark, Sharon Storke, Barbara Bullett, and Doris Robinson was invaluable in typing and compiling the manuscript.

Foreword

IN the six years since the adoption of the Community Mental Health Centers Act of 1963, mental health professionals, joined by the behavioral scientists, have become the innovators widening the concepts of modern medicine not only in degree but in a radical change of substance and practice.

A social policy toward the mentally ill in the United States has developed and is now based on a "right" and a "place." The "right" is the right to treatment and the "place" is the local community. Additionally, there is increasing public expectation that treatment of mental illness, no less than physical illness, be adequate for the needs of the individual patient.

In requiring that treatment facilities be established within the local community, the public is also beginning to realize that mental health services will be provided as a responsibility of that community—to be financed through any one of a variety of patterns, using public, private, and personal funds, as appropriate.

Americans are in the midst of a social revolution characterized by unrest, dissent, alienation, and an explosive reaction to inequalities of opportunity among various groups within the population. Our first priority, therefore, is to expand our newly established social policy concerning the mentally ill into a social policy for mental health. This approach has already begun to develop.

Probably the most significant signpost of this development was the establishment, through provisions of the Community Mental Health Centers Act, of consultation and education services as essentials of a program of community mental health centers. Here for the first time provisions of preventive services became mandatory in a publicly supported mental health program.

The adoption of preventive services as a stated public policy has not only added a new dimension to the mental health program, it has set a new direction for all health programs in the United States. This trend became evident in the early months of the new national mental health program when federal and state funds were made available to finance comprehensive mental health planning in each state. Thousands of volunteers joined mental health professionals and members of other professions in surveys of mental health resources and mental health needs.

The results of these planning efforts established the community mental health movement as a vehicle and model to demonstrate that communities can expand and improve many kinds of services, using the techniques employed by the first citizen planners for mental health.

Mental health planning for the first time brought professionals of all disciplines and other citizen leaders to the realization that there are mental health implications in almost every facet of community life. As community mental health centers become operational and begin to provide services to the residents of the community, it also becomes evident that many kinds of problems cause people to come to these mental health centers for help.

The staffs, in addition to treating the classic range of mental illness, are helping clients with problems about housing, bill collection, reading difficulties, drug abuse, alcoholism, and many others that seem to be side effects of both the affluent and deprived society. Psychiatrists, psychologists, social workers, psychiatric nurses, and a growing wealth of newly interested ancillary personnel are living and working with people of all races in a diversity of communities. Even in their brief experience, these workers have learned that if the demands and expectations of the American people are to be met, effective mental health services must include a wide range of human services. The challenge facing all health professionals in the 1970's will require specialists in all segments of the health community to develop a national program of health services, based on a positive statement of objectives to meet social needs through social health policy.

In *Perspectives in Community Mental Health* the editors have brought together the comments, experiences, and points of view of professionals who are making significant contributions to the development of community mental health service programs as operating realities. Their discussions are of great value to individuals who in the next decade will participate in expanding the origins of community mental health care into a nationwide program of human services designed to make living better for an entire population.

STANLEY E. YOLLES, M. D., *Director*
National Institute of Mental Health

Contents

PART VI. RESEARCH AND EVALUATION

PERSPECTIVES
IN
COMMUNITY
MENTAL HEALTH

Introduction

IN recent years, community mental health has become a catchphrase for innovation in the mental health field. Fired by the 1961 report of the Joint Commission on Mental Illness and Health, the nation was stimulated into a growing realization that the old approach of large mental hospitals was no longer acceptable. A "bold new approach" was outlined by President John F. Kennedy in his message to Congress in February 1963, which led to the passage of the Community Mental Health Centers Act of 1963, and the more recent act for staffing of such centers. The upshot of such legislative support has been the beginning of a major development of far-reaching, comprehensive services for the mentally ill and retarded.

Community mental health can be viewed as an approach in which greater emphasis is placed upon the interrelations between the individual and the community in which he lives. The patient and his emotional disturbance can no longer be viewed in isolation, but require a broader understanding of the environmental or community factors which may also play a part. By the same token, the patient cannot be treated in isolation. His treatment requires the utilization of a broad range of community agencies and caretakers. This change in orientation has led to the participation of such diverse agencies as public health, welfare, rehabilitation, urban planning, police departments, schools, and a wide range of mental health clinics, hospitals, and community centers. It has involved both professionals and nonprofessionals, ranging from the usual psychiatrist, psychologist, social worker team to the increased utilization of local physicians, public health nurses, rehabilitation counselors, educators, neighborhood aides, and even parents. The movement has also involved a wider range of social scientists from social psychology, sociology, anthropology, and public health.

Community mental health has, therefore, become a term which refers to a wide range of activities around the problems of mental health, and carried out in the community—that is, in the places in which people carry on their daily lives. The mental health professions have turned away from the more traditional theoretical approaches and have developed a broad-gauged, community orientation. The focus is upon mental health and not merely upon mental illness, and this focus implies that there will be a concern for many aspects of human

3

welfare and behavior. There is a greater emphasis upon preventive measures, methods of coping, community organization and style of behavior in groups, as well as research into ecological factors which may play a role in the enhancement or reduction of mental health.

Although this is still a relatively young movement, the number of community mental health programs has increased markedly in this country and abroad. The impetus developed from the increased federal support will lead to still more emphasis upon such relatively new areas, such as consultation and education techniques in community mental health practice. The broader participation of the citizenry is just beginning to play a major role in the definition of plans and the justification of programs and services in our communities. We are in a new era, one where the solid research and evaluation to support our planning and program development are still at a primitive level. These issues are merely a small sample of the problems that need to be faced in order to mount a major effort which will bear fruit in lowered mental health casualties.

The collection of papers in this book combines a blending of philosophy and practice. Articles were selected that foretold the beginnings of community mental health practice, that expressed thoughts about what is currently happening throughout the nation, and that provided a projection into what could possibly be expected in the near future. Papers and reports dating back to the early 1950's set the stage for the evolution of many of the emergent concepts noted today. At all times the reader is cautioned to check the date of the article he is reading. Like women in the oft quoted maxim, scientists and practitioners too are allowed to change their minds.

Although most editors would prefer that their works be considered definitive books in their own right, we do not feel that way. If this current collection of readings were to be accepted as the epitome of material on community mental health, it would of course inflate our egos—but, the book would not have achieved its goal. In fact, the direction would be contrary to our anticipated aim. Community mental health programs and practices are in such a state of flux that we feel at this time the prime need is for flexibility. Administrators, practitioners, and researchers should not fall into established patterns of behavior but should continue to experiment and to arrive at solutions that perhaps have not yet been considered. Furthermore, we feel that the moving edge is still gaining considerable momentum.

It has been a difficult task to select articles for this collection that would result in a book providing a complete picture of the problem area. No boundaries exist that concretely prevent intrusion of extraneous matter. In truth, we feel that boundaries would be artificial in the current conceptualization of community mental health. Therefore, we sought to choose articles that would stimulate thought, that would make some sparks fly and not be a palliative dose to be treated indifferently.

While the general approach may suggest that a professional audience of mental health workers may benefit most from this book, it is not aimed simply at those individuals. Mental health workers may have their horizons widened when they review the background from which community mental health theory and practice has sprung, but in addition there have been landmark papers written within the journals of various professional disciplines which will serve to stimulate thought among other professionals. Psychiatrists, psychologists and social workers immediately come to mind in such an audience, but this book is also meant for the physician, nurse, educator, and rehabilitation worker. Those social scientists who are just becoming involved in community mental health issues and research possibilities may profit from a broad contact with the field which these selected papers afford. The book is also meant for the student in all of the above professions and scientific endeavors. Finally, one should not forget the many community mental health and retardation board members, volunteers, and other interested citizenry who will be playing an increasing role in program development and support in the future.

Most introductions also express thoughts about the general content of the subject under scrutiny. However, in this case the stirring words of President John F. Kennedy in his February 5, 1963, message to the Congress sums up the situation and seems to have an appropriate place within a book devoted to an area where the President was personally responsible for initiating a forceful push forward.

We as a Nation have long neglected the mentally ill and the mentally retarded. This neglect must end, if our Nation is to live up to its own standards of compassion and dignity and achieve the maximum use of its manpower.

This tradition of neglect must be replaced by forceful and far-reaching programs carried out at all levels of government, by private individuals and by State and local agencies in every part of the Union.

We must act—

to bestow the full benefits of our society on those who suffer from mental disabilities;

to prevent the occurrence of mental illness and mental retardation wherever and whenever possible;

to provide for early diagnosis and continuous and comprehensive care, in the community, of those suffering from these disorders;

to stimulate improvements in the level of care given the mentally disabled in our State and private institutions, and to reorient those programs to a community-centered approach;

to reduce, over a number of years, and by hundreds of thousands, the persons confined to these institutions;

to retain in and return to the community the mentally ill and mentally retarded, and there to restore and revitalize their lives through better health programs and strengthened educational and rehabilitation services; and

to reinforce the will and capacity of our communities to meet these problems, in order that the communities, in turn, can reinforce the will and capacity of individuals and individual families.

We must promote—to the best of our ability and by all possible and appropriate means—the mental and physical health of all our citizens.

I
WHAT DOES COMMUNITY MENTAL HEALTH MEAN?

BETWEEN the opening and closing articles in this book, some of the most critical years in the community mental health movement are spanned. Emerging influences of new concepts are questioned and explained.

History, theory, definitions and questions are discussed in this chapter in order to set the reader thinking how rapidly changes have occurred in mental health endeavors. Within the articles one sees the burgeoning forth of the meaning of community mental health. Concepts are discussed and defined in the friendly environment of intellectual curiosity and acceptance as well as from the more cynical frame of reference of a doubting Thomas.

Many students of community mental health feel that the movement began as a result of World War II, without much history or development prior to that time. Rossi's detailed historical article dwells upon the early establishment of institutions and agencies. In addition, he quotes the ideas of numerous individuals as he also notes the involvement of social science and the development of the mental hygiene movement.

Hobbs contends that mental health has had three revolutions: the heretical notion that insane people are humans and should be treated accordingly; the obsession with the intrapsychic life of man; and, currently, the penetration of public health concepts into the field of mental health.

Community mental health is defined in Brown's article as the child of a "shotgun wedding" of public health and mental hygiene. To explain the conceptual framework, an overview from public health theory is given which contains definitions and describes primary, secondary, and tertiary levels of prevention. Similarly, the brief history of the mental hygiene movement lays the groundwork for a discussion of the interrelationships of the two partners in the wedding. Although the practical applications of public health concepts often seem to rely on communicable disease models, Brown demonstrates the transferability to mental health clinic practice. In considering directions, parameters such as prevention, individual care, group treatment, caretakers,

7

setting of service, timing of services, and the duration of efforts are considered.

Dunham examines the nature of community psychiatry as it is taking shape, paying particular attention to the urban influences. In noting the ever-widening scope of deviant behavior subsumed in the broadening definition of mental illness, the question of uncertainty about what constitutes mental illness is raised. In a sense, the emergence of community psychiatry is credited to the cherished American belief that all problems are capable of solution. However, the author also traces some of the central historical events in the movement. Linking community psychiatry to its future role, the author questions the ability to develop techniques to treat social collectivities, the implication that the psychiatrist will be able to move into the ongoing power structure, the fact that psychiatrists are being pushed in a direction not entirely of their own making, and the implication that psychiatry is being utilized to move us closer to the welfare state.

Part of the confusion in developing a community mental health theory resides in the fact that mental health is used as a goal, as a euphemism for mental illness, as a personality characteristic, and as a characteristic of society. In his article, Newbrough contends that the health-problem orientation and the social-problem orientation converge to form the final common path of community mental health. Building upon the systems theory approach to human behavior, an ecological model is proposed that considers the uniqueness of mental health problems. From this ecological position, the author moves to the declaration that there is no general mental health problem. Therefore, services should be custom tailored, with research telling us how and training providing the skilled artisans.

1

Some Pre-World War II Antecedents of Community Mental Health Theory and Practice

ASCANIO M. ROSSI

EARLY DEVELOPMENTS [1]

WHEN discussing the historical development of community mental health activities, it is convenient to dichotomize this development into two periods: pre-World War II (early) and post-World War II (later). For those with even a cursory acquaintance with the development of community mental health, the reason for this dichotomy should be obvious.

Before World War II the development of community mental health activities proceeded along several paths in a comparatively slow, irregular, and not always self-conscious manner. Since the war, however, the growth in community mental health activities has not only been phenomenally rapid, but the impetus for the growth has been a comparatively clear-cut desire for community mental health activities as such.

The very noticeable change in the rate of development that has occurred since World War II undoubtedly is one of the factors underlying a misconception on the part of not a few persons. This misconception is that community mental health philosophy and activities began almost *de nouveau* after World War II, and that as such they lack the stability of an historical foundation.

Nothing could be further from the truth. Community mental health philosophy and activities had been developing gradually since at least the beginning of this century and possibly earlier. What accounted for the phenomenal growth of community mental health activities after World War II was not the appearance of a new philosophy of treatment or the sudden conversion of

---

[1] In reading about the development of community mental health activities as described in this paper, the reader would do well to keep in mind the far-reaching changes that were taking place in almost every other segment of American life (e.g. art, education, jurisprudence, literature, etc.) as the first half of the twentieth century unfolded (e.g. see 1, 40, 46). The student of American society will undoubtedly notice the similarity between the nature of the changes taking place in the mental health field and the changes taking place in other areas of society.

Reprinted from *Mental Hygiene,* 1962, *46,* 78–98, by permission of the publisher and the author. © 1962, National Association for Mental Health. Dr. Rossi is Chief Psychologist, Boston City Hospital and Associate in Psychiatry, Department of Psychiatry, Harvard Medical School.

mental health personnel to an unsubstantiated messianic vision but rather, and more simply, it was the increase in the number of available mental health personnel and the willingness and ability of local, state and federal governments to finance this method of dealing with the mental health problem.

INSTITUTIONS AND AGENCIES

As we look back to the mental health field at the turn of the century, the first thing that strikes us is the noticeably wide gap that was perceived between normal and deviated persons. The latter were considered casualties of the natural selection process and were placed in isolated asylums far from the mainstream of life.

Consistent with the Darwinian orientation which was dominant at that time, mental deviations were thought to have a biological or hereditary basis and represented failures in the struggle for existence. It followed from this orientation that there was little that could be done for mentally deviated individuals, and, furthermore, little *should* be done for them to insure that their defective heredity would not be perpetuated into future generations.

This view found overt expression through eugenic societies which constantly used insanity as a prime example of the necessity for the widespread adoption of eugenic legislation and practice. In addition, of course, the old-as-history view that insanity was the result of sin had not yet died out.

With either view, however, the end result was the same: a general acceptance of the belief that little could or should be done for the insane.

The physical isolation of insane asylums was a concretization of the wish of society to isolate and wall-off the problem of insanity. This wish was common not only among the lay public; it was also widespread among the professions. On the whole, this area was almost completely neglected by medical personnel.

Those physicians who did venture into this area did so primarily as administrators or as part-time staff physicians concerned solely with the physical conditions of the patients. The few hardy souls who attempted to treat the insane were apt to be considered somewhat unusual by their colleagues and, in many cases, were isolated from their profession.

Following from the conceptualization of insanity as being an all-or-nothing affair, the facilities provided for the care of the insane were also all-or-nothing. Either a person was insane or he was not insane. If he were insane he was removed from society and committed to an asylum for custodial care. Half-way houses, clinics, outpatient departments, and the like would have been very inconsistent with the prevailing view. If a person were not insane, then he was responsible for his own welfare. Those persons who were unable to function adequately in society but were not considered "insane," lived out their days in jails, poorhouses, attics, prisons, or other similar places.

Even within this atmosphere, however, the seeds of change were being sown by forward-looking men. The view that man was a product of his environment as well as his heredity and that the environment was amenable to modification began to affect the field of mental health, just as it was to affect almost every segment of our society. In the 1890's, a few medical men with vision—such as Frederick Peterson and John Chapin—began advocating a new type of institution for the care of the insane. This new institution, called a "psychopathic hospital," was to be located in the community it served, in contrast to the location of asylums, and its primary function would be the provision of treatment rather than custodial care.[2]

We can get some idea of the radical innovations implicit in this proposal when we consider that within the generally negative atmosphere of the times, these men were proposing that insanity could be treated effectively by: (a) treating patients early; (b) not isolating patients from their families, friends, and community; (c) having the patients' families available for supplying information about the patient's life history; and, (d) stimulating local medical personnel to become interested and involved in the problem of insanity.

While we today would accept these advantages as self-evident, it was only after a great deal of work and much determination that the efforts of these men bore fruit with the establishment of Pavilion F of the Albany, N. Y., Hospital, in 1902. This pioneer move led to the establishment, in 1906, of an independent psychopathic hospital affiliated with the University of Michigan.

The success of this type of hospital was almost immediate. Its novel approach to the problem of mental illness attracted the attention of those who recognized the need for a change but were uncertain as to what direction this change should take. The institution's close affiliation with a university hospital gave the mental health field a needed boost in acceptance and made it possible for the hospital staff to interest medical students in this field through the media of lectures and demonstrations.

As time passed, similar hospitals were established in different parts of the country. The Boston Psychopathic Hospital, which began as a division of the Boston State Hospital, became an independent state hospital in 1912. Johns Hopkins Hospital in Baltimore opened its psychiatric clinic the following year; the Psychopathic Hospital associated with the University of Iowa opened in 1919; the University of Colorado opened its Psychopathic Hospital in 1924.

The importance of these hospitals should not be underestimated. They were instrumental in stimulating a most welcome community interest in the mentally ill as well as the interest of hospital personnel in communities. In addition, as the individuals associated with these psychopathic hospitals became aware of the importance of environmental factors in mental illness, they realized that other, nonmedical professions would have to be represented on their staffs. The interdisciplinary approach to the mental health problem, which is so

[2] For a detailed history of the development of psychopathic hospitals, see Hurd (25), especially 258–80.

fundamental to the present-day mental health field, was first developed within these hospitals.

A further indication of the hospitals' changing role can be gained from a brief glimpse at the beginning of the profession of psychiatric social work and of the aftercare service. The ancestors of psychiatric social work were a group of charitable laywomen who offered their services to asylums on a volunteer basis. Gradually, a few of these women became interested enough in certain patients to follow their progress after discharge. This "aftercare" attention fit in well with the emerging hospital role changes, and the potential value of this service was recognized as too great to leave in the hands of lay persons.

The service gradually became professionalized, and with the New York City hospital system appointment of Miss Elizabeth Horton as psychiatric social worker in 1907, the profession of psychiatric social work was born.[3]

Within five years a Maryland hospital was to develop its aftercare service to the point where a full-time psychiatrist was appointed to administer the service with the help of a social worker. The spread of this service into other hospital systems soon led to the establishment at Smith College of the first formal psychiatric social work training program. The development of this profession and service provided further links between hospital and community and further stimulated hospital personnel to think of environmental factors in etiology and treatment.

Hospitals' and communities' growing awareness of each other was accompanied by the establishment of the first psychiatric clinics.[4] As far back as 1885 the Pennsylvania General Hospital attempted to improve admissions policy through the establishment of a hospital-connected clinic, and in 1897 the Boston Dispensary began a similar service. Twelve years later the New York State hospital system instituted a traveling clinic, and the following year the Massachusetts hospital system followed suit.

Although these early clinics represented an improvement in admissions procedure, they had little in common with present-day clinics. They operated solely within hospital facilities, with hospital medical personnel, and they provided only diagnostic services with no explicit treatment.

A little more recognizable as a precedent of the modern community clinic was the Psychological Clinic established by Lightner Witmer at the University of Pennsylvania in 1896. This clinic had its closest liaison with schools and concerned itself mainly with children—particularly the mentally deficient— who presented learning problems. Its novel features were that it offered remedial as well as diagnostic services and that it dealt with borderline rather

---

[3] Although Miss Horton was not appointed as a psychiatric social worker, she is sometimes considered one of the first in this field because of the nature of her duties. The development of the term and concept of psychiatric social work is usually attributed to Southard and Jarrett, particularly because of their publication *The Kingdom of Evils* (41). For additional information on the development of psychiatric social work, see Deutsch (14), Jarrett (27), and Meyer (37).

[4] For a synopsis of the development of psychiatric clinics, see Barhash (2). For a more detailed history of these clinics, see Davis (13).

than gross disorders. However, the absence of an interdisciplinary staff and the restricted range of problems dealt with, placed this facility outside the mainstream of the community clinic movement.

At the same time that New York was beginning its traveling clinic service (1909), William Healy was establishing in Chicago the now well-known Psychopathic Institute (later renamed the Institute for Juvenile Research). This was to be the first of the community clinics for children. Independent of hospitals, these new clinics were concerned with research into the etiology and treatment of mental disorders as well as with diagnosis.

The use of an interdisciplinary team in dealing with mental health problems was also further developed within these clinics. Although no direct treatment was offered in the early community clinics, treatment recommendations were formulated for the referral agencies, and occasional consultation was provided to the agencies providing the treatment. Established in communities and dealing with noninstitutionalized patients, these clinics were to do much to close the gap between the "insane" and "sane" and to point up the important relationship between social environment and behavior.

The community clinic movement gained momentum slowly previous to the 1920's. William Healy, with his associate Augusta F. Bonner, had established the Judge Baker Guidance Center in Boston in 1917, and other institution-connected clinics began broadening their referral base. However, although the potential value of this service was recognized by various people throughout the country, the shortage of trained personnel and the cost involved in establishing community clinics prevented a more rapid spread of the service.

By 1920 three developments were combining to give new life to the community clinic movement. One, the child-welfare movement, had been developing for at least two decades. Services for children were constantly being expanded, and it was only a matter of time before mental health services for children would be demanded. Another development was the sudden growth in public awareness of the extent of the mental health problem. This growth in awareness followed the publicity given to the findings of military mental health personnel during World War I. The third development was the rapidly growing National Committee for Mental Hygiene [5] which became an effective social force about this time. The combination of these interrelated developments culminated in the establishment of the demonstration clinics of the early 1920's.

Under the auspices of the National Committee for Mental Hygiene and the Commonwealth Fund, demonstration clinics were established in several strategically located cities throughout the country. These clinics provided valuable services to the community; also, they offered special training in the interdisciplinary approach to psychiatrists, psychologists, and psychiatric social workers. This training created a core group of individuals in each of these

[5] In 1950 the National Committee for Mental Hygiene merged with the National Mental Health Foundation and the Psychiatric Foundation to become the National Association for Mental Health.

professions who were to help their respective colleagues recognize the value of the interdisciplinary approach.

After this initial burst of activity in the community clinic movement, there was another period of slow growth. The temper of the times before the 1930's was not propitious for tax support for services of this kind. The few new clinics that were established during this interval came into being through the philanthropy of private foundations or local mental hygiene societies. Still, the value and need of this service was appreciated within the professions and among the informed lay public. As local, state, and federal governments became more aware of their responsibility for the welfare of their citizens, the community clinic movement again gained momentum. With increasing tax support throughout the 1940's and 1950's, the community clinic became a fixture in nearly every progressive large city or county.

From what has been said thus far, it should not be inferred that the clinics mentioned were the *only* clinics established during the first three decades of this century. On the contrary, by 1925 nearly 400 "mental clinics" were in existence (28, p. 428). However, the great majority of these clinics were institution or agency-connected. They did not utilize an interdisciplinary team, and they offered a restricted service to a restricted segment of the community.

For example, approximately 40 per cent of these clinics were affiliated with or were under the auspices of state mental hospitals, and many of these employed only a psychiatrist who offered merely a differential diagnostic service.

An indication of the slow growth of the interdisciplinary clinic, in contrast to the growth of other types, is provided by the following:

In 1932, the *Directory of Psychiatric Clinics in the United States* (38) listed 674 psychiatric clinics which offered some service to children; yet, the following year a special committee of the American Psychological Association was able to locate only 32 psychologists who were employed in any type of psychiatric clinic (10, p. 9).

IDEAS

In the previous section we examined the early growth of interdisciplinary institutions and agencies and the part that they played in focusing attention on the relationship between social factors and mental disorders. Naturally, such institutions and agencies do not create themselves. Rather, they are the concrete manifestations of ideas which were born and which matured within the minds of men.

Who were these men? What conceptions did they have of the roles and goals of the mental health field? We shall turn our attention briefly to these questions with the understanding that within the limited scope of this paper it will be impossible to include the views of all the pioneers in this field.

Rather, we shall include only a sampling of views held by a sampling of these men.

We have already become acquainted with the views of the men who were associated with the development of the psychopathic hospitals—Frederick Peterson, John Chapin, Montgomery Mosher (Albany); W. J. Herdman and A. M. Barrett (Michigan); L. Vernon Briggs, Owen Copp, and E. E. Southard (Boston); S. T. Orton (Iowa), and Franklin G. Ebaugh (Colorado).

These men had recognized the continuum running from health through illness, and they had emphasized the importance of early treatment. Through their writing, teaching, and demonstrations, they constantly expressed their views and influenced the thinking of many of their students and colleagues —in the mental health field. The present-day assumption that every effort should be made to forestall the removal of mentally ill persons from family, friends, and community can be traced back directly to the ideas held by this group of practitioners.

Lightner Witmer, who has already been mentioned in connection with the establishment of the first psychological clinic in 1896, had also recognized the importance of social factors in the etiology of mental disturbances. For many years he sought to convince his colleagues in psychology to forego the confines of laboratories and to venture out into communities in search of relevant social variables. Considered the father of clinical psychology, he presented his view of this new branch of psychology in the first issue of *The Psychological Clinic,* the journal he founded in 1907:

> Although clinical psychology is closely related to medicine, it is quite as closely related to sociology and to pedagogy. The school room, the juvenile court, and the streets are a larger laboratory of psychology. An abundance of material for scientific study fails to be utilized because the interest of psychologists are elsewhere engaged . . . (48, p. 7).

Although Witmer's new field, clinical psychology, was to undergo a period of even closer ties to medicine, to the exclusion of sociology and pedagogy, his original conception of the field has recently gained wider acceptance in theory and practice.

One of Witmer's academic colleagues, G. Stanley Hall, also played an important role in the changing concepts of mental health and illness. No less a personage than Adolf Meyer described Hall's influences in this way:

> . . . a very important factor had entered American thought and interests during the later eighties in the variously rated but certainly remarkable personality of G. Stanley Hall, one of the men who put psychology in the service of men from two angles important to the present-day [mental hygiene] movement. He had a perhaps somewhat premature pioneer urge in the direction of child study; and for a short time, while still in Baltimore, he put himself in close contact with the city institution for mental cases, so as to draw psychiatric experience into the service of his very broad conception of psychology. Out of this developed such early and ephemeral organizations

as the Illinois Society for Child Study (1894), started by W. O. Krohn, and stimulating the writer to a very early interest in contributions on mental abnormalities of children (1895). On the other hand, throughout the nineties there developed courses in psychiatry for psychologists at Clark University. Here was a beginning in the direction of blending interest in the average child with that in the less usual and clearly abnormal, as illustrated in G. Stanley Hall's *Adolescence* (45, pp. 268–69).

Several of Hall's students, such as H. H. Goddard and Edmund B. Huey, were stimulated enough by Hall's views to become pioneers in the establishment of clinics for the study and treatment of borderline mental disorders.

Adolf Meyer's views on early influences in the development of the broader views on the etiology and treatment of mental illness and the nascent interest in promoting mental health should not be taken lightly. Perhaps no other single individual in the early part of this century has played a greater role in these developments than Meyer himself.

As scholar, innovator, inspirator, teacher, and author, his contributions to what today would be termed community mental health were too numerous and varied to summarize here. The interested reader is referred to Volume IV of *The Collected Papers of Adolf Meyer,* titled *Mental Hygiene* (45). From this 557-page volume the reader may begin to get a glimpse of the enormous contributions of this foresighted man. Paper after paper written by Meyer up to 60 years ago would represent advanced thinking even today. In the introduction to this volume, Alexander H. Leighton, a student of Meyer's, has written:

> Enough has been said, without further extending the list, to show what Meyer meant by common sense. Although he often incurred strong criticism, the passage of time during some 50 years has borne him out. After the waves of enthusiasm have spent themselves in issue after issue, the world has come back to where Meyer stood from the beginning.
>
> Thus, after various assaults on the problem of understanding man from such single avenues as instinct, reflexes, and libido, he has been found to be, after all, a symbol-using animal with multiple motives and aspects operating interdependently to form a shifting equilibrium with a social environment which also has a range of form, function, and plasticity; and that life history and the current situation must both be taken into account; and that neither conscious nor unconscious nor more or less conscious behavior can be omitted; and that, finally, culture-personality is one phenomenon.
>
> Some workers in the field have evidently rediscovered many of these things for themselves, or have come upon them in their consciousness without being fully aware of the effect of the flow of students and assistants through Meyer's clinic, while year after year he reiterated his views regarding man in society (45, p. xxviii).

Mary C. Jarrett did much to define the role and training needs of the emerging profession of psychiatric social work. As early as 1913 she was stressing the importance of community factors in the treatment of mental disorders. She hailed the development of psychopathic hospitals and community clinics as an opportunity for the exploration of the influence of community factors on the mental health of the population. A decade later she summarized these views in the following words:

> The clinic plays a particularly important role in the education of the personnel for mental hygiene work. Since social attitudes and behavior are so large a factor in both the cause and treatment of mental disorder, it is essential that the psychiatrist shall have experience with patients living in the community in order to gain a working knowledge of family and community relationships as they affect mental health (28, p. 449).
>
> Research in the study and treatment of mental diseases depends to a great extent upon observation of the personality of the individual in his daily life in the community. It is necessary, in considering the cause and results of mental disorder, to evaluate the physical, social and mental factors that combine to produce the patient's activities. Also, since the object of treatment is to restore as far as possible the patient's capacity for living an ordinary life, it is necessary to have facilities for carrying on experimental treatment in the community (28, p. 450).

Dr. C. Macfie Campbell, an early leader in the development of outpatient psychiatric services in Massachusetts, ventured the following prophecy concerning his field of work in 1922:

> The indoor department of the twenty-first century hospital may be a comparatively minor factor in the general health organization, while the main hospital activity may be in an outpatient department. More and more should the outpatient department be used as the admission route to the hospital, and all patients should be discharged through this department in order to facilitate the aftercare work (43, p. 164).

Four years later, the directors of the Danville State Hospital in Pennsylvania expanded on Campbell's views in their annual report:

> It is incumbent upon a hospital for mental disease to place within the reach of communities included in its district, adequate facilities for the preservation of mental health, for the recognition of early manifestations of mental disorders and for scientific study and advice concerning the problems that arise in schools, courts, and homes as a result of conflict between the normal members of the community and those of its number who, because of mental disease or mental defect, present disorders of conduct that render them distinctly antisocial. The hospital must no longer serve the community apart from it, but rather as a part of it (26, pp. 130–31).

And by 1935, a special committee of the American Psychological Association, which was given the task of drawing up standards for the training of clinical psychologists concluded:

> . . . The art of dealing with human adjustment requires more than a knowledge of human behavior. Adjustment depends, as frequently, upon a

manipulation of the factors without the individual as it does upon the analysis of those within. . . . [The clinical psychologist] should have an appreciation of the influence of community and family life upon the behavior of the individual. It is therefore necessary that he pursue courses in sociology and in social pathology (10, pp. 6–7).

In selecting the above persons and quotes for inclusion in the section, an effort was made to include typical representatives of particular groups and to avoid quoting out of context. The views presented were by no means subscribed to by all persons in the mental health field at the time; yet they were common enough that variations of these views can be found in many publications of that period.

SOCIAL SCIENCE INVOLVEMENT

As workers in the field of mental health became more cognizant of the influences of social mores and institutions on the behavior of individuals, they became more interested in learning about the concepts and techniques employed by social scientists.

Meanwhile, social scientists were beginning to show an interest in mental health problems and concepts because of two separate developments in the mental health professions. One of these developments was the sudden growth of the branch of psychology called "social psychology" between 1910 and 1920. The area of interest of this growing branch of psychology inevitably overlapped the areas of interest that were traditionally associated with sociology and cultural anthropology. As a consequence, exchange of information and professional contacts between the social scientists and social psychologists were initiated and continued to grow over the years.

The second development was the growth in popularity of psychoanalytic attempts to "explain" anthropological and sociological events by the use of psychoanalytic concepts. It would not be an overstatement to say that many social scientists were incensed by the early literature in this area. However, in their attempt to refute the claims of psychoanalysts, some social scientists became conversant with psychoanalytic theory and were won over to the potential value of the theory, if it were tempered with a sound grounding in the social sciences.

Between 1910 and 1920, a few scattered articles, appearing in anthropological and sociological journals, began calling attention to some of the common interests shared by the mental health professions and the social sciences and to the possibility of their eventual collaboration (e.g., 23). In 1920, the American Sociological Society gave its first explicit recognition of these mutual interests by scheduling a symposium at its annual meeting titled "Sociological Significance of Psychoanalytic Psychology" (17, p. 183). In the previous year, the American Anthropological Association and the American Psychological Association had given an indication of their awareness of their mutual interests by holding a joint annual meeting at Cambridge.[6]

In 1922, a full section of the annual meeting of the American Sociological Society was devoted to contributions in the area of "Psychic Factors in Social Causations." By 1927, so much interest had been generated within the ranks of sociologists and psychiatrists that special committees were created within each of their national organizations for the purpose of further exploration of their mutual interests. Thereafter, for every year between 1928 and 1941 but one (1934), the annual meeting of the American Sociological Society included a section on the relationships between sociology and psychiatry. It was during this period that the term "social psychiatry" began to appear with increasing frequency in social science journals (e.g., 11, 16, 18, 21, 24, 33).

Meanwhile, in the field of cultural anthropology, similar signs of growing interest in the areas of mental health were becoming evident. The writings of two anthropologists, Boas (e.g., 8, 9) and Kroeber (e.g., 32), were particularly insistent and effective in calling for a *rapprochement* of anthropology and psychiatry.

Two of Boas' students, in fact, made the first attempts at actually integrating mental health concepts into anthropological studies. Boh of these latter anthropologists, Mead and Benedict, published (independently) the results of their labors in the year 1928 (7, 35). Mead's publication *Coming of Age in Samoa* is considered "the first major piece of empirical research by an American anthropologist to be organized along psychiatric lines" (30, p. 599). Since 1928, there has been a steady increase in the number of articles in anthropological literature that utilize mental health concepts.

Although more and more anthropologists were beginning to utilize mental health concepts and theory in their studies, it remained for Edward Sapir to modify anthropological theory in accordance with the accumulated results of these studies. Thus, in place of an unintegrated exchange of ideas and facts between anthropology and the mental health professions there occurred a basic reconstruction of the postulates of anthropological theory. According to Kluckhohn, "to [Sapir] more than to any other single person, must be traced the growth of psychiatric thinking in anthropology" (30, p. 601).

The change in anthropological theory and the growing interest in mental health matters were particularly effective in shaping the views and activities of students of anthropology. A new generation of anthropologists with an enduring interest and preoccupation in mental health matters came into being.

As early as the 1930's, anthropologists were joining the staffs of mental health centers (e.g., Cora Dubois at the Harvard Psychological Clinic and George Devereux at the Worcester State Hospital). However, it was during the 1940's that the period of active collaboration between anthropologists and mental health workers began in earnest. This collaboration included teaching

[6] A paper presented by an anthropologist at this joint session was titled "Opportunities for Coordination in Anthropological and Psychological Research" (47).

activities (e.g., Kardiner and Linton at Columbia and Murray and Kluckhohn at Harvard) as well as research activities (e.g., 12, 22, 31, 34).

Thus far, this paper has emphasized the development of an interdisciplinary attack on the problem of mental illness and the related development of interest in community and social factors as they affect mental health—two characteristics of the present-day field of community mental health. The third, and probably most characteristic of this field, is the public health orientation, with its strong emphasis on prevention of illness and promotion of health. The development of these latter goals in the mental health field has been so closely tied to the mental hygiene movement that it was thought desirable to deal with this development in a separate section.

MENTAL HYGIENE MOVEMENT [7]

The public health approach had been slowly but steadily pervading the broader field of medicine since the mid-nineteenth century. In America, the dramatic success of the public health approach in combating such dread diseases as yellow fever, tuberculosis, and certain forms of anemia, could not help but attract the attention of some of those interested in the problem of mental illness.

Adolf Meyer was one of these persons, and as early as 1906 he was writing on "The Problem of Aftercare and the Organization of Societies for the Prophylaxis [prevention] of Mental Disorders" (45, pp. 201–207), and two years later in "Aftercare and Prophylaxis" he stated, "Nobody can engage in the work of the aftercare of the insane without experiencing the awakening of an instinctive desire for prophylaxis. The two ideas are parts of one instinct" (45, p. 211).

He later spoke of the necessity of creating community mental hygiene districts in which mental health personnel would coordinate the services of schools, playgrounds, churches, law enforcement agencies and other social agencies in an effort to prevent mental disorders and to foster sound mental health (36).

At about this time, Clifford Beers was released from an insane asylum and was vowing to devote his life and energies to improving the plight of the mentally ill. Although the immediate stimulus for his decision was the wretched condition of the asylums of that time, he was perceptive enough to recognize that the asylums were only a symptom of the ignorance and neglect of the total area of mental health and illness.

Before he published his classic, *A Mind That Found Itself,* in 1908 (3) he had the wisdom to seek the aid and advice of leading figures in the mental health field on how best to proceed with his campaign. From his consultations,

---

[7] For an unusually full description of the history of the term "mental hygiene," particularly during the nineteenth century, see Deutsch (15).

he was able to formulate and to add to his book the outline of the organization and goals of the yet-to-be-founded mental hygiene societies.

William James, who was given a manuscript copy of the book with the outline of the mental hygiene movement included, became enthused enough with what he read to write to Beers, "I think that your tenacity of purpose, foresight, tact, temper, discretion and patience are beyond all praise, and I esteem it an honor to have been in any way associated with you. Your name will loom big hereafter, for your movement must prosper" (5, p. 245). In the ensuing years, James supported the mental hygiene movement, both financially and morally (39).

Adolf Meyer was another of the chief sponsors of Beers' work. It was Meyer who suggested the title of "Mental Hygiene" for the societies and for the movement (4, p. 265), and Meyer gave Beers letters of introduction to some of the leading figures of the day to enhance his efforts in founding and financing mental hygiene societies throughout the country.

In his proposal for the establishment of a national mental hygiene society, Beers wrote:

> A permanent agency for reform and education in the field of nervous and mental diseases is one of the great needs of the day. Such an agency—whatever its form—could do in its own field what the National Society for the Prevention and Cure of Tuberculosis has done, and is doing, in its sphere of activity.
>
> Though the improvement of conditions among those actually insane and confined should ever be an important factor in shaping the policy of such an organization, its most important work would be the waging of an educative war against the prevailing ignorance regarding insanity. This—to cure the disease by preventing it—is the only effective cure known (3, pp. 295–96).

The book which contained this proposal became an immediate "best seller," and later the same year the Connecticut Society for Mental Hygiene was founded in New Haven—the first of many such societies to be established throughout the country and world. Included in the prospectus for the Connecticut Society was the following article:

> A most important function of the society will be the waging of an educative war against the prevailing ignorance regarding conditions and modes of living which tend to produce mental disorders. This common sense prophylaxis—or work of prevention—will, in time, bring under control the now increasing population of our hospitals and asylums (6, pp. 395–96).

To this end, the society set itself the task of:

> . . . securing state legislation and appropriations, of developing co-ordinated local programs and securing support for them, of impregnating the schools and courts with the mental hygiene point of view, and of disseminating sound attitudes toward mental and emotional problems throughout the community as a whole (44, p. 306).

In the following year, 1909, the National Committee for Mental Hygiene was organized under the guiding hand of Beers. The charter members at the first meeting of the National Committee included such notables as William James, Adolf Meyer, and Julia Winthrop (15, p. 358). Until 1917 this committee devoted its resources and energies to the accumulation of factual data concerning the care and treatment of the mentally ill.

Through the generous support of private philanthropy—particularly the Rockefeller Foundation—extensive local, state and national surveys in this area were carried out. The factual data collected provided a sound basis for the Committee's program of public education, passage of favorable legislation, and the improvement of the institutional facilities for the care of the mentally ill.

It was during the course of this work that it first became obvious to the Committee that there was a tremendous need for properly trained psychiatrists, psychologists, and psychiatric social workers, and that this need would become greater with the passage of time. The Committee was to play a leading role in the development of this training by collaborating in the establishment of the demonstration clinics of the early 1920's and through its years of public education aimed at securing financial support for the development of training programs.

During World War I, the National Committee turned its attention to the mental health problems of the armed services.[8] The Committee saw in this period of mass mobilization of manpower, with its attendant stresses and strains, an opportunity to apply recently evolved mental health principles and to demonstrate the value of mental health contributions.

Mental health personnel, principally psychiatrists, who were recruited and organized for this venture by the efforts of the National Committee attracted world-wide attention for their accomplishments in detecting and treating mental disorders in the military. Their record in dealing with "shell-shock" casualties was particularly impressive when compared to other countries. The publicity given to the contributions of mental health personnel during the war did much to create a reservoir of support for these services both among the lay public and within the professions involved.

During this period, the medical director of the National Committee was Thomas A. Salmon who had been employed in the United States Public Health Service from 1903 to 1915. He had early developed an interest in psychiatry and in the mental hygiene movement, and in 1915 he was appointed its first medical director.

Dr. Salmon brought his public health orientation into his new position and helped to identify the mental hygiene movement with the broader field of public health. During his term of office the National Commitee became more explicit about adopting public health methods and goals into its program. The identification of the mental hygiene movement with public health

---

[8] For further information concerning the contributions of the National Committee for Mental Hygiene during World War I, see Strecker (42).

was continued by Dr. Salmon's successors and in 1933, a professor of public health at Yale, C. E. A. Winslow, stated explicitly:

> The mental hygiene movement, then, bears the same relation to psychiatry that the public health movement, of which it forms a part, bears to medicine in general. It is an organized community response to a recognized community need; and it lays its prime emphasis on the detection and the control of those incipient maladjustments with which the physician *qua* physician never comes into contact, unless specific community machinery and far-flung educational facilities are provided for the purpose (44, pp. 304–305).

In 1922, Franklin E. Williams replaced Salmon as the Committee's medical director. Under Williams, the work of the Committee became less closely tied to psychiatry, as it had been previously. The Committee had responded to the then current child welfare movement by waging an educative campaign for the creation of children's clinics. It was during this campaign that nonpsychiatric mental health personnel became more actively involved in the Committee's work. And with the establishment of the demonstration clinics in the early 1920's, the National Committee itself became more interdisciplinary in its views and goals.

By 1930, the mental hygiene movement was so widespread that there were local mental hygiene societies throughout the world. It was felt that there was an increasing need for improved communications and co-ordination of effort among the distant societies, and in May of 1930, the first "International Congress on Mental Hygiene" met in Washington, D.C. The official "Purposes of the Congress" included the following:

> 3. . . . Through a program planned for the purpose, to endeavor to correlate the special knowledge and experience of psychiatrist, psychologist, psychiatric social worker, occupational therapist, public administrator, educator, sociologist, and those of related professions, in determining how best to care for and treat the mentally sick, to prevent mental illness and to conserve mental health (39, pp. 374–75).

Seven years later, the National Committee reflected the shifting emphasis in its activities in the following section of one of its official publications:

> The present program of the National Committee is a fourfold one of treatment and prevention, education and demonstration, and includes, among others, the following basic activities: . . . Integration of mental health principles into the practices of social work, nursing, public health administration, education, industry, and government; encouragement of institutional programs favorable to the creation of a mentally healthy environment and the co-ordination of community forces to this end (39, pp. 326–27).

And in the same publication, C. E. A. Winslow summarized the development of the mental hygiene movement up to that time:

> We start with the institutional care of the violently insane. We move on to the early but obvious forms of disease that come to the psychiatric ward of

the general hospital or the mental hygiene clinic. We pass next to a group of maladjustments that were never conceived as psychiatric a quarter century ago, but that are sufficiently serious to bring the child into conflict with the machinery of the law. Finally, we envisage those still slighter deviations from perfect harmony with the environment which manifest themselves in maladjustment to the social world of the school and nursery. At each step we go deeper toward the roots of ultimate difficulties. At each step we find the prospect of success more hopeful (39, pp. 308–309).

FEDERAL AGENCIES [9]

As we have seen, the trend toward community mental health activities had been slowly developing at least since the turn of the century. From reform movements to improve the plight of the confined mentally ill, through hospital clinics, outpatient services, and community clinics, to the provision of mental health services to schools, courts, industry, and social agencies, the trend became increasingly perceptible.

At each step of the progression, the search for etiological and ameliorative factors in mental illness spread into wider and wider aspects of the social environment. As more and more of these social factors became suspect or identifiable, it became more and more evident that the problem of mental illness and health could not be attacked solely on an individual treatment basis but that it required a co-ordinated series of services on a community-wide basis with a program for prevention as well as cure—a program, which, in turn, required increased governmental involvement in the mental health field.

In 1930, the year that the first International Congress on Mental Hygiene was held in Washington, a Division of Mental Hygiene was created in the United States Public Health Service. The creation of this Division was, in fact, a reorganization of the Division of Narcotics which had come into existence just a year earlier. The Narcotics Division had been created for the purpose, among others, of supplementing local and state efforts in dealing with the mental health aspects of narcotic addiction—and, as such, it represented one of the first explicit federal ventures into the mental health field.

The chief of the Narcotics Division, Walter L. Treadway, quickly recognized that the work of the Division could be greatly enhanced by expanding its interests and authority beyond the narcotics field. Accordingly, when the Division of Mental Hygiene was created, it was given greater authority to co-operate with local and state mental health personnel, and the areas of concern of the Division were expanded to include the mental health aspects of such other areas as alcoholism and delinquency.

In 1938, Lawrence Kolb replaced Dr. Treadway as chief of the mental hygiene division. Under Dr. Kolb's leadership, the Division began to expand its activities into the wider field of treatment and prevention of mental dis-

[9] Much of the information in this section was obtained from an article by Felix (20).

orders. Dr. Kolb was particularly concerned with the need for research in this whole general area, and he was one of the first advocates of the creation of a national neuropsychiatric institute which would stimulate this research by establishing its own laboratories and by grants-in-aid to private investigators. His recommendations in regard to the form and functioning of such an institute were influential in the planning for the National Institute of Mental Health, which was carried on several years later.

Meanwhile, during the 1930's, the Rockefeller Foundation was financing a mental hospital inspection project which was sponsored by several medical and lay groups throughout North America. The results of this project were so beneficial in pinpointing the conditions and needs of mental hospitals in this country and in establishing standards for these hospitals, that the United States Public Health Service assimilated the project's director and services into its organization when the private financing expired in 1939.

This hospital consultation service, under the direction of Samuel W. Hamilton, was to provide a wealth of factual data on the tremendous need for increased professional manpower, services, and facilities in the mental health field, which was to serve as a stimulus for greater federal concern with these problems.

For example, it was disclosed that in 1941 the state mental hospitals employed 74 per cent fewer psychiatrists than recommended, 92 per cent fewer psychologists, and 71 per cent fewer social workers. The presentation of such conditions in a factual form helped to create pressures on Congress for remedial legislation, which the lawmakers found increasingly difficult to ignore.

Thus, before World War II, there was a growing trend for increased federal involvement in the mental health field, and, in all probability, this trend would have continued to grow even without the catalytic effects of the war. However, the unending need for manpower during the war, and the discovery of the toll that mental disorders exact by detracting from this manpower, greatly accelerated the move toward federal involvement.

This acceleration was brought about by two exceedingly important changes in perspectives concerning the nation's mental health problem: the nation's mental health was no longer considered solely a humanitarian concern, but also an economic and military one; and the state of the nation's mental health was seen as directly influencing the functioning of the national as well as local governments. Both of these changes in perspective created a basis and a justification for federal involvement that overpowered any opposing considerations.

While the war was still in progress, the groundwork was being laid for the nature and extent of this federal involvement. A Senate Subcommittee of Wartime Health Education was given the task of exploring means and methods of instituting a national program in mental health which would also include a service program for veterans. The Interim Report of the Subcommittee contained the following recommendation, among others:

At present, psychiatric clinics are altogether inadequate to meet the needs of the returning men, and considerable expansion of such services should be undertaken, primarily as a preventive measure, to guard against the aggregation of disorders which are now relatively minor . . . and this service should be provided through the media of general community clinics (19, pp. 358–386).

Also, in 1944, the United States Public Health Service (by Public Law 410) was given the authorization to significantly alter the methods by which it was tackling the need for greater knowledge on the etiology, prevention, and treatment of mental disorders. Previous to this Law, the Public Health Service had to carry out its own research within its own facilities, but with the passage of the law, the U.S.P.H.S. was able to award grants-in-aid to institutions and individuals to carry out research in the field of mental health.

This important step resulted in a more varied attack on the problems and succeeded in interesting more mental health personnel in devoting their energies and talents to research.

The form of the yet-to-be-founded national program was slowly emerging when Dr. Robert H. Felix succeeded Dr. Kolb as chief of the mental hygiene division in 1944. That a national program would soon evolve was not questioned by this time, and Dr. Felix was especially enjoined by the Surgeon General "to do everything possible to further the development of a balanced and effective national program" (20, p. 675). When the National Mental Health Act was passed in 1946, the mental hygiene division, under Dr. Felix, played a major role in influencing the scope and the intent of the Act. The National Institute of Mental Health was created the following year, and a full-fledged national program was born, with a three-pronged attack of research, training, and community services.

Since the passage of the National Mental Health Act [10] there have been rapid and far-reaching changes in the philosophy, methods, and goals of the mental health field. The term "community mental health" has become ever more popular as a general designation of these changes.

It has been the purpose of this paper to discuss some of the antecedents of these changes and to give the reader an indication of the historical development of present-day community mental health theory and practice.

REFERENCES

1. Allen, F. L., *The big change.* New York: Harper, 1952.
2. Barhash, A. Z., Bentley, M. C., Kirkpatrick, M. E., and Sanders, H. A., *The organization and function of the community psychiatric clinic.* New York: The National Association for Mental Health, 1952.

[10] The National Committee for Mental Hygiene played a leading role in the formulation and passage of this legislation. For five years prior to the passage of the Act, the Committee had sponsored a bill in Congress and in two successive Congressional sessions employed a representative in Washington to engineer its passage. The Committee was also instrumental in bringing the measure to a vote on the floor at a particularly crucial point.

3. Beers, C. W., *A mind that found itself*. New York: Longmans, Green, 1908.
4. Beers, C. W., *A mind that found itself*. New York: Longmans, Green, 1921.
5. Beers, C. W., *A mind that found itself*. New York: Doubleday, 1933.
6. Beers, C. W., *A mind that found itself*. New York: Doubleday, 1937.
7. Benedict, R., Psychological types in the cultures of the Southwest. In *Proceedings of the American Congress of Americanists*, 1928, 23:572–81.
8. Benedict, R., Franz Boas as an ethnologist. In *Franz Boas, 1858–1942*. Washington, D.C.: American Anthropological Association, July-September, 1943. Memoir 61, 27–34.
9. Boas, F., The methods of ethnology. *Amer. Anthropol.*, 1920, 22: 311–21.
10. Brown, A. W., Report of Committee of Clinical Section of American Psychological Association. *Psychol. Clinic*, 1935, 23:1–140.
11. Brown, L. G. The field and problems of social psychiatry. In L. L. Bernard (Ed.), *The fields and methods of sociology*. New York: R. Long & R. R. Smith, 1934. Pp. 129–45.
12. Chapple, E. D. and Lindemann, E. Clinical implications of measurements of interaction rates in psychiatric interviews. *Applied Anthropol.*, 1942, 1: 1–10.
13. Davis, M. M. (Ed.), *Clinics, hospitals and health centers*. New York: Harper, 1927.
14. Deutsch, A. The convergence of social work and psychiatry: An historical note. *Ment. Hyg.*, 1940, 24:92–97.
15. Deutsch, A. The history of mental hygiene. In *One hundred years of American psychiatry*. New York: Columbia University Press, 1944. Pp. 325–66.
16. Dunham, H. W. The development of social psychiatry. *Ment. Hlth. Bull. of the Illinois Society for Ment. Hyg.*, 1940, 18:4–7.
17. Dunham, H. W. Social psychiatry. *Amer. Soc. Rev.*, 1948, 13:183–97.
18. Editors, American Journal of Sociology. Selected references on social psychiatry. *Amer. J. Soc.*, 1937, 42:892–94.
19. Felix, R. H. Psychiatric plans of the U. S. Public Health Service. *Ment. Hyg.*, 1946, 30:381–89.
20. Felix, R. H. Evolution of community mental health concepts. *Amer. J. Psychiat.*, 1957, 113:673–79.
21. Folsom, J. K. The sources and methods of social psychiatry. In L. L. Bernard (Ed.), *The fields and methods of sociology*. New York: R. Long & R. R. Smith, 1934. Pp. 387–401.
22. Fries, M. E. National and international difficulties. *Amer. J. Orthopsychiat.*, 1941, 11:562–73.
23. Groves, E. R. Sociology and psychoanalytic psychology. *Amer. J. Soc.*, 1917, 23:107–16.
24. Groves, E. R. The development of social psychiatry. *Psychoanalytic Rvw.*, 1935, 22:1–9.
25. Hurd, H. M. (Ed.), *The institutional care of the insane in the United States and Canada*, vol. I. Baltimore: The Johns Hopkins Press, 1946.
26. Jackson, J. A. and Pike, H. V. Community service activities of the Danville State Hospital. *Ment. Hyg.*, 1926, 10:130–42.
27. Jarrett, M. C. The social service, 1913 to 1918. In L. V. Briggs, et al., *History of the Psychopathic Hospital, Boston, Massachusetts*. Boston: Wright & Potter Printing Co., 1922. Pp. 172–83.

28. Jarrett, M. C. Mental clinics. In M. M. Davis (Ed.), *Clinics, hospitals and health centers*. New York: Harper, 1927. Pp. 426–52.

29. Kardiner, A., et al. *Psychological frontiers of society*. New York: Columbia University Press, 1945.

30. Kluckhohn, C. The influence of psychiatry on anthropology in America during the past one hundred years. In *One hundred years of American psychiatry*. New York: Columbia University Press, 1944. Pp. 589–617.

31. Kluckhohn, C. and Mowrer, O. H. Culture and personality. *Amer. Anthropol.*, 1944, 46:1–29.

32. Kroeber, A. L. Totem and taboo: An ethnologic psychoanalysis. *Amer. Anthropol.*, 1920, 22:48–55.

33. Krout, M. H. The province of social psychiatry. *J. Abnormal and Soc. Psychol.*, 1933, 18:155–59.

34. Levy, D. M. Sibling rivalry studies in children of primitive groups. *Amer. J. Orthopsychiat.*, 1939, 9:205–15.

35. Mead, M., *Coming of age in Samoa*. New York: William Morrow, 1928.

36. Meyer, A. Organizing the community for the protection of its mental life. *Survey*, 1915, 34:557–60.

37. Meyer, A. A historical sketch and outlook of psychiatric social work. In *The collected papers of Adolf Meyer*, vol. IV., *Mental hygiene*. Baltimore: The Johns Hopkins Press, 1952. Pp. 237–40.

38. National Committee for Mental Hygiene. *Directory of psychiatric clinics in the United States*. New York: Commonwealth Fund, 1932.

39. National Committee for Mental Hygiene. *The mental hygiene movement*. Garden City, N. Y.: Country Life Press, 1938.

40. Reinemann, J. O. Fifty years of the juvenile court movement in the United States. *Ment. Hyg.*, 1950, 34:391–99.

41. Southard, E. E. and Jarrett, M. C., *The kingdom of evils*. New York: Macmillan, 1922.

42. Strecker, E. A. Military psychiatry: World War I. In *One hundred years of American psychiatry*. New York: Columbia University Press, 1944. Pp. 385–418.

43. Thom, D. A. The outpatient department. In L. V. Briggs, et al., *History of the Psychopathic Hospital, Boston, Massachusetts*. Boston: Wright & Potter Printing Co., 1922. Pp. 154–71.

44. Winslow, C. E. A. The mental hygiene movement and its founder. An address given at Yale University in 1933, reprinted in National Committee for Mental Hygiene, *The mental hygiene movement*. Garden City, N. Y.: Country Life Press, 1938. Pp. 303–17.

45. Winters, E. E. *The collected papers of Adolf Meyer*, vol. IV., *Mental hygiene*. Baltimore: The Johns Hopkins Press, 1952.

46. Wish, H., *Contemporary America*. New York: Harper, 1945.

47. Wissler, C. Opportunities for co-ordination in anthropological and psychological research. An address given before the joint session of the American Psychological Association and the American Anthropological Association at Cambridge, Mass., December 30, 1919. Reprinted in *Amer. Anthropol.*, 1920, 22:1–12.

48. Witmer, L. Clinical psychology. *Psychol. Clinic*, 1907, 1:1–9.

2

Mental Health's Third Revolution

NICHOLAS HOBBS

THE exciting thing for me about this session on movement and resistance to change in the mental health professions is the assumption that professional people have a responsibility for the management of innovation. The implication is that the mature profession does not simply respond to the needs of society but claims a role in determining what society should need and how social institutions, as well as individual professional careers, can be shaped to the service of an emerging social order. The responsible professional person becomes the architect of social change.

AN OVERVIEW

I see a two-phase process: the invention phase and the engineering phase. The invention phase is what we are about in this session; the engineering phase invokes, among other things, the development of new training programs and the building of new institutions. I propose to talk about the third mental health revolution, the inventions it requires and their implications for training programs.

The first mental health revolution may be identified with the names of Philippe Pinel in France, William Tuke in England, and Benjamin Rush and Dorothea Lynde Dix in America. It was based on the heretical notion that the insane are people and should be treated with kindness and dignity. Though 170 years old, this revolution has, unhappily, not yet been consummated. Its ideals may not yet be taken for granted and must therefore be given a major emphasis in training programs at all levels. You will recall that the central thesis of *Action for Mental Health,* its story line, is that the mentally ill do not get adequate care because they are unconsciously rejected by family, neighbor and professional alike. I regard this as an oversimplification, but

Reprinted from *American Journal of Orthopsychiatry,* 1964, *34,* 822–833, by permission of the publisher and the author. © 1964, American Orthopsychiatric Association. Dr. Hobbs is Director of the John F. Kennedy Center for Research on Education and Human Development, Peabody College and Provost, Vanderbilt University.

the fact that there are still practices to support the argument of the Joint Commission's report may remind us that the work of Pinel is not yet done.

The second revoluion was born in Vienna—its charismatic leader, Sigmund Freud. Its agents were the wearers of Freud's ring and other disciples who carried his ideas, making a few adjustments of their own, throughout the Western world. Freud was a giant, a companion of Darwin, Marx and Einstein in shaping our culture, our beliefs about man. It is impossible not to include Freud in a training program today, for if his ideas were to be omitted from the syllabus they would be brought in, as the clothes they wear, by every participant who has been exposed to novels, plays, poetry, television, the jokes of the day and even to *Infant and Child Care,* the most popular publication of the United States Government Printing Office.

Revolutions generally tend to excess and Freud's is no exception. A counterrevolution is required to restore balance and common sense. Freud has led us to a preoccupation with the intrapsychic life of man. No, I think "obsession" is a better word to suggest the passionate commitment we have to the world inside a man's skull, to the unconscious, the phenomenal, the stuff that dreams are made of. Everyone must become a therapist, probing the argument of insidious intent, stalking ragged claws scuttling over the bottoms of silent seas. The psychiatrist forgets Adolph Meyer and can no longer give a physical examination. The psychologist lays down his diagnostic tools, forgets research and gets behind a desk to listen. The social worker goes inside and waits for the patient to come. The preacher takes to his study and the teacher to the case conference. The most thoroughly trained person of all, the psychiatrist who has completed psychoanalytic training, becomes a monument of Veblenian inutility, able to treat maybe a hundred patients in his entire professional career. We owe a tremendous debt to Freud, as a son to a wise and insightful father, but to use our heritage we must break with him and discover our own, authentic idiom. The pendulum is already swinging back, and I am here trying to give it a little push.

The third mental health revolution, the one we are now challenged to further, is not readily identified with the name of a person but is evident in the common theme that runs through many seemingly disparate innovations of the last 15 years.

The therapeutic community, the open hospital, the increased interest in children, the growth of social psychiatry, the broadened base of professional responsibility for mental health programs, the search for new sources of manpower, the quickened concern for the mentally retarded, the proposed comprehensive community mental health centers, these developments are evidences of a deep-running change, indicative of this: *The concepts of public health have finally penetrated the field of mental health.* Up to the last decade the mental health effort was developed on a clinical model; now we are committing ourselves to a new and more promising public health model and are seeking specific ways to make it work in practice.

Mental health used to mean its opposite, mental disease; now it means not just health but human well-being. The revolution of our time is manifested not only in changed practices but more consequentially in changing assumptions about the basic character of mental disorders and of mental health. A great stride forward was made when aberrant behavior was recognized not as madness, lunacy or possession by a devil but as an illness to be treated like other illnesses; a perhaps even greater stride forward may result from the growing recognition that mental illness is not the private organic misery of an individual but a social, ethical and moral problem, a responsibility of the total community.

By an accident of history the problem of mental retardation is being brought into prominence, with a clear demand that the mental health professions no longer shirk their responsibility for the mentally handicapped individual. Thus the scope of the mental health field is broadening at the same time that its basic character is undergoing change. Mental retardation is also being redefined to recognize the preponderant involvement of social and educational influences in the overall problem.

It is a paradox that the care of the mentally ill has always been largely a public responsibility but that the concepts of public health, of early detection, of prophylaxis and prevention, of adequate treatment of all regardless of wealth or social position, have never had much influence. Toward the end of the eighteenth century, the *maisons de santé* in Paris did give humane treatment to the insane, but these facilities were expensive and thus not available to the great masses of the afflicted. In America moral and humane treatment was established in a few of the better early institutions, such as the Friends Asylum in Philadelphia, but the indigent insane continued to be neglected, to be housed in overcrowded and filthy quarters, to be bound in camisoles and forgotten. The chains that Pinel had struck off were simply turned to leather. It was in the interest of the indigent insane that Dorothea Dix launched her crusade. Of course, the situation today is much better, but the dominant theme of advantage for the well-to-do and relative neglect for those without substantial means remains depressingly evident. In June, 1963, The National Institute of Labor Education presented a report, "Issues in the New National Mental Health Program Relating to Labor and Low Income Groups," in which the following observations are central to the argument:

> While in principle the state hospital is available to the community at large, in practice its population is overwhelmingly drawn from lower income groups. To bring about a reduction in state mental hospital populations, therefore, requires that treatment and rehabilitation services be created in the community which can effectively reach lower socioeconomic groups. . . . To a larger extent, the orientation and treatment methods of existing community facilities have been based on services to middle and upper class individuals. They have neither attracted blue collar workers nor found them to be suitable clients when and if they presented themselves for help.

Two contemporary books seem to me to present in boldest relief the character of the public health, mental health problem today. One is by Hollingshead and Redlich and the other is by George Albee.

The former, *Social Class and Mental Illness,* is often quoted but not for its main point, a point so startling and so revealing of the character of much of our current mental health effort that one suspects its neglect can only be due to professional embarrassment and consequent repression of the disturbing facts. Hollingshead and Redlich studied all persons receiving psychiatric treatment in New Haven, Connecticut, during a specific period, to find out what determined the kind of treatment they received. One would normally make the simple-minded assumption that diagnosis would determine treatment, that what was done for a patient would be based on what was the matter with him. The investigators found no relationship between diagnosis and treatment. They studied other variables such as age and sex, and found these unrelated to treatment. The one variable related to type of treatment received was the socioeconomic status of the patient. If he were from the lowest socioeconomic group, he received some kind of mechanical, inexpensive and quick therapy such as electric shock. If he were from a high socioeconomic group, he received extended, expensive, talking-type psychotherapy. If the patient were not only affluent but also a member of an old, prestigious family, so situated in life that he bestowed honor on his helper, he received extended talking-type psychotherapy, but at a discount. The relationship between socioeconomic status and type of treatment received was not manifested in private practice alone but was also evident in the treatment provided by clinics and other public supported agencies. Thus all the mental health professions are involved.

The second pivotal book is George Albee's. I regard his monograph *Mental Health Manpower Trends,* prepared for the Joint Commission on Mental Illness and Health, as a most important and instructive book for the shaping of a national mental health program as well as for the development of curricula for the training of psychiatrists, psychologists, social workers and other mental health specialists. The book requires, it seems to me, a fundamental shift in strategy in providing mental health services to the people of this nation.

Albee's main thesis can be stated simply: The prospective supply of people for training in the mental health professions is limited, demands for services will continue to grow more rapidly than the population of the country, and there will not be in the foreseeable future enough mental health personnel to meet demands for service.

It is widely and I think erroneously assumed that the personnel shortages so much with us everywhere are a local and a temporary phenomenon. We assume that it is a matter of waiting a year or so for the training programs to catch up. Albee's point is that they will not catch up. We can't solve the problem in the way we are trying to solve it.

Keep these two disturbing books in mind and then consider: (1) the geographical distribution of psychiatrists and (2) the growth of private practice in clinical psychology. Most psychiatrists are concentrated in urban centers in proportions much higher than the relative concentration of population. Over 50 per cent of the psychiatrists trained under NIMH grants go into private practice. Mental health services flow in the direction of money and sophistication. The most vigorous development in clinical psychology today is the extension of private practice, following the model of psychiatry, which has followed the model of the private practice of medicine. Psychologists in private practice are a major power group in the American Psychological Association. Several universities are working toward the establishment of professional schools for the training of psychological practitioners.

Now there is nothing wrong with the private practice of psychiatry or psychology except that it does not provide a sound base for the development of a national mental health program. The one-to-one relationship, the fifty-minute hour, are a dead end, except perhaps for the two participants or as a source of new knowledge. This mode of offering service consumes far too much manpower for the benefit of a far too limited segment of society. We' must find a more efficient way of deploying our limited resources of mental health manpower.

These two books, more than any I know, tell us what the third mental health revolution must accomplish. We must find new ways of deploying our resources of manpower and of knowledge to the end that effective mental health services, for prevention, for diagnosis, for treatment, for rehabilitation, can be made available to all of the people. Furthermore, we now have two other books that provide us with guidelines to action. They are *Action for Mental Health,* the report of the Joint Commission on Mental Illness and Health, and *National Action to Combat Mental Retardation,* the report of the President's Panel on Mental Retardation.

IMPLICATIONS FOR TRAINING PROGRAMS

To prescribe the content of professional curricula is hazardous at all times and downright foolhardy in a time of revolution. The most useful and productive thing to do is to keep up a lively debate on educational objectives for mental health professions and to leave it to local initiative, to the faculties of graduate and professional schools and to directors of inservice training programs, to determine what to teach and how to teach it. As a contribution to the debate on goals, I would identify nine objectives that should guide the development of educational programs for social work, nursing, psychiatry, medicine in general, clinical psychology and the various adjunctive disciplines.

1. The changing conception of the nature of mental illness and mental retardation will require that the mental health specialist be a person of broad scientific and humanistic education, a person prepared to help make decisions not only about the welfare of an individual but also about the kind of society that must be developed to nurture the greatest human fulfillment.

I am, frankly, gravely concerned about the proposed comprehensive community mental health centers. Here is a bold and imaginative proposal that may fail because top-level mental health personnel may not be prepared to discharge the responsibilities of a comprehensive community mental health program. When the great state hospitals were built across this country in the nineteenth century, someone must have thought them the last word, the best way to care for the mentally ill. There is a chance that the new mental health centers will be nothing more than a product of the general urbanization of America, a movement from country to city. Twenty years from now, people may moan not over bricks and mortar but over glass and steel; there is a real danger that we shall succeed in changing only the location and the architecture of the state hospital. If the new centers turn inward toward the hospital, they too will be monuments to failure. If they turn outward to the community, as some of the testimony before the Congress said they should, who among us will know what to do? Psychiatrists, social workers, nurses and psychologists have been trained primarily as clinicians, as intrapsychic diagnosticians, as listeners with the third ear; we are clinicians, not public health, mental health experts. Who among us knows enough about schools, courts, churches, welfare programs, recreation, effects of automation, cultural deprivation, population mobility, delinquency, family life, city planning and human ecology in general to presume to serve on the staff of a comprehensive community mental health center? The first training program we should plan should be for ourselves. We have nothing more urgent to do.

2. The concept of the responsibility of the doctor for patient, case worker for client, so appropriately honored in traditional educational programs for the physician, social worker and clinical psychologist, must be reconceptualized to define the responsibilities of these specialists as workers with other professionals who can contribute to the development of social institutions that promote effective functioning in people.

The psychiatrist might have limited himself to the treatment of the hospitalized psychotic or the acutely debilitated neurotic, leaving lesser problems of adjustment to teachers, clergymen and counselors of various types. With respect to the mentally retarded he might have limited himself to those so handicapped as to require institutionalization, defining the rest as slow learners and thus the responsibility not of medicine but of education. Psychiatry has, wisely I think, chosen not to take this constricted course but to concern itself with a broad spectrum of problems that are also the historical concerns of other professional groups. Most of the mental health effort, as we now define it, overlaps substantially with the domains of education, religion, welfare, correction, and even recreation, communication, architecture and city planning. There is nothing in most mental health training programs to provide either content or method for dealing collaboratively with other professional groups to solve the problems legitimately defined as both mental health and something else. Indeed, there is much in the education of the doctor, the psychologist and the social worker that actually militates against effective collaboration in these areas of overlapping concern. For example, the honorable concept of the physician's responsibility for his patient, so carefully and appropriately nurtured in medical training, gets extended unconsciously to relationships with other professional people and becomes an issue not of responsibility but of hegemony. What the physician sees as being responsible, his colleague sees as being arrogant. The physician always seems surprised and hurt by this incongruity in role perception, this seemingly unwarranted misunderstanding of his intent. The more thorough his clinical training, the less well prepared he may be for public health responsibilities. Somehow, without sacrifice of clinical competence, the psychiatrist must be trained to meet role requirements of truly co-operative enterprises involving a variety of professional people. Is there anywhere an approved residency program in psychiatry that explicitly trains for this concept of professional responsibility?

Clinical psychology is equally vulnerable to charges of incompetence in collaborative skills. Its arrogance is not that of responsibility but of detachment, a product perhaps of professional timidity and defensiveness, coupled with the platitudinous allegation that we need more research before we can contribute to social action programs. Perhaps only the social worker, before the advent of the sit-behind-the-desk-and-do-therapy era, is prepared for public health, mental health responsibilities.

3. The mental health specialist must be trained in ways to multiply his effectiveness by working through other less extensively and expensively trained people. The one-to-one model of much current practice does not provide a sound basis for a public health, mental health program.

The most promising approach to this problem at the present time is to use the extensively trained, expensive, and scarce mental health specialists to guide the work of other carefully selected persons with limited training. Such manpower is available, even in abundance, and its effective use depends on the ingenuity of the mental health specialist and his willingness to extend himself by working through other people. I would cite the work of Margaret Rioch in training carefully selected housewives to do psychotherapy under supervision; the use of college student volunteers in mental hospitals, and our Project Re-ED in Tennessee and North Carolina in which carefully selected teachers are working with disturbed children with the support of mental health and educational specialists. The place to start is in the universities, medical schools, residency centers and inservice training programs. The challenge to the mental health specialist in training should be, after establishing his own basic clinical competence, to work out ways in which he can multiply his effectiveness, say by a factor of six, by discovering means of working through other people.

4. Current developments will require that mental health training programs be revised to give attention to mental retardation commensurate with the degree of responsibility that the mental health professions have already assumed for the retarded. Since mental retardation is a much broader problem than it is usually considered to be in those few medical, social work and psychological training programs that have given it attention, the inclusion of mental retardation in these curricula will require a substantial extension of their conceptual underpinnings. Slums are more consequential than galactosemia or phenylketonuria.

I surmise that few things could so radically alter the character of education in medicine, psychiatry, psychology, and social work as a serious commitment to doing something about the problem of mental retardation. The health professions have laid claim to much of the problem; at least three of the institutes of the National Institutes of Health are involved; a substantial portion of every state's mental health program is devoted to the retarded. Yet in most training programs it receives peripheral attention.

For one thing, mental retardation is not a disease entity. It is a host of conditions manifested in impaired intellectual and social competence. It is due to chromosomal aberrations, intrauterine trauma, prematurity, metabolic disorders, accidents, cultural deprivation, inadequate opportunities to learn and acute emotional disturbances. Mental retardation is widely regarded as a hopeless condition; yet it is hard to think of a human affliction as amenable to productive intervention. But again, a radical reconceptualization of the problem is required. When it is in our interest to make the problem of mental retardation loom large, we cite the figure of 5,400,000 retarded in the country. Yet the major emphasis of most of our programs is on the 400,000 who have some apparent physical anomaly, to the neglect of the 5,000,000 who are primarily a challenge to the adequacy of our social institutions. We are more intrigued by galactosemia than challenged by slums and poor schools. We presume to claim the finest medical care in the world but stand eleventh among nations in infant mortality, evidence of widespread inadequate prenatal care that also produces prematurity and much mental retardation. Assumption of responsibility for the retarded will require that our major professional groups make as their cause equal access to medical services and educational opportunity for all people without regard to means or social status.

5. Curriculum constructors in social work, psychiatry and psychology must come to terms with the issue of the relationship between science and practice. Are the scientist and the practitioner to be one or are their functions separable? Just at the time when psychologists seem ready to back off a bit from their insistence that the two functions should go together, there is an opposite trend developing in medical education. The issue is absolutely basic and must be clearly resolved before the content of training programs can be discerned.

6. The main source of nourishment for the mental health professions has been clinical practice leavened and limited by research. The shift toward a public health emphasis in mental health programs will require that the mental health specialist work through social institutions. He must acquire an appreciation of how disparate groups of people organize to achieve common goals and he must know how to encourage this process. He will need to be adept at institution building, at social invention, at the ordering of individual and community resources in the interest of mental health. I have found instructive a study by Harland Cleveland of the successful foreign service officer, who is in a position very much like that of the public health, mental health officer. He is confronted with a tremendous problem, his resources are limited, his staff is inadequate and he is expected to make a difference in the

lives of a substantial number of people. Cleveland found that the highly effective foreign service officer had, among other attributes, a strong institutional sense, a sense of the ways in which social groups invent institutions to serve their ends and a notion of how this process can be furthered in the interest of his concerns. It seems to me that the public health, mental health specialist must develop a comparable sensitivity and skill.

7. An increased public health emphasis in mental health programs will accentuate the need for prevention and thus lead to a greater emphasis in professional training on problems of children, on childhood disorders and early indications of later difficulties and, especially, on normal patterns of development.

I would urge that we invest approximately 25 per cent of our resources to mount a holding action against the mental health problems of the adult, devoting the major portion, at least 75 per cent, of our resources to the mental health problems of children. This is the only way to make substantial changes in the mental health of our adult population a generation from now. I have made this suggestion on a number of occasions and no one ever takes exception to the substance of the argument. But, alas, children are unprofitable clients and, furthermore, they don't vote, so I expect they will continue to be neglected unless the public health challenge grips the mental health professions.

8. The new curricula should paradoxically reinstate an age-old study, that of morals and ethics, not professional ethics but classical ethics. There are two reasons for this. First, the therapeutic relationship, whether between two people or in a broader social effort, is at heart an ethical enterprise, with respect to both method and outcome. Second, we face the awesome prospect of becoming efficient in our efforts to influence human behavior. With increasing effectiveness we must become increasingly concerned with the consequences of our work. We cannot responsibly remain satisfied with vague definitions of what we mean by mental health.

9. Educational programs for mental health specialists should anticipate an increasing obsolescence rate for knowledge and build habits of continuing scholarship and independent study. The more productive we are in mental health research, the more ingenious in the development of new social institutions, the more quickly will training programs become obsolete. The mental health specialist must be a continuing learner; training for independent learning must be a major commitment of mental health educational programs. National conferences are pleasant but they can only suggest new directions for study. Learning is ultimately a lonely enterprise.

From these nine considerations, these nine objectives for the training of mental health workers, there is instruction perhaps for the improvement of training programs, but there is a more insistent challenge that we re-examine the total structure of our mental health program to test its adequacy to get done the tremendous task that confronts us.

I thus come to a potentially distressing point. There is a possibility that the improvement of training is not our problem at all. I see little profit, from a public health viewpoint, in the following:

To train better and better psychotherapists to treat fewer and fewer people.

To improve the training of nurses to take care of increasing numbers of hospitalized old people who are no longer ill.

To hone to a fine edge the group work skills of an attendant who must watch more than 80 mentally retarded adults in a cyclone fence compound.

To improve the skills of the obstetrician in providing prenatal care to the poor in big cities when his contact with the mother is limited to 30 minutes before the arrival of the baby.

To train for exquisite precision in diagnosis when differentiated treatments are not available for differential diagnoses.

And so on for the social worker, the recreational worker, the occupational therapist, the community volunteer.

I come back to the possibility that we may not be able to solve the problem the way we are trying to do it, no matter how adequate our training. We must pay attention to the organizational structures for providing services, to the more effective deployment of our limited resources of highly trained people, to invention of new patterns for the provision of mental health services. These new patterns of organization may then have more influence on training than any other single consideration. Indeed perhaps a major goal of all inservice training programs today should be to train for the invention of new and more efficient forms for providing service, and then for skill in the diffusion of innovation.

A CASE STUDY IN INNOVATION

I should like, in conclusion, to present a case study in social innovation, to illustrate the thesis that it will be of no moment simply to train ourselves to do better what we are already doing. There must be invention of new forms for the provision of mental health services, forms that will treat realistically the problems of cost, of limited resources of highly trained talent, and of the necessity of extending mental health services to all of the people and not to a privileged few. Actually I might cite many new inventions, for the necessity of building public health concepts into mental health programs has already commanded attention and stimulated innovation, but I shall limit myself to one example simply because I know it well and can describe it fairly. I refer to our Project Re-ED, which is a compressed way of saying "a project for the Re-education of Emotionally Disturbed Children."

Project Re-ED was deliberately planned to meet a pressing social need that had been identified some eight years ago by a study of mental health resources in the South conducted by the Southern Regional Education Board. That study revealed an acute shortage in the region of specialized services for emotionally disturbed children. There were a few hospital units but most children in trouble were placed in detention homes, in institutions for the retarded, on wards with psychotic adults, or were left at home to fester there, occasionally seen by an itinerant teacher. The specialized services of all 16 states would not meet the requirements of the least populous state. While the situation has improved in recent years the problem remains acute. Furthermore, it is nationwide. The problem promises to be chronic, for we aspire to apply the clinical model to all disturbed children, and this simply can't be done because of limitations on the supply of personnel—even if it were desirable, which I question. We must turn to a public health, mental health model if we are to make any substantial headway at all. Re-ED is one such approach; there could of course be many others.

Two residential schools for emotionally disturbed children have been established, one in Nashville, Tennessee, the other in Durham, North Carolina. Each school will serve 40 children between the ages of six and 12, who are too disturbed or disturbing to be retained in a public school and who come from families that are too disrupted for the child to benefit from day care. The schools are staffed entirely by carefully selected young college graduates who have skills in teaching, recreation, camping, physical education, crafts and so on. They have been given nine months of specialized training for their work, and are called Teacher-Counselors. There is one social worker to mobilize community resources in the interest of the child and his family and one liaison teacher to coordinate a Re-ED school with the child's regular school. The Teacher-Counselors are backed by consultants: psychiatrists, psychologists, social workers, pediatricians and curriculum specialists. This is a sketch of the basic plan.

Now let us look at some of the principles that guide the program and warrant, I believe, the use of Re-ED as an example of a deliberate turning away from a clinical model toward a public health, mental health model for the provision of services to emotionally disturbed children.

1. The program draws on a source of manpower that is in reasonably good supply and does not compromise on the quality of the person who works with the child 24 hours a day.

2. Re-ED is basically a plan by which highly trained mental health specialists can multiply their effectiveness by working through other less well-trained people. If we could get most mental health specialists thinking along these lines, and then if we could invent the institutions to support them, the mental health personnel problem might be solved.

3. Re-ED concentrates on children from six to 12, hoping to prevent more serious later difficulties by early intervention. This is the mental health analog to the public health strategy of early case finding.

4. The program in Re-ED is organized around ecological rather than intrapsychic concepts. The task is not to "cure" the child (a clinical goal) but to get into reasonably functioning order the circumscribed social system of which the child is an essential part (a public health goal). The effort is to get

the child, the family, the school, the neighborhood and the community just above threshold with respect to the requirements of each with respect to the other. When it is judged that the system has reached a level of functioning so that the probability of its successful operation exceeds the probability of failure, the child is returned home. A little improvement in all components or a dramatic improvement in any one component may make the system operational for the child. With this concept, it makes sense to plan for an average length of stay for a child in a Re-ED school of from four to six months.

5. A public health effort must have a public vocabulary. All of the theory of Re-ED, the objectives of the program and the processes by which these objectives are furthered, have been put into a simple vocabulary using English words as English words are commonly used.

6. A public health effort must be economically feasible. We think Re-ED is. The existing clinical model for the residential care of disturbed children costs from $25 to $80 a day, with an average of around $50. We think that Re-ED schools can be operated for around $12 to $15 per day. More important than the daily cost is the cost per child returned to his family and school as described above.

I describe Project Re-ED not as a solution to the problem of the emotionally disturbed child. It obviously is not that. An array of services will be required—as in any good public health program—to do the job, including hospitals and better public school programs for the disturbed child. I see it, rather, as one social invention that can make a difference. For an effective public health, mental health program in America, we need similar innovations in a number of fields: in the prevention of mental retardation due to inadequate prenatal care and to acute cultural deprivation; in the care of the chronic schizophrenic, the alcoholic, the drug addict; in programs to arrest deterioration in the aged and for the care of hospitalized oldsters who are no longer ill. By such innovations the concept of public health can come to the field of mental health.

3

Philosophy and Scope of
Extended Clinic Activities

BERTRAM S. BROWN

In the last century, the prevailing counsel was "Go West young man." In the present century, all you hear is "go out into the community." But no advice is given whether to go out the front door or the back door. Or whether to go west, east, north, or south. That is what I am going to talk about today —direction. I will give you a road map in order that you will have a conceptual framework for your journey. I will remind you that it is too cold up north in the "psychotic badlands," and it is too hot in the "southern suburbs" where the modern mothers already know that you are there for anticipatory guidance —and it had better be good. But like a good clinician, I won't tell you which way you should go. I will retreat behind that wonderful psychotherapeutic panacea, "It is *your* decision."

The subject or topics by which the two dimensions of the promised road map will be sketched are first, public health, and second, mental hygiene. A psychiatric journal in 1950 described the relationship between these two fields —public health and mental hygiene—as a "shotgun wedding." After many years, there seems to be no signs of an immediate divorce, and the child of this union, named *Community Mental Health,* is still thriving. We will first discuss some aspects of the history and philosophy of public health, then take a similar overview of mental hygiene, and finally examine the relationships between the two fields.

PUBLIC HEALTH

One would think that the history of public health is synonymous with that of medicine. While they are obviously related, they have taken a slightly separate course. The history of medicine shows a somewhat irregular but more or less cumulative stream of outstanding physicians and steady accumulation of scientific knowledge and practices. Public health, on the other hand, has

Reprinted from C. F. Mitchell (Ed.) *Extending Clinic Services into the Community.* Austin, Texas: Texas State Department of Health, 1961, 5–9, by permission of the author. Dr. Brown is Deputy Director, National Institute of Mental Health.

been present ever since the community recognized serious threats to itself. For the most part, these were the severe plagues and pestilences which often wiped out as much as a quarter of the population in a given city or area. When these occurred, the community felt extremely threatened, and concerned citizens banded together feeling something must be done. The history of public health is really the story of "community health action (19)." The action taken would often bear little relationship to the underlying etiology or causes of the outbreak or disaster, and thus was often quite ineffective.

Modern public health, as we think of it today, really had its origins in the last half of the nineteenth century. It has often been referred to as the "sanitary revolution." It was intimately related to the discovery of microorganism as the causative agent of disease. From its beginnings, public health involved communities. Its effectiveness was proportional to the soundness of the knowledge about factors or causes involved in the particular community problem which was being attacked.

The mental hygiene movement, then, might be seen as the communities' response to the threat of mental illness and delinquency. Even more important is that its effectiveness is proportional only to the extent that communities have sound knowledge of the factors involved.

DEFINITIONS OF PUBLIC HEALTH

Let us, for the moment, look at some modern definitions of public health. One would think that the intimate relationship of community action and health hazard would have led public health theorists to realize how intimately related the field was to the social sciences. However, it is only recently that this has been clearly recognized. A forceful advocate of this point of view was the famous physician Winslow who in 1920 gave his definition as follows:

> Public health is the science and art of (1) preventing disease, (2) prolonging life, and (3) promoting physical and mental health, through organized community efforts for (1) the sanitation of the environment, (2) the control of communicable infections, (3) the education of the individual in personal hygiene, (4) the organization of medical and nursing services for the early diagnosis and preventive treatment of disease, and (5) the development of social machinery to insure everyone a standard of living adequate for the maintenance of health (22).

There have been other definitions, from which some significant parts are now taken. The House of Delegates of the American Medical Association defines public health as "the art and science of maintaining, protecting, and improving the health *of people through organized community efforts.*" Other definitions bring forth the aspect that public health is concerned with health problems with which the individual alone cannot hope to cope (22). Still other key phrases are "systematized social action" (17, pp. 5–6), "community responsibility" (20), and the like.

LEVELS OF PREVENTION—CONCEPTS OF NATURAL HISTORY

Running through the many definitions of public health is the concept of prevention, which is so important in the field of public health that its definition has been extended to include rehabilitation. Prevention is seen as having several levels, sometimes five, sometimes three, and sometimes two. Let me illustrate these levels with a graph.

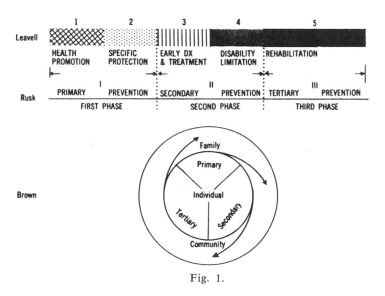

Fig. 1.

Primary Prevention

The first two levels of prevention are often joined together in the term, *primary prevention.* The two components of primary prevention are (a) health promotion and (b) specific protection (16).

a. Health promotion. The procedures in promotion are not directed at any particular disease or disorder, but serve general health and well-being. Examples might thus be health education, good nutrition, optimal personality development, housing, and the like.

b. Specific protection. This is prevention in a stricter sense. Here, we use measures applicable to a particular disease or group of diseases in order to intercept the causes before they involve man. The points of attack involved in any preventive effort concern the familiar agent, host, or environment. The agent may be attacked, for example, by purifying water for bacteria or even getting rid of radioactive wastes. We are most familiar with the hosts being specifically protected with the tetanus and polio shots given to children. We may prevent diseases by altering the environment, such as removing air pollutents, or in the psychiatric sense, providing continuous mothering for a child separated from his parents.

Secondary Prevention

The second level of prevention, often called *secondary prevention,* is the one with which we are most familiar. This, in essence, is *"early recognition and prompt treatment."* A subgroup, here, seen as the fourth level is *disability limitation,* i.e., the prevention or delaying of consequences of clinically advanced or non-preventable or non-curable disease.

Tertiary Prevention

The third level, often called *tertiary prevention,* more often rehabilitation, or as Dr. Rusk said, "The third phase of medicine," is seen as the prevention of complete disability after anatomic and physiological changes are no longer reversible. Its positive objective is to return the affected individual to a useful place in society.

I think this road map of primary, secondary, and tertiary prevention or as it is at other times called, prevention, treatment, and rehabilitation, will prove an adequate conceptual scheme into which we may fit our mental health work.

MENTAL HYGIENE

A brief historical overview of mental hygiene similar to that taken for public health (1, 4, 5) shows that the term itself was first used by Dr. William Sweetzer in 1843 in a book entitled *Mental Hygiene,* a work documenting the fact that emotions had effect on physical functions. Thus, for the moment, we may say that it began with a *clinical frame of reference.* By 1863, Isaac Ray, one of the founders of the American Psychiatric Association, gave this definition:

> Mental Hygiene must be defined as the art of preserving the mind against all incidents and influences calculated to deteriorate its qualities, impair its energies, or derange its movements. The management of the bodily powers in regard to exercise, rest, food, clothing, and climate; the laws of breeding, the government of the passions, the sympathy with current emotions and opinions, the discipline of the intellect—all these come within the province of mental hygiene.

In this somewhat broader definition we can discern the movement from an individual or clinical frame of reference to *a* stress on *environmental factors.*

Not too many years later the definition had expanded to include what we might call a *sociological frame of reference.* I refer to the 1876 definition of Dr. Gray, who was at that time editor of the American Psychiatric Association *Journal of Insanity.* He pointed out that mental hygiene was not limited to individual life but that there was also a "mental hygiene in communities" and that this necessitated that students of mental hygiene must enter "the wide domain of sociology and social science."

His definition continues,

> Mental hygiene may be variously classified, but as a whole, it embraces all that is related to the development, exercise, and maintenance of mental activities, in individuals, communities, and nations, and must therefore be considered from an individual, social, and national point of view. It involves education, social culture, religion, and national life—mental hygiene covers all the broad fields of human energy embracing all the professions in every branch of industrial life.

We note, of course, that he left out the international point of view. This possible relation of mental hygiene to society and social action has been re-discovered every ten years. Any field embracing individual physiology to national policy is broad indeed. For over one hundred years the problem has been to distinguish between broadness of vision and noble goals from grandiosity and pomposity.

A psychologist in the 1920's after struggling with a definition finally decided "mental hygiene is what the worker makes it" (18, p. 288).

The bulk of what might be called mental hygiene efforts in the nineteenth century centered around the well-known efforts of Dorothea Dix. What is not often realized is that her goal was the building of a sufficient number of "insane asylums" to accommodate all the mentally ill whom she found so poorly cared for in jails and poorhouses. The origin of our great state hospital system, the nightmare of the present century, was, in a sense, the outgrowth of the most enlightened efforts of the last century.

The last quarter of the nineteenth century has been referred to as "the golden age of medicine." The years 1875 to 1900 saw almost annual discoveries of specific bacteria which were so-called "causes of disease." This exciting quarter century also saw the bringing to light of the "Shame of our Cities" and other finds from the muckraking of such men as Lincoln Steffens and Upton Sinclair.

As previously noted, the great microbiological discoveries gave impetus to the public health movement. At roughly the same time, the muckraking discoveries gave birth to a period of social reform. The fusion of these two movements was the setting in which the mental health hygiene movement started.

I have in mind, of course, Clifford Beers' hospitalizations at the turn of the century and his book *A Mind That Found Itself* published in 1908 (2). Beers' book was an instantaneous success in that it not only did the muck-raking job of exposing the evils but proposed some wise remedies. I will only use one quote by which I would like to show the analogy to public health thinking of the concept of mental hygiene at this time; or to put it another way, the conceptual dependence on the advances in physical medicine that had just been so miraculously brought about. Mr. Beers offered in his book that:

> A permanent agency for reform and education in the field of nervous and mental diseases is one of the great needs of the day. Such an agency—whatever its form—could do in its own fields what the national society for the prevention and cure of tuberculosis has done and is doing in its sphere of activity. Though the improvement of conditions among these actually insane and confined should be an ever important factor in shaping the policy of such an organization, its most important work would be in the waging of an educative war against the prevailing ignorance regarding insanity—this, to cure the disease by *preventing* it, is the only effective cure known. The watchword of such an organization might well be the significant phrase, mental hygiene.

We see in these early origins of the mental hygiene movement an anticipation and hope for a focus on prevention. But, in a sense, all the early *activities* centered around the care, treatment, and rehabilitation of those already desperately ill. The "insane asylums" were the first line of real attack and it was only several years later that actual outpatient work began in the community.

At the time of World War I and shortly after, there was a concatenation of events bringing together the field of social work and mental hygiene. Thus, in the early 1920's we saw the development of the child guidance movement. In general, 1920's saw an accelerated trend toward organizing mental hygiene clinics in the community (21, 23). Early efforts centered around guidance and education, and the pendulum has swung between prevention and treatment through the last 40 years. I would like to summarize this early history of the mental hygiene movement in this century by using the framework we developed in our discussion of public health. In early years, the aspirations and hopes were perceived primarily as educational to the public, i.e., primary prevention. However, the actuality was organization around secondary prevention treatment, i.e., improving facilities in the mental institutions; as well as tertiary prevention, i.e., rehabilitation of those who had already been ill. For instance, in the 1920's in one of the first mental health programs in a state department of health in Connecticut (3, 7), the first actual activity was parole supervision of former state hospital patients. The ensuing 40 years has seen a gradual extension of aspirations into realities of community efforts in the educational and preventive fields, but the original ghost has come back to haunt us. To jump right to a modern anecdote, at a recent meeting of the mental hygiene clinics in the state of Massachusetts, the Commissioners stood up and told the practitioners who had been working very hard toward developing consultation and primary prevention in the community that they will, in short order, be charged with developing plans and facilities around aftercare of discharged patients from the mental hospital. While one might look upon this as a new responsibility put upon community mental health clinics, in historical perspective, this is where it all began.

PUBLIC HEALTH AND MENTAL HYGIENE—INTERRELATIONSHIPS

The two fields, mental hygiene and public health, have joined together in what is now known as the community mental health movement. Before this came about, we saw the growth of clinical psychiatry from its initial emphasis on the individual and intrapsychic mechanisms, to a new emphasis on the concept of interpersonal relations.

Historically speaking, the humanitarian concerns of mental hygiene for education of the masses, and, hopefully, for prevention, came together with the individual focus of clinical psychiatry, psychology, and psychiatric social work in what is known as the child guidance movement of the 1920's. Here the preventive goal was to be achieved by working with children. It is difficult for us to believe how very recent is the expansion from a focus on individual children to the current child guidance focus on the family as a key unit. To illustrate, Dr. George Stevenson wrote in his book, *Child Guidance Clinics— A Quarter Century of Development* (1933):

> Should the clinic as it gains skill in the application of its techniques to adult problems, see all comers without reference to age and thus become a center for family rather than child guidance? . . . The clinic must spend its energy at the point of largest social return. Society's stake in the child is generally considered to be greater than its stake in the adult: the child may become a fully productive man or woman; the emotionally handicapped adult has already been to some extent discounted. Children's problems, moreover, can be treated more quickly and with greater hopes of success than those of adults. Treatment of the child, in a well-oriented clinic is reflected in better child care throughout the community. For such reasons, the degree of specialization involved in the maintenance of clinical service definitely for children seems justified now and in the future, and in general— whatever may be the marginal practice—the clinic treats adults only to give effect to an endeavor to treat children.

Many practitioners still subscribe to this doctrine, but many of us no longer feel so sure that "the child can be treated more quickly and with greater hopes of success." Child guidance has moved to a group frame of reference, i.e., the family, and has focused on key parent-child relationships. This difference of emphasis on child or family and adults continues today in planning the organization of new community clinics. Should they be essentially child-centered or should they be all purpose?

The relationship of the two fields has been discussed in the literature by perhaps its most eminent contemporary practitioner, Dr. Robert H. Felix, director of the National Institute of Mental Health (7, 8, 9). In an article entitled, "Mental Hygiene as a Public Health Practice," he defines the relationship between the two fields in terms remarkably similar to that foreseen by Clifford Beers at the turn of the century. To quote Dr. Felix,

> Mental hygiene as a part of public health practice bears a relationship to clinical psychiatry similar to that which tuberculosis control bears, for example, to the treatment of clinical tuberculosis.

He points out in this article written in the 50's that "a disease becomes a public health concern when its rates reach a point when individual efforts cannot cope with the disease unaided, when economic dependencies or other social problems created by the illness become a community burden, and often when the sick individuals become a source of danger or contagion." He goes on to say that "a disease becomes a public health *responsibility* where these factors are present, and furthermore there are practical ways in which the community can attack this disease or reduce its effect." Dr. Felix also noted that the pendulum had swung in forty years, from concentration on improved mental hospitals, namely the initial emphasis of Clifford Beers, to the realization of out-patient and preventive programs.

PRACTICAL APPLICATIONS OF PUBLIC HEALTH CONCEPTS IN MENTAL HEALTH

At this point, let us discuss the practical application of these public health concepts to the mental health field as they finally appear in clinic practice.

One difficulty often noted by mental health personnel in thinking about public health applications to their work is the heavy dependence of public health concepts on infections or communicable disease. However, some public health problems, such as problems involved in nutrition, may serve as a more appropriate analogy. As a clear way to point out the applicability of public health thinking in the field of mental health, I would like to use an example used by Dr. Hugh Leavell in a fascinating article called "What Public Health Needs from Psychiatry" (15). He points out the interchangeability of the viewpoint of the public health administrator in viewing nutrition and mental health.

> Everyone needs a certain amount of information about each field to carry on daily life most effectively. The broadly applicable knowledge should be universally available, using all channels of popular dissemination with special emphasis on the community school. Rather more concentrated and precise help will be needed by a very considerable segment of the population in periods of stress and crises of various sorts. This can be provided by those with general training—physicians, ministers, public health nurses, teachers, etc. Specialists can provide in-service training and consultation to the general worker on some problem cases. A small group with threatened or actual disease will require individual consultation and treatment by specialists in mental health or nutrition. Still small will be a group who needs hospitalization and those who are discovered to have already suffered damage from irreparable psychiatric or nutritional disease will have to be rehabilitated to their fullest potential.

Incidentally, following this article on what public health needs from psychiatry was another article entitled "What Psychiatry Needs from Public Health" (14). The author, Dr. Kirkpatrick, pointed out quite clearly after listening to the emphasis of the public health on community groups, etc., "if the psychiatrist wished to work with groups of people he would have become a clergyman or a labor organizer but then he might not have been a psychiatrist." Dr. Alan Gregg (10), who listened to both sides of this discussion, then neatly pointed out, "Now, who will tell each side what it needs but doesn't realize it needs." He noted that "human beings are rather touchy when obliged to listen to a discussion of what they needed but didn't know they needed."

My own recent experience in the state of Massachusetts has served to acquaint me with one community mental health program. Much of what I say has been spelled out clearly by Mr. Hallock and Dr. Vaughan (11) in an article entitled "Community Organization—A Dynamic Component of Community Mental Health Practice." Massachusetts has developed a three-phased or balanced program. They have developed, first of all, a program *promotion* by means of mental health education. Techniques include everything from mass media, small discussion groups, PTA's, and face-to-face contacts. The second phase is that of mental health consultation, also geared toward the goal of prevention. Much of the present conference will center around the specific key operation which is of essential importance. It leans heavily on such things as concepts of preventive intervention—"Crisis Theory" and other things you will hear about. The third phase is treatment and techniques of ordinary clinical care. If we look at this three-phased program of (1) promotion or mental health education, (2) prevention or preventive intervention through consultation, and (3) treatment through clinical care, we can fit this easily into the first two levels of prevention in the public health framework we have noted. Both mental health education and mental health consultation fall under primary prevention. Mental health education might, in terms of the five levels, be said to represent nonspecific promotion of mental health. Mental health consultation might be said to be specific prevention. The second phase, effective treatment, is self-explanatory. However, at this point, it would be well to reiterate that, from the start, this program left out a rather crucial area, namely, tertiary prevention or rehabilitation. This is what I referred to earlier when, at a technical assistance project such as this, the Commissioner of the state pointed out that they would soon have to develop services in this area.

PARAMETERS OR CONCEPTUAL FRAMEWORK FOR FINDING DIRECTION

Let us now return to the original problem of north, east, south, and west. Our road maps, so far, consist of several parameters. First, we might note how we can look at different levels of prevention; from a form of general

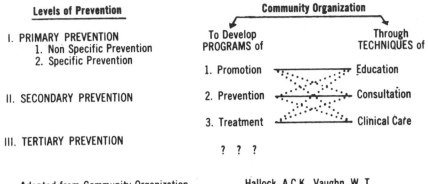

MENTAL HEALTH PROGRAMS AND SPECIFIC TECHNIQUES

Levels of Prevention   Community Organization

I. PRIMARY PREVENTION   To Develop   Through
    1. Non Specific Prevention   PROGRAMS of   TECHNIQUES of
    2. Specific Prevention
                                    1. Promotion   Education

II. SECONDARY PREVENTION   2. Prevention   Consultation

                                    3. Treatment   Clinical Care

III. TERTIARY PREVENTION   ? ? ?

Adapted from Community Organization—   Hallock, A.C.K., Vaughn, W. T.
A Dynamic Component of Community   American Journal of Othopsychiatry
Mental Health Practice   Vol. 26, No. 9, October 1956

Fig. 2.

education toward promotion of health, to rehabilitation of those already chronically and seriously ill. Which direction will you take? Clearly, most of us have our feet firmly planted in the middle; that place where we are most comfortable, namely, diagnosis and treatment. Shall we move to the right and establish relationships with our state hospitals toward rehabilitation and prevention of rehospitalization? I have heard it said by one authority at the National Institute of Mental Health that the best place to spend our money is not on the prevention of hospitalization about which we know nothing but rather the prevention of rehospitalization. I pointed out to him that, perhaps, some of us ought to try to work at least on an experimental and pilot level on the other side of the spectrum and see what we could do toward preventing hospitalization in the first place. This would be leaning to the left, namely, toward primary prevention, perhaps using the techniques of consultation.

A second parameter would be whether to deal with the individual, groups, or the community. Child guidance has traditionally dealt with the family group extending at least to the mother-child and in some places giving more than lip service to the father. At our own community clinic, the Mental Health Study Center, family group therapy is used routinely and is finding new popularity in several places in the country.

A third parameter is the concept of caretakers. Certainly, there are key people who have traditionally handled people in trouble. These varied from unofficial caretakers, like bartenders, to our more traditional clergymen, physicians, and nurses. Shall we extend this concept to include the true caretakers—the political forces? Here we get into such areas as the role of mental health personnel in such things as city planning. Such psychiatrists as Dr. Leonard Duhl are actively involved in this field (6). It is more than fantasy to conceive that one form of assistance to a mayor may be a psychiatrist, since this has already happened in New Orleans.

A fourth parameter is determining the place or setting where we render services. If we do offer service to the schools, is there any more value to going out into the school situation itself to see the teachers, administrator, or principals, or would just as much be accomplished seeing the teachers at one's own clinic? After receiving a year of training in how important it was to be out at the school and to be in the social setting in which the teacher operated, I came to my present setting and found that the school guidance counselors came to us. I'm not sure which is better, but even though we see the counselors in the clinic, philosophically at least, one can consider this extended clinic practice. The renaissance of interest in home visiting might be considered an aspect of concern with this parameter of appropriate place or service.

A fifth parameter is the timing of the services. How important is it to arrange our services so that we are available to patients and families at the time of crises or upset? What does the waiting list period mean to what types of patients? Who is to take care of emergencies? Would psychotherapy be more effective in the middle of the night?

A sixth parameter is the length of our efforts. Shall it be short-term therapy or long-term therapy? Since a very few people, families, or even caretakers if treated over a long period of time would soon use up all the available professional time, attempts have been made to best use professional time in short-term processes. Here, the concept of intervention at keypoints as well as with key people has arisen, perhaps best thought through by Dr. Caplan, Dr. Lindemann, and his associates as preventive intervention in a crisis. Here, one hopes to intervene, altering the equilibrium so things turn out better in the end than they were at the start.

PANDORA'S BOX OF PROBLEMS

Throughout this talk there have been several difficult problems. We have pointed out how much of the progress of public health has been based on the soundness of the knowledge of etiology. Certainly, this is where we are weakest in psychiatry and thus have the most difficulty in developing clear-cut preventive programs. The standard tool in public health practice for measuring the effective program has been epidemiology. Epidemiology is a study of the distribution and rate of an affliction throughout a population. This is difficult to do in a field such as psychiatry where even definition of illnesses is not agreed upon by the professional personnel. One way this vexing difficulty shows up is in how troublesome it is to evaluate our efforts in the field of extended clinic activities (12). There have been experiments in certain places, such as San Mateo County, California, to develop an epidemiology or system of measuring disturbed behavior which might measure the effects of program on the rates of disturbed behavior and psychiatric illness in the community. However, even there it has not been very successful, and we face always the vexing problem of evaluating our efforts. Perhaps we will not advance very much in this field until we have defined, not only the common psychiatric illness such as schizophrenia, but mental health. I'm sure you are all familiar with Jahoda's book *Toward the Social Psychology of Mental Health* (13) which is a long effort toward defining mental health but in the end points out how difficult it is.

So there you have it. Shall you move toward people sicker than you usually see in the clinic or toward those who are relatively healthy but in whom you wish to prevent future mental illness? Shall you see them in the clinic or at their homes or places of business? Shall you continue to see only patients or will you attempt to establish relationships with the caretakers in the community? If you do decide to establish relationships, sharing your knowledge of human psychology and emotions with such personnel as teachers, you will still be left with the problem of whether to see them at school or back in your office. I wish you good luck on your journey and hope you don't get lost.

REFERENCES

1. Andriola, J. The development of the concept of mental hygiene. *Ment. Hyg.,* 1955, 39:657–64.
2. Beers, C. *A mind that found itself.* New York: Doubleday, Doran, 1948.
3. Cunningham, J. C. The Connecticut State Department of Health mental hygiene program. *Amer. J. Pub. Hlth.,* 1942, 32 (6):606–10.
4. Deutsch, A. *The mentally ill in America.* New York: Doubleday, Doran, 1937.
5. Deutsch, A. *The history of mental hygiene: One hundred years of American psychiatry.* New York: Columbia University Press, 1944.
6. Duhl, L. J. City responsibilities in problems of mental health. Paper presented at the 34th Annual Municipal Congress of the American Municipal Association in San Francisco, California, December 3, 1957.
7. Felix, R. H. Mental hygiene and public health. *Amer. J. Orthopsychiat.,* 1948, 18:679–84.
8. Felix R. H. Evolution of community mental health concepts. *Amer. J. Psychiat.,* 1951, 113 (8).
9. Felix, R. H. Mental hygiene versus public health practice. *Amer. J. Orthopsychiat.,* 1951, 21 (4).
10. Gregg, A. Psychiatry in public health. *Amer. J. Psychiat.,* 1950, 107:330–33.
11. Hallock, A. C. K. and Vaughan, W. T. *Community organization: A dynamic component of community mental health practice. Amer. J. Orthopsychiat.,* 1956, 26:691–708.
12. Howe, L. P. *Evaluation in community mental health programs.* New developments in community mental health. Proceedings of a Conference, Lenox, Mass., November 24, 1959.
13. Jahoda, M. *Current concepts of positive mental health.* New York: Basic Books, 1958.

14. Kirkpatrick, M. E. What psychiatry needs from public health. *Amer. J. Psychiat.,* 1950, 107:327–29.
15. Leavell, H. R. What public health needs from psychiatry. *Amer. J. Psychiat.,* 1950, 107:321–26.
16. Leavell, H. R. and Clark, E. G. *Textbook of preventive medicine.* New York: McGraw-Hill, 1953.
17. Mustard, H. S. *Government in public health.* New York: Commonwealth Fund, 1945.
18. Paynter, R. H. The clinical psychologist at work. *Personnel J.* 6:288, 1927.
19. Rosen, G. *A history of public health.* New York: MD Publications, 1958.
20. Smilie, W. G. *Preventive medicine and public health.* New York: Macmillan, 1952.
21. Stevenson, G. S. *Child guidance clinics; A quarter century of development.* New York: Commonwealth Fund, 1934.
22. Winslow, C. A. *The untilled fields of public health science. Mod. Med.,* 1920, 2:183–91.
23. Witmer, H. L. *Psychiatric clinics for children.* New York: Commonwealth Fund, 1940.

4

Community Psychiatry:
The Newest Therapeutic Bandwagon

H. WARREN DUNHAM

THE proposal to add community psychiatry to the ever-widening list of psychiatric specialties deserves a critical examination. Thus, my purpose in this paper is fourfold. First, I intend to examine the nature of community psychiatry as it is taking shape. Second, I want to consider our continuing uncertainty about mental illness which is manifested in a widening of its definition. Third, I discuss some of the historical landmarks and cultural forces that have brought about the proposal for this new subspecialty of psychiatry. Finally, I examine some of its hidden aspects with respect to the future role of psychiatry.

COMMUNITY PSYCHIATRY—THE NEWEST SUBSPECIALTY

Let us begin by examining the nature of community psychiatry that is apparently emerging as judged by a mounting chorus of voices from those who jump on any bandwagon as long as it is moving. In doing this I will focus first on community psychiatry in relation to community mental health and the various programs, plans, and social actions that are currently getting under way, with emphases that are as varied as the cultural-regional contrasts of American society.

A pattern concerned with maximizing treatment potential for the mentally ill is gradually taking shape. This newest emphasis points to a declining role of the traditional state hospital and the rise of the community mental health center with all of the attendant auxiliary services essential for the treatment of the mentally ill. In its ideal form the community mental health center would provide psychiatric services, both diagnostic and treatment, for all age groups and for both inpatients and outpatients in a particular community. In addition, the center would have attached closely to it day and night hospitals, convalescent homes, rehabilitative programs or, for that matter, any service

Reprinted from *Archives of General Psychiatry*, 1965, *12*, 303–313, by permission of the publisher and the author. © 1965, American Medical Association. Dr. Dunham is Professor of Sociology, Wayne State University.

that helps toward the maximizing of treatment potential with respect to the characteristics of the population that it is designed to serve. Also attached to this center would be several kinds of research activities aimed at evaluating and experimenting with old and new therapeutic procedures. In the background would still be the state hospital which would, in all likelihood, become the recipient for those patients who seemingly defy all efforts with available therapeutic techniques to fit them back into family and community with an assurance of safety to themselves and others. This reorganization of psychiatric facilities as a community mental health program also implies an increased and workable coordination of the diverse social agencies in the community toward the end of detecting and referring those persons who need psychiatric help.

This ideal structure does appear to be oriented toward the urban community. Therefore, the need arises to clarify the size and type of the population that would be served. Further, a breakdown of the population into the several age and sex categories along with several projected estimates of the number of mentally ill persons that will occur in these population categories would be required. Estimates should be made for the psychoneuroses, the psychoses, the psychopathies, the mentally retarded, and the geriatrics cases that will be found in a community.

Indeed, we should attempt to mobilize and to organize our psychiatric resources in such a manner that they will maximize our existing therapeutic potential for any community. At all events, such a structure seems to suggest to certain professionals at the National Institute of Mental Health that if there comes into existence a realistic community mental health program, there must be a community psychiatry that knows how to use it. While the logic here escapes me, it seems to be quite clear to Viola Bernard who states that, "Recognition of the need to augment the conventional training for mental health personnel to equip them for the newer function of community mental health practice parallels wide-scale trends toward more effective treatment methods at the collective level to augment one-to-one clinical approaches" (3). Dr. Bernard goes on to say that community psychiatry can be regarded as a subspecialty of psychiatry and that it embraces three major subdivisions—social psychiatry, administrative psychiatry, and public health psychiatry.

While Dr. Bernard may see clearly the nature of a community psychiatry that transcends the traditional one-to-one clinical approach, this is not the case with departments of psychiatry in some medical schools as the recent National Institute of Mental Health survey attests (10). In reviewing the limited literature it is all too clear that different conceptions abound as to what community psychiatry is and while these conceptions are not always inconsistent they nevertheless attest to the fact that the dimensions of the proposed new subspecialty are by no means clear-cut. These conceptions range all the way from the idea that community psychiatry means bringing psychiatric techniques and treatments to the indigent persons in the community to the notion that community psychiatry should involve the education of policemen, teachers, public health nurses, politicians, and junior executives in mental hygiene principles. A mere listing of some of the conceptions of what has been placed under the community psychiatry umbrella will give a further notion of this uncertainty. Community psychiatry has been regarded as encompassing (1) the community base mental hospital, (2) short-term mental hospitalization, (3) attempts to move the chronically hospitalized patient and return him to the community, (4) the integration of various community health services, (5) psychiatric counseling and services to nonpsychiatric institutions such as schools, police departments, industries, and the like, (6) the development of devices for maintaining mental patients in the community, (7) reorganization and administration of community mental health programs, and finally (8) the establishment of auxiliary services to community mental hospitals, such as outpatient clinics, day hospitals, night hospitals, home psychiatric visits, and the utilization of auxiliary psychiatric personnel in treatment programs (10).

Perhaps we can come close to what someone visualizes as the content of community psychiatry by quoting an announcement of an opening for a fellowship in community psychiatry in Minnesota. In the announcement the program is described as follows: "One year of diversified training and experience, including all aspects of community organization, consultation, and training techniques, administration, research and mass communication media." Such a psychiatric residency program certainly represents a great difference from the more traditional training program and points to a type of training that might be more fitting for a person who wants to specialize in community organization.

There is no clearer support for this conception than Leonard Duhl's paper (6) where he discusses the training problems for community psychiatry. In this paper he speaks of three contracts that the psychiatrist has, the traditional one with the patient, the more infrequent one with the family, and still more infrequent one with the community. In connection with his community contract, the psychiatrist states, according to Duhl, "I will try to lower the rate of illness and maximize the health of this population." Duhl continues, and I quote, because the direction is most significant.

> In preparing psychiatrists for these broadened contracts, a new set of skills must be communicated. For example, he must learn how to be consultant to a community, an institution, or a group without being patient-oriented. Rather, he must have the community's needs in central focus. He must be prepared for situations where he is expected to contribute to planning for services and programs, both in his field and in others, that are related: what information is needed; how it is gathered; what resources are available and so forth. Epidemiology, survey research and planning skills must be passed on to him. He must be prepared to find that people in other fields, such as the legislature often affect a program more than his profession does. He must find himself at home in the world of economics, political science, politics, planning, and all forms of social action (6, p. 6).

While these remarks of Bernard and Duhl may not represent any final statement as to what community psychiatry will become, they point to a probable direction that this newest addition to psychiatric subspecialties may take. However, in this conception of the community psychiatrist as a person skilled in the techniques of social action there lie so many uncertainties, unresolved issues, and hidden assumptions that it is difficult to determine where it will be most effective to start the analysis, with the role of the psychiatrist or with the nature of the community.

Perhaps sociologists can garner some small satisfaction in the fact that the psychiatrist finally has discovered the community—something that the sociologist has been studying and reporting on for over half a century in the United States. However, once the psychiatrist makes this discovery he must ask himself what he can do with it in the light of his professional task, how the discovery will affect his traditional professional role, and how working on or in the community structure can improve the mental health level of its people. Now, it seems that those leaders of psychiatry who are proposing this new subspecialty imply several things at the same time and are vague about all of them. They seem to be saying, in one form or another, the following:

1. We, psychiatrists, must know the community and learn how to work with the various groups and social strata composing it so that we can help to secure and organize the necessary psychiatric facilities that will serve to maximize the treatment potential for the mentally ill.

2. We must know the community because the community is composed of families which, through the interaction of their members, evolve those events and processes that in a given context have a pathic effect upon some of the persons who compose them.

3. We must know the community in order to develop more effective methods of treatment at the "collective level," to eliminate mentally disorganizing social relationships, and to achieve a type of community organization that is most conducive to the preservation of mental health.

4. We must know the community if we are ever to make any headway in the prevention of mental illness. For we hold that in the multiple groups, families, and social institutions which compose the community, there are numerous unhealthy interpersonal relationships, pathological attitudes and beliefs, cultural conflicts and tensions, and unhealthy child training practices that make for the development of mental and emotional disturbances in the person.

An analysis of our first implication shows that no new burden is placed upon the psychiatrist but it merely emphasizes his role as a citizen—a role that, like any person in the society, he always has had. It merely emphasizes that the psychiatrist will take a more active part in working with other professionals in the community such as lawyers, teachers, social workers, ministers, labor leaders, and business men in achieving an organization of psychiatric facilities that will maximize the therapeutic potential in a given community. To be sure it means that in working with such persons and groups, he will contribute his own professional knowledge and insights in the attempt to obtain and to organize the psychiatric facilities in such a manner as to achieve a maximum therapeutic potential. Thus, this is hardly a new role for the psychiatrist. It only becomes sharper at this moment in history when a social change in the care and treatment of the mentally ill is impending, namely, a shift from a situation that emphasized the removal of the mental patient from the community to one that attempts to deal with him in the community and family setting and to keep active and intact his ties with these social structures.

The second implication is routine in the light of the orientation of much of contemporary psychiatry. Here, attention is merely called to the theory that stresses the atypical qualities of the family drama for providing an etiological push for the development of the several psychoneuroses, character disorders, adult behavior disturbances and in certain instances, psychotic reactions. Thus, it follows that to change or correct the condition found in the person, some attention must be paid to the family as a collectivity, in order to grasp and then modify those attitudes, behavior patterns, identifications, and emotional attachments that supposedly have a pathogenic effect on the family members. From the focus on the family the concern then extends to the larger community in an attempt to discover the degree to which the family is integrated in or alienated from it.

However, it is in the third implication that many probing questions arise. For here the conception is implicit that the community is the patient and consequently, the necessity arises to develop techniques that can be used in treating the community toward the end of supplementing the traditional one-to-one psychiatric relationship. This position also implies a certain etiological view, namely, that within the texture of those institutional arrangements that make up the community there exist dysfunctional processes, subcultures with unhealthy value complexes, specific institutional tensions, various ideological conflicts along age, sex, ethnic, racial and political axes, occasional cultural crises, and an increasing tempo of social change that in their functional interrelationships provide a pathogenic social environment. Thus, when these elements are incorporated into the experience of the persons, especially during their early and adolescent years, they emerge as abnormal forms of traits, attitudes, thought processes, and behavior patterns. In a theoretical vein, this is the Merton (17) paradigm wherein he attempts to show the diverse modes of adaptation that arise as a result of the various patterns of discrepancy between institutional means and cultural goals.

The influence of the social milieu in shaping, organizing, and integrating the personality structure, of course, has been recognized for a long time. What is not so clear, however, is the manner in which such knowledge can be utilized in working at the community level to treat the mental and emotional maladjustments that are continually appearing. In addition, the nature and function of those factors in the social milieu contributing to the production of the bona fide psychotics are by no means established.

These issues point to some very pressing queries. What are the possible techniques that can be developed to treat the "collectivity"? Why do psychiatrists think that it is possible to treat the "collectivity" when there still exists a marked uncertainty with respect to the treament and cure of the individual case? What causes the psychiatrist to think that if he advances certain techniques for treating the "collectivity," they will have community acceptance? If he begins to "treat" a group through discussions in order to develop personal insights, what assurances does he have that the results will be psychologically beneficial to the persons? Does the psychiatrist know how to organize a community along mentally hygienic lines and if he does, what evidence does he have that such an organization will be an improvement over the existing organization? In what institutional setting or in what cultural milieu would the psychiatrist expect to begin in order to move toward more healthy social relationships in the community? These are serious questions and I raise them with reference to the notion that the community is the patient.

If a psychiatrist thinks that he can organize the community to move it toward a more healthy state I suggest that he run for some public office. This would certainly add to his experience and give him some conception as to whether or not the community is ready to be moved in the direction that he regards as mentally hygienic. If he should decide on such a step he will be successful to the extent that he jokingly refers to himself as a "head shrinker" and that he becomes acceptable as "one of the boys." But if he does, he functions as an independent citizen, in harmony with our democratic ethos, bringing his professional knowledge to bear on the goal he has set for himself and his constituents. However, successful or not, he will certainly achieve a new insight concerning the complexity involved in treating the community as the patient.

While I have poked at this proposition from the standpoint of politics, let me consider it with respect to education. If this becomes the medium by which the pathology of the community is to be arrested, one can assume that it means adding to and raising the quality of the educational system in the community. The dissemination of psychiatric information with respect to signs and symptoms, the desirability of early treatment, the natural character of mental illness, the therapeutic benefits of the new drugs, and the correct mental hygiene principles of child training have been going on not only through the usual community lectures and formal educational channels but also by means of the mass media—radio, television, the newspapers, and the slick magazines. I hasten to add, however, that this may not be to the advantage of the community, for it may do nothing else but raise the level of anxiety among certain middle-class persons, who, when they read an article on the correct procedure for bringing up children realize that they have done all the wrong things. Also, the media are frequently sources of misinformation and sometimes imply a promise that psychiatry cannot fulfill.

Further, I observe that in this proposal for a community psychiatry, the psychiatrist seems to be enmeshed in the same cultural vortex as is the professor. For it is becoming fashionable for a professor to measure his success in having hardly any contact with students—he is too busy on larger undertakings, research, consultations, conferences, and the like. Likewise, some psychiatrists think that they have arrived if they have no contact with patients. For example, I have heard of one psychiatrist who has not seen a patient for several years—he spends his time educating teachers, nurses, policemen, business men, and the laity in psychiatric principles.

The third and fourth implications of the new focus provided by community psychiatry are closely related because each position partially views the structures and processes of the community as containing certain etiological elements that make for the development of certain types of mental and emotional illness. However, the third implication, as we have shown, points to the development of treatment techniques on the collective level, while the fourth emphasizes that knowledge of the community is essential if mental illness is ever to be prevented.

There is no doubt that the word prevention falling on the ears of well-intentioned Americans, is just what the doctor ordered. It is so hopeful that no one, I am sure, will deny that if we can prevent our pathologies this is far better than sitting back and waiting for them to develop. But, of course, there is a catch. How are we going to take the first preventive actions if we are still uncertain about the causes of mental disorders? How do we know where to even cut into a community's round of life? And if we did cut in, what assurance do we have that the results might not be completely the opposite to those anticipated? Of course, there is always secondary prevention—that is, directing our efforts to preventing a recurrence of illness in persons who have once been sick. This is a laudable goal but in connection with mental and emotional disturbances we are still uncertain as to the success of our original treatment efforts.

PREVENTION OF BEHAVIORAL PATHOLOGY—
SOME PREVIOUS EFFORTS

There is no doubt that the possibility of prevention is something that will continue to intrigue us for years to come. Therefore, it is not without point to take a look at several other programs that, while they have not all been exclusively oriented toward the treatment of the community, have been launched with the hope of preventing the occurrence of certain unacceptable behavior on the part of the members of a community. I cite two experiments which are widely known with respect to the prevention of delinquency.

The first is Kobrin's statement concerning the 25 year assessment of the Chicago Area Project (15). Kobrin has presented us with a straightforward, modest, and sophisticated account of the accumulated experience provided by this project in the efforts to bring about a greater control of delinquency in certain areas of Chicago. This project has been significant on several counts, but in my judgment its greatest significance was that it helped to initiate various types of community organizational programs that logically proceeded from an empirically developed theory of delinquency. This theory, in general, viewed delinquency as primarily a "breakdown of the machinery of spontaneous social control." The theory stressed that delinquency was adaptive behavior on the part of adolescents in their peer groups in their efforts to achieve meaningful and respected adult roles, "unaided by the older generation and under the influence of criminal models for whom the intercity areas furnish a haven." This theory, in turn, rests upon certain postulates of sociological theory which emphasize that the development and control of conduct are determined by the network of primary relationships in which one's daily existence is embedded.

The significance of this experiment was that this theory of delinquency provided a rationalization for cutting into the community at certain points and seeking persons there who were ready to organize themselves to secure a higher level of welfare for themselves and their children. The results of this experiment are relevant to those advocators of the preventive function of a community psychiatry because there was not only the difficulty of determining what actually had been accomplished in the way of the prevention of delinquency but also a difficulty in assessing the experience in relation to community welfare.

Kobrin, in his opening sentence has stated this problem most cogently.

> The Chicago Area Project shares with other delinquency prevention programs the difficulty of measuring its success in a simple and direct manner. At bottom this difficulty rests on the fact that such programs, as efforts to intervene in the life of a person, a group, or a community, cannot by their very nature, constitute more than a subsidiary element in changing the fundamental and sweeping forces which create the problems of groups and of persons or which shape human personality. Decline in rates of delinquents—the only conclusive way to evaluate delinquency prevention—may reflect influences unconnected with those of organized programs and are difficult to define and measure (15).

The point here is that in a carefully worked out plan based upon an empirically constructed theory it is difficult to determine what has been achieved. One can hazard the observation that if this is true with respect to delinquent behavior where mounting evidence has always supported the idea that its roots are deeply enmeshed in the network of social relationships, how much more difficult it will be in the field of psychiatry to make an assessment in preventive efforts when we are much more uncertain concerning the etiological foundations of those cases which appear in psychiatric offices, clinics, and hospitals.

The well-known Cambridge-Somerville Youth Study (19) provides the second example of a delinquency prevention program. While this study did not focus upon the community as such but rather on certain persons therein, it did proceed from a conception of a relationship between a person's needs and a treatment framework for administering to those needs. In this study an attempt was made to provide a warm, human, and continuing relationship between an assigned counsellor and a sample of delinquents and to withhold this relationship from another comparable matched sample. These relationships with most of the boys in the treatment group lasted for approximately eight years. At the conclusion of the experiment there was an attempt to assess the results. These were mainly negative. The number of boys in the treatment group appearing before the crime prevention bureau of the police department were slightly in excess of the number of boys making such appearances in the control group. The only positive note was that the boys in the control group were somewhat more active as recidivists than were the boys in the treatment group.

Although the results of this study were inconclusive and told us nothing particularly about the communities to which these boys were reacting, they did document the failure of one type of relationship therapy to reduce delinquency. While these results provide no final word they do point up the necessity for the various techniques in psychiatry to first acquire a far greater effectiveness than they now possess before starting to operate on a community level where there will be a great deal of fumbling in the dark before knowing exactly what to do.

It seems most appropriate in the light of the task envisioned for community psychiatry to call attention to the professional excitement that was engendered when the Commonwealth Fund inaugurated a child-guidance program in 1922. The Child Guidance Clinic was hailed as a step that eventually should have far-reaching consequences. For who saw fit to deny at that time in the light of certain prevailing theories and the optimism provided by the cultural ethos of the United States that if emotional, mental, and behavioral disturbances were ever to be arrested and prevented at the adult level it would be necessary to arrest these tendencies at their incipient stage, namely, in childhood. This all appears most logical and reasonable. However, 40 years after the opening of the first child guidance clinic we have such clinics in almost every state and they are very much utilized as evidenced by the long waiting lists. Nevertheless, not only does juvenile delinquency remain a continuing community problem but also the adult incidence rates of at least the major psychoses appear to remain approximately constant during this period, especially if the study by Goldhamer and Marshall (9) is accepted as valid.

I cite these three different kinds of experience primarily for the purpose of emphasizing the necessity to review our past efforts in attacking certain behavioral problems at a community level and also to point to some of the difficulties that are inherent in any proposal that emphasizes the development of psychiatric treatment techniques for the "collective level."

THE WIDENING DEFINITION OF MENTAL ILLNESS

Efforts in the direction of carving out a subspecialty of psychiatry known as community psychiatry take place in a cultural atmosphere which has seen a definite attempt to widen the definition of what constitutes mental illness.

This is shown by the tendency in our society to place any recognized deviant behavior into the sick role. By doing this we not only supposedly understand them, but we can also point to therapies which will be appropriate for their treatment. Thus, the past two decades have witnessed attempts to place in the sick role delinquents, sex offenders, alcoholics, drug addicts, beatniks, communists, the racially prejudiced, and in fact, practically all persons who do not fit into the prevailing togetherness that we like to think characterizes middle-class American life. The danger here is that we only add to our state of confusion because the line between who is sick and who is well becomes increasingly a waving, uncertain one. Thus, we appear to be constantly moving the cutting point toward the end of the continuum that would include those persons who in some subcultural milieus are accepted as normal.

There is much current statistical evidence that supports this notion of a widening definition for mental illness. For example, if one examines the community epidemiological surveys of mental illness in the 1930's and compares them with the community epidemiological surveys in the 1950's one is struck with the fact that four to five times more cases are reported in the latter years (18, p. 90). In my own epidemiological study of schizophrenia, where I have examined many epidemiological studies from all over the world I have noted the great differences that are reported with respect to total mental disorders in the surveys, a marked decrease in the differences between the surveys when only psychoses are reported and a still further decrease in the rate variations when the reports are based upon only one mental disorder, namely, schizophrenia. In this latter case, the variations are slight and all of the rates are quite close together. One might point to the Mid-town Manhattan Survey (20) where two psychiatrists reviewing symptom schedules on a sample population as collected by field workers found that approximately 80 per cent of the sample were suffering from some type of psychiatric symptom. This extreme figure can be contrasted with the 20 per cent reported as incapacitated. The providing of adequate psychiatric services for even the latter figure would place an impossible burden on any community.

Several factors help to explain this widening definition of mental illness which has been so apparent during the past two decades. One factor, of course, has been the adaptation of psychiatry to office practice following World War II (1). Another factor is that the mounting frustration resulting from the failures to achieve therapeutic results with the bona fide psychotics has led to a widening of the psychiatric net in order to include those persons with minor emotional disturbances who are more responsive to existing treatment techniques. These people are suffering from what has been termed "problems of living," and they do not represent the bona fide mentally ill cases (22). In this connection it is interesting to note that George W. Albee, at an American Medical Association meeting in Chicago, stated:

> What we clearly do not need more of in the mental health profession are people who go into private practice of psychotherapy with middle-aged neurotics in high income suburbs. While there are humanitarian and ethical

reasons for offering all the help we possibly can to individuals afflicted with mental disorders, it seems unlikely that we will ever have the manpower to offer individual care on any kind of manageable ratio of therapists to sufferers.

In the light of Albee's observation it is instructive to note Paul Hoch's evaluation of the therapeutic accomplishments of mental health clinics in New York State (11). With respect to psychotherapeutic techniques he states:

I do not mean to deny that psychotherapy brings relief to those suffering from emotional disorders or that it may not be the treatment of choice in certain cases. What I am questioning is the preoccupation with intensive psychotherapy in clinics which are part of the community health program. After more than fifty years of its utilization we still have no foolproof measure of its effectiveness, of its superiority over other forms of treatment or even that a long term is better than brief psychotherapy (11).

He goes on to point out that while in the previous year 30,000 patients were released from the state hospital, nevertheless, only 8 per cent of the cases that were terminated by psychiatric clinics came from inpatient facilities. He notes also that the volume of patients being treated in the state hospitals is greater than ever before, in spite of an almost unanimous need to develop alternatives to state hospital care. His evidence supports this contention of a widening definition of mental illness, implying that the outpatient clinics are not treating cases that are likely to need hospital care but are treating numerous cases that are experiencing emotional problems. These are, for the most part, tied up with the daily round of human existence and can never be completely eliminated except in a societal utopia. One conclusion appears inescapable— the more clinics, the more patients. In addition, this widening definition of mental illness has served as a type of fuel for the development of the idea of a community psychiatry.

HISTORICAL AND CULTURAL INFLUENCES

There is the problem as every historian recognizes of how far back one should go in enumerating those events which helped to shape a present situation, because every historical event is both a consequence of some previous happening and a cause of something that is to take place in the future. However, I begin my history of the proposal for a community psychiatry with the accumulated psychiatric experience which came out of World War II. Psychiatric experience during the war showed that a large number of inductees were afflicted with various types of neuropsychiatric disorders. This finding was reported by Dr. William Menninger, head of psychiatric services of the United States Armed Forces, in a book dealing with his war experience and anticipating the uses to which psychiatry might be put in meeting the new problems

and tensions that were arising in American society and in the societies throughout the world. In this volume Menninger (16, chap. 13) asks if psychiatry
after the war is to continue its preoccupation with the end results of mental
disease or is "to discover how it can contribute to the problems of the average
man and to the larger social issues in which he is involved." Thus, Menninger
anticipated that the new role for psychiatry would be expanded to deal with
family problems, industrial conflict, community conflict, and in fact, any
situation where conflict, difficulties, and tensions arise between people. Thus,
the publication of this work seemed to play a role in turning psychiatry away
from its traditional concerns and in directing its attention to problems of the
community.

The work of Menninger, Thompson (23), and others tended to anticipate
a more positive and frontal attack upon mental health problems in American
society. The writings of these men set the stage for the passage of the National
Mental Health Act in 1948 which has played a significant role in stimulating
professional training, research, and treatment programs in psychiatry and its
allied fields. After the passage of this act which raised mental health to the
status of a public health problem numerous events followed swiftly. Certainly
the new monies available through the federal government and foundations
made it possible for scholars from all over the United States and Europe to
meet more often to deal with specific problems in the mental health field.
This exchange of scholars acquainted psychiatric workers in the United
States with the various programs and plans that were being carried on in
Europe for handling mental health problems, such as Querido's program for
community psychiatry in Amsterdam, the development of the open door
hospital in England, auxiliary psychiatric units such as night- and day-hospitals,
rehabilitation houses, and various kinds of industrial units to train the mental
convalescent for jobs. All of these developments proved most exciting and
interesting, stimulated thinking, broke through conventional and traditional
notions of the past, and paved the way for taking many new looks as to how
we could more adequately treat the mentally ill in order to more quickly
return them to their families and communities.

In fact, these developments began to undercut various conceptions of
chronicity and we recognized that hospitalization for mental illness need not
be a lifetime affair. We should call attention also to the research on the mental
hospital conducted by social scientists which provided a rationale for the
hospital as a therapeutic community, a development that Maxwell Jones (13)
in his work in England has already anticipated. However, these studies that
came during the 1950's in the work of Stanton and Schwartz (21), Dunham
and Weinberg (19), Belknap (2), John and Elaine Cumming (5) and W.
Caudill (4) increasingly began to pose the issue as to whether the therapeutic
community could be considered as a real factor in the treatment process. These
studies further called attention to the rigid traditional structure of the state
hospital and how it actually contained within itself those cultural forms that
tended to discourage patients toward moving to a level of acceptable behavior.

Finally, there came the report of a Joint Commission on Mental Illness and Health (12, p. 338) in 1961, along with the Surgeon General's recommendation in January, 1962 that the states explore a more complete utilization of all community resources dealing with the mentally ill toward achieving a maximum in the prevention and treatment of such illnesses. And as a final stimulus came the speech of the late President Kennedy (14) to Congress in October of 1963 in which he outlined a broad program with respect to community centered hospitals, research and training, covering both mental illness and mental retardation.

In the above account I have attempted a cursory examination of the central historical events that have led to the development of community psychiatry. However, in a broader perspective these events can be regarded as the consequences of the cultural forces embodied in certain beliefs and traditions that are deeply embedded in the texture of American society. In a sense the emergence of community psychiatry as a subspecialty of psychiatry is a reflection of the cherished American belief that all problems are capable of solution if we can just discover the key by means of the scientific methodology at our disposal. The ever-multiplying programs of health insurance during the past 20 years have also laid an economic foundation making it possible to bring mental patients out in the open instead of hiding them away as we have done in the past. Under these conditions the essential qualities of American culture, individualism, optimism, humanism, and the equalitarianism have merely provided the additional push for the emergence of community psychiatry.

SOME HIDDEN ASPECTS FOR THE FUTURE ROLE OF PSYCHIATRY

In this account I have pointed to the several conceptions which seem to be implied in the development of a community psychiatry. I have emphasized that the tieing of community psychiatry with the several evolving plans throughout the country to reorganize the mental health facilities toward the end of maximizing treatment potential is a significant move. While there is the question as to whether community psychiatry extends beyond current psychiatric practices there may be a gain in identifying the psychiatrist more closely with the different community services and breaking down the isolation in which both the psychoanalytic practitioner and the hospital practicing psychiatrist have been enmeshed. This would move the psychiatrist not only closer to the patient but what is more important, closer to the entire network of interpersonal relationships of the family and the community in which the patient is involved.

However, it is in the other visions that have been held up for community psychiatry wherein I think, as I have indicated, great difficulties are in the offing. Here I am most skeptical concerning the adequacy of our knowledge to develop significant techniques for treating social collectivities or for developing techniques on the community level that will really result in a reduction of mental disturbances in the community. It seems that such expectations are likely to remove the psychiatrist still further from the more bona fide cases of mental illnesses that develop within the community context. Much of his effort will be spent on dealing with the noncritical cases. This trend has already been going on for some time as I have indicated in discussing the widening definition of mental illness. Until we have a more sound knowledge which will indicate that the minor emotional disturbances are likely to develop into the more serious types of mental disturbances we will be dissipating much of our collective psychiatric efforts.

Then, too, there is another hidden aspect of these projected conceptions of community psychiatry which deserves careful exploration. I refer to the implication that the psychiatrist will be able to move into the ongoing power structure of a community. The profession must confront the issue as to whether its effectiveness will be less or greater if some of its members should succeed in obtaining roles within the power structure of any community. Here, I would suggest that such a psychiatrist would find himself in a system where his professional effectiveness would be considerably reduced because he would be involved in a series of mutual obligations and expectations in relation to the other persons composing the power structure. He would thus lose the role that in general characterizes the professional in other areas, that of being an adviser and a consultant with respect to any psychiatric problems or issues that the groups, institutions, and associations of the community confront. What I am trying to indicate is that in becoming a part of the power structure he is likely to lose more than he gains. That is, his gains would be in respect to power, personal prestige, and recognition but his losses would be in the growing rustiness of his diagnostic and therapeutic skills with patients.

Another implication of these aspects of community psychiatry is the fact that psychiatrists are being pushed in a direction not entirely of their own making. The national efforts and monies that are being directed to the states and communities for the reorganization of the mental health facilities have engendered a high degree of excitement among professional social workers, mental health educators, psychiatric nurses, and numerous well-intentioned persons who see new professional opportunities for service and careers. Thus, the psychiatrist is led to think, because of these pressures, that he should prepare himself with new skills in order to provide the required leadership to these various professionals who are planning to work toward this new vision to maximize the treatment potential in the community for the mentally ill.

Finally, there is the implication that psychiatry is being utilized to move us closer in the direction of the welfare state. This may not be undesirable in itself but it seems most essential that psychiatrists should be aware of the role that they are asked to play. We can anticipate that while the doctor-patient relationship will still be paramount in most medical practice the psychiatrist is likely to move into roles unforeseen but which will be required by the new structural organization of psychiatric facilities with the proposal for a community psychiatry. In such new roles the psychiatrists may become agents for social control, thus sacrificing the main task for which their education has fitted them.

In this paper I have attempted to show the link between community psychiatry and the new evolving community mental health programs. While one can see in this linkage a most significant development I am somewhat skeptical toward those emphases in community psychiatry which aim at the development of treatment techniques on the community level. In discussing the widening definition of mental illness I have tried to show that this is one of the crucial factors that has accounted for this movement toward a new type of psychiatric specialty. I have seen, in this widening definition, an opportunity to overcome a frustration that engulfs psychiatrists with respect to their inability to make much therapeutic headway with the traditional mental cases. Finally, I have attempted to consider some of the hidden implications for psychiatry in the proposal for this new psychiatric specialty.

REFERENCES

1. Barton, W. E. Presidential address—Psychiatry in transition. *Amer. J. Psychiat.*, 1962, 119:1–15.
2. Belknap. I. *Human problems of state mental hospital.* New York: McGraw-Hill, 1956.
3. Bernard, V. Some interrelationships of training for community psychiatry, community mental health programs and research in social psychiatry. In *Proceedings of Third World Congress of psychiatry*. Montreal, Canada: McGill University and University of Toronto Press, 1961. Vol. 3, pp. 67–71.
4. Caudill, W. *Psychiatric hospital as a small society.* Cambridge: Harvard University Press, 1958.
5. Cumming, J., and Cumming, E. *Closed ranks: Experiment in mental health education.* Cambridge: Harvard University Press, Commonwealth Fund, 1957.
6. Duhl, L. J. Problems in training psychiatric residents in community psychiatry. Paper read before the Institute on Training in Community Psychiatry at University of California, Texas, Columbia, and Chicago, mimeographed, Fall-Winter, 1963–1964.
7. Dunham, H. W. *Sociological theory and mental disorder.* Detroit: Wayne State University Press, 1959, chap. 6.
8. Dunham, H. W., and Weinberg, S. K. *Culture of state mental hospital.* Detroit: Wayne State University Press, 1960.
9. Goldhamer, H., and Marshall, A. *Psychoses and civilization.* Glencoe, Ill.: Free Press, 1953.
10. Goldston, S. E. Training in community psychiatry: Survey report of medical school departments of psychiatry. *Amer. J. Psychiat.*, 1964, 120:789–92.

11. Hoch, P. H. In therapeutic accomplishments of mental health clinics. *Ment. Hyg. News,* June, 1963, pp. 1–3.
12. Joint Commission on Mental Illness and Health. *Action for Mental Health.* New York: Basic Books, 1961.
13. Jones, M. *Therapeutic community: New treatment method in psychiatry.* New York: Basic Books, 1953.
14. Kennedy, J. F. Message from President of United States relative to mental illness and mental retardation: February 5, 1963. *Amer. J. Psychiat.,* 1964, 120:729–37.
15. Kobrin, S. Chicago area project—25-year assessment. *Ann. Amer. Acad. Political Soc. Sci.,* 1959, 322:20–29.
16. Menninger, W. *Psychiatry in troubled world.* New York: Macmillan, 1948.
17. Merton, R. K. Social structures and anomie. In *Social theory and social structure.* Glencoe, Ill.: Free Press, 1949. Pp. 125–50.
18. Plunkett, R. J., and Gordon, J. E. *Epidemiology and mental illness.* New York: Basic Books, 1960.
19. Powers, E., and Witmer, H. *Experiment in prevention of delinquency.* New York: Columbia University Press, 1951.
20. Srole, L., et al. *Mental health in metropolis: Midtown Manhattan study,* vol. 1. New York: McGraw-Hill, 1962.
21. Stanton, A., and Schwartz, M. S. *Mental hospital: Study of institutional participation in psychiatric illness and treatment.* New York: Basic Books, 1954.
22. Szasz, T. S. *Myth of mental illness: Foundations of theory of personal conduct.* New York: Harper, 1961.
23. Thompson, C. B. Psychiatry and social crisis. *J. Clin. Psychopath.,* 1946, 7:697–711.

5

Community Mental Health:
A Movement in Search of a Theory

J. R. NEWBROUGH [1]

MENTAL health, as a descriptive phrase, means many things depending upon the speaker, the context, and the audience. It is constantly used in several different ways:

1. *Mental health as a goal.* This is a set of ideas and beliefs that life in the future can be a better and more satisfying experience than it is now. This is the definition used for programs to promote mental health.

2. *Mental health as a euphemism for mental illness.* Mental health is often used to refer to work by professionals and citizens groups alike to help people in trouble or to prevent them from getting into trouble.

3. *Mental health as a personality characteristic.* Jahoda (12) describes two ways of viewing mental health in personality terms. It may be seen as a relatively constant and enduring function of personality yielding classifications of the health of a person; *or* it may be seen as a less permanent function of personality and the situation yielding a classification of the adequacy of actions or behavior.

4. *Mental health as a characteristic of society.* Situations or societies are often called healthy or sick. Frank's *Society as the Patient* (7) and *The Sane Society* by Fromm (8) are examples of this. With this meaning, one talks about society either: (1) as a unit which is ill, or (2) as an environment which makes people ill.

I cite these uses as evidence for the ambiguity of the term *mental health*. For purposes of this discussion, I will talk about mental health as referring to mentally ill or mentally disordered behavior, and will consider the definitions of such problems as: (1) health problems, and (2) social problems.

Community mental health has become a term which refers to all the activities carried out in the community [2] in the name of mental health. These

Reprinted from *Community Mental Health: Individual Adjustment or Social Planning?* Bethesda: NIMH, 1964, 1–18, by permission of the author. Dr. Newbrough is Associate Professor, George Peabody College for Teachers.

[1] I am indebted to D. N. Lloyd, F. V. Mannino, and Howard J. Ehrlich for critically reading this paper.

[2] The community here means the places in which the person carries on his daily life—of being with his family, or earning a living, or living among friends and neighbors.

' activities include diagnosis and treatment in clinics and agencies, day or night care in hospitals, consultation around various personal and behavioral problems, research on mental problems through such means as case registers or surveys, and training of professionals to work on mental health problems.

It is the purpose of this symposium to provide a rather general view of community mental health as it is conceived in the United States—a view of services, research, and training. The function of the discussants is to consider what the implications of these activities and ideas are for application in their own work and in the mental health work of their countries.

MENTAL ILLNESS AS A HEALTH PROBLEM

The history of mental ill-health first as *insanity* and, more recently, as *mental illness,* shows that the problem has, for nearly two centuries, been regarded as a biological malady which requires medical treatment (2, 17). The mind was thought to have a neurological base; mental disorder was then considered to be a biological disorder.

In professional medicine, a major concern has been to define mental disorder properly so that the appropriate treatments could be devised. Benjamin Rush in 1783 began a life of work which approached mental illness scientifically to understand and treat it. He was apparently the first physician in the U.S. to do so, and thus the organic tradition in psychiatry was begun (17). Prior to 1800, however, the general climate of opinion held that insanity was virtually incurable and thus did not warrant serious attention or work (2).

Over the next decade or two, however, the effects of the Enlightenment began to be felt in the United States. There was a growing conviction that man was perfectible, that he could control the environment and that life on earth could be perfected (2). Out of this grew the "moral treatment" approach, a social treatment similar to what is now called milieu therapy or therapeutic community. It was designed to appeal to the moral sense of the patient through example and to teach him to return good for good; it gave value to the physical setting and the social influences of the hospital or educative agents (2).

Development of moral treatment was limited to a few institutions and enlightened practitioners. Diffusion of the new knowledge was uncertain and not widespread to either the general medical pracitioners or the lay public. Dain describes the nineteenth-century lay thought as similar to that of eighteenth-century medicine: insanity could not be cured and, thus, lunatics suffered long and severe confinements.

Dorothea Dix came upon the national scene in 1841 to provide a major impetus for a redefinition of insanity by the lay public. Up to that time, asylums were privately funded and existed only for the wealthy. Treatment institutions for the poor would require funding from public moneys. Therefore Miss Dix set about emphasizing insanity as a social problem. She, in fact, blamed society for almost all insanity and held it responsible for its victims, the mentally ill. Her work built on the professional thought begun by Rush, and led to the widespread recognition of the need for public mental hospitals.

The next major social event to further the cause of the movement to reform the care of the mentally ill was the publication of the book *The Mind That Found Itself* by Clifford Beers. This was supported by a number of eminent men of the day (including Adolph Meyer and William James) and was the beginning of a formal citizens organization, now called the National Association for Mental Health.

Adolph Meyer was an important figure in the development of the definition now used for community mental health. His conceptions of psychobiology represented a formal attempt to see mental illness as a condition where environmental aspects were as important as individual biological ones. He viewed the unit of concern (man-in-nature) as an ecological one; that is, man in his natural settings (20). This system of thought has led to the interest in sociology by workers in mental health—and to an interest in the effects of the environment upon mental disorder (19, 21).

"Social psychiatry," "community psychiatry," and "community mental health" are ways of referring to the fact that sociological thinking is increasingly permeating the mental health field. A recent bibliographic effort attempting to prepare a reference guide to the field found that social science concepts were pervasive in the writing on, and were of relevance to, community mental health (10). There has also been the realization that since this health problem occurs in the community it becomes a public health problem. As a public health problem, mental health takes on the status of a major social problem; a social problem, however, with the concepts of prevention and cure taken from an orientation toward individual health. Most of the applied professional writings in community mental health talk about the social aspects of individual health problems.

MENTAL ILLNESS AS A SOCIAL PROBLEM

Mental illness is nowadays regarded both by professional workers and the general public as a national social problem *as well as* a health problem. The effects of the lay movement as well as the professional climate of opinion can be seen in the following facts:

1. There is a National Mental Health Week designated by the President of the United States to call attention to the problem.

2. There have been a series of national laws to provide for programs in mental health:

    a. *National Mental Health Act of 1946* established the National Institute of Mental Health and its program of services, grants and research on problems of mental maladjustments.

b. *National Mental Health Study Act of 1955* established the Joint Commission on Mental Illness and Health to analyze and evaluate the needs and resources of the mentally ill and to make recommendations for a national mental health program.

c. *Mental Retardation Facilities and Community Mental Health Centers Construction Act of 1963* provided local services to deal with problems of mental retardation and mental ill-health.

The legislation has been supported with massive amounts of public money, and represents a major investment of national resources in the recognition and solution of problems of people.

Most of this activity received its major push into public consciousness with World War II. Here the problems of mental ill health became very apparent with 850,000 men rejected by the draft as unfit for military service, and the large number of psychiatric casualties from the war which had to be cared for by the Veterans Administration.[3] Over the twenty years since the war, mental illness has experienced the momentum of the increased federal and citizen support as mentioned above. The terms of mental disorder—anxiety, depression, compulsion, schizophrenia—have become common household words.

Where mental health is defined as a social problem, problems of behavior are seen to be signs of social disorder. The behavior of the mentally ill represents socially intolerable deviance from patterns of normal or expected behavior. Treatment from this approach is then organized to deal with the deviation—either to make it conform or to separate it from the rest of society.[4]

COMMUNITY MENTAL HEALTH AS THE FINAL COMMON PATH [5]

It would appear that the mental health movement [6] has been a unifying force, a final common path, for these two rather different orientations toward mental illness. The *health-problem orientation* is one where there is concern about individual well-being, with curing illness, and with establishing a state which has been called "high-level-wellness" (4, 13). There are themes of individualism which have appealed to the general public and have been consonant with the national ideal of the good man.

The *social-problem orientation* has the efficient functioning of the society as its goal. It is concerned with the social cost of deviant behavior. The monetary cost, as one aspect of the total social cost, has been well calculated

[3] Forty-three per cent of all Army discharges were for neuropsychiatric disorders (19).

[4] For more discussion of this orientation see references 1, 5, 23, and 24.

[5] For a more extensive discussion of the two separate orientations and their interaction, see Sanford (22). He also deals with the difficulties encountered in planning for mental health services which arise from "these two viewpoints."

[6] By "movement" is meant the activities (public, private, and individual) carried out in the name of mental health.

by Fein in *Economics of Mental Illness* (6). Social disorganization, as another cost, has been discussed by Leighton in *My Name is Legion* (15), *People of Cove and Woodlot* (11), and the *Character of Danger* (16). The goal is the balance of the system; problems are thought about in terms of deviance and conformity.

There is often the situation where the public official who is planning programs views mental disorders as problems of society and of moral turpitude. He seeks support from the citizen who thinks about the programs as being helpful to the solution of personal problems. Whether the two goals can be served in this one movement is entirely an open question, especially when there is no special distinction drawn between them and where services are discussed generally as "mental health" programs.

THE LACK OF THEORY

Mental health has been an ambiguously defined term since the movement began. Kingsley Davis (3), almost thirty years ago, discussed this as a major problem—a problem which kept the movement from being very successful in achieving a goal of prevention. The problem seems to reside in the minds of the mental health workers. Though they think and say that they are working to prevent mental disorder, Davis argues that they *actually* are engaged in the prevention of moral delinquency. Pressures are exerted on people to behave properly in the name of scientific knowledge, but proper behavior is judged by the values of the social group.

If one looks closely at what is going on within the mental health movement, one sees various groups of people with differing training engaged in different activities with differing goals. The general orientation, however, is that they are working *against* mental illness. They may want mental health as a positive state for different reasons, but all can agree to being against mental illness.

In the United States, as in all industrialized societies where the standards of living are generally high, the people are faced with a new problem. This new problem is the planning for the future in such a way that positive improvements will take place. Planning has been extremely difficult to do; it becomes involved with the selection of philosophical goals, and uses scientific knowledge mainly in the process of getting to the goals. Science, per se, is not very helpful in deciding just what the goals should be. Decisions are more usually made when all the interested parties can agree to some compromise direction.

The history of the world has been based on a continual struggle for survival. With this, the emphasis in society was on "getting rid of the bad." Marginal groups like the aged, the crippled, the retarded, and the insane were, in some societies, expendable.[7] Industrially based affluence has allowed society

[7] I am grateful to D. N. Lloyd for bringing this thinking about cultural evolution to my attention. For a more general treatment of cultural evolution see Mackie and

to retain marginal groups—but its philosophy, as a carryover from the past, is still to do away with them. There is either pressure to change their behavior, so that the problematic people will stop causing trouble, or to maintain them separately, as in prisons or mental hospitals. The more sophisticated techniques now include ways to change other people's views of the behavior as well as to change the behavior itself. The possibility that the marginal or deviant group might be used as a functional and constructive part of the society has not yet occurred to most people.[8]

At the present stage in the development of programs for dealing with mental health problems, there is no specific theory about mental health which overrides all others. The approaches to prevention and treatment of conditions in a population have come from public health. This orientation has worked well for the eradication of communicable disease, since the system components of host, agent, and environment approximate rather well the way the biological system of the human individual functions and the way it responds to disequilibria. In the application of public health thinking to mental health, it has been found that the concept of a disease entity with causal agents has not been very helpful in studying or treating mental disorder. This failure has led, I think, to the increased interest by medicine in psychological and sociological theory.

It has been asserted with increasing frequency that the biological model (called by some, the medical model) is inapplicable to mental disorder, and should be replaced by social or cultural models. I will offer an interpretation of the biological model which makes it compatible with other systems theory whether it is mechanical or social. To begin with, biological, organic, and medical practitioners, it seems, have come to regard the biological functioning of the human as based on a number of invariant relationships. Introduction of drug A will yield effect B. These strong relationships, however, are imposed by the extremely limited variations within the living organism. Temperature, blood sugar, and oxygen levels are examples of processes that can vary only over a restricted range without threatening the identity of the entire unit. Very small deviations from the norms can be detected and are called symptoms of systemic disequilibria, or disease.

But consider the entity of a social system such as the family. Variation is

---

Rafferty (18). Such a teleological interpretation of evolution may offend many readers especially cultural anthropologists, but I have used this oversimplification to highlight the point that while the technology and resources of our society have advanced to a point where life patterns can be radically altered, the ideas and values of people stand in the way.

[8] The U.S. seems still to be eradicate-the-bad oriented. Community action and development, preventive medicine and public health programs are often viewed with suspicion. A war on poverty, however, is eminently understandable and receives widespread support. Erikson (5) has begun to think about how the state of deviance is useful to society and discusses the possibility that society recruits and maintains people into this status in order to maintain its identity. If this be the case, then perhaps deviance can be defined so that it is a more pleasant experience for people, or so that they can rejoin the general society without social stigmata after serving their time as a deviant.

tremendous. Time and space locations of the entity and its subparts are extremely variable. Everyone, for example, is together only for brief times such as at meals, in the evening, on weekends, when going on trips. Most of the functioning, therefore, is between subparts of the unit—with some members away from the interaction process for long periods. The subparts do not have the same history of experience. Coping can be brought about with many different means that are not necessarily harmful to the entity. If two family members do not get along with each other, they can set up schedules by which they reduce or avoid contact. Such separate functions biologically could not be tolerated. Consider the serious effects on the system of such a separation between one's head and his hand. The result would be palsy or paralysis.

With the variations so much greater within the social system, the determination of regularities within it is a much more complicated affair. One must try to keep constant a multitude of things; the number of people, their ages, background experiences, etc. Similiarities between naturally organized social units are difficult, perhaps even impossible, to find. Perhaps the only way to *experiment* with such social groups is with the simulation of them in the laboratory so that the important variables may be controlled.[9] First, however, the important job is the systematic identification, description, and classification of the social units in man's natural environment and the ways in which they interrelate. When this has been done, one then should have sufficient knowledge about how to go into experimentation.[10]

My contention here has been that systems theory is a productive way of looking at social functioning; it is consonant, not disjunctive, with the *biological model*.

THE ECOLOGICAL MODEL

Building upon the systems theory approach to the study of human behavior, I would like to propose an *ecological model* as being both helpful in conceptually dealing with the complexities of social systems and in mounting descriptive research inquiries into man's social behavior.

First, one must begin by accepting the fact that each social system is unique—that it is organized in a particular way, that it has a personality like a person and that no other system is like it. This is the psychology of individual differences applied to a social group. The regularities for which one searches are patterns of function and interrelationships, not patterns of in-

---

[9] Simulation with an electronic computer as the integrating force has become popular in such areas as business management training, the study of political processes, and the training of military personnel to operate a radar station (9). Probably the next set of developments in community mental health will be the use of simulation to study the development and control of mentally disordered behavior.

[10] Perhaps what is needed is a kind of human relations area files for the communities in which we carry out our research.

dividual behavior. Symptomatology in physical illness often *seems* invariant because of the very restricted variability within the biological system; therefore, one can have generally applicable symptoms across different people.

Symptomatology of social system dysfunction can be regarded as a similar process in that some behaviors or patterns of behavior can reflect systemic dysfunction. But first one must know what the regular functions of the system are. Before we can tell whether a husband's physical aggression toward his wife is appropriate, we must establish what are the usual patterns of interaction within that household. To generalize, the point, then, is that mentally ill behavior can be so judged only in relationship to the context in which it occurs; its expression will tell us: (1) that its form is a deviation from expectations in that particular environment, and (2) will tell us something about the nature of those expectations. Thus, the standards or norms for behavior are specific to the social group; the modes of deviance are expressions of those norms. The extent to which people outside the family (e.g., physician or clergyman) are called to help deal with deviant behavior provides indications of the variability of behavior which is tolerated by the community.

Ecology has its roots in plant and animal biology in the study of the adaptation of organisms to their environment. Human ecology is derived from geography and sociology as well. These go together to provide a means for studying the unit of man in his environment. Theodorson (25) distinguishes the *biotic* level of human organization where the struggle for existence is primary, and the *cultural* level, where human behavior is interrelated in social forms. We must be concerned with both in our ecological model in order to provide a basis for inquiries into the nature of man's living patterns, and their disruption into mentally disordered behavior (14).

The major reason for using the model of ecology in community mental health is to begin from a point which assumes that virtually all problems of people are *specific* to themselves and their particular situation. From this position, there is no *general* mental health problem. Communities must be seen as personalities, as unique organizations of forces, needs, and resources. Services should be custom tailored, research should tell us how the tailoring might be done, and training should provide the skillful tailor.

REFERENCES

1. Becker, H. S. *Outsiders: Studies in the sociology of deviance.* New York: Free Press, 1963.
2. Dain, N. *Concepts of insanity in the United States, 1789–1865.* New Brunswick, N. J.: Rutgers University Press, 1964.
3. Davis, K. Mental hygiene and the class structure. *Psychiat.,* 1938, 1:55–65.
4. Dunn, H. L. *High level wellness: A collection of twenty-nine short talks on different aspects of the theme "High-level wellness for man and society."* Arlington, Virginia: R. W. Beatty Co., 1961.

5. Erikson, K. T. Notes on the sociology of deviance. *Soc. Problems,* 1962, Spring, 307–14.
6. Fein, R. *Economics of mental illness.* New York: Basic Books, 1958.
7. Frank, L. K. *Society as the patient: Essays on culture and personality.* New Brunswick, N. J.: Rutgers University Press, 1948.
8. Fromm, E. *The sane society.* New York: Rinehart, 1955.
9. Guetzkow, H. S. (Ed.) *Simulation in the social sciences.* Englewood Cliffs, N. J.: Prentice-Hall, 1962.
10. Harvard Medical School and Psychiatric Service, Massachusetts General Hospital. *Community mental health and social psychiatry.* Cambridge: Harvard University Press, 1962.
11. Hughes, C. C., Tremblay, M. A., Rapoport, R. N., and Leighton, A. H. *People of cove and woodlot.* New York: Basic Books, 1960.
12. Jahoda, M. *Current concepts of positive mental health.* New York: Basic Books, 1958.
13. Kaufmann, M. A. High-level wellness, a pertinent concept for the health professions. *Ment. Hyg.,* 1963, 47:57–62.
14. Kelly, J. G. A preface for an eco-system analysis of community mental health services. 1963.
15. Leighton, A. H. *My name is legion: Foundations for a theory of man in relation to culture.* New York: Basic Books, 1959.
16. Leighton, D. C., Harding, J. S., Machlin, D. B., Macmillan, A. M., and Leighton, A. H. *The character of danger.* New York: Basic Books, 1963.
17. Lewis, N. D. C. American psychiatry from its beginnings to World War II. In S. Arieti (Ed.), *American handbook of psychiatry,* vol. I. New York: Basic Books, 1959.
18. Mackie, J. B., and Rafferty, F. T. Specific and general evolution: The psychological implications of two kinds of cultural change. Baltimore: Psychiatric Institute, University of Maryland Medical School, 1964.
19. Mora, G. Recent American psychiatric developments (since 1939). In S. Arieti (Ed.), *American handbook of psychiatry,* vol. I. New York: Basic Books, 1959.
20. Muncie, W. The psychobiological approach. In S. Arieti (Ed.), *American handbook of psychiatry,* vol. II. New York: Basic Books, 1959.
21. Rossi, A. M. Some pre-World War II antecedents of community mental health theory and practice. *Ment. Hyg.,* 1962, 46:78–94.
22. Sanford, F. The rising tide of mental health. *Publ. Hlth. Reports,* 1957, 72:605–8.
23. Scheff, T. J. Social support for stereotypes of mental disorder. *Ment Hyg.,* 1963, 47:461–69.
24. Scheff, T. J. The role of the mentally ill and the dynamics of mental disorder: a research framework. *Sociometry,* 1963, 26:436–53.
25. Theodorson, G. A. (Ed.) *Studies in human ecology.* New York: Row, Peterson, 1961.

II
ELEMENTS OF PLANNING AND PROGRAM DEVELOPMENT

ALTHOUGH numerous elements of planning are included in this section, it is certain that many others have been omitted. The section moves from the social and ecological requirements of the community to a discussion of planning issues, legislation, and finances, to administrative considerations, and finally to the physical needs of bricks and mortar in the program.

Taken as a whole, the selections illustrate the complexities of developing a mental health program that represents an accurate response to existing and future problems in an area.

To assist in the assessment of community dynamics, Klein formulates a conceptual framework. Fabrics of his framework include physical characteristics of the area about the mental health center, the self image of the community, the social-psychological structure, and the interplay of forces in the community. By collecting this data, a "sense of community" can be secured which will have implications for a more effective development of a community mental heatlh program.

Consistent with an ecological thesis, Kelly offers four principles for community mental health programming. First, he notes that the total community has to be considered as the client; second, that mental health services are designed to reduce high demand for total community service. A third point relates to the creation of professional and research services to local community resources; and, lastly, the author cites the principle of planning for change.

Relating to more effective use of community resources, Greving delineates a two-fold problem: how to keep people out of hospitals, and how to get people out of institutions as soon as possible. Communities must deal with the problem at three levels: the economic level, the adjustment level, and the level of mental illness. Therefore, an integrated system of discovery and identification of ambulatory clinical treatment of nursing home care and of hospital care is a prime requirement. The end result should be a flow of needs and problems to the right service at the right time.

Nationwide planning efforts from 1963 to 1965 were made with an almost evangelistic fervor. Now, aspirations and promises need to be converted into action. Schulberg presents varying concepts of community mental health programs and comments on their implications. Realignment of available resources will result in major and minor changes affecting nonmental health as well as mental health care-giving agents. Renewed importance of citizen committees will help in implementing goals.

Social and professional aspects of community mental health administration are influenced by factors which are often overlooked or operate behind the scenes. Dörken calls attention to the need to explore the potential mental health effects of adverse social conditions and the relatively few investigations and evaluations resulting in continuous program analysis. In addition, he discusses the family therapy-agency complex, the mental health center-hospital relationship, the oft proclaimed but seldom activated concept of prevention, and, finally, routine but important items such as financing, location, salaries, and professional standards.

A key problem in providing comprehensive community health and welfare services is that they need to be subordinated to the needs of individual clients. Techniques for developing interrelations and cooperation generally involve planned communications activities designed to recognize different agency interests. Administrative and/or financial arrangements that build interdependency and interchange into the system are stressed. Halpert and Silverman cite various examples to illustrate alternative methods of achieving interagency cooperation.

Financing of mental health services is important because of its magnitude, its costs in dollars and in human terms, and the historical assumption of the major burden by the public sector. Atwell cites statistics relevant to state mental hospital systems, to private institutions, to services in general hospitals, to private practice, and to community services. In describing the impact of federal funding programs on the budgets of state and local governments, he notes that the community services may cost more in the short run. However, over the long run, mental hospitals as we know them today may be eliminated.

Hall examines how mental disorders and their treatments fit into the overall structure of health insurance and prepayment. Although there is no such thing today as an overall program of psychiatric insurance, there is insurance which provides benefits for psychiatric treatment. Hall discusses the requisites of insurance, the problems of definitions, the scope of existing coverage, and the question of the need for a large deductible.

Architectual considerations, as distinct from functional needs, are often not taken into account in building mental health centers. Wheeler realistically discusses the external environment and the internal environment, including lighting, sound control, materials, and forms. More than most, Wheeler feels the mental patient needs an environment of security, comfort, freedom, and beauty to help him get well.

Finally, Falick states the case for a team approach to designing a mental health center, an approach in which the architect and the client clearly and cooperatively define the problems and goals of the center. The final design should evolve as a synthesis of the best possible solutions, with understanding the needs of the community and of the individual patient as the key to success.

6

The Community and Mental Health:
An Attempt at a Conceptual Framework

DONALD C. KLEIN

THE clinical worker new to community work and his citizen collaborators in the community may question the need for a special conceptual view
of community to guide them in their work. As lifelong participants in multiple
communities, they justifiably may lay claim to knowledge based on first-hand
experience. To suggest that they do not have, on the basis of their experiences,
sufficient understanding of the communities in which they work may seem
strange to some. The suggestion is analogous to that of dynamic psychology
when it questions the adequacy of the average person's common sense view
of himself. This paper is based on the assumptions: (a) that it is important
for professional mental health workers to maintain an objective and comprehensive view of community processes; and (b) that it is often difficult to
do so, especially when the worker is confronted by community issues and
events which are personally involving or which appear to threaten the very
program to which he is committed.

The image of community which is developed in this paper is intended to
serve as a rough territorial map which may help the mental health worker
maintain some bearings as he functions within the complexities of the community. It is an attempt at a dynamic synthesis of a clinical point of view,
with research and theory drawn from the social sciences, and empirical observations made within an ongoing community mental health program at the
Human Relations Service of Wellesley, Inc.

It is believed that any comprehensive view of a community for mental
health purposes should take into account (a) the physical and topographical
characteristics of the setting, (b) the community's "self-image," that is, the
view of the community held by its inhabitants, (c) the nature of community
groups and their characteristic interaction patterns, and (d) the dynamic
interplay of dominant community forces. In the discussion of each area which
follows, there is no attempt to be categorically comprehensive. Rather, the
effort is made to indicate the scope of the phenomena and their implications
for the development of mental health programs.

Reprinted from *Community Mental Health Journal,* 1965, *1,* 301–308, by permission
of the publisher and the author. © 1965, Behavioral Publications, Inc. Dr. Klein is
Program Director, National Training Laboratories, Institute for Applied Behavioral
Science.

PHYSICAL CHARACTERISTICS OF THE COMMUNITY

Where is the community located geographically and with respect to such things as: (a) natural resources, (b) trade and travel routes, and (c) other communities? It should be apparent to the casual observer that the natural resources available to any community dictate to a large extent the character of its economy. The suitable natural resources of some communities are organized around tourists and the tourist trade. Other communities find themselves engaged in mining and the extracting and processing of these natural resources. Other communities are manufacturing centers, and so on.

Trade and travel routes determine the extent to which residents of the community may be in contact with other areas and surrounding regions. Is this the kind of community which is accessible to the outer world? Is this a remote and isolated community into which strangers or "furriners" rarely come? Finally, is the community larger, smaller, or the same size as the surrounding communities? Is it a "satellite community," adjacent to a county seat, or a larger city or town in which are located most of the educational, trade, and cultural resources of its region. Perhaps it is one of the many burgeoning suburban towns growing up around our metropolitan areas from which wage earners emerge in the morning and to which they return at night; the so-called "bedroom" communities of modern America.

PHYSICAL SIZE

Size of a community can be expressed in population density and in trends of population growth or shrinkage, as well as in sheer physical dimensions. Most communities have grown since World War II, sometimes markedly so. Therefore, in most cases it is appropriate to consider what resources, what agencies, and what people in the community are paying attention to population trends? Is there any integrated plan with respect to this? What are some of the effects of this community's growth? What happens to the new people? Are there conflicts between newcomers and the old timers?

POPULATION DENSITY

The factor of population density is just beginning to be studied from the standpoint of mental health. Plant and animal biologists have some notion about the importance of this factor. When two kinds of distribution of the same number of items in the population exist, the conditions under which these trees and other plant and animal life live are very different. A striking and often used example, involves two groves of redwood trees, each consisting of one hundred trees. In one grove the trees are much closer together while in the other they are spread out over a considerable area. The sun penetrates one grove and not the other. Certain kinds of fauna and flora will flourish in one environment and not in the other. There have been some studies of urban communities which suggest that different kinds of behavior and emotional difficulties occur in the center of congested community areas than occurs in outer rings of a community. Outer rings are usually less densely inhabited, and inhabited by different kinds of individuals.

LOCATION AND RESOURCES

Another significant physical characteristic is the location in the community of the various services, agencies, and institutions: schools and hospitals, the main shopping areas, the main arteries within the town, and connecting roads that link one section of a community to another. The consideration of location is obviously important when thinking about the placement of a mental health center, since experience indicates that different clientele are attracted to a clinic depending upon its physical locus within the community. In some places, both the disadvantaged and elite groups in the population often reside in sections which are isolated from the main body of the community and which have few roads connecting them to the rest of the town. Such isolation may well affect the extent of use to which a mental health center or other community resource may be put by either group.

TOPOGRAPHY

Common sense recognizes the influence of topography upon community life. In literature it is common for authors to think of regional differences in terms of topographical features, i.e., the frequent reference to the "*rock-ribbed, reserved New Englander.*" Whether or not topography influences character formation, it does affect real estate values and population distributions. In many communities, for example, the more economically favored sections of the population are more apt to live in the geographically more elevated sections of town.

THE COMMUNITY'S VIEW OF ITSELF

Attention should be directed to the "phenomenology" of the community, that is, the ways in which residents view their community (6, 7). Such perceptions constitute a kind of community self-image, usually based on history and traditions handed down from the past. How are such self-images organized? Each community seems to be able to say about itself, "We are such and such kind of folks." Some communities think of themselves as friendly places; others consist of people who "mind our own business"; a few communities have been studied where the residents accept a self-appraisal which essentially states "we are a bunch of no-goods"; another community may consist of "hustlers and go-getters"; and still another may be inhabited by "rugged individualists." It seems reasonable to expect that such differing community self-images would lead to quite varied responses to the introduction of mental health programs.

GUIDING VALUES

There are the values upheld in the community which guide and direct action: "We hold these truths to be self-evident" in *our* community. Some causes are readily mobilized around certain dominant values and still other causes will not flourish because they seem to be inconsistent or opposed to them.

Several often divergent and even conflicting values may coexist in a single community. Often separate values are upheld by different segments of the population but sometimes the same individuals may appear to subscribe to apparently conflicting value orientations. How does this affect the mental health field? As an example, one might think that the acceptable value of the need "to care for our own" would facilitate the organization of a local mental hygiene clinic to treat adults and children. On the other hand, such an enterprise might seem to conflict with a different value orientation espousing free enterprise because the mental health center becomes viewed as an expression of socialized medicine. Conflicting values in the same individual as well as in the same community are integrated in a variety of ways. But such integrations of dissonance are only beginning to be understood by students of personality, let alone observers of the modern community.

A value conflict frequently observed in such institutions as mental hospitals and prisons is the conflict between the "soft" treatment-oriented, remedial values as opposed to the sterner, more "hard-headed," punitive and judgmental values. Both coexist and are strongly upheld in American society. Usually, mental health centers seem to have relatively little difficulty in entering into contact with the educational segments of the community, but have much more difficulty in establishing cooperative relationships with the law enforcement segments. It may be speculated that communities do not encourage a close cooperation between the "soft" values of the mental health center and the "hard" values upheld by the more punitive agents. Mental health enterprises in some communities may be allowed to flourish just because they do not unduly affect the conflicting values as often expressed and fulfilled by the law enforcement people, among others.

COMMUNITY STYLE

Each community seems to say in one way or another, "we have our own ways of doing things." It is useful to look at how decisions are made in a community and how new ideas may be proposed and implemented in the population. In one community, luncheon meetings seem to be favored; in another, letters to the editor have greater impact; and another may launch a new idea with great public fanfare in a central auditorium accompanied by considerable community-wide publicity.

In the organization of mental health associations and mental health centers, it would seem important to: (a) pay attention to the community's view of itself, (b) determine what kind of folks the inhabitants of this town feel they are, (c) ascertain which truths are upheld as self-evident when applied to human nature and community life, and (d) note the acceptable ways in which new ideas are proposed and decisions are made.

STRUCTURAL CHARACTERISTICS OF COMMUNITY GROUPING

The social-psychological structure of the community can be view from the standpoints of the socioeconomic characteristics of the population, and patterns of interaction between groups, agencies, and institutions. Looking first at socioeconomic characteristics, the observer would do well to note the nationality groups represented, the religious institutions present, the educational levels of the population, the occupations pursued, and the age distribution. Such factors would appear to influence the way in which the mental health resources as well as other community services are used. On the other hand, these factors also affect the nature of the problems to be found in the population. There is a growing body of evidence to suggest that mental illnesses are distributed differentially in the population according to socioeconomic characteristics. The studies by Hollingshead and Redlich (3) indicate that, in New Haven at least, there is a far greater prevalence of diagnosed cases of schizophrenia among working class segments of the population than among middle and upper class groups. Even the nature of treatment provided by professionally trained people in the hospital setting differs according to the socioeconomic background of the patients.

It is useful for the observer of the community to attempt to map or diagram the patterns of interaction between groups, agencies, and institutions. What are some of the social-psychological features which can be noted from a structural point of view?

AUTHORITY

First, there are those segments of the community occupying positions of authority *vis-a-vis* other segments. Authority in this sense is being used to designate the formal responsibilities given to governmental and other bodies. Authority may or may not be accompanied by an equally high level of prestige.

Such authority is often accompanied by power, but is by no means synonymous with it.

POWER

Power is the ability to influence decisions and actions of other people. Viewed in another sense, it is the extent of the individual's or group's ability to block or facilitate the gratification of the needs of other people. Power over all mankind would be secured almost immediately by the individual or group who learned how to control the supply of air which people breathe. Obviously, power viewed in this way can be seen to vary according to the area of need in question. For example, the county commissioners may have great influence and power over the mental health center where finances are involved but it may be counterbalanced by the commissioners' recognition of the professional skills which can be provided by the staff. Such a reciprocal or interdependent situation is perhaps the optimal one for the development of close working relationships and shared problem solving between the governmental body and the mental health center; a sharing based on recognition of mutual needs.

Power patterns in communities differ according to the degree to which they are stable and fixed, or unstable and fluctuating. Expanding population areas, for example, often seem to be typified by highly unstable power structures. They are often marked by sharp cleavages between the newcomers and the old timers. As a result, social planning for health, education, and social welfare enterprises may become inadvertently enmeshed in the already existing struggles for power on the part of different factions. A mental health center thus may become a political issue, although it would hardly appear that one political party would in actuality tend to be more mental health oriented than another. Such cleavages may run through all aspects of community life and may set up barriers to planning in the area of mental health until the reasonable issues regarding the mental health needs of the community are clearly separated from the less reasonable ones grounded in such factors as unstable power distribution.

The well-known studies by Hunter (4), Freeman, et al. (1,2), and others indicate that recognized top power figures or decision makers in most communities are drawn from the following groups: those controlling natural resources, those controlling financial reserves, those in charge of means of production, as well as certain prestige figures and certain professionals, with an occasional political leader thrown in for good measure. Hunter maintained that such top power figures do not usually operate visibly in the community or through official channels. Later students of the subject have not confirmed his thesis, however.

A significant power group in the typical modern American community consists of those realtors who act as so-called "gate-keepers," occupying a role which may impinge upon the mental health of newcomers and others. To a greater or lesser extent, they determine into which communities people will move and into which neighborhoods they will settle. Often the realtors feel that economic security and success is bound up with their skill in assigning suitable newcomers to various sections of town. The criteria the realtor uses in his gate-keeper role and the consequences of the sorting process for mental health is not yet sufficiently understood.

PRESTIGE

Most community agencies seek to attract to their boards or other sponsoring bodies prestigious figures in the community. Prestige is usually based on social position, family background, and inherited wealth. It may also reside in individuals whose deep devotion and good sense is recognized when it comes to matters affecting the entire community. Hunter stresses that prestige-figures often may have a latent power position in their communities which they choose to use only on certain occasions.

COMMUNICATION

The communication network of a community represents an extremely important feature which often is dimly perceived and ill understood. Who talks to whom, about what and under what circumstances? Not only do people of similar socioeconomic characteristics sometimes reside close to one another, they also frequently interact with and communicate with one another more readily than with other groups in other sections.

Certain individuals or places in the community serve as communication centers. For example, in one New England community the largest supermarket was found to be the gossip center. Any item of information discussed in the supermarket would spread through the community. In other towns the barber shop, the beauty parlor, the local bar, and even the town dump may serve as gossip or communication centers.

In considering communication, it is customary to distinguish between formal and informal communication. The community observer would do well to note which open formal communication channels exist between various groups. Some groups have well established intercommunications; between others there are no such channels. When formal communication channels do not exist, informal contacts between single individuals often are relied upon. Very often one group believes it has "communicated" with another group through an informal contact of this nature when in actuality no transmission of information has occurred on an intergroup basis. As a result, under some conditions, the first group may reject the second group and may fail to note possible points of alliance because it has misinterpreted inadequate communication to be rejection. Hunter's study of a southern city (4) provides a case in point. He found that the top power figures in the white community rarely knew and therefore could not communicate with their counterparts in the Negro community. Conversely the Negro power figures were not in touch with the white leaders. Both top power groups instead were in contact with "second echelon" power-figures in the other communities. Under such circumstances, it was very difficult indeed for these two subcommunities to come together to identify mutual needs and to solve mutual problems. It is clear that the board of a mental health agency cannot assume that effective communication with a group exists simply because a member of that group is "represented" on the board.

THE DYNAMIC INTERPLAY OF COMMUNITY FORCES

Because community structure and dynamics are closely interrelated, some issues of the dynamics of the community have been touched on in the fore-going discussions of power and communication. In order to consider this topic more systematically, it is useful to consider the community as an integrated field of forces. This assumption leads one to attempt to identify the instru-mentalities whereby the various community values, interests, and groups be-come coordinated. Some communities have truly coordinative community councils or health bodies. In other communities, apparently coordinative groups in actuality represent restricted segments of the population. One may well raise the question of the extent to which the board of a mental health service should seek to serve the community in a coordinative way. To what extent can such a board attempt to assess and interpret community needs in the area of mental health? Is such a coordinative function possible when the agency must, at the same time, represent one of the value areas of the community and, in so doing, compete in the market place with other values and interests?

One of the most significant integrative dynamics of a community from a mental health standpoint concerns the processes whereby help is made avail-able and sought by those in need. More simply stated, what kinds of problems are brought to which resources in the community? Some observers have sug-gested that in the lower socioecenomic groups as much as 80 per cent of the complaints brought to the general practitioners and health clinics have no organic basis but are instead an expression of social and emotional malfunc-tion. Problems which arise from bereavement are obviously more apt to come to the clergyman. In recent years family agencies in many communities noted that they tended to serve lower socioeconomic groups and, in some cases, have attempted to alter this state of affairs. On the other hand, it appears that mental hygiene clinics are turned to most readily by middle class segments of the population. The community observer or planner may wish to ask him-self and the community whether such patterns of helping should be altered or whether they should be reinforced and strengthened? The board and staff of a new mental health center may wish to consider what will happen to help seeking and help giving patterns as the center becomes established in a community. Should the mental health center take over responsibilities for certain psychiatric problems from the care-taking groups already dealing with them in one way or another? Or should the mental health center be in the position of strengthening these care-taking groups in their mental health operations?

The community is a dynamic system; each segment is related to each other segment. Moreover, the community is what Kurt Lewin (5) called a "unified field." By this he meant that a change in one region would affect all other regions. Since the community is a dynamic system and a unified field, it follows that the entry of a mental health team will induce effects of one sort or another throughout the community. These reactions probably will be quite varied depending upon the ways in which the agency is perceived and experienced. One segment of the community may rush forward to collaborate with the mental health effort, and to make use of the resource. Another segment may attack the agency and perhaps even attempt to have it ejected as something alien or dangerous. Still another segment might simply seek to establish as much social psychological distance as possible between it and the agency. Whatever the pattern of response, the notion of the dynamic community would compel the assumption that these responses, in toto, represent an overall pattern rather than haphazard reactions or reactions based primarily on idiosyncrasies of individual citizens or community leaders.

In the community there are groups which are highly receptive to certain influences from the outside, whereas other segments of the community are correspondingly hostile to or avoidant of outside influences. Which groups are receptive and which hostile depends on such factors as the nature of the community and of the outside influence itself. With respect to mental health issues, the pattern of response in various places throughout the country has appeared to be that of relatively greater receptivity on the part of the educational and certain religious systems, antagonism and attack on the part of exponents of law and order, and avoidance on the part of those people and groups most concerned with the maintenance of such cherished community values as neighborhood integrity, real estate land values, and the like.

As a dynamic system, a community exists in some kind of equilibrium or balance of its forces, which, while not static in nature, do act to maintain some form of homeostasis. In some communities, however, the regulatory mechanisms seem relatively poor and there are extremes of oscillation back and forth as, for example, in political power between radical and reactionary groups, or in the commonly observed alternation of government by reform movements and entrenched political bosses. In such communities, a mental heatlh enterprise may enter as part of one phase in the oscillation and later may find itself under severe attack as the system moves back to the other extreme. Moreover, the entry of a mental health center may itself induce oscillation as opposing and restraining forces are mobilized. If not reckoned with, such oscillation might ultimately lead to unforeseen limitations on or even ejection of the center. It is wise for the board and staff of a mental health center to maintain continuing assessment of forces and factors opposing movement towards mental health values with the goal of understanding and, conceivably, altering and reducing rather than overriding them.

A social scientist may view the mental health movement with some skepticism. There are some who go so far as to postulate that the equilibrium of communities depends upon the existence of social pathology, delinquency, mental illness, and other deviant behaviors. This postulate suggests that the stable segment of the society in some way "needs" the unstable. Another way of putting this thesis is to ask, "How can we understand and practice virtue if we cannot observe and know about sin?" Those upholding this position assert that, even when causes of certain kinds of social pathology are well understood, communities seem remarkably unable to mobilize to deal effectively with them. They note, as further corroboration, the ready tendency of social groups to establish scapegoats and marginal members of one sort or another.

The writer's own observations indicate that in virtually every neighborhood area studied residents can and do identify individuals or families disliked by their neighbors. Those disliked are viewed as marginal or deviant in that they cause trouble, seem peculiar, are emotionally upset, or simply are "not like us." Neighborhoods appear to respond in a variety of ways to behaviors which are considered to be deviant, objectionable, or "sick." Under some conditions certain neighborhoods seem to be able to integrate marginal people and to deal effectively with certain problems. Under other circumstances some neighborhoods appear to reinforce and enhance the marginality through a hostile system of isolation and "quarantine." Such community processes are at present little understood. It seems clear, however, that neighborhood patterns and expectations may have considerable influence on the social learning of children, the quality of coping behavior, and the emotional well being of individuals and families. The child who is having difficulties in relationships with parents, and is expressing these difficulties via destructive and aggressive behavior in the neighborhood, may find that neighborhood a force for health, or an additional force for emotional maladjustment, depending on how neighborhood forces are mobilized.

The foregoing cognitive map of community is necessarily limited. In addition to omissions arising from the author's inadequacies, there are inherent limitations common to most maps. The function of a map is to assist the user to accomplish certain specific purposes. Thus a map of transportation facilities may not include the elevations and other details needed for a topographical map. The objective of this paper has not been to provide specific guidance for the mental health worker in the community. Rather, it has been to stimulate his interest in the community and underscore patterned interactions having to do with certain fundamental functions for which communities exist. Clinically trained psychiatrists, psychologists, and social workers develop an ingrained feeling for the dynamics of personality as they are expressed in the behavior of their patients. It is hoped that, for some, these remarks will point the way towards the development of a similar "sense of community" as manifested by the behaviors of clients, consultees, board members, and the many other citizens with whom they work.

REFERENCES

1. Freeman, L. C. et al. *Local community leadership.* Syracuse: University College, 1960.
2. Freeman, L. C. et al. *Metropolitan decision making.* Syracuse: University College, 1962.
3. Hollingshead, A. and Redlich, F. *Social class and mental illness: a community study.* New York: John Wiley & Sons, 1958.
4. Hunter, F. *Community power structure: a study of decision makers.* Chapel Hill: University of North Carolina Press, 1953.
5. Lewin, K. *Field theory in social science.* New York: Harper, 1951.
6. Sanders, I. *Making good communities better.* Lexington: University of Kentucky Press, 1953.
7. Sanders, I. *The community: an introduction to a social system.* New York: Ronald Press, 1958.

7

Ecological Constraints on Mental Health Services

JAMES G. KELLY

THE concept of ecology is particularly relevant for defining a community mental health program. While the federal legislation for the construction of community mental health centers implicity approaches a conceptual statement, the legal language of the legislation does not make explicit reference to public health principles or an ecological thesis (*Federal Register,* 1964). . . . I will view community mental health programs as a problem for human ecology.

An ecological analysis of mental health services refers to at least three different types of problems. One type of problem is essentially an analysis of social or organizational systems, such as a study of the relationship between mental heatlh services and other community services. The assumption for this type of problem is that any change in the operation of one service unit will affect the operation of all other service units. An increase in admissions to one local mental health facility, for example, can be attributed to a decrease in service opportunities at another facility or may indicate changes in stress tolerance for the social structure of the local population. This type of problem is often defined as operations research.

A second type of ecological problem is the study of the relationship between the physical environment and individual behavior. Studies of population density, response of local population groups to public housing, or effects of urban renewal upon styles of living are examples for evaluating the effects of nonpersonal structures upon behavior (7,14,38). The assumption for this type of problem is that urban design has observable constraining or unfolding effects upon social behavior (24,25).

A third type of problem is the study of the relationship of the individual to his immediate social environment (13). Here emphasis is upon interrelations between individuals in specific behavior settings (30,31,34,35). The most apt example of this type of work is Barker's taxonomic studies of a midwest town (2,3,4); as well as the work of naturalists and animal ecologists in their investigations of the social behavior of animals (11,21,23). The most

Reprinted from *American Psychologist,* 1966, *21,* 535–539, by permission of the publisher and the author. © 1966, American Psychological Association. Dr. Kelly is Associate Professor of Clinical Psychology, University of Michigan.

well-documented and replicated finding of this wide range of work is that group size has significant effects upon individual behavior in such diverse units as high schools and bee colonies (5,12,36). The small social group has fewer status differentials, fewer expressions of maladaptive behavior, and a higher work output per unit than larger social groups. For this last type of problem, the assumption is that social structure and individual behavior are reciprocal. It is this premise that is most provocative for considering community mental health programs.

Each of these three types of problems defines a specific social environment, examines the discrete psychological activities within that environment, and then studies the behavior of individuals who are members of the particular social environment. The ecological thesis is that there are predictable patterns of individual behavior which are characteristic of any one social situation and that the expressive behavior of individuals changes in a newly defined social setting.

The federal legislation with the opportunity to construct approximately 1000 mental health centers over the next three years will definitely affect the visibility and, hopefully, the effectiveness of mental health services in most metropolitan areas. Unless there is a clear conception of programming that is independent of brick and mortar, these centers may perpetuate treatment methods which are increasingly outmoded, rather than initiating a new conception of psychological service. While I recognize that the National Institute of Mental Health is actively supporting changes in treatment concepts, we who can benefit from the legislative program are not always ready for the challenge of innovation unless the philosophy for the social change is readily apparent (22,37).

As an initial attempt to express a point of view, I will offer four principles for community mental health programming that are consistent with an ecological thesis.

PRINCIPLE ONE: THE COMMUNITY AS THE CLIENT

The first principle is that assessment methods are focused on the total population rather than on those persons who presently receive a mental health service. Special attention is given to changes in the quantity and form of maladaptive behavior in the population. Under this principle, the staff of the community mental health program in cooperation with other community resources is concerned with predicting the effects of the physical and social structure of the community upon persons who have different styles of living. The community mental health staff also is concerned with anticipating the effects of services upon the adaptive behavior of the population. It is an assumption of an ecological analysis that the expression of adaptive behavior will vary from place to place. Hence, services should also be designed to be multiple and varied. In order to implement this principle, new kinds of basic data will be needed, such as analyses of population movement and knowledge of how persons in the local community manage crises (20). The primary research task is to accurately assess the type of behavior which will be adaptive in one situation and maladaptive in another.

The model for such a program is not clinical psychiatry, psychiatric social work, or even clinical psychology. Instead, it is community development. Mental health services become one part of a total array of services dealing with the emergent behavior of a local population. The generation of new services are closely linked with a continuous evaluation of behavior perceived by representative segments of the local population as problem behavior. In addition to the linkage of mental health services with other community services, there are other alterations in the assessment process. The psychologist active in community mental health work is equally concerned with the analysis of behavior settings as he is with the individual motivations of a client, and he spends as much time in the community as he spends when he is insulated from the community in his private office. In sum, the program is sufficiently accessible to the population so that adequate analysis can precede intervention (8).

PRINCIPLE TWO: REDUCING THE USE OF COMMUNITY SERVICES

One of the advantages of such an approach is that persons who have demonstrated a high risk for service can be identified in their natural setting. The second principle that I am proposing is that mental health services are designed to reduce a high risk for community service. In some communities high-risk groups consist of persons who have demonstrated that they are chronic recipients of multiple community services. In other localities or for other groups of a population a high-risk status may consist of persons who have had multiple contacts but with only one type of service. In both instances, failure to respond to therapeutic efforts may represent multiple factors, including the provision of professional help divergent from the client's culture. A client's apparent maladaptive behavior also may indicate attempts to attain an adaptive solution to an anticipated new role. Deficiencies in mental health services to persons in lower-class cultures can be attributed to inaccessible professionals that has reduced the creation of workable interventions (29,32). Another basis for proposing as a fundamental principle of community programming services to high-risk groups is that mental health services should focus on negatively valued behaviors that are visible but are unserviced. Commitment to the community's unsolved problems helps acquire knowledge that is necessary for effective prevention. The administration of community health programs has indicated that prevention services that reduce the incidence of maladaptive behavior require changes in the social structure of the local population. Before recommendations for change can be considered, knowledge of the current ineffective social structure is essential.

PRINCIPLE THREE: STRENGTHENING COMMUNITY RESOURCES

In addition to a preference for the continuous analysis of community behavior and a commitment to services for the high-risk populations, a third principle for community mental health programming is the creation of professional and research services to local community resources. By initiating the informal coordination of current services, the community mental health program helps to create specific *new* community services as needed. The range of such new services is open. Consultation programs and educational services have been identified in the federal legislation, but these are not exhaustive. Collaboration activities, the creation of staff development institutes, and provision of multiple research services are other examples. To the extent that mental health programming is participating as a community resource, the mental health program takes the leadership in creating a valid basis for problem-solving. Implementing this principle has direct effects on professional training. In addition to competence in psychotherapeutic techniques, this new professional also acquires competence in other methods for producing change (1). Knowledge of consultation concepts, collaboration methods, community organization skills as well as basic methods for community development become essential (15,19). As the mental health professions acquire these skills, they also become more familiar with the role of the layman and the indigenous leader as effective change agents (17). Active participation in community programming not only has the advantage of developing effective services, but it also increases the chances of the mental health professions becoming more closely aware of the consequences of any particular intervention upon the client's behavior. In this way programming helps to clarify the relative effectiveness with which services are responding to the expression of community problems.

PRINCIPLE FOUR: PLANNING FOR CHANGE

As the community mental health program participates in a continuous assessment of adaptive behavior of the local population, and as services are provided to high-risk groups as well as selected community resources, the program achieves a fourth important function: planning for change (18). I do not mean scheming for change, or proclaiming utopias, but I refer to mobilizing anticipatory problem-solving not only for clients but for professionals as well (28, 33). This principle also refers to a responsible caution for the outcome of programs and considers the effects of valid as well as invalid outcomes upon the organization of services or the structure of the community. I would hypothesize that as the planning function accelerates in a community, the local area will become more efficient and productive but less comfortable. While the planning function can facilitate economic development and more effective use of resources, the planning process itself changes the social structure and can lead to temporary disruption of the regulation of normative behavior.

The planning function becomes particularly salient in large metropolitan areas where mental health services are increasingly a part of government operations along with other health and welfare services. As funds for mental health services become a major budget item, closer attention will be given to the clarity of program objectives as well as the criteria for program evaluation. Establishing this type of planning function should help to manage an increasing problem for public mental health services, namely, distinguishing political objectives from professional objectives *prior* to program development. For the ecologist who is involved in the analysis of community structure and the development of services, the planning orientation is basic. The elements of the planning cycle include data sources which provide continuous input of the interdependent and reciprocal effects of three elements: the plan, community services, and the population at risk.

THE ECOLOGY OF THE INDIVIDUAL: ASSERTIONS

The above comments have been presented as one alternative conception of community mental health work based upon the ecological thesis that adaptive programs change (9, 10). The concept of ecology is also particularly valid for the assessment of individual behavior in social situations and provides a redefinition of clinical practice. The client is viewed as an individual in a specific social situation, with the consequence that expressive behavior is assessed in terms of the structure and function of the social setting in contrast to an analysis of intrapsychic motivations. In the same way, explanations of behavior change are not restricted to the interaction between an expert and a client but are viewed as taking place in multiple settings. A change agent becomes a person who alters behavior independent of formally designated helping roles. The social effectiveness of indigenous leaders under this model becomes as relevant a research topic as the efficacy of treatment institutions or treatment techniques.

One of the primary features of an ecological conception of behavior is the redefinition of pathology. Behavior is not viewed as sick or well but is defined as transactional, an outcome of reciprocal interactions between specific social situations and the individual. Adaptive behavior then can be expressed by any individual in a restricted number of social settings or in a variety of environments and can vary from time to time as well as from place to place. The research task is to clarify the precise relationships between individual behavior and social structure that differentially affect various forms of adaptive behavior. The work of Orth in his studies of the Harvard Business School (27), Mechanic in his analysis of a graduate department in the behavior sciences (26), Becker's analysis of the socialization of medical school students (6), and Barker and Gump's pioneering analysis of a midwestern high school (5) illustrate the potential for studying adaptation to social structures.

The present writer is conducting a study of teenagers' social adaptation to high schools. The study is concerned with the response of socially and geographically mobile youths to the life of a high-school environment. The purpose of this research is to clarify the socialization process of high-school youths that is relevant for understanding the variability of adaptation in different high schools, changes in adaptation over time and across situations, as well as the effects of various patterns of mobility history upon adaptation. To date, pilot work and scattered impressions from the literature suggest that the social structure of the high school is a primary setting for the learning of subsequent adaptations (16). This study is another example of research that I consider relevant for understanding individual behavior in large social units, and is the type of work that is basic for an ecological conception of community mental health programs. This type of study, and the point of view that has generated this research, I hope may contribute to a psychological understanding of the social environment and help to grasp a clearer sense of man's versatility.

REFERENCES

1. Albee, G. W. Psychotherapy: Panacea or dead-end? Presidential address presented at Ohio Psychological Association, Columbus, Ohio, April 1964.
2. Barker, R. G. Ecology and motivation. In M. R. Jones (Ed.), *Nebraska symposium on motivation: 1960*. Lincoln: University of Nebraska Press, 1960. Pp. 1–49.
3. Barker, R. G. On the nature of the environment. *J. of Soc. Issues,* 1963, 19:17–83.
4. Barker, R. G. Explorations in ecological psychology. *Amer. Psychol.,* 1965, 20:1–14.
5. Barker, R. G., and Gump, P. V. *Big school, small school.* Stanford: Stanford University Press, 1964.
6. Becker, H. S., Blanche, G., Hunger, E., and Strauss, A. *Boys in white: Student culture in medical school.* Chicago: University of Chicago Press, 1961.
7. Calhoun, J. B. Population density and social pathology. In L. J. Duhl (Ed.), *The urban condition: People and policy in the metropolis.* New York: Basic Books, 1963. Pp. 33–44.
8. Caplan, G. *Principles of preventive psychiatry.* New York: Basic Books, 1964.

9. Dubos, R. *Mirage of health.* Garden City, N. Y.: Harper, 1959.

10. Dubos, R. *The torch of life.* New York: Simon & Schuster, 1962.

11. Etkin, W. (Ed) *Social behavior and organization among vertebrates.* Chicago: University of Chicago Press, 1964.

12. Forehand, G. A., and Gilmer, B. von H. Environmental variation in studies of organizational behavior. *Psychol. Bull.,* 1964, 62:361–82.

13. French, J. R. P. The social environment and mental health. *J. of Soc. Issues,* 1963, 19:39–56.

14. Fried, M. Grieving for a lost home. In L. J. Duhl (Ed.), *The urban condition: People and policy in the metropolis.* New York: Basic Books, 1963. Pp. 151–172.

15. Gelfand, S., and Kelly, J. G. The psychologist in community mental health: Scientist and professional. *Amer. Psychol.,* 1960, 15:223–26.

16. Kantor, M. B. *Mobility and mental health.* Springfield, Ill.: C. C. Thomas, 1965.

17. Kelly, J. G. The community mental health center and the study of social change. Paper read in Community mental health: Individual adjustment or social planning? Symposium presented at IXth Inter-American Congress of Psychology, Miami, December 1964.

18. Kelly, J. G. The mental health agent in the urban community. In L. J. Duhl (Ed.), *Urban America and the planning of mental health services.* (Symposium No. 10) New York: Group for the Advancement of Psychiatry, 1964. Pp. 474–94.

19. Kelly, J. G. Graduate training in community mental health. Position paper presented at Conference on Professional Preparation of Clinical Psychologists, Chicago, August 27–September 1, 1965.

20. Klein, D. C., and Lindemann, E. Preventive intervention in family crisis situations. In G. Caplan (Ed.), *Prevention of mental disorders in children* New York: Basic Books, 1961. Pp. 283–306.

21. Klopfer, P. H. *Behavioral aspects of ecology.* Englewood Cliffs, N. J.: Prentice-Hall, 1962.

22. LaPiere, R. T. *Social change.* New York: McGraw-Hill, 1965.

23. Lorenz, K. A. *King Solomon's ring.* New York: Crowell, 1952.

24. Lynch, K. Environmental adaptabilty. *J. of Amer. Inst. of Planners,* 1958, 24:16–24.

25. Lynch, K. *The image of a city.* Cambridge, Mass.: M.I.T. Press & Harvard University Press, 1960.

26. Mechanic, D. *Students under stress: A study in the social psychology of adaptation.* Glencoe, Ill.: Free Press, 1962.

27. Orth, C. D. *Social structure and learning climate: The first year at the Harvard Business School.* Boston: Harvard University, Graduate School of Business Administration, 1963.

28. Perloff, H. S. Social planning in the metropolis. In L. J. Duhl (Ed.), *The urban condition: People and policy in the metropolis.* New York: Basic Books, 1963. Pp. 331–347.

29. Phillip, D. L. Rejection: A possible consequence of seeking help for mental disorders. *Amer. Soc. Rev.,* 1963, 28:963–72.

30. Raush, H. L., Dittmann, A. T., and Taylor, T. J. Person, setting, and change in social interaction. *Human Relations,* 1959, 12:361–78.

31. Raush, H. L., Farbman, I., and Llewellyn, L. G. Person, setting, and change in social interaction. *Human Relations,* 1960, 13:305–32.
32. Riessman, F., Cohen, J., and Pearl A. *Mental health of the poor.* New York: Free Press of Glencoe, 1964.
33. Seeley, J. R. What is planning? Definition and strategy? *J. of Amer. Inst. of Planners,* 1962, 28:91–97.
34. Sells, S. B. Dimensions of stimulus situations which account for behavior variance. In S. B. Sells (Ed.), *Stimulus determinants of behavior.* New York: Ronald Press, 1963.
35. Sells, S. B. An interactionist looks at the environment. *Amer. Psychol.,* 1963, 18:696–702.
36. Thomas, E. J., and Fink, C. F. Effects of group size. *Psychol. Bull.,* 1963, 60:371–84.
37. Vickers, G. The psychology of policy making and social change. *British J. of Psychiat.,* 1964, 110:465–77.
38. Wilner, D. M., Walkley, R. P., Pinkerton, T. C., and Tayback, M. *The housing environment and family life.* Baltimore: Johns Hopkins Press, 1962.

8

Basis and Plan for More Effective Use of Community Resources for Mental Health

FRANK T. GREVING

THE PRACTICAL ISSUE

ONE of the most serious problems facing the ten state governments represented at this conference is the mounting capital and operational costs of hospitals for the mentally ill. These northeast states, spend an aggregate of approximately $230,000,000 annually for the care of about 195,000 patients in long-term mental institutions. Each year these states admit about 52,000 patients. Thirty-five per cent or 15,000 of these are readmissions. Twenty-nine thousand are discharged annually.

Public concern about the mentally ill is undeniable; the cost of building and maintaining our state hospitals is mounting steadily. This defines the most clear-cut, urgent and practical issue in the whole broad and still very vaguely defined area of mental health—how to control and prevent an increasing need for state hospital care and its attendant financial burdens.

Our assignment is to discuss how this may be accomplished through the better use of local community resources. The problem posed thus is two-fold: first, how to keep people out of the state hospitals wherever possible, when they can be treated as well or better by non-institutional resources in their local communities; second, how to get people out of the institutions as soon as possible and turn them over to responsible after-care and follow-up resources.

In connection with these two questions we may note another practical issue. These same northeast states have currently budgeted a combined $23,750,000 for local community mental health services. This amount is from several sources —state governments, $12,000,000 or 51 per cent; local tax funds, $9,000,000 or 38 per cent; federal appropriations, $994,000 or 4 per cent and from local voluntary sources, $1,800,000 or 7 per cent. Not only does the state directly pay for the bulk of these local mental health activities, but much of the local tax money is spent in "matching" state expenditures, thus giving the state at least an indirect control over the policies governing it. Therefore, to a very

Reprinted from *Mental Hygiene*, 1958, *42*, 570–577, by permission of the publisher and the author's widow, Mrs. Adele Greving. © 1958, National Association of Mental Health. Mr. Greving was Associate Director, Community Research Associates, Inc., N.Y.

considerable extent, when we ask the question, "how can a state make use of local resources to control and prevent the need for hospitalization?," we are asking, "how can the state make better use of the local services it is now either financing or subsidizing?"

It is, I believe, fair to say that no state has yet come up with a comprehensive plan through which to achieve these objectives. This mental hospital problem is not new, but public and administrative awareness of its proportions is relatively new; realistic implications are still surrounded by uncertainties and confusion. Many of the states represented at this conference have developed and are experimenting with particular measures they hope will keep people out of their hospitals or accelerate the rate at which they can discharge them. But good administrators are the first to admit that these efforts fall far short of what they would like to achieve.

Community Research Associates claims no omniscience in this matter; we have no inside access to any magic wand with which you can solve this problem. All I can attempt to do is to clarify some of the issues and suggest some principles for planning which have evolved from our experience in many local community studies and in some of the special administrative research we have been undertaking.

Let us first see what is known about the problem of mental illness that your state hospitals have to deal with.

It is a practically significant fact that the great bulk of instiutional care is required by psychotics. A small segment of the patients are classified as psychoneurotic—about 5 per cent. The psychotic patients can be divided roughly into two main groups. One consists of those with psychoses with a predominantly organic base. They correspond significantly to an older age group characterized by progressive physical and emotional deterioration. The other group comprises those with severe functional disorders. Here the onset is at a younger age and therefore, unless effective hospital treatment and appropriate community resources are available, care of longer duration will ensue. The median age for state hospital admissions in the U.S. for arteriosclerotic and senile patients is 72 and 76 respectively; for the functional psychotic-psychoneurotic group is 50 and 36 respectively.

These basic characteristics of the state hospital load have several important implications for the better use of community resources. Is state hospital care the most effective and appropriate care for all of these older patients? How well are we planning return of the younger patient to his family and to responsible community life? Is there any responsible community service that provides effective continuum of service concerned with family, relatives, job finding? Or in other words—what services *ought we to have* at the local level, to form the basis for an integrated plan for constructively controlling the flow of cases in and out of the state hospitals? State facilities for the mentally retarded are subject to similar considerations.

Community Research Associates' experience suggests three functions that local community resources ought to be able to perform on a planned basis and that, if they were available and used, might substantially reduce hospital loads:

The provision of nursing home care for long-term cases where there is minimal hope for rehabilitative treatment and where protection and security measures are not a primary consideration. This would relieve state hospitals of the care of many of the older group with chronic organic diseases.

The discovery and treatment of cases at the earlier ambulatory outpatient stage as a means of preventing or delaying their need for institutional commitment. This applies mainly to the functional disorders and to the mentally retarded.

The assumption of cases for follow-up treatment and supervision at the earliest possible time. This applies to both organic and functional states. For the latter, ambulatory outpatient care; for the former, nursing home and bedside supervision.

PRESENT COMMUNITY RESOURCES

If in broad outlines these are the basic types of local service which would help prevent or delay the need for hospitalization and accelerate the possibility of discharge, let us look briefly at the services we now have in our local communities and the extent to which they are being used for these purposes.

We must of course distinguish between urban and rural counties. Generally speaking, the former are much better supplied with mental health facilities than the latter.

URBAN CENTERS

Most urban centers now have outpatient clinics of some kind. The fact is, however, that they tend with few exceptions *not* to accept, or at least to avoid, psychotic or pre-psychotic cases—the type of cases which constitute the overwhelming bulk of flow into the state hospitals. Studies made of child guidance clinics have shown that in this particular field of community mental health service as many as four out of five cases could have used a resource requiring less psychiatric skill and training. Actually we are making an uneconomical use of very scarce psychiatric personnel. Outpatient clinic services should be used for people who are ill and whom it would otherwise be necessary to commit to institutional care. Not many community clinics, either public or subsidized voluntary are fulfilling this obligation as a community resource.

Moreover, most local clinics are not effectively linked either functionally or administratively with the state hospital system and therefore are not integrated into any systematic plan for prevention or follow-up treatment. Only a few states have partial provision for state hospital after-care, and this usually is administered out of the state hospital and not linked with systematic utilization of such local clinical resources as may exist.

Nursing homes, many of which operate with some public subsidy, are available but they have not generally been developed to care for aged mental cases. California did take the bull by the horns and refused to admit these cases to its state institutions.

Our own experience suggests that at the community level the larger proportion of psychotic cases, or cases evidencing pre-psychotic symptoms, instead of being under the care of mental health clinics actually are to be found in the care of three main types of agencies; private casework agencies, public welfare departments and local correctional authorities. The first two types of agencies by definition are working with families and individuals with symptoms of social maladjustment, disordered behavior or emotional disturbances of some sort. We do not know exactly what proportion of their caseloads would show diagnosed psychotic or pre-psychotic symptoms; there never has been any systematic attempt to discover this. Recent data of our own from a representative number of family casework agencies suggest that the proportion in this group may run to 15 per cent or 20 per cent. We also know that local jails and workhouses as well as juvenile detention homes are filled with constant repeaters. We know enough from their case records to be sure that a significant proportion are in, or border upon, a psychotic classification. Public welfare departments not only have a major responsibility for the care of aged people with their accompanying vulnerability to organic deterioration, but in their aid to dependent children and child welfare service loads are very substantial groups of families highly vulnerable to severe mental and emotional pathology. We have no doubt that a significant proportion of them falls in classifications of severe pathological disorder.

Although we feel reasonably sure that a quite substantial portion of the persons in the community with mental illness severe enough to make them at some stage potential candidates for state hospitals are to be found in caseloads of these three types of community agencies, it is an almost universal fact that these agencies do not assume any responsibility for performing either of two functions that would help keep them from filling up the hospitals: namely, discovery or identification and clinical treatment.

Most private casework agencies could systematically screen out or identify the psychotics and suspected psychotics in their caseloads if there were any inducement or requirement that they do so. These agencies usually employ well-qualified caseworkers whose training includes perception of such symptoms. This is not true of the local public welfare or correctional departments.

There identification would require new procedures; this should not, however, present insuperable obstacles.

As to the second function, none of these agencies is now equipped to give effective psychiatric treatment to the persons in their caseload who may require it. From the standpoint of sound planning we believe it uneconomical to try to equip them to do so. But unless there is some local community clinic that will concentrate on the treatment of ambulatory psychotic and pre-psychotic cases, the only recourse these agencies now have is to try to get these cases admitted to your state institutions. This they now do to some extent and in a generally haphazard manner.

RURAL COUNTIES

The main difference between urban centers and rural communities is that in the latter there seldom are mental hygiene clinics or private casework agencies. The principal public services through which cases flow to institutional care are welfare departments and courts. Provisions for preventive and delaying services are almost entirely lacking except where a traveling clinic occasionally gets around to provide diagnostic services.

Practically speaking, the distinction is an academic one. While urban centers have resources that *might* be used to help control the flow in and out of state hospital care, they are not being so used. With fewer resources in rural areas, the net result is the same.

COMMUNITY PLANNING PRINCIPLES

An underlying reason for the present failure either systematically to identify psychotic or suspected psychotic cases in the local agencies or to provide competent local treatment for them is that in our community plans the area of severe pathology has become lost in a confused concern about the very much larger and ill-defined problem of social unadjustment, disordered behavior, emotional disturbance, mental health, or whatever other name you may choose to call it.

Undeniably communities do and must provide services to many families, adults or children with behavior and adjustment problems who are not and never will be severely mentally ill. But the attempt to deal with all these symptomatic evidences of trouble in the name of mental health has created great confusion. Thus we have a myriad of different agencies and jurisdictions dealing with different symptomatic episodes at different times or concurrently in the same individual and in the same family—each with its own brand of treatment plan. The amount of hidden and often rationalized waste attending this process is tremendous. Yet today we clamor for more specialized care facilities—a new panacea being the residential treatment center—not yet defined, very costly and most readily resorted to, often because we failed to use the basic services we already have.

This multiple and wasteful activity leads to many vague apprehensions by professional workers, no less than by the man in the street, about an unknown mass of troublesome behavior. Our own studies have shown that a relatively small number of families and individuals keep producing the bulk of the problems requiring agency activity. This activity, often by many agencies with the same family, creates the impression of vast numbers of cases when actually it is in part a symptom of uncoordinated activity, often with different facets of the same core problem. This leads to an unscientific promotion of so-called needs of all kinds. Funds are raised and appropriated under a myriad of well-intentioned or vested interest motivations. This is neither conducive to sound community planning nor to gaining the confidence of the taxpayer.

At Community Research Associates we believe that you can chart your way out of this confusion only by accepting and acting on a few simple principles.

The first principle is that the organized community—that is, the community which puts up either tax or voluntary money for organized services—must deal with this whole problem of behavior, mental well-being, or however you may conceive it, at three levels:

THE ECONOMIC LEVEL

That is, the community must provide financial assistance to handicapped people who cannot meet accepted minimum requirements of food, clothes, shelter, medical care and other necessities.

This is the primary responsibility of our public assistance programs, now underpinned by modern social security insurance.

THE ADJUSTMENT LEVEL

That is, the provision of service and protection for people who behave in an unsocial manner; who do not give adequate care to their children; who are emotionally disturbed, unstable or disorganized, but who are not mentally ill in the sense that makes them potential candidates for state hospitals.

This level is, or should be, the responsibility of an admitted plethora of agencies, who do and should place their main reliance on social casework personnel: private child welfare and family service agencies; public child welfare services: adult and juvenile court and probation services; special police and youth services; programs for the handicapped, and so on.

THE LEVEL OF MENTAL ILLNESS

That is, the provision of psychiatric medical service to persons with severe pathology. Most of these cases fall within or border on the psychoses, as we now understand that term.

In the state government this is the clear responsibility of the state mental hospital, but in the local community, as we have already indicated, responsibility is not fixed with corresponding clarity.

Our second community planning principle is that the agencies with primary responsibility for each of these basic service levels should stick to their own job and not try to move into the other's territory. In urban communities a great deal of mental hygiene money and expensive psychiatric personnel is widely spread over an extraordinary variety of agencies who do not deal directly with mental illness and who use these resources simply as an adjunct to some program with a completely different purpose.

The function of psychiatric consultation which cuts across many community services has been a singular source of confusion. Its use and purposes are not the subject of this paper except to point out that until its effect can be measured we should be cautious about claiming for it any sizable change in the incidence of mental illness. There is an important place for psychiatric consultation to other professions but by itself it can be like a ship without a rudder in a sea of ill-defined primary agency functions, to which it may seek to attach itself.

In terms of the subject matter of this paper, application of that principle also means that the public welfare department or court, family casework agency, school system or settlement house should not be satisfied merely to stay out of the business of treating the mentally ill, but should get into the business of systematically discovering and identifying mental illness in their caseloads and should see to it that proper psychiatric treatment is given by an agency which has that primary responsibility.

APPLICATION OF THESE PRINCIPLES

When we begin to think about the application of these principles, the overwhelming need for an integrated system of discovery and identification of ambulatory clinical treatment, of nursing home care, of hospital care stares us starkly and immediately in the face. A system integrated at the community level as between those agencies whose primary role should be the discovery, identification, screening and referral of suspected cases of severe actual or potential mental illness and those agencies whose role should be clinical treatment, inpatient treatment or nursing home care; integrated as between the state and local levels so that cases will flow into the state hospitals only after maximum use has been made of local treatment resources and with the assurance that maximum use will be made of the hospitals to facilitate discharge.

At this point in time we are indubitably a far cry from the achievement of such an integrated system. The historic roots and concepts out of which has grown the complex pattern through which we deal with mental illness, symptomatic evidence of disordered behavior, emotional unbalance and social maladjustment practically speaking could not lend itself less to coherent integrated planning and administration. Even at this point in time, however, surely no harm can come from trying to stake our broad planning goals with such policy and organizational directives as seem relevant to their ultimate achievement.

At the community level, it seems to us that the first goal should be a clear design for dealing with psychotic or other cases of severe mental illness. In urban communities, depending on their size, this should require:

1. An outpatient clinic or clinics for adults and children under public or combined public and private auspices. Intake to this clinic, or these clinics, should be limited to ambulatory cases of such diagnosed severity with respect to harmful influence upon the individual, his family or the community as to require medical treatment and supervision. The type of psychiatric team required to staff such a diagnostic and treatment clinic is well established and understood.

This clinic or these clinics should not accept cases in which the problem is primarily one of social maladjustment or symptomatic behavior that can or should be handled as well or better by adjustment agencies primarily using social casework personnel. The "should be" part of that phase is of practical importance. Social casework no less than psychiatric personnel is in short supply. But our experience makes us certain that no good comes from a well-staffed psychiatric clinic's handling general adjustment problems simply because no adjustment agencies are well equipped to do so. That simply compounds confusion and leaves the community with neither job done well

2. There should be inpatient resources in connection with the community's general hospitals. These should be used for cases susceptible to improvement and discharge under supervision after relatively short-time care.

Obviously these inpatient services and the clinical or outpatient services ought to be closely integrated. This does not necessarily mean that the clinic should be set up as an outpatient department of a hospital; many practical circumstances must be taken into account in settling that issue.

3. Psychiatric consultation and in-service training facilities should be provided to the community's adjustment services. This might be provided by the psychiatric clinic or outpatient service. Our experience, however, suggests that consultation often leads to the development of pseudo-treatment functions.

As stated earlier, clarification of primary community functions should always precede the use of consultation. Only then can the latter become a plus.

4. This leaves one area of service about which there is now considerable confusion. In larger urban and suburban communities there is a growing demand for "consultation," "advice" or "counseling" about a great variety of personal, child-rearing and family problems. This stems mainly from families in the middle and upper economic, educational and social brackets. A good deal of this business now goes to child guidance clinics, some to family casework agencies. Much of the actual or potential demand undoubtedly is unmet.

While such a flow of cases may result in some identification of actual or potentially severe mental illness, "counseling" or "consultation" does not require expensively organized clinical service. The present demand for such service comes mainly from people who can afford to pay for it. From the standpoint of the assignment given to me in this paper, the main issue here would seem to be how to organize local services to meet this need so that they will not drain off tax money and skilled personnel needed to concentrate on the job of controlling and preventing the development of cases of severe pathology to a point requiring hospitalization.

These three or perhaps four types of desirable community resources have been developed primarily for urban communities. The chief difference in planning for rural counties relates to the question of how to provide ambulatory clinic or outpatient service. This raises questions of size, volume, structure and financing, which are well beyond the province of this paper.

If these be the broad goals of an integrated plan of control and prevention toward which to work at the community level, what are the corresponding goals at the state level? It would seem to be logical:

That state authority and use of funds for all inpatient and community mental health programs be guided by a single overall policy; that the continuity of treatment and care in the community, in the hospital and again on return to the community is planned to give the patient the benefit of the fullest possible use of all community resources.

That prior to admission to a state hospital, a comprehensive psychiatric and social diagnosis of the patient be made to determine, where possible, the use of community rather than mental hospital treatment and care.

That in planning for return of hospital patients to the community, state-appropriated community mental health funds be assigned a priority of use for continued treatment and care where needed.

That adjustment services in public welfare, in the judicial and school system be used for two purposes: (1) to identify and properly refer cases of serious pathology; (2) wherever appropriate, to assist in keeping the patient out of the hospital or to provide needed service to him after he leaves the hospital.

In summary, to constructively control the need for mental hospital care requires an integrated plan with clearly conceived resources and functions at both the local and state level. Its potential contribution will depend in no small measure upon the degree of responsibility and clarity with which each unit performs its unique job. The alternative is confusion, overlapping functions, problems of administration and accountability—not to mention the disservice and frustration of which the patient becomes the victim. A key result of the constructive use of this mental health framework should be a far more purposeful flow of needs and problems to the right service at the right time—not too late and not too soon.

Finally, there is a strategic concept which underlies these considerations. Only the governors and their chief administrative aides encompass the scope and authority related to the majority of these problems: state mental institutions, outpatient services (state operated or subsidized), correctional and state institutions for the mentally retarded, probation, parole, public health and public welfare and such adjustment services as the state possesses among its many departments concerned with health and welfare.

9

Future Steps in Implementing Mental Health Plans

HERBERT C. SCHULBERG

A future historical analysis of significant trends in the mental health field will have to note that the period of 1963–65 was marked by an unprecedented amount of nationwide activity in the planning of new programs. Thousands of professionals as well as lay citizens participated in intensive efforts to redirect traditional patterns of care for the mentally ill into a new pattern of community mental health programs. The nature of these planning activities, the types of procedure which they followed, and the gamut of problems encountered have been, and will continue to be, discussed for some time to come (2, 3, 4, 6). The tremendous accomplishment of planning projects during the past two years bears ample testimony to our nation's concern for the mentally ill and is, hopefully, equally indicative of the profound interest which will continue to be displayed during the coming years.

And yet, while the numerous participants in the recently completely planning projects are permitting themselves a well-deserved sense of satisfaction at getting a job well done, there must also remain a gnawing sense of curiosity and concern as to what happens next. Various reports have emanated that a feeling of revulsion is being expressed toward planning in several parts of the country. It seems that you can talk to people about planning for just so long before you have to start doing. People can be involved at a feverish pitch for only a limited period of time before they start demanding results.

Planning projects around the country have successfully developed an almost evangelistic fervor and it behooves us all to now start converting our aspirations and promises into concrete deeds which will tangibly benefit the mentally ill and promote mental health. This paper briefly outlines some thoughts about community mental health programs and some of the steps which may be necessary to bring projected plans to fruition.

Reprinted from *Community Mental Health Journal,* 1966, *2,* 157–162, by permission of the publisher and the author. © 1966, Behavioral Publications, Inc. Dr. Schulberg is Associate in Psychology, Harvard Medical School.

THE NATURE OF COMMUNITY MENTAL HEALTH

It would not be unreasonable to assume after two years of planning for community mental health programs that there is a reasonable sense of agreement among planners as to what these programs are all about. And yet, strangely enough, this assumption is far from valid.

In spite of the widespread support which is now being evinced for community mental health programs, this concept still represents many different things to different people (1, 7). To some, the essence of a community mental health service is its physical location in the very midst of an urban population center, thus bringing regular psychiatric services closer to patients and permitting the utilization of facilities such as the general hospital.

To others, the distinguishing feature of the community mental health service is not so much its actual physical propinquity to the mass population, although this is certainly necessary. Rather, the essence of the program lies in its philosophy that provision of comprehensive mental health services (direct and indirect) requires the cooperation and participation of all segments of the community's power structure and caregiving system. Consequently, the skills of more than the traditional psychiatric team are utilized.

To still others, the essential quality of a community mental health program is not rooted primarily in the character of the services which it provides, but more importantly in the fact that a local citizen group assumes responsibility for program planning and development. Program direction by a local board rather than by the central office of the Department of Mental Health is the primary criterion of a community mental health program to this third group.

In view of the fact that we are treading on relatively new ground in the field of community mental health, it is strongly urged that the issues remain open to discussion and the programs flexible. In effect, we are functioning with considerable experience but not with completely informed judgment. We must insure the likelihood of increased knowledge and improved programs through (a) a systematic and well-supported program of basic research in mental health, (b) a careful evaluation of programs so that we may learn from our successes and failures, and (c) an opportunity for experimental demonstrations that can depart from conventional procedures and provide new knowledge.

Although differences should continue to exist about the central emphasis and precise functions of a community mental health program, certain principles are accepted by all and they will lead to profound program changes in the coming years. It is thought that widespread agreement could be reached about these points:

First, the patient must be the focus of a multifaceted program designed to meet his current needs; the patient must not be fitted into an institution's administrative needs.

Second, a community mental health program must be comprehensive. It should include inpatient, outpatient, emergency and partial hospitalization services, and education and consultation services. The program must serve all age groups, all diagnostic groups, and especially those unable to afford private care.

Third, continuity of care must be provided from the beginning to the end of psychiatric intervention. Private practitioners have long adhered to this principle and it is time that we incorporate this principle into institutional practice as well.

Many crucial implications stem from the envisioned changes in program practices and some of them should be highlighted. Since all appropriately trained personnel must be used in an optimum fashion, a fresh analysis of job descriptions is vital. All mental health professionals will be required to function in new ways. Currently defined areas of interest will be broadened and one may expect a redefinition of the particular prerogatives now assumed by psychiatrists, psychologists, social workers, nurses, etc. Individual competence rather than disciplinary prerogative must become the criterion used to define ability.

In developing necessary programs, the community mental health professional accepts responsibility for helping those of all ages and diagnostic categories wherever problems arise in the community. He does not wait for patients to come to his office. Professionals participating in community mental health programs will differ from traditional colleagues in providing direct and *indirect* service, to large numbers of people with whom they have no personal contact. New programs will not be able to wait for patients to come to them since responsibility is assumed for populations at risk and not only for individual patients.

Such an ambitious program cannot be undertaken by the mental health center alone, certainly not upon the traditional basis of diagnosis and treatment of individuals. The use of complementary resources in the health and welfare system will be imperative. Mental health professionals must utilize other resources not as a second best choice but rather out of sincere recognition that the mental health center is just one of the appropriate resources in the community. Thus, in addition to using a direct approach to patients, mental health specialists will utilize indirect methods such as consultation to foster and support the contributions of other caregiving resources.

Many other implications in this concept of community mental health have occurred to planners during the course of their deliberations. Let us return for the moment, however, to the substance of future programs. Most of the states in the country have followed the Federal Guidelines in defining comprehensive community mental health programs. Thus, at least the five essential services will be provided to populations of approximately 75,000 to 200,000 people.

In most communities, especially rural ones, it will not be feasible or appropriate for a single facility to alone provide all of the essential elements in a comprehensive program. It may be much more practical for a number of existing, and possibly new, agencies to coordinate their programs in such a manner as to provide a complete range of services.

A statewide planning project can concern itself only with the *general* nature of comprehensive programs. Local people must determine the specific character of their community's services. The precise manner in which publicly and privately supported agencies coordinate their services can only be determined at the local level. In most states, regional planning committees have been grappling with these very issues during recent months. The solutions which are arrived at through local deliberations will ensure that services are provided as they are clinically indicated and not as they are administratively regulated.

THE NEXT STEPS

Widespread hope has been raised by the planning goals of establishing community mental health programs in which patients stay at home, are treated at home, and become well at home. What are the next steps necessary to achieve these goals? Two broad necessary approaches can be focused upon. The first deals with the manner in which we deploy our limited resources, and the second with the future need for citizen participation in program planning and implementation.

THE DEVELOPMENT OF RESOURCES

In most areas of any state, a comprehensive mental health program will require the coordination of several resources. To be truly effective, major and minor realignments must be undertaken in agency relationships and it is suggested that some are crucial.

Relationships between mental health and nonmental health resources have generally developed more by chance than through any mutual recognition of the benefits that planned cooperation could produce. As mental health programs assume responsibility for the provision of services to all members of the community, the collaboration of a wider range of nonmental health resources must be obtained.

Mental disorders of lower socioeconomic groups are so intertwined with real social problems that they rarely can be solved through the skills of the psychiatrist alone. In the foreseeable future, it is possible that the mental health problems of these groups will be the responsibility of agencies such as the welfare department, settlement house, and public health nursing organization. In these instances, the primary job of the mental health professional could very well be to provide other community resources with consultation, training, and additional types of direct and indirect support. The mental health center itself will be focusing less of its resources upon patient care, and more upon the indirect techniques of consultation and community organization with nonmental health resources. This type of approach would seem to have particular merit in rural parts of the country.

As mental health programs develop interest in the area of primary prevention and initiate activities which traditionally have been within the domain of social and welfare agencies, inevitable conflicts will arise which could be potentially detrimental to effective program coordination. A realignment of agency relationships can minimize this conflict if meaningful communication and increased mutual trust are exercised by all participants.

Mental health facilities should routinely participate in local community councils as one way of promoting mutual trust and establishing communication. This step will also enhance the integration of mental health services with related programs such as housing, poverty, and delinquency control. It is vitally necessary that staff members at the mental health center initiate the reaching out to other significant community resources rather than waiting to be involved.

Components of the publicly, voluntarily, and privately supported mental health systems have coordinated their efforts harmoniously, but by and large relationships have not been cultivated as carefully as is necessary. A history of legal and attitudinal obstacles has limited the role of voluntarily and privately supported resources and prevented their being used in an optimal fashion. The Federal appropriation of construction funds for new mental health centers has again focused attention upon the cleavages between these systems and pointed up the need for resolution of outstanding differences.

In seeking a resolution of these differences, the basic principle which must be adhered to is that active participation of all publicly, voluntarily, and privately supported mental health resources is imperative for the provision of comprehensive services to any community. No single system can cope with the vast extent of current needs. This situation will continue for many years to come.

With the program goal of local inpatient units in all service areas throughout the state, the facilities of the general hospital will be critical, especially in non-metropolitan areas. Inpatient services of a community mental health program should be located so that they are accessible to the medical services of the general hospital and thus avoid duplicating scarce resources.

Private practitioners should be permitted to hospitalize and treat their patients in the facilities operated by state-supported programs when clinically indicated. Such a procedure has been opposed in some states on the grounds that granting private practitioners staff privileges would produce major disrupting results. However, a Massachusetts survey of psychiatrists in private practice (5) revealed that only a minority routinely participated in the hospital treatment of their patients and their effect upon hospital routines was minimal.

The use of general hospitals and private practitioners is recommended for providing specific elements of a comprehensive program. These resources will not replace the other facilities which still will be necessary to provide other essential services. General hospitals and private practitioners must cooperate with the total systems so that their services become an effective part of a comprehensive program.

Voluntary and private social service agencies will be confronted by a variety of possibilities if they choose to become integral members of their community's comprehensive mental health program. The fact that such agencies already do provide major mental health services has been clearly demonstrated in a number of studies. Any of the following options might be considered by a particular facility in determining its future roles:

1. Continue current intake and treatment practices, with the agency determining its own policy, and patients making financial arrangements directly with the agency.

2. Continue to function independently but develop a contract with the area mental health board to provide treatment to selected patients on a fee-for-service basis.

3. Continue to function as an independent facility but arrange a contract with the area mental health board whereby publicly-supported personnel are assigned to the facility to treat patients unable to pay for private services.

4. Alter the facility's administrative structure so that it is financed and operated as a publicly-supported mental health resource and is thus brought under the control of the area mental health board.

Other options are possible and the choice of a particular one will be dependent upon local circumstances.

The manner in which existing state hospitals will be utilized in comprehensive programs represents one of the most serious challenges confronting planners throughout the country. It is suggested that within a statewide scheme for comprehensive services, mental hospitals be viewed as serving two distinct purposes. The first is the provision of the five essential services in a comprehensive mental health program to the geographic area in which it is located. This will be possible when new local inpatient programs relieve state hospitals of much of their current admission loads. The second purpose of a mental hospital would be to provide continued treatment facilities for its own local area as well as for neighboring community mental health programs.

It will be important to facilitate the free movement of patients between outpatient clinics, acute inpatient services, and continued care facilities. In those instances where a state hospital provides continued care for several community programs, the hospital might well consider establishing a geographic unit system on the continued treatment service as one way of facilitating two-way communication and transfer of patients with local centers. When geographical distance is not an issue, the state hospital and its neighboring community mental health centers could experiment with an arrangement whereby each center is responsible, or participates, in the professional staffing of its unit.

CITIZEN PARTICIPATION

The goal of statewide community mental health centers will not be achieved within one or two years but is rather a goal to be pursued during the coming decade. A phasing process will be necessary and the speed with which it proceeds is dependent upon such factors as community participation, citizen interest, the availability of financial support, and the recruitment of necessary manpower.

What is the role of citizen committees in helping to implement the plans which are being formulated? First it should be noted that the very idea of citizen volunteers and local participation in the shaping and operating of community programs is not a new one. Public welfare boards, public health boards, public school committees, and most recently, the federal requirement of citizen participation in urban renewal and poverty programs attest to this concept. The mental health field, although relatively recent in its development, is no exception.

Planning projects have devoted much thought to the creation of optimal administrative structures which will enhance the opportunities for citizen participation. Varying patterns will be tested relative to the role of citizens on the governing boards of mental health centers and their authority will range from decision-making to being purely advisory in nature.

In addition, regional citizen groups will be called upon to assume major responsibility in developing grass root support for recently promulgated plans. Public information programs will have to be directed at two prime audiences: the mass media and civic organizations. An organizational campaign must be mounted to enlist the cooperation of such groups as mayors and selectmen, service clubs, PTA's, labor unions, and chambers of commerce. A speakers' bureau should be developed and trained in every program area to reach widespread audiences. Mental health associations, which have long engaged in these activities, can be instrumental in helping planning groups achieve ultimate success.

A technique which has proved particularly effective in some parts of the country has been the holding of a series of public hearings in major communities. It is suggested that regional committees in every state initiate, or continue, public hearings at which they would present their recommendations and explicitly indicate how proposed plans would affect various groups and facilities. Giving local citizens and representatives of community agencies the opportunity to express their reactions is of considerable value in airing the issues and moving toward consensus. Community mental health centers—no matter how well financed, how efficiently administered, and brilliantly staffed —cannot translate the late President Kennedy's request for "a bold new approach" into a job well done unless residents of the community accept its existence, its purpose, and the patients whom it treats.

Much has been accomplished in the last two years through comprehensive planning but even more remains to be undertaken in the coming decade. It is believed that we are now in the midst of a long, historical social evolution. The thrust is clearly with us. It is hoped that we will do it justice.

REFERENCES

1. Dunham, H. W. Community psychiatry: The newest therapeutic bandwagon. *Arch. Gen. Psychiat.*, 1965, 12:303–313.
2. Fogelson, F. Statewide planning in mental health: An early report. *Soc. Wk.*, 1964, 9:26–33.
3. Glasscote, R., and Kanno, C. *The plans for planning: a comparative analysis of the state mental health planning proposals.* Washington: Joint Info. Service, 1963.
4. Schulberg, H. C. State planning for community mental health programs: Implications for psychologists. *Community Ment. Hlth. J.*, 1965, 1:37–42.
5. Schulberg, H. C. Private practice and community mental health. *Hosp. Comm. Psychiat.*, 1966, 17:363–66.
6. U. S. Department of Health, Education, and Welfare. *NIMH Progress reports on state mental health planning 1964.* Bethesda: HEW, August, 1964.
7. Whittington, H. G. The third psychiatric revolution—really? *Community Ment. Hlth. J.*, 1965, 1:73–80.

10

Behind the Scenes in Community Mental Health

HERBERT DÖRKEN

THE World Health Organization's philosophy is that health should be regarded not just as the absence of disease, but as a positive state of well-being. This far-reaching concept was reflected in the activities and concerns of World Mental Health Year; it is reflected in the studies of the Joint Commission on Mental Illness and Health. Jahoda's review (4) of the *Current Concepts of Positive Mental Health* (one Commission report) points to the broad social orientation that is implicit in these new community mental health programs. Here then is the ultimate goal: the conservation, development and full utilization of human resources.

Cast in these terms, the concept of community services emerges and is in line with public health philosophy. Public health, however, is concerned with the prevention of disease and the promotion of health through work primarily with the community rather than with the individual. For mental health personnel, this is in essence a new type of social contract involving the added dimensions of sound public relations and employer-employee accountability, since beyond the traditional diagnostic and treatment (clinical) services there lies a whole gamut of community services: consultation to agencies and professions in the community, collaboration and cooperation with them in the development of services, coordination and integration of related services, participation in community planning, the provision of public and professional education, and emphasis on survey, evaluation and research. I might add that we especially need to learn more about using and developing the strengths and abilities of men, instead of eternally studying their weaknesses and sicknesses. A concern with human assets is more in keeping with positive mental health than endless dwelling on the ramifications of psychopathology. With this comment on the direction of much of our current research, I will return to the theme.

Reprinted from *American Journal of Psychiatry,* 1962, *119,* 328–335, by permission of the publisher and the author. © 1960, American Psychiatric Association. Dr. Dörken is Chief, Bureau of Research, California Department of Mental Hygiene.

PUBLIC SUPPORT

The involvement of society facilitates, indeed, renders possible, service to it. The mental health associations often provide the medium through which public interest may become manifest. Certainly, in Minnesota, we owe much of our progress to the active support of the Minnesota Association for Mental Health. From the inception, when they supported the legislation under which we now operate, to their consistent and persistent interpretation to the public of our financial needs and present and projected services, they have been a moving force. At critical stages in program development it is advisable to involve key professional groups such as the state psychiatric, psychological, social work and medical associations in planning. They are often able to provide constructive guidance, and potential differences and difficulties may be resolved beforehand. Public support then and, of course, professional participation are the cornerstones of a community mental health program. But both the social and the professional aspects are influenced by factors, though known, which we tend to overlook—factors that operate, so to speak, behind the scenes.

SOCIAL IMPACT AND CHANGE

The increasing scope and expanding knowledge of mental health concerns has led to increasing specialization and to a process of differentiation and upgrading (5). Also, the complex cluster of interlocking bodies of knowledge and the growth of specialization is such that collaboration among a number of disciplines is now required. Current trends appear likely to continue. This increasing emphasis on the psychological, social and occupational factors in mental health suggests an expanding and more significant role for the behavioral sciences.

In terms of the American value system, the capacity of the individual to achieve is one of the most fundamental conditions of the good society. Since mental health is one of the foundations of this capacity, its importance takes on a broader meaning. The gathering impetus of the mental health movement shows plainly that it is a developing social force. People consider now that they have a right to a reasonable adjustment. They believe that science and the mental health professions can improve their lot. As a result, communities are becoming increasingly active in demanding and in organizing comprehensive mental health programs.

The needs, resources and social groups in a society are in continuous change. This should be reflected in appropriate program changes or there will be the equivalent of a cultural lag. Unfortunately, there is a tendency for professional roles and services to become stereotyped, if not biased. Such professional expectancy leads to static patterns and narrow definitions which stifle creativity. A spirit of restlessness must be induced or maintained, for if progress is our aim, then programs must have a "growing edge" in search of new ideas, improved services and better utilization of the full range of community resources.

We are over-prone to consider mental disorder as the prime factor leading to treatment or demand for mental health service, when, in many instances, the degree of community tolerance will provide the basic impetus to seek professional assistance. There is a distinct relationship between social conditions and the ways in which mental disorder is dealt with by the community (1). Mental illness in social terms is behavior deviant from the norm. Expectations within a particular society and the context of the action are factors bearing heavily on local attitude and determination which in turn are related to need, demand and utilization of service, and ultimately, serve to shape professional services and practice.

Taking the larger picture into consideration brings the total range of disordered behavior into focus. These ramifications are an integral part of society. To the extent they are overlooked, we fail to provide an effective community service. The professional staff, then, might be viewed as change-agents who would attempt to induce constructive social change in the community. We have only begun to explore the potential mental health effects of adverse social conditions. Certainly, failures in adjustment, shifts in values and cultural patterns, and social dysfunction, as well as disharmony within families, are hardly individual matters. The findings of research on group dynamics and communications, then, are quite germane and should become a part of our practice and program planning.

PREVALENCE-INCIDENCE

Without proper survey and data, we do not know the nature and extent of actual problems requiring attention; we do not know whether we need a particular mental health service. Certainly, it is not another "industry" to be attracted to town. Cursory surveys may magnify the problem by use of prevalence statistics, but the number of active cases is not an appropriate basis for making probability statements for which incidence rates—the number of new cases during a specified interval—are essential, though seldom obtained (3). Each community has its backlog of cases with protracted mental disorder. If this backlog could be worked through at the case level by effective management, treatment, placement or referral, the mental health center would begin to deal with the natural base rate or incidence of mental disorder in the community rather than its prevalence.

Related is the need for continuous program analysis; failure to evaluate past work and future needs critically results in errors and mistakes never becoming known and, presumably, never corrected. Stock taking is essential, not only of the mental health services but of the major social, economic and demographic community data as well; this is in constant change, the urban population drift being merely one index. The everyday operations and concerns of community services are rife with intriguing and very practical research problems. Here again, pathetically little is being done.

FAMILY THERAPY-AGENCY COMPLEX

Without trying to minimize the extent of the problem, several studies have shown (2) that a relatively small number of families and individuals keep producing the bulk of agency activity. This activity by many agencies with the same family, the multi-problem family, creates the impression of vast numbers when actually it is a symptom of uncoordinated activity, often with different facets of the same core problem. The need for an integrated system of discovery, identification, ambulatory treatment, nursing home and hospital care is pressing. That the multi-problem families involve a small segment of the population suggests that it may be more feasible than many of us think to serve the total community, as problems of the large majority may be more amenable to assistance.

The history of health and welfare service development is replete with examples of rivalry, competition, duplication, and fragmentation. For sake of clarity perhaps in the mental health field, attention has been focused mainly on the individual. Yet, in our society, the family is the basic social unit. Each family will have its unique patterns of interaction. Evaluation and treatment, if geared to this natural social unit, would not only avoid many of the handicaps of partial or incomplete service, it would facilitate the resolution of the emotional and social problems not just of the patient, but of other family members, and lead to a realignment of family patterns of interaction, thereby facilitating progressively more favorable adjustment.

If service is to be comprehensive it should be available to all within the community; all ages, all relevant disorders of behavior, all agencies and professions. Fragmented service may be easier to initiate (e.g., for children, the retarded) but more difficult to sustain, since it depends more on a specific interest group than on community wide support. In order to gain the stability that comes from community wide support and involvement, the service must be widely available and not the agent of any one group or profession (related service) or even identified in the public mind as such (restricted service). The location of the community mental health center often has a significant bearing here in shaping the public image of its service. Location in a welfare building, school or hospital, to illustrate, generally creates the assumption, respectively, of service for the indigent, the children, the sick—thus impairing a community-wide orientation and service.

CENTER-HOSPITAL RELATIONSHIP

Considerable attention is paid to the coordination between mental health centers and state hospitals, particularly in regard to aftercare. In some states this may be their major function. By contrast it is seldom thought that centers may be dealing with essentially different segments of the population. In Minnesota, but 5 per cent to 8 per cent of center admission are referrals from state hospitals, while conversely, termination by referral to hospital varies from 6 per cent to 10 per cent of cases closed. The trend, if any, is for centers to refer progressively fewer patients to state hospitals. Our recent statistics would indicate that the centers deal with a population largely different from that of the mental hospitals and that they are reaching a large segment of the community having emotional, mental and social disorders, and it may be assumed, not previously reached.

The progressive emphasis on community services notwithstanding, there has been a sharp rise in the diagnostic and treatment services provided by the centers. The number of new cases accepted in 1959–60 was more than double the pace of the previous year (10) while 1960–61 showed a 64 per cent gain over 1959–60 with but one new center and a 25 per cent increase in staff. The total of new admissions (4,731 and now projected at over 5,200) has risen to more than double the first admissions (2,188) of the mentally ill to all state hospitals (7 hospitals, 9,600 beds) and is substantially above total admissions (3,142) and even hospital admissions plus return from provisional discharge (3,975). This is roughly an average rate of 28 new admissions per center per month, carried by a total of only 43 professional staff (latterly) at 14 centers, devoting but an average of 48 per cent of professional time to clinical services.

PREVENTION-CONTROL

Much lip service is given to the need for a preventive approach to mental illness, for programs of public and professional education, for coordination and consultation, for the concentrated development of additional community resources, and for research; yet, when any mental health center is established there is often an overwhelming demand for clinical services which may become so exclusive that program control and direction are basically lost.

In developing the service, at the outset, in response to community need, there is usually the hope that it will help to control the problem and have a preventive impact. But this development is open-ended, a progressively increasing amount of service is provided, yet responsibility for its effectiveness is basically evaded. Service does not, by itself, lead to prevention or establish control, is usually without focus and direction and, most important, is without responsibility for results. Specifically, what are the problems and their proportions? How are these conditions modified, controlled or improved? It is essential that the critical factors be isolated in order to enhance the impact of our services and techniques.

Then there is the concept of accountability, a most challenging proposal (10), though generally a most unwelcome and unpopular notion among clinicians who are prone to be ego oriented rather than task oriented. A statement of activities is not synonymous with accountability. Yet, without defined goals and accountability, control and direction are lost and prevention fades into obscurity. Moreover, and this is seldom appreciated in the field, to the public official accountability is a reality of everyday, whether knowledge is incomplete, adequate or even accurate; answers, often critical, must be given. We have only begun to consider the potential of a reorientation of total community health and welfare services leading to a solution of the community problems stemming from disordered behavior. Rather than deal with symptoms of behavior, attention must be focused on the pathological processes giving rise to social disorder. This need for service has been separately interpreted by each agency. Finally, the problems related to criminal and antisocial activity accounts for two-thirds of the annual incidence of disordered behavior, yet communities have generally ignored this area in planning services. Buell's findings in the Community Research Associates studies hold much promise and have tremendous implications.

UNFOUNDED CLAIMS

At times, some of us venture beyond the realm of our skills and a "halo effect" may mask our inadequacies. At other times, overextended claims may be made for certain services, and this can prove awkward later on, especially if no provision is made for the demonstration of results.

All too often, in the mental health field, our procedures are founded on unconfirmed hypotheses rather than valid explanations. Therapeutic zeal may militate against scientific determination, particularly in regard to the efficacy of psychological forms of treatment. Despite the high fashion and great investment of time over years in long-term, intensive, dynamic psychotherapy, there is no evidence that it is superior to less rigorous methods, in fact it would seem that methodology is being preserved for its own sake. It is, of course, asking a great deal of many psychotherapists and analysts to cooperate in trying to find out whether they may be deceiving themselves as to the usefulness of their life's work. Rogers and others, however, have made some definite progress in their attempts to isolate (or insulate?) the factors necessary for therapeutic personality change.

LOCATION-DISTANCE

Service, to be provided, must be available. Logical planning would fix location at the hub of the professional and medical community for the area and at the center of trade and transportation. Such logical planning (sociological) may be set aside by local prejudice, political considerations and chamber of commerce activity. Witness state and provincial hospital programs, the majority of such hospitals in North America being located in towns of under 10,000 population (10), in the shadow of isolation, with resultant removal from the sphere of related services essential to programming.

The growth factor of organizations perhaps has led to the development of over-large mental health services responsible for vast geographical areas, the patient alas fading into insignificance. The lesson for future community mental health planning is that small centers, well dispersed, will render better service —a service more dependent on individual skill than on organizational size or structure. The natural geographical boundaries will vary from place to place. In Minnesota, with its relatively low population density, a radius of 60 miles was found to be the effective limit, about an hour's drive by car. Adequate coverage at greater distance could only be achieved by regular staff travel into the outlying area.

Distance, while it has a very direct relation to frequency or use of clinical service (diagnosis and treatment), also has a qualitative effect, the greater the distance, the more serious the disorder, and the more inappropriate it becomes for an outpatient service. There is a significant relationship between the increase in distance and the severity or flagrancy of the disorder which compels people to overcome this barrier. Outpatient services are more frequently unsuitable and follow-up more impractical. If anything, distance causes an even greater impairment of community services (consultation, in-service training, community planning, coordination)—the services essential to maintenance of a public health orientation in program—the services more closely involved with social structure.

FINANCING

Stable and sufficient financing is basic to the proper development of a full service and the initial budget is critical. If realistic provision is not made at the outset for the predictable complement of professional and clerical personnel at regionally competitive salaries and with necessary equipment and supplies, then neither personnel nor facilities will be sufficient and an overburdened agency will be repeatedly turning to its backers, hat in hand, for one item or another—a process guaranteed to antagonize and discourage staff, board and local government. By contrast, a complete initial budget facilitates recruitment to complement and purchase of all necessary equipment (budgeted funds not expended may simply be returned to source or placed in a special fund for future contingency). Then, in the second and third years, the funds previously necessary for equipment, say $4,000 (likewise fee revenues), are available as a cushion to accommodate salary increments with the result that the cost to the sponsors remains stable for at least three years while the center establishes and proves itself. At this point, the likely attitude, on returning to the sponsors —if necessary—seeking a moderate adjustment of budget, will be one of reasonable expectation and efficient management.

A positive relationship exists between community visability, knowledge of services, public support and local financial backing. Quite apart from the wider range of services received through a program stressing community services such as consultation, community planning and promotion, in-service training of community professional groups and social science research, the program by the very nature of its activities is highly visible and known to many key figures locally. The details of clinical services, by contrast, are never known. They are (as they should be) strictly confidential. Few then learn of the value of this service; the client is seldom outspoken and those who are to provide financial backing have but a statistical report and formal description of the services for consideration. It is a difference which may well be critical.

Services do not operate properly without sufficient fiscal support and reasonable assurance of continuity, while insufficient staff or facilities results in qualitative as well as quantitative program curtailment. Modern programming in the community mental health field is supported by some foreward-looking legislation (8) that typically, on a matching-grant basis, leads to a partnership between state and community with the dual advantage of central leadership and local involvement. Local identification and responsibility is encouraged, leading to a more flexible adjustment of service in keeping with local needs. Then too, within budgetary limits, expenditures are subject to local determination where the community may place greater value on professional talent and service because they seek it.

The cost of staffing may seem higher, for decentralization requires a greater number of costly well-trained personnel since more responsibility is delegated. Turnover is generally less, however, and the effective productivity of smaller quality units higher.

A larger proportion of cost is allocated to personnel (who do the work) rather than being tied up in equipment and major capital expenditures (buildings). In the Minnesota program, salaries typically account for 80 per cent of a mental health center's budget, while the total annual cost per capita, for the area served, at full scale operation is only 90¢ to 95¢. In terms of cost per hour based on total expenditures and total professional hours in fiscal 1960–61, the median hourly cost was $9.77 while local cost was under $5.00 per hour. Considering the extent of service, it seems an excellent return.

PROFESSIONAL PARTICIPATION

Community mental health programs are designed to provide a broad range of services at the local level. The open-ended, complex and flexible nature of these programs, however, calls for fully trained personnel in all disciplines. There is no institutional control to fall back on, no available professional senior to turn to; "you are it," you stand or fall on the ability to assume responsibility, provide service, cooperate with others and "fit in" with the community.

The diversity of local demands and problems underscores ability and accomplishment more, in effect, than professional background (7). Also, particular abilities and talents do not necessarily follow professional stereotypes in hierarchical fashion, nor definition of function by profession. Generalization frequently required on the part of staff may be one factor accounting for the less strict division of roles and responsibilities among professions in this type of program. Professional growth and maximum achievement, however, are encouraged by delegation of responsibility. The opportunity inherent in a diversified program for utilization of training and skills not only precipitates growth, but also facilitates recruitment, provides greater job satisfaction and encourages tenure. The administrative task is to create a climate in which each staff member is free enough and challenged enough constantly to precipitate himself into just manageable difficulty, an expectancy of excellence which leads to its pursuit. Quite apart from the impact this may have on the pace, nature and direction of program development, it creates a favorable professional climate, in turn lending desirable reinforcement to the service.

Even before it was so clearly documented by Albee, the severe professional shortages in the mental health field were widely felt, if not known. In the face of the magnitude of this dilemma it is incredible that greater measures have not been taken in both the recruitment and training of personnel. The modest "indenture-stipend" programs, now fairly common, only scratch the surface. What attempt is made to heighten the potential interest of the undergraduate, let alone those in high school? And few are the mental health services that have well-developed training programs in coordination with the universities for the main mental health professions. To project the continuation or development of a network of services without an active plan for and role in training is rather irresponsible. Are we too busy with the difficulties of personnel shortages to take measures to solve the problem?

A frequent stopgap is the "hand-overhand" competition with neighboring mental health services for personnel. Even this expedient which only shifts the shortage fails because there is failure to appreciate that the competition for such manpower is basically not with other comparable services but with industry and private practice. Moreover, some services, despite the noise from wheel-spinning, have not yet really answered the prime question: Do they really want well-qualified psychiatrists, psychologists, social workers and others —and all that this implies?

SERVICE AND SALARY

All too often, neither training, responsibilities, conditions of employment nor salary bear a realistic relationship. The more common pattern is: professional standards, too low; responsibilities, too varied and far in excess of training; personnel, equipment and space, insufficient; and salaries, noncompetitive. There are many very serious ramifications to this. Two conditions seem most common:

1. A salary unlikely to attract well-qualified personnel: to fill positions, professional standards are progressively lowered, but once inferior staff has been recruited, the agency is deprived of the caliber of staff originally wanted, and more serious, the least qualified are the least mobile. Intended responsibilities become inappropriate. Whoever heard of someone with a year or two of medical training (incomplete training) being recognized as a physician? The same principle holds equally for psychologists, social workers and medical specialists.

2. Seduction by fringe benefit: the basic position and/or remuneration is uninviting. By recourse to various "arrangements", the wrapping for the package is made attractive. Once recruited, the man's talent and identification are divided, his income cumulative. And the basic task?—probably still unmet. This solution is an insidious one, having the seeds of self-destruction. It leads to professional drift away from the agency and obscures identification. Service becomes less reliable and the arrangements progressively more difficult to justfy —certainly to the public. Both service and staff are prostituted, yet eventually may be held accountable.

PROFESSIONAL STANDARDS

Suppose we accept the notion of the "team" and that various professions can make a serious contribution to mental health services. If so, all must be fully trained and sufficiently experienced for an atmosphere of cooperation and respect to prevail, indeed, be possible. The conviction that only fully trained persons can adequately bear full professional responsibility results in comparable competency among the professions and artificial hierarchies tend to dissolve. Administrative responsibilities may then be determined on a "best man" basis. Responsibility is thus directly related to talent and an effective and efficient service can be expected.

Paradoxically, it might be added, that though mental health personnel, with all too few exceptions, exhibit a general disinterest or dislike of broad administrative and fiscal matters, the number of able or qualified administrators falls substantially short of those who believe that the role is properly theirs. Academic training in psychiatry, psychology or social work is rarely germane to administration. Thus, it is difficult enough to secure an able administrator from the three professions, let alone any one.

When we deal with services, positions and qualifications, we are faced with the trials of job classification or merit system procedures. The aim is very clearly an orderly arrangement by duties and responsibilities of all positions. But this fair and logical aim is all too often fraught with two major handicaps. In the first place, technology and the professions are in fairly rapid change with the result that Civil Service structures lag behind professional developments and there is often a rigidity, because of the mere size of the structure, that impairs adjustment to professional developments or makes it almost impossible to accommodate them. More serious, however, is the strong conflict in value systems between the ways in which competence is assessed by the profession and by Civil Service. This is most evident in the two differing views of a college degree, particularly a graduate degree. The common professional assumption that specific academic achievement per se qualifies an individual for a job is a presumption not always shared by Civil Service. In fact, professional requirements are often considered discriminatory, supposedly blocking the appointment unjustly of persons who, it is averred, can do the job though they have not met the usual professional requirements.

This procedure runs contrary to the notion that with intimate knowledge and experience, a profession knows its resources and limits best. Rather, the classification officer becomes the ultimate judge. Regardless of the inaccuracy, this is hardly an approach designed to elicit the cooperation and interest of well qualified (by the professions' standards) personnel.

In some professions, notably medicine, and in some services, such as Minnesota's Community Mental Health program (9), this conflict has been solved by resort to legislation (or rule and regulation) of the professional standards. Any amendments, as deemed necessary, may then be sought directly by the professions or the department concerned. In setting standards for public service in this way, it is likely that the minimum requirements will be high and the maximum open. The only clear way for change then is up; that is, improved standards and standards having professional recognition.

SUMMARY

Comprehensive community mental health programs follow the pattern of public health philosophy which places the need for community service paramount to individual considerations. Public support and professional participation are seen as the cornerstones of such a program, but both the social and professional aspects are influenced by factors which we tend to over-look. In the community mental health field we have been all too prone to develop services without consideration to solving the vast community problems created by a wide range of disordered behavior. Proper integration and control of local services could have a preventive impact. This must become the ultimate goal, for without it, there is no solution.

REFERENCES

1. Glidewell, J. Relationship between social structure and community mental health. Regional Workshop on Leadership Training, St. Louis, Mo., 1957.
2. Greving, F. Basis and plan for a more effective use of community resources for mental health. Northeast State Governments Conference on Mental Health, New Hampshire, 1957.
3. Jaco, G. *The social epidemiology of mental disorders.* New York: Russell Sage Foundation, 1960.
4. Jahoda, M. *Current concepts of positive mental health.* New York: Basic Books, 1958.
5. Parsons, T. What's New. *Abbot,* 1960, 220:6.
6. Slack, D., and Schwitzgebel, R. *Reducing adolescent crime in your community: A handbook.* Tuscaloosa: Educational Design of Alabama, 1960.
7. Southard, C. A view of local community mental health programs. In *Progress and problems of community mental health services.* New York: Milbank Memorial Fund, 1958.
8. Highlights of recent community mental health legislation. APA and NAMH Fact Sheet no. 8. Washington, D. C.: American Psychiatric Association, 1959.
9. *Minnesota community mental health services.* St. Paul: Department of Public Welfare, 1960.
10. *Planning of facilities for mental health services, Surgeon General's Ad Hoc Committee Report.* Washington, D. C.: DHEW, PHS Publication no. 808, 1961.

11

Approaches to Interagency Cooperation

HAROLD P. HALPERT AND CHARLOTTE SILVERMAN

ESTABLISHING a comprehensive community mental health program entails developing complex relationships with other community agencies and institutions. Besides creating the mechanisms required for efficient casefinding and referral, prompt and appropriate treatment, and continuity of care, the mental health program must mobilize resources to meet the medical, financial, housing, and other needs of the person who is mentally ill or emotionally disturbed.

One of the key problems in providing community health and welfare services has been the lack of effective coordination that would subordinate services to the needs of individual clients. Agency domain, institutional inertia, and professional specialization tend to preserve impermeable boundary lines between services. If the comprehensive community mental health program is to succeed, its planners must explore new ways to create interagency cooperation and to organize community facilities.

Discussing the organizational problems of providing medical care and social services, Levine, White, and Paul (2) indicate some methods that might be used to achieve greater interagency cooperation. They include:

Improving the knowledge that organizations have of one another's functions and problems.

Recognizing and analyzing domain differences and trying to resolve them.

Educating the community leaders about the interdependence of the community health and welfare agency systems.

Educating referral sources about agency functions.

Informing the community in general about the resources of the agency.

During the process of planning comprehensive state-wide mental health programs, including mental health centers, states focused much attention on the need for such educational efforts. However, agencies' knowledge of one another's functions and procedures carries no guarantee that they actually will coordinate their activities.

Reprinted from *Hospital and Community Psychiatry,* 1967, *18,* 84–87, by permission of the publisher and authors. © 1967, American Psychiatric Association. Dr. Halpert is Chief, Systems Research Section, Applied Research Branch, National Institute of Mental Health. Dr. Silverman is Deputy Chief, Population Studies Program, National Center for Radiological Health.

Recent attempts have been made to conceptualize principles involved in interagency coordination. Litwak and Hylton (3) hypothesize that there will be pressure for it when the separate agencies are actually interdependent and cannot carry out their missions without the help of other agencies; when the agencies become aware of their interdependence; and when they operate with standardized units of activity, such as intake or diagnosis, that can be exchanged among themselves.

Levine and White (1) have examined the principle of exchange as a framework for developing agency relations. They theorize that the elements essential to the operation of the agencies concerned can be used to fuse stronger bonds between them. These elements include clients, who may be exchanged by referral; professional workers, whose services may be exchanged and shared through consultation and other methods; and facilities, equipment, and funds, which may be shared or exchanged by grants and other techniques.

Many mental health agencies and programs have devised practical methods for interweaving their services with other agencies and programs. In many instances they do exchange clients, staff, or facilities. Some arrangements are made by implied contracts, others by more formal agreements.

Among the more familiar methods are the cooperative arrangements established between official agencies at the state level. In a number of states the agency responsible for operating the mental hospitals has developed rehabilitation programs for hospital patients in cooperation with the state vocational rehabilitation agency, usually a branch of the state department of education. Under such an arrangement, a rehabilitation counselor is stationed at the hospital to assist patients at all stages of their occupational readjustment to life in the community. The West Virginia mental hospitals have entered into a formal agreement with the Division of Vocational Rehabilitation whereby they jointly operate a rehabilitation facility as a separate unit. In Kentucky the official rehabilitation agency operates sheltered workshops and halfway houses for mental patients.

The New York State Department of Mental Hygiene has set up agreements with the Social Welfare Department to provide psychiatric services for senile people in facilities operated by the welfare agency; with the Health Department, which provides certain services to the retarded; and with the Department of Education, which provides special education for retarded and emotionally disturbed children. In Minnesota and Wisconsin arrangements with the health departments permit public health nurses to provide follow-up care for discharged mental hospital patients. Interdepartmental agreements in West Virginia permit use of resources and personnel of the Department of Welfare to help plan for patients about to be discharged from mental hospitals and to assist patients already discharged.

In Wisconsin the placement of adult retardates in nursing homes close to their own homes was made possible through cooperation between the mental health agency, the private nursing homes, the state Board of Health (which licenses and supervises the nursing homes), and the county public welfare departments, which administer financial aid to the disabled. In a number of states, special services for aged patients, who constitute a large percentage of the mental hospital population, have been supported by payments resulting from cooperative agreements between the hospitals and departments of assistance and Social Security programs. Those arrangements among official state agencies entail some sharing of clients, professional workers, and facilities and funds; they usually are formulated in administrative memorandums or statements of agreement.

At lower administrative levels, cooperative interagency arrangements have been set up between public and private agencies and between two or more private agencies. The state-supported mental health center in Springfield, Illinois, provides diagnostic and consultation services to a day center operated by a local association for retarded children; day centers operated privately or by voluntary associations accept discharged state hospital patients. In Rochester, Pennsylvania, the William Lintz Sheltered Workshop has formally contracted with the local family service agency to purchase counseling services for its clients. The workshop thus could qualify for a state grant-in-aid, and the family agency was able, with additional community funds, to employ another staff member to provide the required service.

Coordination has been built into some interagency service arrangements. For several years, for instance, the psychiatric service of Montefiore, a general hospital in New York City, has shared staff salary costs with social, recreational, and vocational agencies that serve its patients during and after hospitalization. The shared staff are on the payrolls of both the hospital and one of the cooperating agencies; one of the agencies (a recreation center) occupies land owned by the hospital. In Chester County, Pennsylvania, a mental health center and a family service agency cooperate to staff a one-day-a-week central intake office in the small town of Kennett Square.

Some mental health agencies operate under an implied contract by which the referring agency is obligated to assume responsibility for some of the clients' needs in return for consultation or treatment services provided by the special agency. The Chicago community mental health program, for instance, requires referring groups to provide transportation, baby-sitting services, or similar practical essentials for low-income clients whom they accept for psychiatric evaluation and treatment.

The cooperative programs of the Albert Einstein College of Medicine, Bronx Municipal Hospital, and the nearby Westchester Square Public Health Center in New York City represent a more complex example of interagency contractual arrangements. The college of medicine staffs the hospital, and, as an adjunct to the psychiatric service, its division of social and community psychiatry operates a day hospital and research center housed at the public health center. In return for its quarters, the research center provides counseling services to local agencies; this activity, in turn, has opened the way for joint service and research projects with the public health nursing staff, the clergy, the police, the schools, the courts, and other public agencies. The budget for those activities comes from funds administered by the city's Department of Health and its Department of Hospitals; from the state-aided community mental health program; from Yeshiva University, a private institution of which the college of medicine is a part; and from federal research grants.

Einstein also is conducting an experiment in interlocking mental health and social services as part of its mental health work at Lincoln Hospital, another city hospital that it staffs. The Lincoln project has opened store-front neighborhood information and service centers in its densely populated, low-income neighborhood to help people find appropriate help for all types of social and psychological problems. The centers are financed by an antipoverty grant and are staffed by nonprofessional indigenous aides. The services do not overlap those of other agencies; instead they effectively screen applicants and refer them to the right agencies. The program is an interesting example of a mental health service experimenting in community organization.

Similar in purpose is the employing of a "re-entry expediter" by the H. Douglas Singer Zone Center in Rockford, Illinois, which serves ten counties in the state. The zone center is responsible for integrating all official mental health agencies and services in a sizable area of the state, besides operating a comprehensive complex of services in the center itself. The re-entry expediter will coordinate all facilities in the zone—inpatient and outpatient mental health services, social-agency services, and public services—for the development of a program to rehabilitate and return to community life persons of diminished social competence.

The Lincoln project service centers and the zone center expediter are, in effect, the poor man's and the sick man's guides to help in a pluralistic system of health and welfare services. The health and welfare agencies themselves are attempting to deal with the general problem of coordination to avoid duplication of community services provided to multiproblem, multiagency families. An interagency committee was formed in Orleans County, a rural area of Vermont, to develop a mutual reporting system. Its goal is to identify high-priority problem families, defined as those whose members are involved with four or more agencies, and, by case conferences, to decide on treatment plans.

Many other examples of interagency coordination could be cited. Those mentioned have been selected to illustrate practical attempts to solve problems in the following ways:

By helping the mental patient make a vocational, financial, recreational, and general social readjustment to life in the community;

By providing counseling and mental health services to clients of health, welfare, and other social service agencies;

By providing social services to clients of mental health agencies;

By helping a person with mental health problems locate assistance tailored to his needs;

By helping agencies focus their services more effectively on persons whose needs constitute a high-priority social problem.

Those practical techniques of coordination may provide models of inter-relationship and cooperation that might be useful in planning for integrated mental health services. In general they involve planned activities based on the explicit recognition that interests of agencies may differ, and they involve administrative or financial arrangements designed to build interdependency and interchange into the structure and function of health and social service agencies.

REFERENCES

1. Levine, S., and White, P. E. Exchange as a conceptual framework for the study of interorganizational relationships. *Administrative Sciences Qtly.*, 1961, 5:583–601.
2. Levine, S., White, P. E., and Paul, B. D. Community interorganizational problems in providing medical care and social services. *Amer. J. of Publ. Hlth.*, 1963, 53:1183–95.
3. Litwak, E., and Hylton, L. F. Interorganizational analysis: A hypothesis on coordinating agencies. *Administrative Sciences Qtly.*, 1962, 6:395–420.

12

The Financing of Mental Health Services: A National View

ROBERT H. ATWELL

I WOULD like to present to you what may seem to be a somewhat grandiose conceptualization of the present and future pattern of financing of mental health services. I believe this approach is useful, indeed it is the only way that I can discuss the subject in concrete terms, but I would like to make more than the usual disclaimers about the figures and assumptions used. In the first place, neither the figures nor the assumptions represent the official views of the National Institute of Mental Health or any other part of the federal establishment on the future patterns of financing. Secondly, the figures are in many cases based or projected on the basis of very poor data. Thirdly, it has been necessary to make a number of assumptions throughout the paper with which one may obviously differ at various points. Nonetheless, for purposes of discussion and as orders of magnitude, I believe the approach presented has a certain validity. I would only beg your indulgence not to be unduly disturbed if at some later point in time, after more careful research and the development of better information, it is necessary to make major revisions in some of the assumptions.

I would like to begin my remarks by pointing out the three most important facts relevant to the financing of mental health services. The first is the importance of the subject. At least 1 per cent of the population can be expected to actively seek mental health services when a reasonable volume of these services are available. Nearly one-third of the hospital beds are occupied by the mentally ill. These are simply evidences of the utilization of services, which is known to account for only a small fraction of the total incidence and prevalence of the disorder. The second important fact is the substantial sums of money now being spent on mental health services. I would estimate that such services account for 8 per cent of total expenditures for personal health care, excluding nonpsychiatric treatment of psychosomatic ailments. Between

Reprinted from a speech in Baltimore at the National Commission on Community Health Services, 1964 by permission of the author. Mr. Atwell is Vice Chancellor, University of Wisconsin.

35 and 40 per cent of all public expenditures for personal health care are accounted for by mental health services. The third fact of paramount importance is that mental health services in this country are characterized by being to a unique degree in the public sector both in operational and financial terms. This, of course, stems from the traditional rejection by society of the mentally ill, with the consequent establishment of what used to be called asylums for putting them out of sight and mind. The public sector, in its role of taking on those functions not wanted or found to be profitable to the private sector, was given the responsibility for the mentally ill, and this responsibility has persisted in large measure despite the fact that our view of mental illness has markedly changed. Thus, whereas only 20 per cent of all personal health care expenditures in this country are publicly financed (and half of these expenditures are for military personnel, their dependents, and veterans), about 70 per cent of the expenditures for mental health services are publicly financed.

Thus, in summary, the problem is important in magnitude, costly in dollar and human terms, and one for which the public sector has historically assumed the greater burden of responsibility.

I would like now to indicate each of the major components of the nation's budget for mental health services. For purposes of a rough approximation, I would estimate national expenditures for nonfederal mental health services as shown in Table 1.

TABLE 1. EXPENDITURES FOR MENTAL HEALTH SERVICES

Type of Expenditure	Amount in 1962* (*in millions*)
Expenditures of state and county institutions	$1,077
Expenditures of private mental institutions	278
Maintenance of patients in psychiatric services of general hospitals	150†
Outpatient community mental health services	100†‡
Private psychiatrists' fees	200§
TOTAL	$1,805

* See Table 2 for source of data, except as otherwise noted. All amounts exclude expenditures under the Veterans Administration and the Department of Defense, as well as expenditures of institutions for the mentally retarded and operations of specialized programs (e.g., alcohol clinics, narcotics programs) where these are administered separate from mental health services per se.

† There is some double counting in this category because some of the public funds devoted to community services are being spent for the care of patients in general hospitals.

‡ Figure obtained from budgetary information submitted to the U.S. Public Health Service.

§ Rough estimate based on updating of figures used in *Economics of Mental Illness* by Rashi Fein, 1958, Basic Books, Inc.

The data on the state and county institutions are reasonably hard, while that on the general hospitals, the community services, and the private psychiatrists are quite soft. Nonetheless, the figures are reasonably satisfactory for discussion, if not for research purposes.

THE STATE MENTAL HOSPITAL SYSTEM

The state system is the overwhelming fact in the financing of mental health services. It is fashionable these days to condemn the system by pointing to its many deficiencies in physical plant and staff. Without in any way denying these deficiencies, two things should be said. The first is that the state hospitals still are the only resource available to the vast majority of the mentally ill in this nation. Secondly, there has been marked improvement in the conditions in a large proportion of these institutions. Over the last ten years, states have nearly doubled their expenditures to maintain patients in these institutions. The $5.51 per-patient-day expenditures for the half million people in these institutions is still woefully inadequate when contrasted with $35–$40 per-patient-day expenditures in general hospitals or $14 per day in Veterans Administration neuropsychiatric institutions, but the improvement is dramatic. However, the improvement is even more dramatic to one visiting one of these institutions today and comparing it with ten years ago. The opening of doors made possible to some degree by the psychoactive drugs has probably done more than anything else to improve the climate of the mental hospitals.

In looking at the financing of the state hospital systems, it is interesting to note what has happened to expenditures for additions and improvements. In 1956, which is roughly the period when the decline in patient populations stemming from the psychoactive drugs, the opening of doors, and other dramatic changes began, the expenditures for additions and improvements was about $84 million. In 1962 this figure had declined to $70.3 million. Thus, what apparently has happened is that states were able, through the decline in patient populations, to put a much higher proportion of their funds into patient services without adding to the number of beds. It is quite a tribute to the states that they have continued to increase their patient services expenditures in the face of declining populations, because the tendency of many budgeteers would be to cut funds for services in proportion to the cut in patients. This decline in capital expenditures varies considerably from state to state and it is interesting to note that whereas California, with a rapidly growing population, has decreased its capital expenditures for state institutions from $9.6 million to $2 million in the seven-year period, New York, with a lesser rate of population growth, increased its capital expenditures from $15.8 million to $19.4 million over the same period.

While the population of the institutions has continually dropped since 1955, this decline has not been dramatic in absolute terms and unless other alternatives are developed rapidly, population growth may well reverse the downward trend of the patient curve. Thus, limited though they may be, the state institutions are going to be with us for a long time to come and their financial burden on the states will not diminish in the foreseeable future, even if the decline in patient population continues, because of the recognized need to improve the quality of services, and the continued growth in admissions to these institutions.

THE PRIVATE INSTITUTIONS FOR THE MENTALLY ILL

These are many in number but few in terms of patients. There are about 260 institutions, as compared with 285 state and county institutions, accounting for only about 16,000 beds, as contrasted with over half a million beds in the public institutions. There is, however, a fairly high turnover in these institutions, with over 70,000 admissions per year as contrasted with about 285,000 admissions in the public institutions. The somewhat higher quality of care in many of the private institutions as contrasted with the public institutions can be seen in the fact that the $280 million being spent in these institutions is many times more per patient than that being spent in public institutions. It is questionable that the private institutions will ever be a major

TABLE 2. SIGNIFICANT STATISTICS ON INSTITUTIONS FOR THE MENTALLY ILL 1962

	NUMBER OF INSTITUTIONS	ADMISSIONS Total	Per 100,000 population*	PATIENTS END OF YEAR Total	Per 100,000 population*	EXPENDITURES FOR MAINTENANCE OF PATIENTS** (in thousands)
State and county institutions†	285	283,863	137	515,640	284	$1,076,579
Private institutions‡	258	71,679	38	15,833	7	278,421§
General hospitals with psychiatric facilities ‖	585	210,305	111	8,563	5	150,000♯

* 1961 figures.

† Data are from *Patients in Mental Institutions, 1962,* Part II, U.S. Department of Health, Education, and Welfare, Public Health Service, National Institute of Mental Health.

‡ With the exception of the last column, data are from *Patients in Mental Institutions, 1962,* Part III, U.S. Department of Health, Education, and Welfare, Public Health Service, National Institute of Mental Health.

§ Figure is residual of $1,355,000 in expenditures of all non-federal psychiatric hospitals (*Hospitals,* Journal of the American Hospital Association, August 1, 1964, Vol. 38, pt. 2, table 1, page 482) less previously cited figure for expenditures for state and county institutions.

‖ Data are from *Patients in Mental Institutions, 1962,* Part III, U.S. Department of Health, Education, and Welfare, Public Health Service, National Institute of Mental Health.

♯ Estimate computed as follows: 210,000 admissions; average stay of 20 days, $35 per patient day costs.

** Figure includes additions and improvements.

resource, because of the relatively high cost of their services, their geographic concentration in a few states (New York and California account for 40 per cent of the institutions and 25 per cent of the beds), and their frequent isolation from the mainstream of social welfare services.

THE PSYCHIATRIC SERVICES IN GENERAL HOSPITALS

These services are the brightest stars in the mental health horizon in the last ten years. While the 10,000 beds in about 600 general hospitals known to have psychiatric services are small in number, because of rapid turnover (an average stay of probably about three weeks) they account for almost as many admissions as to the state mental institutions. For a number of reasons, the future of such services is bright. The best professional judgment in the field supports a close alliance between mental health and general health services, an alliance which is nowhere better illustrated than in the general hospital. Moreover, the growth of insurance coverage can be expected to be most important in the area of inpatient services in general hospitals, which reflects the degree of acceptance—from the point of view of the insurance industry—of any service rendered in a general hospital. It is worth noting in connection with any discussion of the importance of the general hospital that the Community Mental Health Centers Act of 1963, which I will discuss shortly, assigns special consideration, in terms of federal construction as-

TABLE 3. SIGNIFICANT STATISTICS ON OUTPATIENT PSYCHIATRIC CLINICS 1962

Number of Clinics	*1,656*
STAFF	
Psychiatrists	7,828
Full-time	(933)
Part-time	(4,684)
Trainees	(2,211)
Clinical psychologists	3,424
Full-time	(1,165)
Part-time	(1,703)
Trainees	(556)
Psychiatric social workers	4,403
Full-time	(2,254)
Part-time	(1,516)
Trainees	(633)
Professional man-hours per week per 100,000 population for median State	113
PATIENTS	
New admissions	269,313
Patients under care during year	506,103
New admissions per 100,000 population	160
Patients under care per 100,000 population	306

sistance, to those community mental health centers which are part of or associated with a general hospital.

PRIVATE PSYCHIATRY

The fees paid to private psychiatrists account for a large amount of money, but I think everyone would agree that private psychiatry is not now, and will not be in the future (even allowing for some growth in insurance in this field), financially within the reach of a large portion of the population.

COMMUNITY SERVICES

I would like at this point to discuss the present methods of financing community mental health services, reserving for later the impact of recent and probable future federal legislation. Most of the $100 million presently being spent for community mental health (exclusive of general hospitals) is publicly supported. Probably most of the funds are spent in the nearly 1,700 outpatient psychiatric clinics, and undoubtedly a large but unknown portion of the funds are recovered in fees. A second important fact about community services is the relatively small volume of such services. The median state has less than three professional man-years, including all types of mental health skills, going into outpatient psychiatric clinics per 100,000 population. Eleven states are spending less than $200,000 in state, local, and private funds on community mental health services. Three states (New York, California, and Illinois) account for more than 50 per cent of the $100 million being spent on community services.

The public sector's responsibility for the support of community services is fairly equally divided between states and localities, with the federal contribution being limited to date to the $6,750,000 available through a formula grant program, a figure which has not changed markedly in the 15-year history of the program.

The most common form of state support of community programs is a device known as the Community Mental Health Services Act. Twenty states have such acts, which usually provide for state matching grants for specified types of local mental health services, most commonly outpatient and consultation services. Capital expenditures are usually excluded from state participation. States which have such acts account for most of the funds being spent on community services.

Another method of financing community mental health services (including private psychiatric services) is through insurance and prepayment mechanisms. By way of prefacing my remarks on this subject. I would note that health insurance now covers more than three-fourths of the population, but covers only one-fourth of the medical bill. Restrictions against mental illness in many forms of coverage have resulted in a much lower proportion of the mental health bill being met through insurance. Gradually these restrictions are being removed, particularly with respect to inpatient services. It is not unreasonable to expect that within ten years a large portion of the hospital room and board charges for the psychiatric services of general hospitals will be met through insurance. Presently more than 60 per cent of the room and board (per diem) charge of the general hospital is paid for through insurance for all types of hospitalized illness.

However, the outlook is not so bright for outpatient and partial hospitalization services, not to mention the almost total absence of coverage for the services of psychologists, social workers, and other professionals who are increasingly important in the treatment of the mentally ill. Moreover, there is almost no coverage of day care at the present time and outpatient coverage is, with a few notable exceptions, quite limited in terms of availability, and unfavorable in terms of high co-insurance and initial deductible features which discourage early referral and treatment. Coverage in these areas and the recognition of paramedical personnel will probably be somewhat slow to develop given the conservative nature of the insurance industry. It should also be pointed out that voluntary health insurance is not a major factor as yet in the payment of outpatient services in the case of physical illnesses. Moreover, as coverage in these areas does increase, premiums also increase, thereby putting health insurance even more beyond the reach of those who may need it most, those same persons the community mental health center is designed to serve.

THE EFFECT OF PRESENT FINANCIAL MECHANISMS
ON PATIENT CARE

As is true in other fields of medicine, there are two kinds of mental health care, one for those who can pay and another for the so-called indigent. For the latter, there is the state mental hospital; for the former, there are a number of other alternatives. The double standard probably is exacerbated in the mental health field by the obvious disparity in quality between the two types of care. For example, there are few welfare agencies which will pay $35 to $40 for their clients in the psychiatric services of a general hospital when the client can be sent off to the state hospital for $5.50 per day; in large measure, the figures are probably indicative of the difference in quality of care. Most of the community clinics throughout the country, not to mention the offices of private psychiatrists, are populated by the upper and upper-middle classes. The relative unavailability of mental health coverage through insurance or prepayment mechanisms tends, of course, to accentuate the double standard.

Thus, even with a heavy proportion of public subsidization, mental health services are woefully inadequate for the vast majority of people.

A NEW APPROACH TO MENTAL HEALTH SERVICES

Into this somewhat discouraging picture, there has emerged a new ray of hope. In early 1963, President Kennedy sent to the Congress his historic Special Message on Mental Illness and Mental Retardation. The basic thrust of that message was that there should be created throughout the country community mental health centers which would provide the full range of mental health services at the community level. These centers were envisioned as a genuine alternative to the state mental hospital system; in fact the President spoke of reducing the population of these institutions by 50 per cent within a decade or two. Federal support totaling $757 million was requested for the construction and initial operation of these centers. The congressional response was to authorize substantially less than the President had requested and to delete the proposed program of federal grants to support the initial staffing

TABLE 4. STATE AND LOCAL MENTAL HEALTH SERVICES

	1962	1975	Increase
		(in millions)	
TOTAL*			
Maintenance of patients in state institutions	$1,000	$1,400	$ 400
Community services			
Operations†	100	800	700
Construction (including federal funds)	—	200	200
	$1,100	$2,400	$1,300
FINANCED FROM STATE AND LOCAL FUNDS			
Maintenance of patients in state institutions	$1,000	$1,400	$ 400
Community services			
Operations	100	400	300
Construction (state and local matching of federal funds)	—	100	100
	$1,100	$1,900‡	$ 800
DEFICIT (to be met through a combination of private contributions, fees, insurance, and federal funds)	—	$ 500	$ 500

* For the sake of simplicity, figures have been rounded and thus are somewhat at variance with Table 1.

† Increase is not as large as it appears because the 1975 figure includes significant volume of psychiatric services in general hospitals, which are excluded from the corresponding 1962 figure.

‡ Figure is assumed to be limited to the same roughly 1.5 per cent of state and local budgets which currently obtains. State and local budgets are assumed to grow from $75 billion estimated 1963 level to $130 billion by 1975, which is consonant with recent growth patterns. Variations from this assumed rate of growth will, of course, markedly affect figures in this table.

of centers. The Community Mental Health Centers Act of 1963 authorizes appropriations of $150 million over the three fiscal years beginning last July 1, with the current year installment being $35 million. Grants are made, pursuant to a state plan, to support from one-third to two-thirds of the construction costs of those facilities, which are part of a program providing at least the essential elements (defined in regulations as inpatient, outpatient, day care, emergency, and consultation and education services) of comprehensive mental health services.

It goes without saying that this program will have a significant impact on the direction of mental health services, not to mention the budgets of states and localities. The average annual figure of $100 million for this program, including the nonfederal share, compares favorably with the $70 million currently being spent for additions and improvements to the state hospitals. On the other hand, the sums available are in no sense adequate to achieve the goals of the President's message. This is true both on the level of the adequacy of construction funds to create sufficient community centers to achieve a marked reduction in the state hospital populations, and on the level of the ability of communities to finance the operation of centers. Nonetheless, it is reasonable to assume, allowing for continuation of the federal program at a somewhat higher level after the expiration of the current three-year authorization, that within 20–25 years the nation will be reasonably well equipped in terms of community mental health facilities. The method of paying for the services in these facilities, as I will indicate later, has yet to be worked out.

THE FISCAL IMPACT OF NEW PROGRAMS

Assuming the acceptance of the goal of community-based mental health services, what will this mean to the budgets of state and local governments?

While state budgets for mental health services (principally the state mental hospitals) have increased markedly, particularly on a per-patient basis, this increase has not kept pace with the even more rapid growth in total state and local budgets. Indeed, the tendency since 1956 has been for the maintenance of patients in state mental hospitals to decline as a proportion of total state expenditures. However, when allowance is made for the growth in state support of community mental health programs, we have a situation where total mental health activities have probably remained a fairly constant 1.5 per cent of the total state and local budgets.

If we assume that state and local budgets continue, the recent growth pattern of these budgets in 1975 will be on the order of $130 billion. If mental health holds its own as a proportion of this total, one can reasonably expect states and localities to put $1.9 billion into such services, an increase of about $.8 billion over roughly a 12-year period. The non-federal share of the construction of community mental health centers will require about

$100 million under reasonable assumptions of program growth. Even with continued modest reductions in the populations of the state mental hospitals, it is difficult to see how the states can avoid increasing their expenditures for the maintenance of patients in state institutions by anything less than $400 million over the next 12 years, even allowing for some federal support under various types of medical care programs. Thus, there would appear something on the order of $300 million available for added state and local support of community services, a major increase over present levels.

If the goal of a community mental health center for every 100,000 persons were 50 per cent realized in 12 years, which does not seem unreasonable from this perspective, the costs of operating these 1,000 centers would be on the order of $800 million annually. States and localities could reasonably be expected to finance $300 million of this increase. This leaves a residual of $500 million annually to be met through fees, insurance, or federal subsidies.

It need hardly be pointed out that the $400 million assumed increase in the cost of the state budgets is a very conservative figure. Indeed, if the pattern of the last six years were to hold true, the figure could well double its present level over the next 12 years, even assuming a continued decline in the patient population.

Under the assumption of a constant proportion of the state and local budgets being given to mental health, further increases (over the modest estimate which I have postulated) in the state hospital system can be said to be made at the expense of community programs. This only reinforces the most important thought that I would like to leave with you, namely, that community mental health services can be made broadly available in the next 10 to 20 years only with some assistance from the federal government. After a period of experience with these services and the development of other solutions, such as nursing homes for the geriatric population now in the state hospitals, it may be possible to channel some savings from the operation of these hospitals into community programs, but I do not believe we should count on such savings in the foreseeable future.

I would not wish to venture a guess on the proportion or amount of federal assistance that would be necessary to provide the level of community services which I have postulated. It is obvious that insurance, fees, and voluntary contributions can also play a major role in financing these services. It does seem evident, however, that these sources will not be sufficient in themselves.

I have not ventured a prediction of the expenditures in 1975 for all types of mental health services, including private sector expenditures. It seems abundantly evident, however, that if services are to be more equitably distributed to the population, the public sector will have to continue to be the major source of funds. As I have indicated, I do not believe that insurance represents anything more than an important partial solution to the financial problem, and in the absence of such insurance the majority of the population will not be in a position to pay for the full cost of services through fees.

I would note that even on the assumption of holding mental health expenditures, there would be an increase in the per capita spending of states and localities for mental health services from the present $5.90 to about $7.80 by 1975. This, of course, reflects the fact that the expenditures of states and localities for social welfare services generally are increasing even faster than the growth in population. In the case of mental health, this seems fully warranted considering the low base of services at the present time. There is little doubt that in the short run the community mental health center is a more expensive method of treating a given number of patients than the state system. Over the long run, however, the existence of these community services may make it possible to eliminate the state mental hospital as we now know it today. I would suggest that while there are obvious long-run economies in this prospect, these are as nothing compared with the reduction in suffering and the salvation for society of countless persons who might otherwise be doomed to years of unproductive dependency.

13

Mental Disorders and Health Insurance

CHARLES P. HALL, JR.

THE economics of health and the science of medicine continue to ride the flood crest of revolutionary changes which have faced them for the past quarter century. In retrospect, it appears that it was inevitable for these changes to occur simultaneously.

Though medical science has always been dynamic, the scientific developments of recent years have outpaced anything in the past. Initial breakthroughs with penicillin and the sulfas were followed by a seemingly endless flow of new antibiotics, corticosteroids and other drugs. At the same time, undreamed-of progress has been made in surgical and diagnostic procedures as well as in immunization and other preventive techniques. In the field of mental health, too, progress has been rapid. Electroshock, the development of individual and group psychotherapy and milieu therapy, and public support are major innovations which have drastically altered the entire structure for dealing with the mentally ill.

Scientific progress, however, is not a free good. Research costs and the high cost of many new forms of treatment, including heart-lung machines, intensive care units and others, put a rapidly rising price tag on the acquisition of high quality health care. These pressures, much aided by the inflationary nature of the economy during much of the period and the rapid growth of "installment living" as an American way of life, gave rise to new methods of financing health care.

The phenomenal growth of health insurance and prepayment plans during recent years hardly needs documentation (3,12). Despite rapid progress, however, no one suggests that our financing devices are perfect. On the contrary, criticisms of their efficacy in meeting the needs of the nation are many. On every hand they face attack for inadequately serving the aged, failure to assure quality care, inability to control costs, encouraging overutilization of some services, discouraging other necessary forms of treatment and so on, ad infinitum. Unquestionably, many of these criticisms are justified. It is just as

Reprinted from *American Journal of Psychiatry*, 1966, *122*, 1021–1027, by permission of the publisher and the author. © 1965, American Psychiatric Association. Dr. Hall is Associate Professor, Temple University Business School.

certain, however, that some of them reflect an attempt to make the insurance and prepayment mechanisms the scapegoats for ills which are not entirely within their control.

The purpose of this paper is to examine how mental disorders and their treatment fit into the over-all structure of health insurance and prepayment. The broader question of the best way to finance the total structure of mental health care in the United States is not considered in depth at this time. At the outset, then, it is important to put the main issue in perspective. There is no such thing today as psychiatric insurance. There is, however, health insurance which provides benefits for psychiatric care. The extent of protection for psychiatric treatment does not and will not stand independent of other provisions in health insurance contracts.

The American Medical Association has long been vitally interested in health insurance and prepayment as well as in mental health. In addition to being closely involved in the origin and development of Blue Shield, the AMA has, over the years, worked with the Blue Cross and commercial health insurers through its Committee on Insurance and Prepayment Plans. Official recognition of interest in mental health, via the creation of a standing committee and then the Council on Mental Health, stems from the early 1950's, although considerable activity preceded this formal move. The AMA's first National Congress on Mental Illness and Health was held in October 1962, even before President Kennedy's message on mental health was delivered to Congress. It was devoted to establishing state by state mental health priorities and needs. In many states this activity was helpful in subsequent planning operations.

As for the AMA's position on the desired relationship between health insurance and mental health, it was clearly stated several years ago, as follows:

> In the years to come increased coverage of the cost of mental illness by private insurance companies should substantially augment private funds available for mental health needs. The American Medical Association supports the principle that voluntary health insurance programs should be expanded on a basis analogous to ordinary medical and surgical care to include the cost of mental illness (9, p. 20).

REQUISITES OF INSURANCE

Before determining the extent to which mental disorders can be treated the same as other diseases under health insurance, it is necessary to inquire into some basic requisites of insurance. Since insurers are not eleemosynary institutions, all contracts require some controls which enable the benefits to be properly rated. This is just as important in providing mental health benefits as it has been in developing medical and surgical coverage. In addition to requiring adequate spread of risk and some degree of certainty that all insured persons will not suffer loss simultaneously, most insurance policies rely rather heavily on internal definitions of coverage. These definitions may relate to the types of conditions which are covered, the types of services which are covered or the location in which the care must be rendered. In many cases all three items are rigorously defined. Historically, these definitions have been particularly vague or lacking in the field of mental disorders. Fortunately, this problem is now being met. Another traditional concern of insurers has been that losses must be fortuitous—that is, accidental or largely beyond the control of the insured.

While many other factors could be added, this brief list serves to highlight some of the special problems, real or imagined, which arise when coverage for mental disorders is fitted into a health insurance contract. Surely a sizable proportion of the medical treatment provided in this country fails to completely satisfy the fortuitous requirement. Perhaps a majority of the surgery performed each year is elective, at least with respect to its timing. Health insurance and prepayment have successfully overcome this difficulty. In the realm of psychiatric treatment, however, there is still hesitation to be as liberal. Why? Psychiatric treatment is thought by some to be largely elective. Furthermore, there are some groups where unusually high levels of utilization have been recorded. The reasons for this are not always clear, but a desire to be fashionable or to possess a "status symbol" has been blamed in some cases. Since this is related chiefly to Hollywood it can be largely disregarded. A more important fact is that the mental disorders are still thought of by the public very much as tuberculosis was 50 years ago.

DEFINITIONAL PROBLEMS

Definitional problems, however, present the greatest obstacle to insurers. How clearly can mental disorders be defined? What is their nature, extent and cause? When are mental disorders cured, and to what extent are they curable? For that matter, when do they start? What is the cost of treatment? What modes of treatment are available, and what facilities exist which can provide acceptable treatment? Who can provide treatment? Perhaps we should get even more basic. To what extent *should* private health insurance and voluntary prepayment plans try to finance the prevention, treatment and rehabilitation of mental disorders? These are all difficult questions, but it is essential that at least some answers be found.

There are a few who object to the insistence that mental disorders be defined. They might argue that such things as "fevers of undetermined origin" are often covered under regular health insurance. Some also argue that a specific diagnosis is not as important as the determination of the proper treatment for a particular individual. This can vary widely even between persons with the same disorder. The question, however, is not purely academic, nor is it strictly financial. As one Blue Cross plan found, it also gets to the heart of public relations. When this plan asked for a rate increase at approximately the same time that it extended broader coverage to the treatment of alcoholics and drug addicts, it was greeted with headlines in the next day's newspapers: "Blue Cross hikes rates to cover drunks!" Surely insurers have enough problems without this.

Some psychiatrists are also concerned with the vagueness which permeates their speciality, and they actively seek an improvement in this situation. As one has said:

> The definition of a case which states that "everybody is sick" is a deterrent to progress in psychiatry. It reduces the urgency for diagnostic classification and etiologic search. Worst of all, it rationalizes a pattern whereby the healthiest patients receive the greatest amount of active treatment and the sickest the least (7).

It is clear that definite strides have been made in the field of mental health. There is increasing recognition of the fact that mental disorders have much in common with other disorders. They can strike anyone at any time, and they can often be prevented as well as cured. This is certainly a far cry from the prevailing belief of the fairly recent past that persons with mental problems were insane and deserved nothing more than commitment to a "warehousing" type of government institution located—preferably—well out in the country. There is still a need, however, to make clear to laymen and insurers the distinction between those with mental disorders and those who simply have "problems"; between those who are ill and those who are retarded; between those who are susceptible to treatment and those who within the present bounds of knowledge are not susceptible to treatment. These distinctions will play a major role in determining who will finance care and how it will be handled. It is clear that the insurance mechanism is not well suited for providing long term custodial care, for example, and it is questionable whether it is capable of solving the needs of the retarded. Even under more conventional subjects for health insurance the provision of preventive benefits has developed rather slowly. Experience in other lines of insurance, however, demonstrates that prevention is feasible where results are identifiable and measurable.

As Lisbeth Bamberger has stated:

> The question of how mental health services should be financed is still an open one. It may not be as open as it was a few years ago, but it is still open enough to make worthwhile the examination of basic premises and assumptions (2).

Let us not become so preoccupied with the insuring of these services that we begin to force solutions at the expense of other needed financing media. Private insurance can never be the sole financial prop for mental health.

EXISTING COVERAGE

Having explored some problems and limitations, let us now examine what has been done already to provide insurance coverage for mental disorders. For while there is still much to be done, the fact that much has already been accomplished should not be overlooked. Many commercial insurance company hospitalization plans have always provided coverage for mental disorders. This is especially true under group contracts, which account for by far the greatest number of insured lives. As early as 1962 a study conducted by the Life Insurance Agency Management Association (8) indicated that over 94 per cent of the companies surveyed which offered group basic hospital insurance included coverage for mental and emotional disorders. Less than three per cent of these companies imposed any special limits on this coverage. The percentage of companies that provided coverage for mental disorders under individual basic hospital policies was somewhat lower, but still substantial—74 per cent. This corresponds with a normal pattern of more liberal benefits under group insurance. Extensive coverage is also provided under commercial insurers' major medical and comprehensive plans, though the vast majority of these plans impose special limitations on treatment of mental disorders, including different coinsurance requirements and/or internal limits on charges for a single visit to a psychiatrist. Usually maximums based on a specified time period—frequently one year—are also used. Coverage under regular medical benefits contracts is limited.

On March 19, 1965, Steven Sieverts of the Blue Cross Association reported that:

> In 80 per cent of the Blue Cross Plans psychiatric inpatient care in a general hospital, frequently for a somewhat limited number of days per year, is now included as a basic benefit in the most widely held subscriber contracts (11).

Much of this development has come only in the last ten years. Blue Shield plans have provided relatively limited regular medical benefits for nervous and mental conditions, with broader coverage under most of their extended benefits contracts.

Progress, then, has been made, but much of the hospitalization coverage has been more apparent than real. We all know that the development of psychiatric units in general hospitals has been relatively recent. According to a recent survey by the NIMH and the AHA (13), a total of 1,005 general hospitals in the United States admitted psychiatric patients for diagnosis and treatment in 1963. In 1962 only 585 general hospitals were known to admit psychiatric patients. Moreover, the definition of "hospital" in many insurance contracts completely excluded coverage in state mental hospitals or private psychiatric hospitals.

Perhaps the most significant attempt to meet the many definitional questions directly has been through four intensive days of meetings which were held at the headquarters of the American Psychiatric Association in the fall of 1965. This insurance conference brought together a group of experienced senior members of the APA and a number of consultants knowledgeable in the field with the avowed purpose of hammering out some clear answers to definitional questions which will be helpful to insurance and prepayment organizations. In addition to definitions, the group attacked such problems as limits of coverage, criteria of treatment, services, standards and the like.

This represents the first coordinated attempt by the profession to answer these important questions. When these answers are provided, one of the major excuses for not making available adequate coverage for treatment of mental disorders will have been destroyed. Hopefully, the results of these sessions will be regarded as a consensus of opinion on these important questions. They will be made available after official judgment has been made by the Council of the APA, probably in early 1966.

One of the real problems facing insurers today is to keep their policies up to date with developing modes of treatment. In this realm they must necessarily be followers, not leaders. They need the guidance of professionals to indicate the paths which must be explored. As it is found that outpatient clinics, day care centers, emergency services and other alternative facilities provide equivalent and sometimes more beneficial treatment for mental disorders than traditional inpatient confinement, policy provisions must be altered to reflect this new knowledge. Certainly some current insurance provisions have more historical than practical value. Here again, the results of the APA insurance conferences will provide valuable guidance.

The insurance industry is traditionally conservative, perhaps necessarily so, and this is again exhibited in its cautious approach to the expansion of benefits for mental disorders. To be even more specific, the inclusion of outpatient benefits has been particularly slow in coming. However, fragmentary though mounting evidence from a number of widely scattered studies seems to indicate that some of the fears may be unfounded.

One of the most ambitious research projects in this field was conducted by Group Health Insurance, Inc., in New York City from July, 1959, through December, 1961. The American Psychiatric Association and the National Association for Mental Health, aided by a grant from the National Institute of Mental Health, cooperated in the project. The study documented utilization and costs under a plan which tried to minimize the financial and personal barriers to treatment. Many interesting statistics emerged from the study, and a report on the project concluded:

In the present stage of acceptance of psychiatry, there appears to be little danger that the costs of insuring the extent of coverage offered by the project would be prohibitive if spread over an average cross section of the 1960 population (1, p. 258).

This is a qualified but significant statement. What was the extent of coverage offered? GHI paid $15 (75 per cent) of a $20-per-hour fee which had been agreed on by participating APA psychiatrists. They also paid 75 per cent of the agreed charges for 45-minute and 90-minute group therapy sessions. The maximum benefits under the plan were $225 per person. For hospitalized cases, the payments ranged from $15 to $25 a day. Note that first visit coverage was provided, as was coverage for "any conditions treated by a psychiatrist." The major control beyond the coinsurance and maximum limit was to reimburse only participating psychiatrists and hospitals.

At least three other plans provide helpful data. The General Electric Company has accumulated considerable experience with a plan providing broad coverage for mental disorders. Arlene Holen and Agnes Brewster have reported favorably on a study of the plan offered by the Tennessee Hospital Service Association (4). Dr. Philip S. Wagner has spoken widely about the psychiatric program of Retail Clerks Local 770 and Food Employers Benefit Fund in Los Angeles, one of the most important and successful projects ever conducted in this field.

In essence, then, there is factual support for the conclusion that broad inpatient and outpatient coverage of mental disorders is possible. While there is question that many plans in the foreseeable future will follow the GHI experiment and provide coverage for "any condition treated by a psychiatrist" without further definition, we do know that a pattern of first-dollar coverage is developing in this field. Both the recommended guidelines for broader insurance coverage developed by the National Institute of Mental Health (14) and the contract recently negotiated by the United Automobile Workers (5) provide for full coverage of early treatment followed by increasing participation of the insured, with maximum benefits prescribed at relatively modest levels. Let us analyze this development briefly.

Historically, insurance was designed to protect against catastrophic losses. On a purely theoretical basis, many would argue that first-dollar coverage is not economically sound. In fact, there has been rapid growth of the major medical approach which incorporates deductibles and coinsurance in recent years, after the early rise of first-dollar coverage. This statement should not be misinterpreted. There are many persons who are firmly dedicated to first-dollar benefits, service benefits and/or the prepayment concept. This is understandable, but it must be justified on something other than purely economic grounds. Having stated this, it should quickly be pointed out that economic theory is seldom the only or even the overriding concern in choosing between different benefits. Let us explore briefly the reasons why it is particularly desirable that this economic criterion be disregarded, at least for the present, in designing benefits for mental illness.

Except for the continuing concern over rising costs, the main preoccupation in most areas of health services is with overutilization or abuse of services and facilities, however, ill-defined the term "overutilization" often may be. Quite the contrary is true in the field of treatment of mental disorders. There is almost universal agreement that the public underutilizes mental health services in relation to its need. Shortages of adequate facilities and qualified personnel in some geographical areas may create excessive pressure on available resources, but this is a separate issue.

What accounts for this difference? Throughout the history of man a special fear of mental illness has existed. Perhaps lack of understanding has been the underlying cause, but we do know that a social stigma has always been reserved for persons afflicted with mental disorders. Even in our "enlightened" age, vestiges of this stigma remain in many segments of the community.

NO NEED FOR LARGE DEDUCTIBLE

Thus, it seems not only unnecessary but perhaps even undesirable to consider adding a financial hurdle, in the form of a large deductible, to the already formidable social barrier which must be overcome if adequate early diagnosis and treatment of mental disorders is to be achieved. This observation may not always be true, but for the present it seems valid. Removal of the financial barrier alone, however, will not be sufficient to improve existing conditions. It is increasingly being recognized that the entire organization of services is in need of sweeping changes if the masses needing care are to be reached effectively.

Critics within the psychiatric profession and medicine in general as well as laymen and their representatives have attacked the traditional structure of mental health services (10). There is now fairly widespread agreement that the proverbial "psychiatrist's couch" and the one-to-one approach are appealing and useful only to certain fairly restricted segments of the population. They developed largely in an upper-middle-class atmosphere and are not only ineffective for treating many forms of psychiatric illness but also forbidding and frightening to large masses of the working population.

There is, moreover, a mounting body of evidence which indicates that the people who are most in need of psychiatric help are the very ones that the "system" in general and many psychiatrists in particular are unsuited or ill-equipped to handle at the present time. Much progress, however, is being made in developing new techniques. Crisis clinics, walk-in centers in easy-to-reach locations, more effective psychotherapeutic drugs, increasing availability of group and family therapy and other recent techniques show great promise for the future. Of course, many of these developments are of such importance that they transcend the issue of health insurance, which is the immediate concern of this article.

There is yet another justification for reversing the usual application of deductible or coinsurance provisions when dealing with mental disorders. Whereas severe physical illness is frequently terminated by death after substantial expenses have been incurred, this is almost never the case with mental disorders. Given the current state of the art, many mental disorders are more analogous to chronic physical ills which are characterized by periodic relapses and return to the hospital. New techniques have succeeded in making significant inroads on the number of long-run residents in state mental hospitals, and many persons are returned to useful lives, but no one argues the fact that many victims are faced with a lifetime of purely custodial, as opposed to therapeutic, care, given the present state of psychiatric knowledge. This unfortunate group seems likely to continue as a responsibility of the state. The apparent role of private insurance, then, is to provide adequately for early diagnosis and intensive treatment before relinquishing the "incurables" to the state.

Finally, it is again neecssary to put our primary concern in perspective. Insurance benefits for psychiatric treatment are not provided in a vacuum. They are, for the majority at least, negotiated as one small segment of a group health insurance contract which is, in turn only a small portion of a much broader package of employee benefits which includes wages, pensions, vacations, working conditions and so on. What it boils down to is that we are negotiating for a scarce resource—money.

As Herbert Klarman put it in his recent outstanding book, *The Economics of Health:*

> Economists have observed that in the real world the issue is seldom, if ever, the total amount that a nation or group might spend for a given purpose, but whether it should spend more or less than currently. They start with what is and proceed to consider alternatives step by step, by small increment or decrement. Not only is this approach sound for the economist; it is also constructive politically, since it permits adjustments and compromises (6, p. 176).

We must not only speak to the insurers. We must educate the buyers of care—the employers and the unions. Since most group policies are experience rated, insurers will often provide benefits even though they may not think them wise. The insurer will recoup excessive claims costs by adjusting the rate. At least one reason for the slow development of coverage for mental disorders is the lack of demand for it. Perhaps dental coverage is more attractive to the buyer at a given point in time. In effect, the buyer dictates the coverage —he "pays his money and takes his choice." Viewed in this context, the UAW should be congratulated for its leadership in creating an effective demand for coverage of mental disorders.

In conclusion, there is a well-established tendency for service to follow the dollar in the field of health insurance. Let us guard against permitting the dollar to shape the services we provide. Certainly labor, management and the medical profession can all agree that it would be far more desirable for the profession to take the lead in designing the structure of mental health services which will best serve the mental health needs of the people. If this groundwork is properly laid, and the appropriate facilities and personnel are provided, the necessary dollars will be forthcoming to finance psychiatric services, whether via the insurance mechanism, government support or some other combination of sources.

REFERENCES

1. Avnet, H. H. *Psychiatric insurance.* New York: Group Health Insurance, Inc., 1962.
2. Bamberger, L. Financing mental health services and facilities: Problems, prospects, and some policy proposals. Presented at the AFL–CIO meeting on mental health, New York, N. Y., May 20–22, 1964.
3. *Health insurance news.* New York: Health Insurance Institute, May 1965.
4. Holen, A., and Brewster, A. Utilization and costs of psychiatric services under a broad insurance program. In *Psychiatric studies and projects,* vol. 3. Washington, D. C.: American Psychiatric Association, 1965.
5. International Union, United Automobile, Aerospace and Agricultural Implement Workers of America. News release, January 18, 1965.
6. Klarman, H. E. *The economics of health.* New York: Columbia University Press, 1965.
7. Lapouse, R. Who is sick? Presented at the 41st annual meeting of the American Orthopsychiatric Association, Chicago, Ill., March 20, 1964.
8. Myers, E. S. *Insurance coverage of mental illness, 1962, a special report.* Washington, D. C.: Joint Information Service, 1962, pp. 11–14.
9. Program of the Council on Mental Health. Chicago: American Medical Association, June 1962.
10. Riessman, F., and Scribner, S. The underutilization of mental health services by workers and low income groups: Causes and cures. Paper distributed at a meeting of National Association of State Mental Health Program Directors, Chicago, Ill., March 3–4, 1965.
11. Sieverts, S. Psychiatric care and voluntary prepayment. Presented at the 42nd annual meeting of the American Orthopsychiatric Association, New York, N. Y., March 19, 1965.
12. *Source book of health insurance data.* New York: Health Insurance Institute, 1964, pp. 11–12.
13. U.S. Department of Health, Education, and Welfare. News release. Bethesda, Md.: National Institute of Mental Health, November 7, 1964.
14. U.S. Department of Health, Education, and Welfare. *Improving mental health insurance coverage.* Washington, D. C.: Government Printing Office, 1965, Public Health Service pub. no. 1253, appdx. B.

14

Architectural Considerations in Planning for Community Mental Health Centers

E. TODD WHEELER

IN planning a mental health center we start with the mental patient, recording his differing requirements in the functional program which must precede the planning of the building. In programing we need a full understanding of the scope and character of the proposed methods of mental care. Eventually the process of programming and planning leads to a hospital building, but in between initiation and completion there are many steps to take before there can be a useful and beautiful building. And these steps include careful attention to much more than the functional program. This is where architectural considerations begin to appear.

The technics of translating the functional requirements of a hospital into building plans and eventually, through construction, into a hospital building have been well covered in hospital planning literature. What is not so well understood is the effect on design of the purely architectural considerations as distinct from the functional ones. Probably this comes about because hospital representatives quite generally limit their planning participation to the functional aspects, leaving the other aspects to the architect. In many respects this practice is proper but it has its drawbacks. Too often the inevitable shortage of time for planning permits only hurried attention by the architects to those very elements of hospital design which make a hospital building into a piece of architecture, even therapeutic architecture. This paper explores the architectural considerations referred to and illustrates the special technical requirements of a mental health center in relation to the general planning approach.

Several assumptions have been made; first, that the community needs for mental care have been established; second, that the program for mental care has been formulated; third, that a fully developed functional program is available; and finally that a competent planning team has been assembled. An even more fundamental assumption is that numerous environmental forces,

Reprinted from *American Journal of Public Health,* 1964, *54,* 1987–1995, by permission of the publisher and the author. © 1964, American Public Health Association. Mr. Wheeler is Partner and Director of Health Facilities Division, E. Todd Wheeler and the Perkins and Will Partnership, Chicago, Illinois.

not controlled by the actual program of mental care, have a strong bearing upon its effectiveness. The hypothesis presented here is that the mentally ill person will respond to his environment no less surely than the well person and quite probably with greater sensitivity. The objective of the architect is to understand such responses and to design a health center accordingly which will aid the mental care.

COMPREHENSIVE FUNCTIONAL PROGRAMS

During the past two years our firm has enjoyed an exciting and formative experience in helping to develop the comprehensive functional program and some of the building plans for a new system of Mental Health Centers in Illinois. Seven groups of buildings serving six zones are planned to encourage close relationships between the state mental services and the communities involved. It is hoped that may patients can remain at home during treatment or be returned home in a relatively short time. As a result, great emphasis was placed upon providing facilities for outpatient services and upon an open character of the bed services. But emphasis was also placed on the quality of building design and its effect upon the patients. It was here that architectural considerations became clearly evident and as planning progressed, these too were given due attention.[1]

The Illinois system illustrates well the advantages of preparing a carefully formulated functional program before building plans are started. There are several steps in the programming. First comes a complete description of the patient to be served in the Mental Health Center, his classification by disease and perhaps by degree of illness, by age and by presumed length of stay. The anticipated numbers of patients in each separate category are given and the desired relationships among the various groups are described. Any special predilections for building design may be mentioned and all functional requirements are indicated. In practice the statement of requirements becomes extensive, covering in complete detail the care to be given in the Mental Health Center. The functional program alone for the seven Illinois Zone Centers ran to 50 pages and the total description of the program investigation and findings filled 212 pages. Its formulation took four months of intensive work by a programing group. For this paper we need emphasize only that a full development of such information must precede consideration of the architectural factors.

[1] With strong support from Governor Kerner, this program was initiated in 1961 by the state of Illinois, Department of Mental Health, under Dr. Francis J. Gerty, who recently retired as its director. The seven health centers embrace most of the state. Dr. Gerty's successor, Dr. Harold M. Visotsky, is advancing this program with vigor and the construction of all seven centers will be undertaken progressively. Ground was broken in July, 1963, for the Zone II Center in Chicago which is to be completed in 1964 and will be directed by Dr. Arthur Woloshin.

THE EXTERNAL ENVIRONMENT

The next step after programming is to translate functional requirements into physical relationship diagrams which will eventually lead to schematic plans. Here the analysis of needs and relationships establishes what departments should be located on various floors, how many floors the building should have, how large each department and each floor should be, and the degree of flexibility possible within the mandatory functional relationships. In this process the architect begins his search for form which is finally consummated in the building design, and it is here that he can be discouraged and even stopped by the pressures of time unless he persists in the pursuit.

One reason that architectural considerations are often slighted is that they are not obvious or precise. On a given project and within the stipulated functional program there may be half a dozen workable and acceptable plan solutions. Thus the building design is neither foreordained nor limited but may well be any one of many schemes. This fact is what gives the architect flexibility in his design of the architectural form, both external and internal, and makes it possible for him to search for form among many variables without violating good functional planning.

The architect has so many different elements to deal with that it is difficult to describe his work in one phrase, but if one phrase could apply it would be the design of environment. Currrently this word is used rather expansively as total environment, including cities and regions, but in my reference it applies to the immediate environment of the building itself, inside and out. The architect is concerned with all factors, both tangible and intangible, which affect those persons who use the building. He designs for both utility and effect. By such design he seeks to control the human reaction to the building. Externally his concern is largely with visual reactions to building form, color, texture, and size. But internally there are strong physical elements to be considered, including the atmosphere, lighting, color, texture, sound and quality of materials, as well as plan arrangement. Both external and internal design are concerned with human scale, which is a function of size, and with character, which is even more intangible.

The design of environment also relates to the use of land, involving principally the direction of building spread, whether vertically or horizontally, and the complexity of the total result. And finally there are the derivative qualities of style and beauty. These are the architectural considerations to be discussed.

The architect makes a multiple approach to all these problems of design. He is trained to recognize the interweaving influences among them. He discovers early that the design of a building is not a simple sequence from A to B to C and finally to Z, with each step following logically on the previous one. There may be such simple sequences in parts of the design process and it is generally true that the analytical steps do precede esthetic design, but at some point a design concept is evolved almost intuitively, based upon study but drawing upon creative resources also. The architect pursues analysis and synthesis, the two main lines of design thought. He develops and rejects numerous designs until an acceptable one, both internal and external, is evolved. Incidentally, studies are under way in using analog computers to expedite this often laborious process of trial and error selection. However it is done, the process is a dual one involving both analysis and concept. The two are equally essential. No amount of preliminary calculating can substitute for conceptual design at the proper point, but even the most perceptive and farsighted concept will be fruitless unless it springs from and builds upon sound functional analysis. The two go hand in hand and the end design owes much to both.

After the scheme and concept have been determined, one of the first of the architectural considerations is development of the building site. Early in the planning there must be made a careful study of the ground on which the building is to rest. There are several site characteristics to account for. One is topography. It is elementary to say that the building should fit the ground and that its design should reflect the land configuration; yet elementary though it may be, this point is sometimes overlooked. For example, a sloping site makes possible grade entrances at two or more different floor levels. A building design which called for grade entrances to various parts of the building all at the same level would not fit on a sloping site without extensive cut and fill to make a level shelf. Good planning from the outset would recognize this fact and seek a workable scheme with dispersed entrances at several levels. The converse is true with a level site.

Another characteristic of site is its aspect or outlook. Where a superior view exists it seems only sensible to consider orienting the building so that patient rooms can benefit from the outlook. Similarly where the site permits the use of outdoor spaces for recreation, the building design should take this into account. In the Illinois projects major advantage was taken of open spaces in the location of dwelling units and in their internal planning. More prosaically the possible locations of automobile parking lots will establish the directions of approach to the building. This in turn should be reflected in the location of both main and service entrances.

The size of the site and the intensity of ground use also affect the building design. For the mental hospital it often seems desirable to keep the buildings low and intimate in scale with ready access to the outdoors, a possible plan only if the land is sufficient to care for buildings horizontally dispersed. Ten patient dwelling units at grade level will obviously require more land than those same units stacked in a ten story tower. Thus limitations in the quantity of land available may force a vertical scheme. The same line of reasoning cannot, however, be applied to entrance drives and walks nor generally to automobile parking, although occasionally multilevel parking garages may be justifiable.

Many long hours are spent discussing parking. This is one of the architectural considerations on which everyone is an expert. Let the architect overlook the problem or defer its solution and he is quickly called to task. In fact the architect is expected to know the proposals for expressways in the community as well as for public auto parking and to locate the hospital so that all who approach it via the highway systems will be able to leave the expressway at the nearest cloverleaf, hurry to the hospital parking lot, and reach the hospital entrance in no more than 50 steps. Clearly the ideal hospital would be one in which every user could park his car right outside the door. Sometimes I despair of the way the automobile dominates our lives and our planning of buildings. It is only one force among many, yet it cannot be ignored.

Other site factors which affect design are the subsoil bearing strength, which may limit building height; the subsurface water condition which may prevent the construction of basement space; the esthetics of the site, its natural features of contour, trees, and aspect; and the economics of land use. These are architectural considerations which can be satisfied equally well by many different functional plans. The site character finally established is bound to affect the spirit of the patient in the hospital, not only esthetically but psychologically in its sense of space use and physically in the distances involved.

There is still another factor in site design not so readily discernible. If the building plan combines many diverse elements into a complex scheme, the very size of the result may have a depressing effect upon the users of the building. The mental patient's spirit is fragile. It is sensitive to a great many influences, some mild, some strong, and we architects are not always wise enough to know when to stop in design at a point which will be restful. Sometimes the very nature of the building leads us on and we overdesign, to our later regret. In such case, where other considerations dictate complexity and dispersion of plan, the architect must avoid confronting the individual viewer with the full complexity of the building at any point, but give him instead the chance to respond to a limited portion of it, comprehensible to him and in human scale, a part of the whole but not overpowering. The use of inviting views from one unit to other elements of the complex is desirable, but the plan should not force the full scope of the complex building upon the viewer nor even permit its perception except perhaps in a view from the air. Most of the state of Illinois plans illustrate this point. Thus intimacy of character is desirable even when the total building is large and complex. Many medieval towns have this quality, including some which are fairly large. It is a quality which makes a person feel at home even though he may get lost in the maze.

Inevitably factors of cost also affect the relative dispersion of buildings on the site. Not only does a dispersed plan take more land but it also calls for slightly more floor space for a given program. Yet for the mental hospital in most cases this extra space seems defensible if it can be used to create an environment beneficial to the patient's state of mind. The plans for the Illinois projects are dispersed in varying degrees. There is none which is concentrated and stacked vertically.

THE INTERNAL ENVIRONMENT

I have dealt with site problems at length because of their generally limiting nature but there is a second architectural consideration of even greater importance, namely the internal environment. Here we deal with many factors, of which an all-pervasive one is the atmosphere. When we handle air we must control its temperature, its moisture content, its movement; we are conscious of odors, smoke, and dust; we are less conscious of but do respond to air pressure and ionization. Surely one of the most complex building design problems today is to establish systems of air handling and processing which will control all these items for the benefit of the patient. This is especially true when individual room regulation seems desirable. Mental patients are often sensitive to atmospheric discomforts. There are emotional responses to changes in pressure, illustrated by the common feeling of apprehension before an advancing thunderstorm which is in part at least a response to falling air pressures and to excessive ionization. The correlation between emotional stress and sweat gland activity is well enough known to make the point that control of the atmospheric environment may be important in mental care.

Such control is more than a physiological problem. It is an architectural and engineering problem presently solved better in theory than in practice as we still have trouble with our air-conditioning systems. Yet we have come a long way since the 1930's and there can be no question that we are moving surely and rather rapidly in the direction of complete control of temperature, humidity, and air movement. Before long this will be a commonplace and another of our luxuries will have become a necessity. The same can be said for the other atmospheric factors, especially pollution by smoke, dust, and odors; so far, however, little or nothing is being done to control air pressure or ionization except in space capsules. Yet these, too, can be controlled and we can anticipate that mental patients as well as others will eventually be able to enjoy their own completely controlled atmosphere. For this the individual helmet, the space suit, or the small room may be the answer.

LIGHTING

Another major element of environment is its lighting. In a mental hospital special thought must be given to both natural and artificial lighting. It is desirable to have ample outlook and cheerfully lit interiors without introducing glare. I am encouraged by the fact that this has been achieved in many of the building designs for the state of Illinois program, in which natural light in most of the rooms for group activities is supplemented by controlled artificial light. The human eye is marvelously adjustable to a wide range of light intensity but the mechanism by which such adjustment is made, namely the closing or opening of the iris, involves muscles which do not work instantaneously. It takes several seconds for them to respond to bright light and contract the iris or to relax it when the brightness lessens. Repeated demands for sudden adjustment cause fatigue in the eye muscles. Accordingly, in both natural and artificial lighting, sharply contrasting bright and dark surfaces should be avoided. Even without contrasts the glare from direct light is fatiguing and in the extreme can be permanently harmful to the eye.

Within the limits of comfort, however, lighting should be as bright as is called for by the activity involved. Desirable levels of lighting for reading, sewing, writing and other activities found in the mental hospital are well established technically and should be followed within reason but the architectural design problem is deeper than these technicalities. The greatest impact of the design of a building, inside and out, is visual and thus we come to a third architectural consideration, building form. The qualities of atmosphere, already discussed, may compel attention by their deficiencies but when effective they are best subdued to the point of not being noticed. But as long as we build above ground and walk about in the daytime we shall be conscious of form. A building is seen only as light is reflected from it and thus the lighting, both natural and artificial, becomes an integral part of design. Hence form can be changed by varying the lighting. This is most dramatically illustrated in exterior lighting but is in fact more important in the mental hospital interiors, where care must be exercised to define form properly without causing glare. This is a serious architectural consideration.

Light also has the qualities of color and movement. Color comes from the local or native color of materials when seen under white light or it may come from the use of colored lights. Movement may come from the slowly changing direction of sunlight or from changes in intensity of artificial light or from actual movement of the light sources. Control of such effects is a commonplace in the theater and in advertising signs but less so in the hospital. We do not begin to utilize this design tool to its full potential. Many mental patients are quite sensitive to light and color and the architect must therefore know something of the psychology of color in order to design the building adequately, combining variety and stability of design to achieve a beneficial harmony. Clearly the interior should be cheerful but restful and only rarely stimulating. Future technology will most certainly develop this useful tool more fully than now. It would be well for us to know more than we do about the reaction of mental patients to color. The use of local color in pigment is quite commonly studied for its psychological effect but the use of colored lights for therapy seems to be an open field.

SOUND CONTROL

Still another factor of environment which becomes an architectural problem of some magnitude is the control of sound. Objectionable sound is called noise and noise may greatly influence the mental patient. Most loud sound is objectionable and most soft sound not, but there are exceptions to this. In the midst of a symphonic climax, triple forte, a crash of cymbals may give just the right touch and, conversely, in the dead silence of night the tiny chirp of a cricket may be most disturbing. So with sound as with light we must watch out for contrast. There are also problems of sound transmission which may be disturbing and may cause loss of needed privacy. At low frequencies sound and vibration may join offensively. There are technics quite well worked out for control of sound but they are not always observed in the hospital. Some of them are costly. Certainly in a mental hospital the opportunity for quiet should be offered the patient who needs it, without forcing others to modify their activities in order to achieve quiet. For this goal, plan arrangement and adequate protection against sound transmission offer the best solution. In the hospital-clinics being built for Illinois the arrangement of dwelling units has been consciously planned to create privacy both of view and of sound in many of the patient areas. This is possible in the dispersed plan only if adequate land is available. Needless to say the design of rooms to be used for speaking and listening must be done with thought for the acoustics. As for compulsory music, euphemistically called background music and sometimes justified as acoustical perfume, I think it an abomination and the less heard of it the better.

MATERIALS AND FORM

Another architectural consideration and an important factor in design, both exterior and interior, is the texture of materials and of form. These two textures are similar but different in scale. Texture of materials derives from the manner in which they reflect or trap light. Their texture is usually discernible close up, though it also reads at a distance. Texture of form is created by the pattern of light and shade on the whole surface of a building and is generally best perceived from some distance. In principle both textures are created by highlights and shadows and both affect the general impression created by a building design. Textures may be coarse or fine grained, hard or soft, dull or brilliant. In materials the hard textures tend to repel and the soft to attract, though both have their place. The hard surfaces also reflect sound and often light, while the soft generally absorb both. In the mental hospital the soft textures are generally preferable, but restlessness of texture should be avoided. Texture of form is found in the larger elements like an entire wall whose texture is made up of openings, changes of surface and angle, modifications of materials both in color and texture, all of which when seen together creates an over-all feeling of texture. In form the simple textures are generally preferable and the busy ones less so. A major curse of today's buildings is the number of different materials and textures we use with such prodigality and artlessness that the total effect is of ostentatious waste and ugly at that.

Another architectural consideration is that characteristic of a building design which we call quality, meaning usually high quality. It is elusive yet perceptible. It derives from a multitude of well executed details, well selected materials and thoughtful planning. It need not imply luxury, though it often does. It does imply long life and pleasure in its use. The apparent quality of a building becomes especially important in the mental hospital because of the sensitivity of many of the patients. Too often in the past we have followed a line of reasoning which, though logical enough, has led to oppressive designs. It goes like this. First, it is known that some mental patients seek to destroy themselves or, failing that, seek to destroy their environment. Thus, it is reasoned, the environment should be made indestructible, with glazed tile walls, concrete floors and ceilings, no accessories to remove or get hung on, and everything should be locked. In a building so designed the patient reacts to this environment with understandable fury and becomes even more psychopathic. Thus we establish a cycle of failure. It would seem obvious that such design should be avoided, yet how can the patient's urge to destroy be thwarted without resorting to prison design? In part this can be done by giving apparent freedom to the patient, accompanied by the necessary personal supervision. In part it can be done by good design of environment, relying upon the experience that many mental patients, like the rest of us, tend to respect obvious quality and will hesitate to despoil a carpet or piece of woodwork when they would not hesitate to attack a concrete floor or a steel cot. Admittedly there are limits to this approach but it seems worth the risk of damage in using attractive and sometimes soft materials for their therapeutic benefits. Occasional damage to the building materials may cost much less than damage to human beings. Here the architect must rely upon the doctor for his guidance. In the state of Illinois buildings a conscious effort has been made to design the interiors attractively and yet reasonably durable, toward the end that the freedom explicit in the mental treatment program would neither be hampered nor readily perverted into destructive license.

DESIGN ELEMENTS

Mention has been made of scale as an architectural consideration. Scale is that quality of design which reflects the relationship between size of building elements and the human figure. We speak commonly of large-scale buildings and of small-scale details but scale is also felt between these two extremes. In the mental hospital scale becomes important because the patient is responsive to anything which belittles him. There is no place in the mental hospital for overpowering monumentality, yet the scale must be such that the building appears dignified. It is a fine line we draw. Scale is felt in the total plan and in the smallest detail, and a mistake in scale, either of surface design or plan arrangement, can spoil an otherwise good design. A good plan relationship and a convenient circulation pattern, easy to follow, will establish a scale which makes the patient feel at home and able to cope with the building, even a large one. The dwelling units of the Illinois Health Centers illustrate this point quite well. They are extensive but inviting.

The combination of all the design elements mentioned generates a total impression, yet there is another quality, already mentioned in the comments on lighting, with which the architect is deeply concerned, namely form. The word is not limited to architecture. For almost any subject, form means the recognizable framework within which the substance is contained and expressed, as in music or poetry or literature. In the dictionary form is "the particular way of being that gives something its nature or character." Physical form refers more to containment than to expression, though both qualities are present. It is concerned with proportion as well as color and textures. In a building, form brings the third dimension to the two dimensional floor plan and gives it a quality within which a man can walk and discover his environment. Through form the architect seeks to express the substance of his building. Without substance form is hollow and meaningless but without form substance is amorphous and incomprehensible. Both are essential. So for the mental hospital the form of the building should seek to express the strivings and restraints which are in its plan, the hope and tragedy of its occupants. This is a real challenge to the designer and one not always met.

Our progression through this list of architectural considerations has been from the specific and the literal to the general and the abstract. Without question the specific and the literal are the qualities most often dealt with in building design. Yet the general and the abstract are what establish the lasting quality of an architectural design and they have great effect upon the patient. Admittedly the building must stand up and be a comfortable and safe enclosure. But if that is the end of design the chances are that we shall have an inconsequential if not an ugly building. In a real sense this is why the architect survives and is needed to complement the work of the engineer and the builder.

The best illustration of this point is in beauty. Beauty is almost like honesty and law abidance. Everyone is for it in principle but in practice attention often turns to more practical considerations. Why should we spend hard earned funds, or tax money, on nonessentials like beauty? Why should we even consider so doing? A careful analysis will show that such protestations of scorn for beauty and our alleged preference for economy are fatuous. In almost everything we acquire, whether an automobile or a wife, appearance tips the scale in favor of or against a choice. Whatever the psychology of the act, I contend that we do choose, consciously or otherwise, what we think is beautiful, often at the expense of utility, reflecting thereby an innate human need. This need exists in mental patients, perhaps more than in others. It is a need for gratification, not just of the physical senses but of the esthetic sense also. Hence the architect in designing a mental hospital seeks beauty through form, texture, color, proportion and movement, using all his ability to achieve it for he knows it is an essential. Conscious recognition was given this issue in Illinois by choosing a number of architects to design the seven buildings in the hope that by so doing more varied and perhaps more beautiful designs would be achieved than if all buildings were designed by one firm. The final results are still to be judged but the designs evolved seem to attest to the soundness of this policy.

Even more elusive than beauty is a final architectural consideration, often ignored and seldom achieved, called style. Style cannot be accomplished in one design. It derives from a series of successful designs, not necessarily all the same but necessarily beautiful, each in its own way and each representative of the architect as well as of the program. If an architect can achieve a style, honestly, and keep it growing, he is truly creating. Style is more subjective than the other architectural considerations yet it can be recognized and has an effect upon all who use the building. Style need not be ephemeral. It is almost always individual.

Probably the most lasting qualities in architecture are those of style and beauty. And the greatest impression upon patients and others in the hospital will be found in these qualities. The sincere architect seeks a complete design, providing beauty as well as utility. Unquestionably it is our duty to consider all factors and to meet all functional and utilitarian requirements, but unless we provide something more than utility we have failed to serve the total needs of the patient.

Thus we return to the patient. More than most, the mental patient needs an environment of security, comfort, freedom, and beauty to help him get well. It is the task of the architect to design such an environment to the best of his ability, and it is a surpassing opportunity as well.

15

Team Planning:
Translating Needs into Physical Facilities

JAMES FALICK

COMMUNITY mental health centers are new kinds of facilities. Reflecting an overall reorganization of health care, mental health services are now to be community based, community operated, and community oriented. Traditionally, mental health care and facilities have been "hidden." Now, identity and visibility are to be given to promote care, prevention, and removal of the stigma so long associated with mental illness.

The decision to add mental health services to the health resources of a community raises questions:

Should mental health facilities be a part of a total health services center?

Should the hospital and the community mental health center be combined?

Should they be independent?

Should they be affiliated but retain separate identities?

What are the aims of the mental health center, and how can architecture promote them?

Answers to these questions depend on many factors within the community —on levels of sophistication, on how services have been organized previously, on the strengths of sponsoring agencies, on power structure, and, naturally, on financing. As each community must find its own direction and methods to provide services, each will have a unique physical plant.

If administrators and architects are to translate patterns of service into facilities, they have to understand not only the new direction, but the planning process as well. There are many complex steps between the decision to build a community mental health center and the existence of an operating plant. If these steps are ordered and rational, if the forces that shape the building are understood, then a good solution can result. Too often in the organization of a facility, little time or effort is given to analysis of community needs. Too often, design consists of applying interior or exterior decoration to match a preconceived esthetic.

The architectural process is divided, roughly, into programming, schematic

Reprinted from *Hospitals,* 1968, *42,* 69–74, by permission of the publisher and the author. © 1968, American Hospital Association. Mr. Falick is Associate Partner, Caudill, Rowlett, Scott Architects, Houston, Texas.

design and design development, preparation of construction documents, and supervision of construction. The architectural firm with which the writer is associated believes programming is the most critical phase in the design of a community mental health center; it is during programming that both architect and client develop a thorough understanding of client and community requirements. During programming, the concepts and conditions that influence design are sought out and discovered. Programming is problem seeking, and design is problem solving.

Architectural programming is procedurally distinct from functional programming (administrative planning) or computer programming (preparing data for electronic processing). However, it is similar to the latter two programming concepts in that architectural programming does integrate a great number of facts and requirements into an organized relationship, which the architect can translate with fidelity into the required physical design.

To be effective, architectural programming requires the joint effort of two groups—the health facility staff and the architectural staff—with the client planning therapy modalities and the architect analyzing site and space requirements. Through this teamwork approach, facts are defined and concepts identified; data are analyzed to determine needs and separate them from superfluous wants; space and cost budgets are balanced; and the uniqueness of the project is sought.

The client group may include administration, board, staff, consultants, and even outside agencies. Few of the participants are trained in architecture and many may not have been involved previously in a building program. Therefore, education is a part of the programming process. The architect teaches the client the potentials of architecture, and the client teaches the architect his special role as a team member. The architect must share in the total experience—he must know the community and the institution and have an opportunity for informal interaction with the client on a continuing basis; the architect can facilitate this relationship by setting up a temporary office at the client's home base, rather than talking and then going back to his office to draw.

For the team method to work, communication between groups has to be effective. Techniques that help achieve good communications are based on the need to translate the oral and written to the visual. These techniques include:

1. Designating a responsible individual from each group.
2. Using diagrams to state the affinities of functional elements.
3. Stating every fact and idea as a single succinct diagram.
4. Organizing diagrams of concepts as a documented record.
5. Using that record to demonstrate understanding and provide feedback.

Programming is most effective if attacked in two stages. The first involves discriminating between basic information and minor details; the second is identification of relevant facts for design development and refinement. Significant first-stage statements thereby form the basis for details of the second stage.

Information comes from many sources and directions. An orderly framework for documentation of information is required, consisting of a step-by-step analysis:

1. Establish aims.
2. Collect, organize, and analyze facts.
3. Uncover and develop concepts.
4. Determine needs.
5. State the problem; solutions can then follow clearly and logically.

ESTABLISH AIMS

A community generally has certain mental health objectives it wants emphasized and policies for achieving its goals. If identified and documented by the team, goals can be inspiration for design. Since goals are usually discussed at the beginning of the project, they must be clearly identified at that time or they will be lost in the avalanche of later details.

A basic goal is community orientation. Architecture once emphasized that mental health facilities were self-contained communities—difficult to get into and out of. An enlightened contemporary attitude now relates them to the outside world, emphasizing that not merely the individual or even the family, but in fact the whole community, is to be the focus of concern. Community orientation implies the need for coordinated services so that patients and their families are not subjected to the "fragmentation" that is often characteristic of traditional modes of treatment and services. This coordination in turn leads to the requirement that the center establish a continuing relationship with the patient-family unit. Design must help make these goals attainable.

A repeated request is that the facility not be "institutional." While effects of environment are not easily measured, psychiatric aims are for a therapeutic milieu—that is, control the patient's environment so that all the sensations he received from it are conducive to treatment and recovery. The architecture, the physical part of the total environment, should contribute privacy, dignity, and security to the achievement of those environmental ends.

COLLECT, ORGANIZE, ANALYZE

Facts alone mean little. They have to be organized and analyzed in relation to the particular project in order to have meaning. In programming for a community mental health center, there are two major sources of factual input.

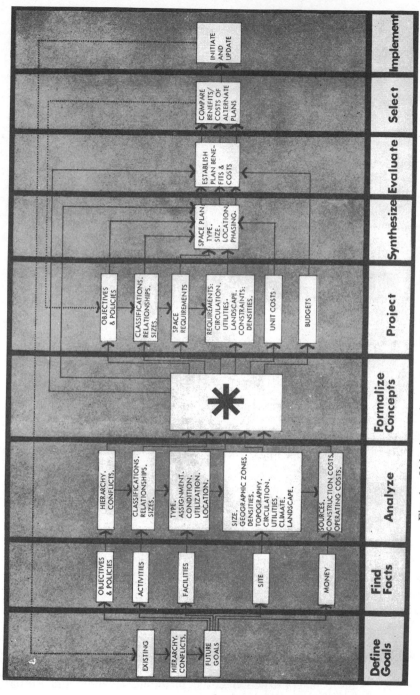

Fig. 1.—If basic requirements are firmly established, details of operational needs and architectural design can follow logically. A graphic conceptualization of this fact aids the architect's communication with his client.

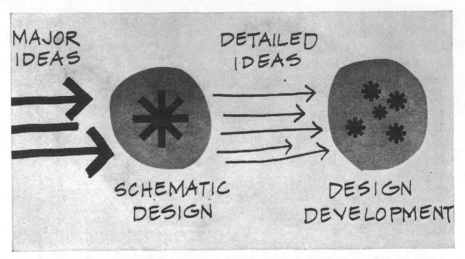

Fig. 2.—A flow-chart representation of problems and goals helps both architect and client visualize important relationships within their task and to establish priorities for solving problems before actual design work can begin.

The architect's contribution is concerned with who, where, when, how many, and how much. For example:

FUNCTION

Functional specifications provide information regarding numbers of patients and staff; numbers and kinds of spaces to be determined; activities that determine size of space; and local, state, and federal requirements that affect computations.

TIME

Time affects program, site, and cost. With time, programs change and physical needs often grow. Since costs usually rise with time, a construction schedule must be established. Even the site may be expanded in time by new acquisitions. We build in the present; yet time, as a test, must be applied to find implications for the future.

BUDGET

Facts about local construction costs, including location and escalation factors, have to be collected (see Table 1). Cost analysis must reflect an appropriate quality of construction, consistent with requirements of long-term maintenance and operating expenses. At this point the budget must be realistic and thorough and must include all cost components—construction, fixed and movable equipment, site development, fees, and contingencies.

TABLE 1. COST ESTIMATE ANALYSIS

A. Building cost		$ 7,200,000
(300,000 SF × $24/SF)		
B. Fixed equipment		576,000
(8% of A)		
C. Site development		
(15% of A)		1,080,000
D. Total construction cost		$ 8,856,000
E. Movable equipment		
(8% of A)		576,000
F. Fees (6% of D)		531,000
G. Owner's expenses[a]		125,000
H. Contingencies (5% of D)		442,000
J. Total budget requirement		$10,530,000

[a] *Surveys, insurance, bond issue, consultants*

SITE

Analysis of physical, legal, and even emotional aspects of the site must be made since the site itself can be an important determinant affecting design. Factors include topography, soil conditions, view, off-and-on-site traffic circulation, and utilities. Local climatic conditions such as prevailing winds, sun angles, temperature, precipitation, and snow are key variables that affect design. Investigation of site and potential limitations should include codes, zoning, and other legal restrictions.

The other major source of factual data, the client, contributes information that is more patient-oriented and that demands architectural response:

PERCEPTION

Before the individual patient defines or understands details of his physical environment, he perceives it as a whole. Design must help the individual know where he is, so that with a comprehensible environment he is neither surprised nor threatened. Therefore, organization of space and circulation patterns have to fit emotional as well as physical needs.

REACTION

The patient's sensory mechanisms are altered from normal. Environmental conditions surrounding the individual can either intensify his condition or aid in his treatment and recovery. Therefore, every physical space will produce a reaction, either positive or negative. There are no neutral areas to which the patient will not react.

ATTITUDE

Mental health services deal with human wants and needs. If positive results are to be achieved, facilities must be designed to cater to patients in the way commercial enterprises are designed to cater to customers. In a commercial enterprise the customer is treated with dignity; he has knowledge of the process in which he is involved and a feeling of normality; he controls what is to happen. The community mental health center, in a similar way, must convey to the patient that his is an acceptable situation, one in which he as an individual has some degree of control over his destiny.

UNCOVER AND DEVELOP CONCEPTS

Facts and concepts are interrelated, difficult to separate. For a start, the functional program can be examined for major concepts. As some concepts recur, they may be used to "test" the program. For example:

FLEXIBILITY

To anticipate growth of services, design should permit easy expansion of the physical plant. The probability of program changes requires that space be convertible. At any time, a space may have to accommodate more than one kind of activity; therefore it must be versatile. The dining area is an example. Dining space is customarily determined on the basis of a defined patient and staff load, but in a community mental health center the size and nature of the patient load may change radically in response to different service, training, and research programs and to varying patient age and disability.

One solution is to make the dining space a cafeteria, with an adjacent coffee shop area staffed by volunteers. With such facilities, family, staff, and even patients could be served at times other than routine meal hours. Vending machines in or near the area would serve for evening and night use. To facilitate staff interaction, combination staff dining-conference spaces could be provided.

CENTRALIZED OR DECENTRALIZED SERVICES

Is the day hospital a separate space or structure, or does it operate within the total facility? Generally, the decision to centralize or decentralize services is made in deference to whichever scheme best promotes the flow and inter-action of personnel and services.

The Maimonides Community Mental Health Center of Brooklyn, New York (Fig. 4), had specific goals which seemed threatened by limitations of budget and site. It was decided that a network of services located in schools, YMCA's, and other places could serve the Maimonides service area better than a single comprehensive facility; the mental health center building would function as the base.

COMPARTMENTALIZATION OR INTEGRATION

A community mental health center has many staff office-treatment rooms. Except for those requiring special equipment or utilities, offices can be grouped by discipline or integrated into a multidiscipline complex. In either case, offices can be organized around small secretarial and reception areas or use a single, central lobby and a secretarial pool.

The Manhattan Community Mental Health Center, a $20 million project scheduled for completion in New York City late in 1972, will have extensive training programs requiring structured as well as informal interaction between disciplines. Therefore, treatment teams will be multidisciplinary and can be changed by administrative decision at any time. Team members will be placed in offices grouped around secretarial and reception areas within separate and identifiable units.

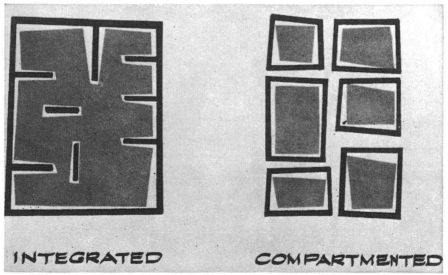

INTEGRATED   COMPARTMENTED

Fig. 3.—A decision must be made as to whether to integrate or compart-mentalize office spaces. The decision must be based not on esthetic considera-tions, but on which scheme best implements the goals to be achieved in the center.

Should elements of the facility be given equal or unequal social value by location? Which elements should be given greater importance? An interesting case in point has been the placement of children's play areas. In a number of cases, it has been believed that outdoor play represents a normal activity, and that locating a play area in the public view, at ground level in front of the facility, will help reduce the stigma associated with mental illness.

DETERMINE NEEDS

It is necessary to balance space and cost. Without an accurate determination of needs during this phase of planning, the design will be based on a vague program and an unbalanced budget. Effective communication between architect and client is critically important at this point. One communication technique the writer's firm uses to display cost-space relationships is the graphic representation of space requirements, by square blocks drawn to a scale corresponding to the actual space needs of the mental health center and labeled according to use. The number and relative sizes of the blocks enable the planners to visualize the space requirements of the center and to make necessary changes in space allocation.

Since the initial budget usually is based on an estimated gross-square-foot cost for construction and on percentages of construction cost for most other items, the visualization of space requirements helps the planners determine whether available funds are sufficient. Realistic estimates must be based on the architect's experience and tempered by the local situation.

STATE THE PROBLEM

The goal of programming is identification of the major problems to be solved in the design. All documented information must be reviewed, and the most important statements to be made regarding the problem must be determined. The Manhattan Community Mental Health Center is a good example of the application of this process. Included in the statements will be at least the following:

FUNCTION

One problem is the need to change public attitudes toward mental illness. People must be made aware of the new nature of mental health care. Architecturally, this problem implies physical contact with the facility. The Manhattan

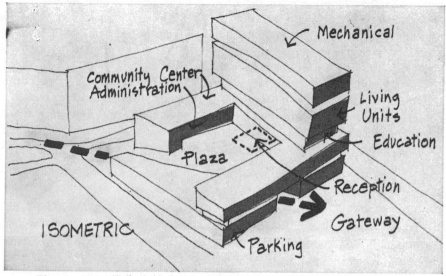

Fig. 4.—The Manhattan Community Mental Health Center in New York City is to be the culmination of operational and design decisions reached through the orderly process of architectural programming. The facility should be completed by the end of 1972.

site was created in the design by closing a main traffic artery and creating a "superblock."

Use of the site for construction is limited by the location of subways below it. This apparent disadvantage was overcome by the creation of a central garden court area through which pedestrian traffic will flow as part of its normal movement. The public will be in daily contact with the facility.

TIME

After visibility and contact, there is need for transitional time and space. Design has to invite, to provide a transition between exterior and interior that allows easy movement into and between services. At the Manhattan Community Mental Health Center, the central court is the transition area. Pedestrians are not forced by the architecture to enter; they are given an opportunity to observe the flow of individuals into and out of the building. The court allows view of movement in waiting and circulation spaces which, in turn, are placed above court level to preserve privacy.

BUDGET

In order to balance need with cost, the architects did an office study and found (1) that staff offices were to be home bases out of which staff would work; (2) that 75 per cent of the time, a given space would be needed for only one to three persons in addition to the staff member; and (3) that once a relationship between the staff member and the patient was established, it would be possible to move the location of therapy without disrupting the process.

As a result, the design includes staff offices that comfortably hold up to four persons, supervisory staff offices for as many as eight, and a number of conference and consultation rooms placed conveniently and used on a shared basis. As a result, approximately 25 per cent more space has been programmed with the established site and budget than was originally considered possible.

SITE

Clear, comprehensive physical organization is necessary. If the site has no limitations, various programmed elements might be arranged horizontally around an enclosed mall as in a suburban shopping center. This mall would serve to promote interaction and orientation while allowing the necessary containment of services.

If the site is constricted, the solution may have to be vertical, an arrangement that may require stacking levels and separating elements despite the affinities defined. To foster visual as well as physical vertical flow, the optimum vertical circulation should be established, and then a central space should be designed that can provide visual orientation as staff and patients move between services.

The cooperative nature of the team process must continue throughout the design development and construction phases to the completion of the physical plant. Along the way, some change almost always takes place as ideas, attitudes, and programs become more sophisticated. Change should therefore be seen as a necessary and expected part of the process. When administrators, staff, and architects work together, with a high degree of communication between team members, they contribute more than the total of what each could achieve separately.

Responsible architecture for the community mental health center must meet many challenges. It must be clear, yet house a complex function. It must respond to the special needs of patients, force interaction rather than repel it, and, especially, openly invite the community to enter rather than hide its function behind walls of embarrassment and fear.

III
TECHNIQUES AND METHODS

RUNNING from the initial organization of community mental health programs through rehabilitation, this section covers a broad spectrum of methods and techniques. Articles deal with the participation of citizens and community agencies as they strive to meet local needs and problems. Education, often maligned as an effective tool, is considered at various levels, and early case finding and some of the newer preventive activities are described and evaluated. The evolving field of mental health consultation is examined from a practical as well as a theoretical viewpoint. Recent advances in treatment techniques are related to some unique new programs. Current emphasis on emergency and precare services are described and a wide variety of existing efforts are detailed. Finally, the end result of all the methods and techniques are scrutinized as rehabilitation programs are described and criticized.

To develop a strong three-phase program of mental health education, consultation and clinic services, active participation from the community is an absolute necessity. Community organization is discussed as a means of achieving a sound program. Hallock and Vaughan in their classic article also raise the issues of who should take the first step in the local effort, the financial role of the community, and the part that state mental health professionals play in setting up the service.

Goldston maintains that all community mental health workers can perform educational tasks and functions. Suggestions are made for strengthening professional training programs. In addition, the various activities of a professionally trained mental health educator are detailed, including public education efforts, staff training, mass media utilization, consultation and patient care education.

Based on five years of experience, Otto and Chalmers describe their mental health education programs for professional groups, mainly members of the teaching profession. In addition to explaining the dynamics of the learning process, the authors list the materials used, describe the techniques of presentation and spell out their observations and analysis of the group experiences.

In view of the research that reports about 50 per cent of police calls deal with emotionally disturbed persons, Friedman's efforts at community mental health education with police are particularly pertinent. At the conclusion of his article, five points are emphasized, including the need to recognize the authoritarian and hierarchical nature of police organizations and the action orientation of the individual police officer.

Studies show that prevention, not primarily treatment, appears to be the logical long-term solution to mental illness. Past investigations have divided the diseases into three classifications: organic brain damage, individual stress, and group stress resulting from cultural and social strains. Lemkau observes that organic causes are fairly well understood, and that present-day knowledge could obviate the detrimental effects of individual stress. However, he notes that where social customs seem to be the dominating factor in psychiatric illness, new research is needed.

As a specific activity, prevention as a concept is vague and still has the task of interesting and involving members of the mental health professions. Bower cites three interrelated ingredients in primary prevention: a healthful birth experience, a healthful family experience, and a successful school experience. Zonal classifications of people and services are used as a framework for a functioning methodology for the development of programs of prevention.

Treatment in child psychiatry still remains of paramount importance in most clinics. In their article, Eisenberg and Gruenberg specifically list disorders for which there is reasonable likelihood of response to treatment, and disorders whose response to treatment are uncertain. The result is a rationale for program planning for children's mental health services.

Caplan has long defined and differentiated mental health consultation from other professional activities in the community mental health field. Four main types of consultation are discussed, including client-centered case consultation, program-centered administrative consultation, consultee-centered case consultation, and consultee-centered administrative consultation. Methods and techniques are described for each example.

A case seminar method of group mental health consultation is presented by Altrocchi, Spielberger, and Eisdorfer and differentiated from group supervision, seminar teaching, and other group activities. Analysis by the authors suggests that phases of consultation are discernible and contribute to problem-solving. The active use of group processes by the consultant clearly delineates this method from Caplan's approach to mental health consultation.

In a survey of the present state of the field of mental health consultation, Bindman covers both theory and practice. Various definitions and models of consultation are presented and the relation to other interpersonal methods such as education, supervision, psychotherapy, and administration are noted. In addition to detailing the consultation process, the author also discusses training and the need for research and evaluation.

In their wide-ranging article, Becker, Murphy, and Greenblatt cover most of the recent activities in community mental health programs. Among the transitional facilities the authors describe are the day hospital, the night hospital, the halfway house, the ex-patient club, family care, and aftercare services. Other activities detailed include preadmission and admission screening services, suicide prevention services, college psychiatric services and psychiatric services in general hospitals. In addition, the concept of a therapeutic society outside the hospital and the role of clergy and general practitioners in mental health are noted.

Ramsey describes a unique sociotherapeutic camping program for the mentally ill in which almost 700 patients participated. In addition to describing the selection of patients and the staff roles, the author also evaluates the outcomes and notes that no patients attempted to run away, no serious accidents occurred, no patient ever asked to return to the hospital, and no psychiatric emergency arose that required medical referral or hospitalization.

Twenty-one programs providing immediate or emergency psychiatric care are reported in Carlton's review of the literature, along with studies on the preadmission period. Precare programs include telephone services, walk-in clinics, screening units, and home visiting teams. Paths to the hospital and the agents of hospitalization are noted in the preadmission review.

In describing a demonstration of paid employment as a rehabilitative technique in a state mental hospital, Hoffman concludes that the two and one-half year project exceeded all expectations. Appendices enumerate the conditions of employment and some of the more important advantages for employers to use mental patients.

In a controversial paper, Olshansky notes that some of the sickest ex-mental patients are able to work. On the other hand, he also questions whether we really need the manpower salvageable through vocational rehabilitation. In addition, the author contends that many of the transitional facilities within the community are not needed. The point is made that professionals should accept the biases of employers and withhold information regarding the patient's history of hospitalization.

16

Community Organization—A Dynamic Component of Community Mental Health Practice

ARTHUR C. K. HALLOCK AND WARREN T. VAUGHAN, JR.

COMMUNITY mental health practice is a new and rapidly growing public health field. It consists of theory and practice derived from both clinical psychiatry and public health. Clinical psychiatry is concerned with the intrapsychic life and adjustment mechanisms of the individual while public health is concerned with the community, groups of individuals, and ecologic relationships of the community to its environment. The theoretical concept which binds these two fields together is the concept of interpersonal relations. The literature of this subject has been growing rapidly (2, 4, 5, 6, 9, 10, 12). Social science obviously becomes of extreme importance to community mental health practice.

Mental health is usually defined with the individual as a primary frame of reference, although in Lindemann's recent review of various concepts of positive mental health (8) he cites definitions from social science, such as that a mentally healthy person is one "in harmony with his culture." In child guidance practice, we have a group frame of reference, the family, and are concerned with interpersonal relations. We speak of healthy or unhealthy families, or healthy or unhealthy parent-child relationships. Evidence that causal factors do exist in the relationships between key figures surrounding the child and the child's emotional well-being is well recognized and accepted. The work of Freud and Burlingham (3), Spitz (13), and Bowlby (1) concerning the mother-child relationship is, for instance, of extreme importance to the community mental health practitioner. Studies of other key relationships, for example, father-child and teacher-child, are currently awaited by mental health practitioners in order to give solid experimental proof to the theories of interpersonal relations and needs of children which form the basis for practice.

If we extend the system of human relationships with which we are con-

Reprinted from *American Journal of Orthopsychiatry*, 1956, *26*, 691–708, by permission of publisher and the authors. © 1956, American Orthopsychiatric Association. Mr. Hallock is retired. He was formerly Chief of Community Organization, Massachusetts Division of Mental Hygiene. Dr. Vaughan is Associate Clinical Professor of Psychiatry, Stanford Medical School. He was formerly Director, Massachusetts Division of Mental Hygiene.

cerned from the family to the community at large, and accept the premise that there exist relationships between social structure and individual emotional well-being within particular social systems, we can begin to form the basis for the development of the field of community mental health practice. The goals now become those involved in fostering "mentally healthy human relationships" within the various formal and informal social systems making up the community. There are different levels of medical care and public health, moving from concern over the community at large to the individual in distress (7). Mental health practice is concerned with developing programs designed to promote the mental health of a community, to prevent specific psychiatric disorders in the community, to develop programs of early diagnosis and prompt treatment, to develop effective treatment programs and to rehabilitate. If mental health practitioners see as their function the job of influencing the nature of human relationships in various community settings, they must have not only a set of professional practices based on sound fact and theory, but, most important, a program designed to reach and influence key areas in community life dealing with families and children. Habitual modes of interaction and interpersonal relations which do not promote mental health and which, indeed, may be pathogenic may be altered by the systematic application of professional techniques.

In Massachusetts, the program which we are developing consists of three parts. We call it a "three-phase" balanced program. The existence of one part is not sufficient, for each part is dependent upon the other. The three parts are mental health education, mental health consultation and clinical services.

1) Mental health education may be thought of as primarily for the purpose of promoting mental health, giving community groups general and specific knowledge about the field of human relations and mental health. Techniques used range from mass media techniques to small discussion groups and individual face-to-face interviews, the latter most frequently occurring in the clinical and community organization settings.

2) Mental health consultation is a new key operation in community mental health practice, of central importance. It has educational facets as well as clinical-therapeutic characteristics. Mental health consultation represents the systematic development of consultation relationships with key individuals in social systems concerned with families and growing children, in which the key individuals can call upon the consultant for help in dealing with the particular problems recognized or felt by the key person. The mental health consultant is crisis-oriented, is concerned first with the key persons and their effective playing of their roles vis-à-vis the child; and secondly, with a clinical appraisal of the child, or the children themselves, in the total situation. The consultant becomes part of the social system, which at a time of crisis is in a state of "disequilibrium." We are currently developing such services in Massachusetts for public schools and various health and social agencies. We think of mental health consultation services as approximating specific prevention, inasmuch as the consultant is concerned with children who are maladapted to the social environment, who are reacting to stresses and who may be further decompensated if release of tensions and removal of stresses in their interpersonal relations are not forthcoming. Counseling with parents and certain aspects of the intake interview may have the quality of the mental health consultation. Casework with parents in the child guidance clinic setting may have more of the characteristics of the mental health consultation than of mental health education or specific psychotherapy.

(3) *Clinical services* form the bulwark of the community mental health program, just as clinical facilities are most important in the broad field of public health. The mental health consultant has clinical services available. The intrapsychic disturbances of children and adults are dealt with by psychotherapy and other therapies in the hospital and clinic settings, altering and making more effective the characteristics of their interpersonal relations in family and other community settings.

In Massachusetts, we have moved from the concept of the traditional three-man clinic team of psychiatrist, psychiatric social worker and clinical psychologist to a concept of a four-man community mental health center team, composed of psychiatrist, social worker, clinical psychologist and community mental health consultant. The community mental health consultant, the fourth man on the team, turns the "clinic" into a "mental health center." He is a nonmedical specialist in community mental health practice, specifically trained in community mental health consultation work. He may have basic training in either psychiatric social work or clinical psychology. We are currently working at the Harvard School of Public Health to develop training programs for this new specialist in community mental health practice.

The program briefly outlined above (see Figs. 1 and 2) cannot be applied to any community without active participation of the community itself. This is self-evident, and is derived on theoretical grounds from the concept of interpersonal relations and the importance of social systems and interpersonal relations to individual emotional well-being.

We can get nowhere with the development of this three-phase mental health program unless we develop the essential machinery for applying the program to the community. In Massachusetts, the participation of the community itself in the development of the machinery is done through the formation, growth and development of organized mental health associations in the various areas of the state. The local mental health association represents the emotional involvement of the community, with its enthusiasms and resistances, only if it is composed of responsible and representative lay and allied professional workers from the community. Through the local organization, community participation can be developed and effective changes in patterns of interpersonal relations and social systems in the community can then follow in time.

Massachusetts has for many years been concerned with mental health issues, their definition, and the development of programs to deal with them.

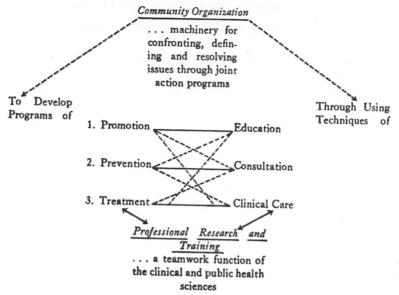

Fig. 1.—Mental Health Programs and Specific Techniques

Massachusetts has certain advantages in that it is a leading training center for psychiatrists and allied workers in the field of mental health. There are many competent psychiatrists in private practice. There is also a highly developed hospital system; many of the 17 hospitals have at one time or another sponsored substantial outpatient services. Since 1913 there has been an active, state-wide, wholly private mental health association, the Massachusetts Association for Mental Health, Inc. This association has been active in the field of community mental health education in all the principal towns and cities of the state, both by direct personal contact and through the distribution of printed material. It has also been interested in helping communities think through their own mental health problems and develop programs for meeting them.

There has been for many years a strong state-wide and district-wide forum for social work discussion, the Massachusetts Conference of Social Work. This organization has each year devoted a week for the discussion of leading current problems of social welfare, with needs for child guidance services always prominent on the agenda. It is a historical fact that community psychiatric services, particularly child guidance clinics, have been considered among the social agencies rather than as medical agencies in this state. Currently the pendulum is swinging back to the proper inclusion of psychiatric services as essential medical care agencies. The Division of Mental Hygiene of the Massachusetts Department of Mental Health has had a community program since 1922, founded by Dr. Douglas A. Thom. Several community child guidance clinics were developed in the thirties which incorporated the

MENTAL HEALTH EDUCATION

1. Mass media: information, orientation; public relations, community awareness and attitude
2. Lay workshops and groups: parent education, neighborhood groups, school groups, civic groups, etc.
3. Professional workshops and groups: work with key people—educators, nurses, courts, social agencies, physicians, lawyers, etc.
4. Integration with consultation and clinical services: educational aspects of "anticipatory guidance," the intake interview, the school consultation, casework with parents, etc.

MENTAL HEALTH CONSULTATION

1. With key individuals in a social system
2. Focus on interpersonal relations in everyday life situation
3. Consultant as part of consultee's human environment
4. Changes in interpersonal relations may influence intrapersonal states

CLINICAL PSYCHIATRY

1. With "sick" member of a social system—the "patient"
2. Focus on intrapersonal states in special life situation (office, clinic, hospital), with availability of physicochemical agents to influence intrapersonal states
3. Therapist as key figure in patient's human environment
4. Changes in intrapersonal states may influence interpersonal relations

Fig. 2.

idea of the professional team as part of a public mental health agency being supported in its work by local private interests. These include the Springfield Child Guidance Clinic and the Worcester Youth Guidance Center. A system of traveling school clinics, begun in 1919, was designed to help the public schools identify and properly handle mentally retarded children. Since 1919, these clinics have examined over 175,000 children. They are currently being discontinued, their functions being taken over by the new area mental health centers.

At the conclusion of World War II, Massachusetts found itself with a tremendous amount of public awareness of the need for community psychiatric programs coupled with an almost complete lack of professional personnel. Both lay and professional people were concerned that community psychiatric services in the state were woefully deficient in quantity and almost completely uncoordinated.

The National Mental Health Act, through the community services grants-in-aid to the State, began in 1947 to give some assistance through reallocations to agencies outside of the activities of the Department of Mental Health. The National Mental Health Act funds were used for the development and expansion of community services. With these funds, the Department, in co-operation with the Judge Baker Guidance Center, prepared a bibliography of printed material relative to community psychiatric services, and with the participation of the Harvard School of Public Health conducted and has published a state-wide survey of community psychiatric resources in Massachusetts (11, 14). During the winter of 1951–52, the new Commissioner of Mental Health obtained the interest and support of the legislature in the development of increased community psychiatric services. The pattern of developing community mental health associations was implicitly set by the agreements reached with the legislature, namely, that the legislature would appropriate funds for key professional personnel who would develop community mental health programs under the supervision of the Department of Mental Health, but who would be assisted by local communities themselves. Furthermore, requests for such community mental health programs must originate within the community itself.

A firm but informal understanding exists between the Department of Mental Health, the State Legislature and the State Budget Authorities which carries the following implications: (1) The State Department of Mental Health stands ready to help communities secure the kind of mental health services that the communities decide they want; (2) when communities are ready by virtue of having developed a community or area-wide organization and have given sufficient evidence of being able to make a substantial financial contribution, the Commissioner of Mental Health will put an item in the budget providing a traditional psychiatric team for the purpose of establishing an area mental health center with the further proviso that the legislators from that area join in supporting such a budgetary item in legislative committee meetings and on the floor. The understanding support from the legislature which secures adequate starting money is the greatest single stimulant that gives all parties involved the faith, hope and energy to give their best toward producing direct, effective, organized and stable area mental health programs.

Community mental health practice begins when the community approaches the Department of Mental Health for aid in development of a program. The Division of Mental Hygiene has a community organization section devoted to this basic preliminary work with the community. The starting money actually begins to be expended for personal services only after many months of work, involving the development of mutual understandings between specific communities and the Department of Mental Health. There are no statutory or even regulational formulas for the development of these understandings between communities and the state. This fact seems to be an important element in the Massachusetts plan. It appears that the lack of any such prescribed rules makes it easier to reach satisfactory solutions in particular instances, because every single project of every community differs from each of the others. The freedom of action provided by absence of any mandatory method facilitates the essential development of spontaneity in the community group as well as in the state workers. Specific understandings are reached, following the formal organization of associations, but no contractual agreements are entered into.

There are no geographical boundaries, no "mental health areas" as one finds in other state-level health programs, like state hospital districts, public health districts. The purpose is to remove as many obstacles as possible to spontaneity and total participation. There is no specific provision with respect to how many cities and towns may combine to provide area mental health services. We are trying to make it possible for any and all communities and groups to combine in truly cooperative teamwork. The function of the Department of Mental Health is to remove obstacles to the natural, free, easy and spontaneous entering into active participation by many groups. These include physicians, clergy, public and parochial school administrators, executives and leading staff members of public and private health agencies, family and child casework agencies, courts and public welfare departments, city, town and county governments, community chests and councils, parent-teachers' associations, service clubs such as Rotary and Kiwanis, and other groups such as state-level planning agencies including, in addition to the Department of Mental Health, the State Departments of Public Health, Education, Public Welfare, the state-wide Youth Authority and, finally, the State Legislature.

The discussions between community people and the Department of Mental Health provide the setting in which many crucial issues are worked out by the participants long before a program is actually in operation. Examples of such issues are: state versus local control, fixing of authority and responsibility, concerns over public medicine, threats to private practice, "socialized medicine," desires for the state to take no part in "giving," and desires for the state to take over completely the program and give to all parties. The total participation mentioned above is crucial to successful organization for community mental health practice. Every interested party should have the opportunity to participate in the deliberations of the association in every phase of the initial study, policy development, program planning and action.

The state really wants to join with the communities in what can best be described as an informal but quite tangible partnership. One of the partners, the community, expresses itself through the development of the incorporated mental health association, one of the principal purposes of which is to assist in the establishment and maintenance of an area mental health center. The formal incorporation of the local community organization takes place, theoretically at least, just about the time when the Department of Mental Health can fulfill its part of the partnership, namely, by supplying the professional team for the new area mental health center. The partnership develops through very simple beginnings, made by some small group or an individual from a community coming to the Department of Mental Health and asking for help in establishing or increasing community mental health facilities. Every effort is made by the community organizer of the Department to create and foster this spirit of partnership, rather than permitting the development of a feeling of different levels of understanding and unequal contributions. The initial explanation to the interested people is that the Department of Mental Health will help the area secure what the area itself decides is needed and desired in the way of new or increased community psychiatric services. The worker representing the state in this growing partnership must be sensitive to the fact that the area representatives themselves have a great capacity to work out difficult issues by themselves independently, given sufficient time. In other words, it is the state worker's primary function to help uncover and support self-reliance and self-confidence on the part of the community people. He must inject himself or allow himself to be drawn into joint action at the most helpful time and to withdraw temporarily at the proper time. He must then be able to transfer his functions, as far as a given area is concerned, to the incoming psychiatrist-director. He must still make himself continually available to the local people as they begin to join with the professional team in their work.

The success of these efforts comes from paying constant and meticulous attention to the needs of the community group during each phase of its growth and development. The arrival of the professional team brings the program from the level of discussion and planning down to an immediate here-and-now reality. A new association is born at the time of its formal incorporation. It has a broad charter in hand and now has to develop further the partnership with the mental health center itself, working with it to develop the specific programs of mental health education, consultation and clinical services. The social forces operating in the community itself become reality factors to be systematically studied and worked with by the partnership, each having its specific area of concern, but both working together. Definitions of role and function of the association and professional staff require many hours of committee meetings, individual meetings with key people, deliberations and resolving of differences of opinion. The professional mental health worker is using his knowledge of individual psychotherapy, human relations and social systems, and his techniques of mental health education and community organization in this important work.

When the Department of Mental Health begins relationships with the local communities, the only reality limitations which are made to the community are the following: (1) the area to be served should include a population of somewhere near 125,000; (2) the professional work of the Department of Mental Health must be limited to work with school-age and preschool children and their families; (3) the program should have the approval and participation of the locally organized medical profession through every stage of its development; (4) an organization truly representing the area should be formed in which the local medical profession would play a leadership role; (5) the chief function of this group would be to help in developing an area-wide mental health program and it would be able by its charter to concern itself with all matters of mental health importance; (6) assurances are to be given that the area association, from any and all sources, will be able to furnish funds or their equivalent in sufficient amount to provide quarters, clerical help and operating expenses, and, as growth takes place, additional professional personnel; (7) it would be understood that the proposed partnership is a real one, that each partner works alongside the other, but that the responsibilities and functions of each do not intermingle—that many issues must be settled by joint discussion and disposed of by decisions jointly achieved; (8) it shall be recognized that the local association and the State Department of Mental Health shall each possess areas of quite separate and independent function. The partnership, then, can grow and develop but at any time can be dissolved.

As suggested above, the partnership begins at the very instant of initial approaches to the Department of Mental Health by community representatives. Experience suggests that the future of the relationships between the state agency and the community in fact depend largely upon the depth, fullness and sincerity of these early attachments which are made between individual representatives of the Department of Mental Health and the individual representatives of the community. It is through the steady growth of these personalized attachments that final workable arrangements are completed. Unless these specific, early relationships are carefully nurtured without changing representatives, either by changes in state personnel or in local personnel, it is extremely difficult and sometimes almost impossible to establish easy and effective relationships later.

Massachusetts has a town system of government and is organized into 351 separate, autonomous cities and towns. The Division of Mental Hygiene believes that a community must have physical boundaries and feels justified in asking local representatives to join with neighboring towns in setting up specific areas embracing approximately 125,000 inhabitants. Some of these areas may have had some previous experience in doing things together, but in most cases the forces for cohesiveness are weak. The task of developing an area concept in Massachusetts is a major one. The figure, 125,000 population, is used as a guide. Flexible adaptations are finally agreed upon, governed by the more realistic considerations of compactness and homogeneity of populations. For instance, a community chest area is often used as an area for a mental health program.

The professional work is limited to children and families merely because of realistic considerations. The need for services to children and families is so pressing and professional personnel so scarce that work with children and families is given priority. The mental health associations can consider problems involving adult mental health facilities and join actively to sponsor adult programs with other groups, such as the neighboring state hospital, the Massachusetts Department of Public Health's Division of Clinics for Alchoholism, and local community hospitals.

The need for participation of the medical profession and of representative members of the community is self-evident. The vitality and breadth of representation in the organization represents the heart and soul of the experiment to develop realistic and total area-wide mental health programs. By the participation of all, we have some hope of putting into practice effective programs which will promote mental health in communities and areas of community life where mentally unhealthy and pathogenic conditions may exist. The active understanding and help of the medical profession are of paramount importance. The practicing physician stands in a very powerful relationship to community interests and families. The physician's role inherently contains powerful potentials for the promotion of mental health through education, consultation and clinical care.

The local financial contribution is not the primary consideration of the mental health organization, but follows naturally after the development of the partnership, the outline of needs and plans, the emotional involvement of various community groups. The contribution is, in a sense, a measure of the intellectual and emotional involvement of the area group. The ease, speed and extent with which the local organization comes through with its share of the material support of the program is related to the degree of involvement of the local organization and has relatively little to do with the wealth or poverty of the area.

The mental health association assumes the major portion of over-all policy making, a substantial part of the day-by-day administration of the mental health center, a sizable portion of the financial support and, most important, the major responsibility for the development of the mental health education program in the area. By the intensity and extent of this involvement, the area organization in all reality develops and maintains a healthy sense of ownership of the whole venture. The community mental health program then belongs to the community. The professional personnel, employed by the state and under the professional supervision and direction of the State Department of Mental Health, is in essence working for the local community as represented by the mental health association. The mental health association determines, through committee work, such matters as eligibility for clinical care, development of fee scale, the choice and maintenance of quarters, the type of program development. Fees are retained by the local association for the furtherance of the community mental health work. Some communities have decided upon fixed fees, others on sliding scale fees. Some communities have made an upper age limit of 16, others age 18. Some communities wanted the professional program to begin with consultation services only; others have wanted to begin with a traditional program. In all these matters, the Department of Mental Health has welcomed, and indeed insisted upon, the participation of the local community in the formation of the specific policy.

The state policy with respect to quarters is that they be sufficient in quality and size for the professional staff to do good work. They must also be fully accessible to any and all families and sections of the area, convenient to transportation. In the various programs we find quarters in a county courthouse, in rooms in an office building, in a private house shared with a family service agency, in public school buildings, in a state mental hospital and in a city-owned community health center. The Division of Mental Hygiene does not believe that quarters in public schools and state hospitals represent the best arrangements for the development of area mental health centers. These opinions are given to the area mental health associations, which have the final say in changing quarters.

The Division of Mental Hygiene through the direct employment of professional personnel maintains control of the professional conduct of the center. The psychiatrist-director becomes the official representative of the Division of Mental Hygiene for the area. He does not become a member of the local association. He attends meetings of the executive committee, professional advisory committee, program committee, educational committee, and ways and means committee of the association and joins in the discussion. He plays the role of a resource consultant, as well as bringing forth and interpreting the policy of the Department of Mental Health. He takes no legal part in the formal action of the local association. He is not the leader in promoting the community aspects of the program. It is rather his job to help the local association take the leadership in the community aspects of the program.

At any one time in Massachusetts we find community mental health organizations in various stages of development. Each stage, as explained above, requires a particular kind of attention. There are enough projects under consideration to make it always possible for the state personnel to engage actively in one or another. It is important, of course, to avoid becoming involved in more projects at any one time than can be properly helped in sound development. The relatively small size of Massachusetts and the convenient clustering of cities and towns make it possible to cover the entire state with a comparatively small central staff.

Massachusetts is one of the few states in which the legislature meets every year. This system may seem archaic, but it does offer the opportunity for special requests for funds to be considered at almost any time. Over the past three years the Commissioner of Mental Health has asked for and received appropriations for three new psychiatric teams each year, designated for specific areas which had progressed to the final stages of development. In addition, requests are now also made for the new community mental health consultant. Three new teams a year have been found to be about right in view of the rate at which new projects come to fruition and psychiatrists and other personnel are available.

The degree to which each area program differs from the other, the intensity and size of these differences are sources of constant amazement. The complete lack of similarity means that each area requires its own unique form of attention. It takes usually two to five years for each area to develop its sound community organization. The Division of Mental Hygiene does not urge or push the communities, does not try to "sell" them. It is only available to be called upon when the community wishes. After the first approach to the Division there are countless numbers of different directions in which the local organization may go in its growth. There is considerable variation in the type of assistance which the state may give the local people; they may arrive at maturity, ready for a professional program, with little or no help at all from the Division of Mental Hygiene. The following is a summary of the status of various projects as of winter, 1954–55:

Project 1. This project has completed its formal area organization after two years of work. Professional personnel allotments have been secured and a half-time director may be available in several months. The community association is well represented by the medical profession, educators and social agencies, but does not have enough lay representation as yet.

Project 2. After three years of work an area association is in the last stages of incorporation. A half-time psychiatrist-director is available. The medical profession has taken a prominent role in sponsoring this project, is somewhat concerned about "state medicine."

Project 3. This project began in 1953 at community request with a limited mental health consultation service, working closely with an area mental health association. It covers a large number of otherwise unrelated cities and towns. The project has had only part-time services, but is to acquire a full-time psychiatrist in the near future. This mental health association has a full-time paid executive. The project is involved in a special arrangement with a state teachers' college to provide mental health training programs for student teachers.

Project 4. Fifteen years of work in a community area almost completely lacking in psychiatric resources culminated 18 months ago in the establishment of a program. There is now a full-time staff, and a lively area association which is developing programs in mental health education, consultation and clinical services.

Project 5. This project developed very fast. Only 18 months elapsed between the first contact with the Department of Mental Health and the opening, in the fall of 1954, of a mental health center with a full-time staff, a strong area organization and relatively sumptuous quarters. The very speed and intensity of work, however, seem to have created other problems for this project, now quite evident. They stem from the deflation of a sense of community achievement following a comparatively spectacular first success. Reappraisal and redefinition of the role of the mental health association are needed, now that the initial goal of establishing a professional center has been achieved.

Project 6. This project presents a very difficult task for the community organizer, namely, to attempt to develop and attach a community mental health association to a clinical center which has been in operation for some time. This entails trying to "pass the ball" as quickly as possible to three contiguous but insulated towns, each of about 50,000 population, in an effort to spark them into joining together to make themselves one community organization for this mental health service, and to vigorously promote a broad program of community mental health education. In addition, financial assistance for the healthy growth of the community program is essential. A certain unhealthy awkwardness has arisen here because the state has been forced to take the initiative for at least some time. A natural feeling exists in the community as follows: "Well, if the state now runs it at least acceptably on its own, why come to us with just one more charity drive?"

There are at least six other projects in six distinct stages of development. There are now ten community mental health centers in Massachusetts. Seven more programs are to begin within the next year or so. Long-range planning calls for between 20 and 25 area mental health centers. In the final analysis, however, the local communities themselves will determine the number and manner in which these future programs are organized.

We are closing our paper with a more complete discussion of the area mental health center directorship. When the psychiatrist-director comes to an area mental health center, he becomes immediately a powerful figure in community life. His power for influencing and changing patterns of human relationships in the community may not be immediately apparent, and may be only gradually expressed through the years as he develops his program and his relationships throughout the community. All points of contact between the director with his professional staff and the mental health association and community are of vital importance. It is at these points of contact that interpersonal relations occur between the professional worker and the community which contain the three components of community mental health practice— education, consultation and treatment. It is through the mental health association that the director systematically develops relationships through the community. The mental health association takes leadership in the education program. The professional staff has consultation interviews with teachers, health and welfare workers, physicians, clergy, court personnel and others. Children and parents come to the clinic setting. They become involved in intake procedure, consultation and counseling, diagnostic and treatment work. The director is extremely concerned with the development of the mental health association and the proper definition of the roles and functions of the association in contrast to the roles and functions of the professional team. He is concerned with areas of tension and communication barriers which may exist between community groups, and between the professional team and the community. He is necessarily a community organizer, viewing the growth and development of the association as a basic component of his community mental health practice. The association is a community body important not simply for publicity purposes and fund raising, but for sound theoretical reasons. The director knows that the public health components of community mental health practice, namely, mental health promotion and specific prevention with their research and service components, cannot be properly developed without the organized participation of the community. The director is interested in many types of relationships in the community. Typical examples of these are as follows:

1. *State-local.* The development of the partnership concept, avoidance of the director's dictating policy, or of allowing the local community to become passive or dependent or both.

2. *Public-private.* Again fostering partnership, insisting that the private association form policy and advise the public agency; that responsibilities for professional programming and clinical care remain with the Department of Mental Health, but questions such as "What programming?" should be decided by the private group.

3. *Lay-professional.* The director is anxious to secure maximum participation of lay interests in the association, both key lay individuals and lay groups. He knows that mental health associations overweighted with professional people in key positions may be a handicap.

4. *Medical-nonmedical.* The director is a physician. Mental health practice and child guidance work represent public health and medical care. The local medical profession needs orientation with respect to the nature and purpose of the mental health program, and an opportunity for rewarding participation.

5. *Interagency.* The director knows that the new mental health center is viewed by agencies as the answer to the handling of many difficult cases. He has to interpret his program, state limitations of clinical care, develop consultation services to complement clinical services, learn to use various community resources, and clarify roles and function of the mental health center in contrast to those of various agencies in order to avoid role confusion, anxieties and tensions.

6. *School-community and school-home.* The director knows that development of relationships with public school systems is complicated and must proceed slowly and with care; education and organizational work involving all levels of school personnel necessarily precedes any clinical or consultation service.

7. *Mental health center personnel.* The clinic people will play new and unfamiliar roles in community mental health practice. The director has studied the community organization; he sends staff people into various areas of community life where he feels their training, experience and personality characteristics will be effective in the program. In-service training and supervision is essential. Modes of defining problems in relationship to clients and referring agencies which may work in the child guidance context are not necessarily appropriate in the mental health center context. The mental health center staff is exposed to the community at large; sees the hopes, expectations and frustrations of community groups, as well as individuals; must realize that solutions cannot necessarily be found within the context of the individual professional role or the role of the mental health center. Community mental health issues which individuals bring up can and should be referred to appropriate committees of the mental health association.

With this review of our experiences in community organization for mental health we believe that we can outline several guiding principles which may be tested by other groups working in different settings: (1) An organized community mental health group is an integral, vital part of a community mental health program. (2) The organized community mental health group joins with the professional team on a partnership basis, each having its own clear function and area of responsibility; each is working side by side with the other within the context of a total community mental health program.

(3) Change in habitual patterns of interpersonal relations in the social systems of a community represents a goal; the professional personnel and the organized group are change-agents. (4) The professional mental health worker is concerned with the psychology of change, in the face-to-face treatment relationship with children and parents in the clinic, as well as in the dyad and group relationships with the organized community group and various community institutions. (5) Increased communication and interaction between key individuals in the community represents a goal; the joining together of many otherwise insulated or isolated community groups to discuss human relations and mental health issues is an essential function of an organized mental health group. (6) A stabilization of professional mental health personnel is essential in order that relationships can be developed between the mental health center and the community; programs cannot be developed when there is turnover of personnel. (7) If the professional mental health worker plays his proper role at each stage of development, the organized mental health groups will take active leadership with initiative and spontaneity in building the mental health program.

This work is new; conclusions can be arrived at only tentatively. There is pressing need for basic public heatlh research to be developed, utilizing social science, biostatistics and epidemiologic methodology. Ten or fifteen years will be needed to evaluate the effectiveness of these programs. However, we do not yet have sound measures of mental health which we can use for comparative purposes ten or fifteen years hence (13,14).

REFERENCES

1. Bowlby, J. *Maternal Care and Mental Health*. Geneva: World Health Organization, 1951.
2. Felix, R. H. Mental hygiene and public health. *Am. J. Orthopsychiat.*, 1948, 18:679–84.
3. Freud, A., and Burlingham, D. T. *War and children*. New York: International University Press, 1943.
4. Kirkpatrick, M. E. What psychiatry needs from public health. *Am. J. Psychiat.*, 1950, 107:327–29.
5. Leavell, H. R. What public health needs from psychiatry. *Am. J. Psychiat.*, 1950, 107:321–26.
6. Leavell, H. R. Contributions of the social sciences to the solution of health problems. *New England J. Med.*, 1952, 247:885–97.
7. Leavell, H. R., and Clark, E. G. *Textbook of preventive medicine*. New York: McGraw-Hill, 1953.
8. Lindemann, E. "Mental health: Fundamental to a dynamic epidemiology of health," In Galdston, I. (Ed.), *Epidemiology of Health*. New York: Health Education Council, New York Academy of Medicine, 1953. Pp. 109–23.

9. Milbank Memorial Fund. Epidemiology of mental disorder. New York, 1950.
10. Milbank Memorial Fund. Interrelations between social environment and psychiatric disorders. New York, 1953.
11. Powers, E. *Annotated bibliography of published material dealing with the establishment, administration and financing of psychiatric clinics.* Boston: Judge Baker Guidance Center, 1951.
12. Simmons, L. W., and Wolff, H. G. *Social science in medicine.* New York: Russell Sage Foundation, 1954.
13. Spitz, R. A. The psychogenic diseases in infancy: An attempt at their etiological classification, In *The psychoanalytic study of the child,* vol. VI. New York: International University Press, 1951.
14. Vaughan, W. T., Jr. *Survey of community psychiatric resources in Massachusetts.* Boston: Massachusetts Department of Mental Health, 1952.

17

Mental Health Education
in a Community Mental Health Center

STEPHEN E. GOLDSTON

THE regulations associated with the Community Mental Health Centers Act of 1963 cite five essential elements of comprehensive mental health services: (1) inpatient services, (2) outpatient services, (3) partial hospitalization services, (4) emergency services, and (5) consultation and education services available to community agencies and professional personnel. The focus of the first four elements is primarily on new methods of clinical treatment and care, whereas the fifth element, consultation and education services, is concerned with the prevention of mental illness and the promotion of mental health. The mandated inclusion of consultation and education services represents a new approach in community mental health programing and a distinct challenge to the responsible staff of a community mental health center. The challenge calls for pioneering efforts in an area which heretofore appears to have been relatively neglected and in which limited opportunities have existed for professional training and practice.

Although the above-named legislation combines both consultation and education services into a single element, clear distinctions exist between these two forms of indirect mental health service. Whereas mental health consultation has been an area of increasing concern and activity over the past decade, few guidelines have been formulated for conducting a community mental health education program. In an attempt to stimulate creative educational programming, this paper offers some approaches to mental health education and to the educational components of community mental health programs.

EDUCATIONAL APPROACHES

From the standpoint of individual and community health, a community mental health center's efforts toward preventing mental illness and promoting

Reprinted from *American Journal of Public Health*, 1968, *58*, 693–699, by permission of the publisher and the author. © 1968, American Public Health Association. Dr. Goldston is Special Assistant to the Director, National Institute of Mental Health.

mental health are the most important facets of a comprehensive community mental health program. Prevention of mental illness implies not only the reduction of those factors which tend to produce mental and emotional disturbances, but also the provision of a climate in which each individual has optimum opportunities for sustained creative and responsible participation in the life of the community and for the development of his particular potentialities as a human being. This latter concept is usually denoted by the public health term "primary prevention" or "health promotion."

The effective operation of a preventive mental health program requires first, a population which knows what to do and is prepared to act at the first sign of trouble and next, the necessary services to provide the requested help. People need to know what services are available, the reasons for utilizing these services before they find themselves in serious difficulty, the effects of environmental stress on human personality and behavior, the critical importance of interpersonal relationships, and the nature of their own emotions and motivations. A preventive approach must incorporate mental health education of the general and professional public into community mental health activities.

For purposes of discussion, this paper identifies a number of mental health education functions, not all-inclusive, which are classified within two broad areas of programing. The first area includes those *general* educational services, activities, and tasks which every community mental health worker might assume in order to increase his effectiveness as a community agent. The second area cites *specific* educational functions which require the skills of a professionally trained community mental health educator.

GENERAL EDUCATIONAL ACTIVITIES

All community mental health workers should share responsibility for educational activities in the following areas:

Community Organization

A sound educational approach is essential if a community mental health center is to work cooperatively within the family of existing agencies of a community. As relative newcomers on the community agency scene, the center staff must interpret their program to the entire community, establish liaison with all types of community agencies concerned with mental health, promote interagency relationships, and facilitate the coordination and proper utilization of the community's mental health services. A mutual information-sharing about agency programs and goals has educational ramifications. In order to function effectively in this capacity, a community mental health worker should become knowledgeable about the general structure and functioning of the community, its power structure, and decision-making processes and bodies. Griffiths has noted that:

The encouragement and promotion of interaction processes that open channels of communication, widen social participation, emphasize the value of individual worth in decision-making, are forces of no mean consequence in the total mental health picture of a community (2).

Community Analysis

The professional mental health worker serving in an educational capacity works in the general community to assess attitudes, and present knowledge and beliefs regarding mental health and illness and the perceptions of mental health services. He participates in educational programs to create favorable attitudes and provides information on available services.

In addition, special studies having an educational component may be undertaken to analyze the effectiveness of a center's program as well as the nature of the population within a center's catchment area, e.g., epidemiological studies and program analyses, general demographic studies, and surveys of unmet community needs and community expectations.

Identifying Foci of Mental Illness

A community-oriented mental health staff will seek to identify the foci of mental illness and stress within a community. Educational efforts may be undertaken, in cooperation with representatives of other community agencies, to ameliorate those conditions which are deleterious to community life. The result of educational endeavors may lead to utilization of clinical and educational services by those in need and/or administrative actions to eradicate harmful conditions.

In many instances a focus of mental illness can be alleviated through educational programs and methods. Often laws and regulations persist long beyond a period of utility, thereby creating harmful conditions. A specific illustration concerns the police department of a large eastern city which requires a police officer who is undergoing care for an emotional disturbance to report this to his superiors, with the consequence that his service revolver is turned in until such time as a "recovery" has been effected. This act of emasculation and humiliation creates a barrier to those police officers who wish to seek help during the early stages of a disturbance. Furthermore, this regulation reflects and perpetuates a false public image of the wildly deranged insane. Studies of these problems could lead to educational programs and measures which could eliminate foci of mental illness and thereby promote mental health and constructive public perceptions of the mentally ill and mental health services.

Establishment of Mental Health Consultation Programs

Educational considerations enter into the planning, organizing, and administering of mental health consultation programs. Since consultation services are often provided to a unit within an organization, the professional mental health worker could perform an educational function as liaison to top staff in the organization receiving such services. For example, a center staff member could fulfill such a role in a relationship with the superintendent of a school system, although consultation services might be provided to school principals and teachers.

Although some experts maintain that any request for consultation services should originate from the potential consultee, circumstances may demand that the initiating agents be the center staff. The task of the center representative is to interpret the nature of consultative services available and the "contractual" obligations of participants in a consultative relationship.

Provision of Mental Health Consultation

To the extent that effective consultation may include teaching and learning, there is an educational component in the provision of such services.

"Clinical-Educational" Functions

In order to serve the needs of the total community, a center could develop educational programs aimed at groups of preadmission patients, predischarge inpatients, and patients' families. Such educational programs would focus on the specific needs of such groups and thereby would extend the center's services beyond concern with only the already-identified patient population requiring direct clinical services.

SPECIFIC EDUCATIONAL ACTIVITIES

The most effective type of systematic community mental health education programs can be implemented when a professionally trained mental health educator is a staff member of a center. Hanlon supports this position by stating:

> The health educator, with years of experience in selling health and health programs, can expand his efforts to include mental health. He can be of invaluable assistance to mental health personnel as they move from their treatment activities into their community role (4).

The mental health educator shares the fundamental goals of the educator engaged in general public health programs, i.e., to stimulate, coordinate, and further the efforts of people to recognize their own or their organization's health problems and to take an active part in dealing with them. Basically, the principles of health education are similar to the principles of education in general. Health education aspires to provide individuals and groups not only with information and understanding but also with the opportunity to examine and evaluate their observations and experiences, to draw meaning from them, and then to act on them.

The unique contributions of the mental health educator are identified in the following specific educational activities:

Professional Training

The mental health educator stimulates, plans, organizes and, where appropriate, assists in conducting professional training programs which impart information, teach skills and technics, and aim to create facilitating attitudes among such community help-giving groups as general practitioners, teachers, clergymen, police, and others. Other relevant functions would include determining the needs of such groups, building curriculum, scheduling programs, and evaluating the effects of such programs.

General Education Programs

In distinction to professional training programs for professional help-givers, the mental health educator might develop what could be termed "general education programs." Such educational programs would aim to promote mental health among *organized* lay groups, such as PTA's, labor unions, and others. Education for personal and family mental health would be the focus, rather than an attempt to assist the audience to further their mental health skills in their work as is typical of professional training programs.

Consultation to Center Staff

By definition, community mental health programs are multidisciplinary efforts. Many issues in program planning and operation have an educational component, and the best resource in the center to deal with educational problems is the mental health educator.

Too frequently either the educational nature of an issue has been ignored, been unknown to the staff, or not been acted upon due to lack of staff expertise in this area. The mental health educator on the staff of a center thus may add a new dimension to the study, investigation, and implementation of community mental health programs.

Staff In-Service Education

Staff orientation sessions and a continuing in-service education program are two other functions to which the mental health educator may contribute his distinct skills. Staff in-service education programs may include visiting speakers and consultants, a journal club, staff review of films and books, and so on. The organization and conduct of these programs are tasks for the mental health educator.

Rehabilitation

The mental health educator would identify and utilize educational methods and technology in patient care programs. Educational approaches include resocialization, emotional re-education, and planned learning experiences, e.g., patient clubs and day care. In addition, the educator would assist re-habilitation staff in working with groups of employers to promote job placement for patients needing a sheltered work environment and for former patients.

Mental Health Education of the Public

Mental health education programs for the general public may have three different emphases: (a) education about mental health—informing people in general about the facts bearing on mental health in their communities so that they may work to improve relevant conditions, e.g., alcoholism, addictions, delinquency; (b) education about mental illness—focusing concern on the care, treatment, and rehabilitation of the mentally ill as well as those institutions designed to provide such services; and (c) education for mental health—helping individuals to manage their own lives better and to achieve better mental, emotional, and social adjustment (1,3,5).

In undertaking general mental health education programs for the lay public, the mental health educator must be alert to these three emphases and plan programs accordingly. Most present-day mental health education programs are concerned with the first two categories named. Greater efforts should be directed toward programs concerned with education for mental health and for fostering human potential for healthy living, e.g., ego strengthening, coping technics, anticipatory adjustment education, and crises avoidance. Such programs would include education about parent-child relationships, marriage and the family, the role of work in our society, stress, and so on.

Communications

1. *Use of Educational Media.* Educational media such as films, pamphlets, television, radio, and others, can be used effectively in a community mental health education program to the extent that the educator maintains and communicates to his colleagues that such media are merely program tools, and not the program itself. There is a great need for evaluation studies of media and such activities would call upon the research and analytical skills of the educator.

The educator's knowledge of media can be applied in the bibliotherapy efforts of a center's clinical staff. Clinicians should become familiar with the phraseology and reading level of mental health publications prepared for public consumption since such materials could facilitate clinician-patient communication. Clinical staff familiar with the utilization of media could be encouraged to distribute, where applicable, appropriate reading materials to their patients. In many instances, such materials may serve an ego-supportive function and also provide needed reality-orientation as well as information to the patient.

For example, the use of good parent-child publications could be helpful to parents with insufficient information about the problems of normal child development.

The mental health educator might also develop materials for specific groups since the mental health "message" must be individualized to the target-group audience. Unfortunately, too few publications are addressed to the particular needs of a specific group and a shotgun rather than a rifle approach characterizes the present state of the field of mental health information. The creation and development of such media, which may be invaluable in promoting a center's in-service and professional education programs, requires considerable knowledge by the educator of each specific group's needs, interests, and particularly, the relationship of their occupational tasks to mental health concerns. Often a job analysis of each target group must precede the development or selection of meaningful materials.

The mental health educator is aware in utilizing educational materials that the mere presentation of facts does not automatically result in changes in behavior, regardless of the allure of the media. He uses such materials knowing that only if an individual is motivated to act on the available information, in order to achieve optimal health, is the information meaningful.

2. *Speaker's Bureau*. Since speakers on mental health topics are frequently demanded by community organizations, center staff should be responsive to such requests. However, to effectively utilize other mental health resources in a community, the mental health educator could establish a speaker's bureau which would serve as a clearinghouse for such public education functions.

3. *Public Relations*. In those centers where there is no specific staff member assigned the public relations function, these responsibilities may be performed by the mental health educator. Such activities would include preparation of news releases, assistance in speech writing, answering public inquiries, and so on.

4. *Professional Writing*. The mental health educator may contribute to the preparation of center policy papers, professional articles, annual and other reports, speeches, and so on. Writing skills are a prerequisite for the mental health educator and facilitating communication is one of his prime skills.

Career Recruitment

The mental health educator could assume responsibility for developing a program within the community to orient interested youngsters to what is involved in a mental health career. Such a program might be conducted in conjunction with local colleges and high schools. Students could be invited to visit the center to witness, where appropriate, the functioning of mental health workers. Perhaps a volunteer program could be associated with a careers program, although the former would not usually be a direct concern of the mental health educator.

TRAINING NEEDS

If mental health workers are to perform educational functions, they must be prepared for the assumption of such duties and be aware of the opportunities to serve in an educational capacity. Mental health expertise in and of itself is no guarantee that the professional person can be a successsful educator.

With the inclusion of educational services as a basic element of community mental health center operations, it would appear that mental health workers should have planned experiences during their formal academic and field training which will provide familiarization with the following relevant concerns: (a) the development and use of simple reading materials; (b) instruction in basic teaching methods, particularly from a demonstration and practical work aspect; (c) emphasis on the organization and conduct of workshops, seminars, and conferences; (d) greater attention to community organization; and (e) supervised field activities in which the mental health workers function as educators.

The growing importance and relevance of the educational approach to mental health issues suggest that there is a need for a new professional worker with special skills, the mental health educator. Lindemann has suggested that such a worker should have preparation in the following areas: vital statistics; social anthropology; social system observations; group behavior; the varieties of mental health operations which have educative results; the group discussion method; and individual consultation at times of special crises. Lindemann suggests that such a worker:

> will learn to be comfortable with the care-taking professions and learn to be comfortable in that particular role which we believe is that of a health educator. He does not have the answers. He has to continue to go to the expert to find out what is known at present, but he can be useful to the expert by providing him with some reasonable guesses concerning the best educative method which is applicable for a particular focus of concern which this expert has in mind (3).

Efforts to explore the training of the mental health education specialist are taking place at the University of California School of Public Health, Los Angeles, under the direction of Professor Guy Steuart (NIMH Training Grant, MH-10301). The program provides trainees with the basic requirements for the M.P.H. in general health education plus specific mental health education courses. The areas of specialization include: (a) growth, development, aging, and mental health; (b) appraisal of community mental health education needs; (c) concepts of mental health consultation; (d) social psychiatry, theory, and practice; (e) sensitivity training; and (f) mental health services as social systems. Field work opportunities parallel each academic content area. Potentially, this experimental program will provide valuable information not only about the training of the mental health educator but also a clearer conceptualization of his role and contribution in community mental health.

SUMMARY

Mental health education is a vital aspect of community mental health programs. This paper contends that all mental health workers potentially may be educators, and they should be aware of the educational functions they might assume in the conduct of community mental health functions. In addition, the numerous tasks which require the services of a professionally trained mental health educator are outlined. Suggestions are offered for augmenting professional training programs to include attention to the educational functions of community mental health workers.

REFERENCES

1. Committee on Professional Education. Proposed report on educational qualifications and functions of public health educators. *A.J.P.H.*, 1957, 47, 1:112–19.
2. Griffiths, W. The public health educator in mental health. *California's Hlth.*, 1960, 17:14.
3. Group for the Advancement of Psychiatry. *The psychiatrist in mental health education.* Report no. 29, 1954.
4. Hanlon, J. G. The role of the mental health service in the local health department. *Pub. Hlth. Rep.*, 1957, 72, 12: 1093–97.
5. Pennsylvania Mental Health, Inc. *Mental health education: A critique,* 1960.
6. U.S. Department of Health, Education, and Welfare. Consultation and Education. PHS Pub. no. 1478, 1966.

18

Mental Health Education with a Professional Group: Some Implications for the Medical Profession

HERBERT A. OTTO AND RIVES CHALMERS

THIS paper is based on five years of experience in mental health education by conducting in-service training workshops, study groups and seminars in school systems, faculties, teachers and administrators in many parts of Georgia. As Assistant Professor of Mental Health at the College of Education, University of Georgia, it has been the responsibility of one of the authors of this paper to administer a Mental Health Education Program. This program is a demonstration project of the Division of Mental Hygiene of the Georgia State Health Department, and is conducted in cooperation with the University of Georgia, College of Education.

INTRODUCTION

From a number of years of experience in the field, the following definition of mental health education emerged:

Mental health education is the process of supplying information and concepts based on the needs of training groups and dealing with the area of mental health and illness in such a manner as to encourage the development of mature attitudes and promote professional competence.

Mental health has come to be considered the nation's number one health problem. The medical profession is assuming a major responsibility for professional leadership in this area. The development of professional leadership brings with it a need to keep informed about what is being done in the field and the realization that training programs can greatly accelerate the emergence of responsible and effective leadership. This paper presents some impressions and observations which are the result of five years experience in the field of mental health education.

Reprinted from *Southern Medical Journal*, 1958, *51*, 1031–1037, by permission of the publisher and the authors. © 1958, Southern Medical Association. Dr. Otto is Director of Research, Stone Foundation, Chicago, Illinois. Dr. Chalmers is a physician at the Atlanta Psychiatric Clinic.

FRAMEWORK OF THIS STUDY

This study is based on mental health education programs which are conducted primarily with members of the teaching profession. Of a total of 86 training sessions, 11 were with public health nurses, 4 with ministers, and 71 with teachers. Requests for mental health education were largely voluntary in nature. Approximately 80 per cent of the requests came as a result of decisions by higher (administrative) authority. Training and consultation requests by school systems were usually addressed directly to the University whereas public health nurses sent their requests through public health channels. All of these programs were in the nature of in-service training. Sixty-eight programs were conducted on the "home ground" of the participants with the remainder evenly divided between on-campus sessions held at other central locations.

Of the 86 programs there were 21 single sessions (lasting up to 2½ hours) and 30 half-day sessions. There were 19 full-day, 10 two-day and 6 three-day training programs. In other words less than a quarter of the total programs were of the single session variety, with better than 55 per cent of the total following the half-day to full-day training pattern.

It should be pointed out that consultation and preplanning with local program committees or other sources of responsible leadership was a standard procedure in the development of training programs. This was done in order to determine local needs and interests and to explore what local resources could be utilized.

MATERIAL RESOURCES USED

Whenever possible, local professionally trained resources were drawn upon. Visiting teachers (school social workers), school guidance workers or locally based mental hygiene personnel were invited to participate in programs as resource persons. For two- or three-day workshops, consultants and resource persons were also obtained from higher institutions of learning located within reasonable travel distance, as well as from the State Division of Mental Hygiene.

A somewhat limited number of material resources were available at the time the mental health education project at the University of Georgia was initiated. The resources consisted of films, pamphlets, and other publications. However, in the short space of five years the number and quality of educational aids has increased markedly.

During all workshop experiences, a continuous program of evaluation of all educational aids was carried on. Whenever possible, group members were asked to evaluate the effectiveness of educational aids. As a result of this activity, it was possible to define a core of five films which seemed to have general appeal to professional groups by stimulating thought and discussion:

1. *Preface to a Life*—United World Film Company.
2. *Feeling of Hostility*—McGraw-Hill Film Company.
3. *Feeling of Rejection*—McGraw-Hill Film Company.
4. *Angry Boy*—Mental Health Film Board.
5. *Fears of Children*—Mental Health Film Board.

A list of approximately 30 pamphlets and books was compiled and kept current. From the list a group of 10 pamphlets was judged to be most valuable and useful. These are:

1. *A Pound of Prevention*—Committee on Mental Health, State Charities Aid Assn., New York City.
2. *Emotional Problems of Illness*—Science Research Associates, Chicago, Ill.
3. *Helping Children Solve Problems*—Science Research Associates, Chicago, Ill.
4. *Keystones in Psychological Thinking About Young Children*—The National Committee for Mental Hygiene, Inc., New York City.
5. *Mental Health Is a Family Affair*—Public Affairs Pamphlets, New York City.
6. *Understanding Hostility in Children*—Science Research Associates, Chicago, Ill.
7. *Teachers and Behavior Problems*—The Commonwealth Fund, New York City.
8. *Teacher Listen—the Children Speak*—Committee on Mental Health, State Charities Aid Assn., New York City.
9. *The Why and How of Discipline*—The Child Study Association of America, Inc., New York City.
10. *Toward Mental Health*—Public Affairs Pamphlets, New York City.

Finally, a continuous survey was made of new books and publications, and a traveling "sample" professional library for use by workshop participants was organized. Displays of pamphlets and books were used at all programs. Participants were encouraged to leaf through and become familiar with resource material. During programs lasting two or three days, workshop participants were encouraged to sign out materials. A folder of "current items" or teaching aids was also kept. This consisted of articles on mental health clipped from local newspapers and popular magazines as well as professional journals. This folder was passed around during the session or workshop. Such articles or items served as springboards for discussion as group members related reading material from the folder to local experiences or cases. For programs of two to three days duration participants were urged to bring articles or clippings on mental health to the sessions for use as teaching aids.

Depending on the available supply, it was made a standard policy to give out at least one free piece of literature such as the pamphlet, "Mental Health is . . . 1–2–3," at every program (4). Any such literature was used as content material at appropriate moments.

TECHNICS OF PRESENTATION

Technics of presentation of the material have varied. The lecture method and a prepared agenda was used in the beginning. This was shortly found to be ineffectual. Use of the lecture method was found to be ineffectual for a number of reasons: (1) Oftentimes local needs and interests did not clearly emerge during preplanning or underwent considerable modifications between the pre-planning consultation and the time of delivery of the lecture. (2) Deeply rooted misconceptions and inculcated misinformation as well as unsound attitudes could not be dealt with via the lecture method. (3) Material on mental health inevitably aroused some feelings of anxiety and hostility in group members. These feelings often needed to be handled "on the spot,"—obviously impossible during a lecture. (4) It was difficult to meet individual needs and concerns via the lecture method. (5) It was observed that the unsatisfied needs and concerns, the anxiety and hostility aroused by the nature of the material, as well as the method of presentation, constituted a barrier to assimilation and learning. Finally, (6) "Experience has shown that a course based on the giving of information by experts leaves trainees dependent, insecure and unskilled (2, p. 240)."

It is of interest to note that during the use of the lecture method, the post-lecture "question period" was either marked by sluggishness and apathy or by an extreme question-pressure as many members vied to gain the floor to air their needs or ventilate their feelings.

A new method of presentation was developed with the view of creating the type of learning climate which would facilitate free thinking and discussion centered around the needs and level of development of the participants. It was found that such a climate could most satisfactorily be attained by concentrating *on the quality of relationships existing between workshop participants in the beginning of the session and by exploring how the quality of relationships influences the learning process*. The objective was for members to "get to know each other," to lessen social and interpersonal isolation, to lower anxiety, and to help group members to assume increasing responsibility in the learning process. To this end, the question of "getting to know each other" was usually the first joint responsibility to be worked through by the group and instructor together.

Another aspect of this method of presentation was to meet the professional group "where it was" in terms of its level of development. The level of development was determined by helping the group to explore both expressed and implied needs in relation to the subject area. This was done by "agenda building." After a brief statement about the program or workshop, participants would be invited to submit questions and sub-areas which they wanted to explore. The group was then asked to organize the questions and areas in such a way as to facilitate learning, interest, and approach to the subject. Following the organization of content possibilities, existing material resources and teaching aids would be discussed by the instructor. Group discussions were encouraged as to which films should be shown and where they would fit into the content organization.

A further change in the technic of presentation was introduced after several groups were encountered which had difficulty building an agenda because of an almost total lack of information about the field of mental health. In these cases a brief survey of the field was given which included some of the areas that might be discussed or investigated. This lecture-type survey was entitled, "Overview of the Field and Suggested Areas of Study."

A modified discussion technic was used during all mental health education experiences. Agenda items were covered as far as possible through discussion led by the workshop instructor. However, leadership was not seen as residing solely in the instructor, but as a coresponsibility of workshop participants. For example, by virtue of his interest, experience and knowledge of an agenda item, a workshop member might spontaneously assume leadership by sharing of his knowledge, answering questions addressed to him, etc. The workshop instructor, at such times, would usually function in the role of a consultant. In this capacity, his aim was always to encourage the group to do their own thinking and to assist them to "pull out" information about an agenda item as far as possible from their own resources, as well as to contribute of his own thinking and knowledge.

In short, the method of presentation developed for mental health education programs can be outlined as follows: (1) "Getting to know each other," and examining how this influences the learning process. (Group shares this responsibility with leader and begins to develop feeling of "we-ness.") (2) Determining the level of need through agenda building. (3) The group organizes the agenda and decides about the use of some teaching aids. (4) Sharing of thinking and experiences through discussion of agenda (concept formation and new learnings). Group shares in leadership responsibility.

OBSERVATIONS AND ANALYSIS OF GROUP EXPERIENCES

Early in the course of his work the writers noted that group after group needed help with the following three basic attitudes or concepts:

1. Attitudes toward mental illness. The majority of workshop participants

seemed to feel that an emotional disturbance was something shameful, something fearful or ludicrous. Attitudes toward seeking psychiatric help were similarly a mixture of shame and fear. This was coupled with misconceptions about treatment and the psychiatrist's role and function.

2. Behavior was often labeled and categorized and therewith dismissed. This relieved the individual doing the labeling of responsibility in seeking to understand the causes of behavior or from participating in the helping process. For example, Johnny was called "a nervous boy," and no further thought given as to the underlying cause of his behavior or in which way help may be brought to bear.

3. Group members had difficulty in recognizing the feelings of others and working with these feelings. This difficulty ranged from a lack of recognition or insensitivity to feelings, to a consciously formulated philosophy such as, "The best way to deal with feelings is to ignore them." Most group members acknowledged that the handling of an emotionally charged situation was a problem.

It seemed to be most helpful to encourage workshop participants to express and explore their own feelings and emotions. For example, talking about feelings they had about emotional illness or seeking psychiatric help, often led to a deeply meaningful exchange and sharing of personal experience. Socio-drama was used to illustrate how certain attitudes and feelings of professional persons can affect their functions in a professional setting. Socio-drama was also used to give individuals practice in the use of new concepts. For example, a teacher or nurse would act the part of a parent or patient in a highly emotionally charged incident. Another volunteer would then act out the role of a professional person who is recognizing and handling the feelings and emotional needs of a parent or patient.

Case studies were used to deepen the understanding of personality dynamics and the causes of behavior. Often participants would present cases with which they needed help. Because of their immediate interest, suitable cases were used as teaching aids whenever possible. In this connection and at other points, the multidisciplinary and team approach to mental health problems was stressed. State clinical resources and the function of the clinic team were explained. Problems of referral to other mental health resources such as school social workers and psychiatrists in private practice were explored. Since this type of information demonstrably increased the professional skills of the learner, the assimilation and retention of such material was high.

An analysis of agenda items listed by all three professions over the course of five years reveals the following topics most often chosen in the order of importance:

1. Causes of mental illness.
2. Symptoms and treatment methods.
3. How can we help a disturbed child or person?
4. Is mental illness hereditary?

5. Our own mental health.

6. How to work more effectively with parents and administrators.

7. What are preventive programs in mental health?

8. What is the state mental health program and what resources are at our disposal?

9. What can you do about a person who needs psychiatric help?

10. Help with specific cases.

The majority of workshop groups listed "Our own mental health" as an important topic for discussion. Interest in this topic seems to be widespread and general and has been so reported in other mental health education programs (3, 5). Exploration of this topic usually began with participants expressing concern about pressures under which they were operating in their professional setting. They were then asked to list hazards to their mental health and to go into their feelings about such hazards. Prophylactic measures were then discussed. Usually a number of clear-cut decisions for change were made by some participants. These decisions often involved manipulation of the professional or home environment in order to produce a less stressful routine or situation.

Due to the nature of the subject studied in mental health education, a number of participants usually joined the group for help with their personal problems. Sometimes open bids for help or therapy were made. These personal problems were not handled during the training sessions, but individuals who had such problems were seen in private and directed to sources of psychiatric, medical or other help.

The teaching philosophy and method of presentation used in mental health education programs seemed to affect group process in a number of ways. Early and extensive leadership testing was noted in the majority of groups. This testing was manifest by either passivity, silence and unwillingness to participate in discussion, or by asking the workshop leader to lecture. It was only after the workshop leader had met this test and had said to the group in effect, "We can work out solutions to these needs and problems together—I am not here to tell you what to do," that the group was able to assume responsibility for doing its own thinking and to become actively involved in the learning process.

Following this particular phase of leadership testing, both rate and level of communication usually increased markedly with approximately 70 to 80 per cent of the group members entering in the discussion at some time during the first two hours. As more group members expressed themselves, communication tended to become more personal, "I want to tell you of this experience I have had with this case," "I want to tell you about this problem." In group sessions of more than a day's duration another cycle of testing of the leader (again open criticism and hostility directed toward the leader) was observed on the second day. As this was handled, a further increase in group cohesiveness and ease of communication could be observed.

It was also noted that the initial leadership testing and phase of heightened communication was accompanied by a strong development of "we-feeling" or group-belongingness. This feeling of being accepted and valued as members of the group gave participants the "safety" to share deeply entrenched attitudes ("I always used to think there was something funny about being crazy, or crazy people") and meaningful experiences. It was an outstanding finding that it took time for group members to develop the feeling of being accepted and to share in a deeply meaningful way in the learning process. For this reason single sessions from one to two hours duration were rarely effective and little seemed to be accomplished during these sessions. The main contribution of these short single sessions was to give participants some idea of the problems and complexities of the field. A limited retention of informational content was observed. However, at the same time group members were left with considerable feelings of dissatisfaction, which can best be illustrated by certain remarks which were repeatedly made by participants, "We didn't have time to get in deep enough," and "We didn't really get a chance to talk about some of the things we needed some help with."

A characteristic pattern of dealing with group tensions was observed in the workshops. Whenever tensions became too strong, humor was used as a release, i.e., the irrelevant or comic remark followed by explosive laughter. Often a "group wit" or comic emerged who acted as a catalyst.

DYNAMICS OF THE LEARNING PROCESS

As the result of interplay of three major factors, most groups working in the area of mental health education seemed to be highly motivated to learn. First, the current widespread interest in mental health has prepared a fertile ground for work. Second, members of professional groups seek training with the objective of becoming more proficient in their ability to handle the human relations factor of their work. Finally, the training method says to the participant in essence, "What are your interests in learning about this area, what are your needs, and what can we do to meet these needs together?"

This approach of focusing on the professional needs and interests of trainees usually results in maximum participation in the learning process. Inattentiveness is rare and is a cue to the instructor that needs are not being met. As has been stated before, it was a major finding that every training group needed help with, (a) attitudes toward mental illness and seeking psychiatric help, (b) using and understanding the concept, "behavior is caused," and (c) recognizing feelings and working with them.

In relation to these three areas, the dynamics of the learning process is complex as basic attitudinal changes are involved. It was borne out repeatedly that if workshop participants were able to explore and share their attitudes and feelings, a certain amount of growth or change would take place. This was evidenced by verbalizations which seemed to reveal attitudinal changes. Baruch's (1, p. 30) concept, that negative feelings and attitudes have to be expressed first, before positive attitudes can develop, sheds some light on this process. Another force which seems to be operating is embodied in the concept that, "sound attitudes are contagious" (often expressed as "mental health is contagious"), i.e., the expression of healthy and mature attitudes and viewpoints by some group members leads to modifications and changes in the attitudes of other group members.

Other factors in the dynamics of the learning process are as follow:

1. Reduction of feelings of isolation between members led to a lessening of tensions and self-consciousness and helped participants acquire a sense of "safety, significance and affection." This facilitated communication and free exchange of thought.

2. By focusing on group needs and interests (through agenda building) participants were highly motivated and more ready to invest of themselves in the learning process.

3. Group members were encouraged to participate in the organization of content material and methods of approach to the study of the subject. This helped the group as a whole to identify with the agenda and diminished resistance to new material.

4. Group members together with the leader worked out concepts and answers to agenda items as a form of "learning by doing."

FOLLOW-UP AND RESULTS

Repeat visits were made to 70 per cent of the communities where mental health education workshops had been held and former workshop participants were interviewed. A number of outcomes and results were revealed. Communities in which mental health education programs were held seemed to become more "mental health conscious." This was evidenced by civic groups conducting mental health programs, showing of mental health films at PTA meetings, etc. In many cases this was directly traceable to workshop participants who assumed leadership, for example, by suggesting mental health as a topic to the program chairman of various organizations, or by functioning as a resource person or group leader in the organization of a mental health program.

In some communities inter-professional cooperation and collaboration was stimulated and strengthened. For instance it was found that teachers worked more closely with the local public health department or public health nurse. In at least four cases disrupted lines of communication between school authorities, public health nurse, physician and welfare department were re-established. In six communities collaborative planning by the school, the welfare department, public health department and general practitioner occurred for the first time. Such collaborative planning usually centered around a child with a combination of emotional and physical problems.

Finally, use of available mental health resources and referrals by workshop participants increased demonstrably. For example visiting teachers (school, social workers) and school guidance personnel were utilized more.

Group members reported certain specific contributions of the training program to their professional functioning:

(1) Better understanding of others and more confidence in handling situations involving feelings.

(2) Recognition of the importance of early detection of symptoms and case finding as an aspect of prevention. Recognition of the importance of preventive programs.

(3) Greater awareness of the need for emotional health and the need for more clinical and psychiatric facilities.

(4) Knowledge of available mental health resources and referral procedures. Knowledge of the state mental health program.

(5) Increased self-understanding and awareness of the importance of the participants' own mental health.

(6) Increased understanding of mental illness, the mentally ill, and treatment methods.

IMPLICATIONS

In our state the mental health committee of the state medical association is actively engaged in providing leadership in mental health. Public and private schools, PTA's, church groups, and community organizations such as the Chamber of Commerce, YMCA, and other civic groups request information, education, and consultation. All physicians are called upon from time to time to provide leadership in this broadening field of mental health education. In recognition of this developing leadership within the medical profession, the state medical association and some county medical societies are planning educational programs for their own membership to provide accurate information and interpretation of developments in the field of mental health and care and treatment of the mentally ill.

Medical and psychiatric aspects of care and treatment of the mentally ill are an integral part of mental health. This cannot be a separate specialized field limited to the professional skill of physicians particularly trained in psychiatry. It is not possible for a person to maintain a recovery from mental illness in a social setting where there are both individual and group forces actively rejecting the patient and promoting mental illness. This rejection and crippling of the patient by the use of social stigma, group resentment and social isolation, is just as effective a means of retarding recovery as the withholding of vitamin B from the patient with pellagra, or the withholding of antibiotics from the patient with lobar pneumonia. We, as physicians, must acquire the knowledge and understanding to combat social stigma and individual and group prejudice in the same way we combat dietary deficiency and bacterial infection. Our approach must combine the technics of prevention with those of treatment and rehabilitation.

The technic described in this paper can provide effective means of promoting the development of informed leadership in the field of mental health. Certain observations and concepts have been presented. These might offer some suggestions and ideas which can be integrated into other programs.

REFERENCES

1. Baruch, D. *New ways of discipline.* New York: McGraw-Hill, 1949.
2. Hollister, W. G. The risk of freedom-giving group leadership. *Ment. Hyg.,* 1957, 41:240.
3. Margolin, R. J. New perspectives for teachers: An evaluation of a mental health institute. *Ment. Hyg.,* 1953, 37:394.
4. Mental Health Is . . . 1-2-3. New York: National Association for Mental Health, 1951.
5. Rankin, P. T., and Dorsey, J. M. The Detroit School Mental Health Project. *Ment. Hyg.,* 1953, 37:228.

19

Community Mental Health Education with Police

MERTON H. FRIEDMAN

THIS report describes one of the important educational activities under-taken by a typical community mental health clinic: that of providing a mental health seminar for police. Justification for the broad educative role of the community clinic has been fully elaborated upon by Bellak (1) and Caplan (2). However, the description of a specific experience with a particular care-giving agency may spotlight both the problems and rewards implicit in such educational activities.

Brookline, economically and socially, is a middle- to upper middle-class community of 50,000 people. It is part of the greater Boston area. Its police department consists of 138 regular officers and patrolmen with an auxiliary force of 50 more. The mental health association is a voluntary, non-profit citizen's organization concerned with promoting the broadest medical, social and educational aspects of mental health in the town. In 1960 the Com-monwealth of Massachusetts approved the request of the association for the establishment in Brookline of a mental health clinic with full professional staff.

The clinic is one of 30 throughout Massachusetts established through a unique cooperative effort between state and community. The state, through its department of mental health, is responsible for the professional staff, for maintaining professional standards and for approving policy. The community, through its mental health association, provides the clinic with office space, equipment and secretarial staff. The clinic staff consists of two part-time psychiatrists, two full-time psychologists and two full-time social workers. It serves all age groups, with a three-fold purpose: (1) To provide direct clinic services to all individuals living in, working in, or going to school in Brookline; (2) To provide mental health consultation to public and private schools and agencies in the community; and (3) To participate in community mental health education through the programs of the Brookline Mental Health Asso-ciation. One result of this third goal is the mental health seminar for the

Reprinted from *Mental Hygiene*, 1965, *49*, 182–186, by permission of the publisher and the author. © 1965, National Association for Mental Health. Dr. Friedman is Chief, Psychology Service, V.A. Hospital, East Orange, New Jersey. He was formerly Chief Psychologist, Brookline Mental Health Clinic, Brookline, Massachusetts.

Brookline Police Department. The one here reported was the seventh such seminar provided through the auspices of the mental health association. The association, from its inception, has sponsored such seminars for the police department. Up to the time of the present project, consultant psychiatrists or psychologists were hired on a fee basis to present the seminars. The experience reported here was the first time that a clinic staff member (a psychologist) was given responsibility for arranging and conducting the seminar as part of his regular duties.

The first step was to call the chief of police of the town, who had been closely involved in working out plans for the previous seminars. He suggested a time most suitable for the seminar, a time when he could reasonably expect to free a number of his men from duty without sacrificing police coverage. It was agreed that the seminar would meet one evening for each of five weeks from 7:30 P.M. to 9.30 P.M. The chief appointed a sergeant as liaison person between the department and the clinic. This officer selected seminar members and worked with the seminar leader on the details and mechanics of the meetings.

The relationship established at several preliminary meetings was absolutely crucial to the success of the seminar. The sergeant had been involved in arranging many of the previous mental health seminars and had a wealth of suggestions about procedures and content based on this experience.

With the information provided by the sergeant and by reports left by previous leaders, it was determined that each of the first four sessions would consist of a film briefly introduced by the seminar leader and then discussed by the group. These films would not exceed 40 minutes' duration. The final session would consist of a summary of points made in the previous meetings as well as a general question and answer period. The over-riding considerations were that the content of the seminars be applicable to police work, and that it cover as representative a spectrum of mental health problems as possible. There were no reading assignments as such, but each of the 10 seminar participants was given a copy of *A Manual for the Police Officer: How to Recognize and Handle Abnormal People* (3). Wherever possible, seminar content adhered to and elaborated upon the excellent material provided in this little book. The four films were obtained either from the library of the Massachusetts Association for Mental Health in Boston or from the National Association for Mental Health in New York.

The first seminar session was based on the film "Booked for Safe Keeping." Emphasis was on major mental illnesses, including the different types of functional and organic psychosis and the potentially violent individual. Discussion was extensive. Several of the policemen related their own experiences. They wondered if their generally direct way of dealing with severely disturbed people was really the most efficient and humane. They were particularly interested in alcoholism, but less from the point of causality than from that of handling and disposition.

Discussion material for the second session emanated from the film "Headed for Trouble." Here emphasis is on juvenile delinquency and the emotional disturbances of childhood and adolescence. This film stimulated extensive comments by the seminar participants. They argued among themselves far beyond the usual closing time about child-rearing practices and the advantages and disadvantages of physical punishment for the disobedient child. The police seemed genuinely (if only tentatively) concerned with the cause of behavior problems in children. They seemed to feel that in the final analysis firmness and action should take precedence over understanding.

The third seminar session was based on a very sensitively produced film "The Cry for Help." This emphasized the depressed and suicidal individual. The discussion of the etiology and handling of suicide was reinforced by a recent suicide in the community. The officers tended to ignore the aspects of the film that dealt with improper *versus* more realistic means of coping with the potentially suicidal individual. They wanted to know more about what makes a person want to kill either himself or others. Yet in their own comments they seemed to attach more importance to what a person does or what is done to him by others than to his feeling state. When very realistic scenes of attempted self-destruction were shown in the film, there was an undercurrent of mumbling. Several of the men looked away from the screen.

The fourth session was based on the film "Anger at Work." This illustrates the way individuals cope with such feelings as resentment and frustration which interfere with their daily living both on the job and at home. Although somewhat guarded on this point, the officers were seemingly able to recognize that people (including themselves) can let their feelings influence their relationships with others. Two of the participants hesitantly volunteered recollections of episodes in which their personal feelings at the time influenced their handling of traffic violators to an unnecessarily punitive degree. Religious and ethnic prejudices were also cautiously alluded to by the group.

The final session was devoted to a general recapitulation of what had been discussed in the previous meetings as well as to a question and answer period. In the latter the police seemed most interested in the role of parents and others in the early development of emotional disturbance. Again their major pre-occupation was with children and how one goes about keeping a youngster on the "straight and narrow." Uncertainties as to child rearing practices seemed uppermost in their minds and they expressed the wish that future seminars devote more attention to this area.

A careful analysis of this particular experience in mental health education leads to observations applicable to any community clinic's effort to work with the local police department. First, and not to be underestimated, is the fact that a regular member of the clinic staff conducted the seminar rather than an "outside" consultant on a fee basis. This staff member thus functioned as a representative of one arm of the community (its mental health clinic) in relation to another arm of the community (its police department). The police responded well to this approach. Their acceptance of the mental health worker as being "on their side" and part of a total community team effort contributed to the success of the seminar. This also served to re-emphasize to the community at large that there was an established and well-defined corps of mental health professional people in its midst to which it could turn for concrete help, as did the police.

A second point to be recognized is the hierarchical prerogatives of police department organization. The police officer respects the principle of chain of command and those who adhere to it. Thus, it is not only courtesy which dictates having all plans fully checked and approved by the chief of police before they are put into effect. Most realistically, the police department is authoritarian in nature. Policemen will give of themselves in large measure if they know that their superior officers are solidly behind a given plan. While the community clinic stands to benefit generally from any goodwill on the part of any important community figures, this seminar would have been a failure if it had received only token support from the chief.

A third point to be considered is the relationship of the clinic representative to the officer who represents the chief of police. This officer, too, can drastically affect the course and outcome of the seminar. His willingness to cooperate, to brief the seminar leader on the mores of the police department, to lend his authority to the plan on a day-to-day basis, to communicate to the patrolmen his perception of the worth of the seminar, and actually to participate in the discussions at each meeting, assures likelihood of a true group effort. In the present instance, the seminar leader profited immeasurably from the suggestions of the sergeant who served as liaison officer. Simply providing this perceptive officer the opportunity to reminisce about his experiences in previous mental health seminars led to a number of guidelines which were subsequently confirmed by the seminar leader's own observations.

These observations can be briefly summarized as follows. The policeman does not want to be talked down to. He feels that his daily experience on the beat brings him into contact with as many emotionally disturbed people as the mental health worker. He has something to teach the professional person, just as the latter has something to teach the policeman. He may not have the "book learning" and "theory," but he has had a wealth of practical experience and would like this recognized. The policeman is not interested in technical language. He likes short, direct sentences with ideas expressed simply and concisely. He is happy to hear the professional person use the language of the policeman; but the professional worker should not expect the policeman to talk like him. The policeman is a man of action, not a man of words. He is interested in *doing* and he therefore appreciates someone who emphasizes *action* and experience rather than deeply thought-out abstractions. He likes someone who can think quickly on his feet and who is not cowed by a mass of blue uniforms or by the policeman's penchant for silence when confronted by a professional person. Finally, the policeman doesn't want to feel that someone is flaunting a superior education before him. He will relate best to the professional worker who emphasizes what he and the worker have in common rather than the ways in which they differ.

SUMMARY AND CONCLUSIONS

This report of a mental health seminar for police as part of the educational services of a typical community mental health clinic emphasizes not only the mechanics of seminar formation and audio-visual content but also a number of observations which are pertinent to achieving a satisfying working relationship with an important care-giving community agency, the police department. Five conclusions may be drawn from the particular experience described:

1. The advisability of having a regular member of the clinic staff conduct the seminar, thus functioning as a representative of one community agency to another.

2. The need to recognize the authoritarian and hierarchical nature of police organization.

3. The importance of establishing a reciprocally respectful relationship, not only with the department chief but also with the police official who serves as liaison officer between police department and clinic.

4. The careful selection of seminar content to assure that it will be applicable to police work and that it will contain a representative sampling of the facts of emotional disturbance both in children and adults.

5. Recognition of the police officer as an action-oriented individual who has had a wealth of practical experience which he is willing to share, who has little interest in abstract professional language, and who will relate in a most rewarding fashion to the mental health seminar leader who stresses what he and the officer have in common rather than those ways in which they differ.

REFERENCES

1. Bellak, L. (Ed.) *Handbook of community psychiatry and community mental health.* New York: Grune & Stratton, 1964.
2. Caplan, G. *Principles of preventive psychiatry.* New York: Basic Books, 1964.
3. Matthews, R. A., and Rowland, L. W., *A manual for the police officer: How to recognize and handle abnormal people.* New York: National Association for Mental Health, 1960.

20

Prevention of Psychiatric Illnesses

PAUL V. LEMKAU

THE major successes in the prevention of disease have been in dealing with that group in which there is one outstanding and overwhelming cause for the disease (7). For the most part, these successes have been in the prevention of diseases of bacteriological or viral origin in which the essential etiological factor is an invasion of the body by an external agent. We have had much less success with illnesses that arise within the body itself, such as arthritis, cancer, diabetes, and arteriosclerosis. In these we probably deal not with a single overwhelming cause but with a series of causes that must in some way act together to produce disease.

It is true that these two general groups of illnesses cannot be entirely separated, and that more and more we begin to recognize, under the leadership particularly of Dubose (3), that even those diseases fundamentally related to the invasion from the outside depend upon the condition of the body invaded. Dubose, by means of ingenious experiments, is bringing back into focus the common folk ideas that drafts cause colds; that, in other words, overexposure predisposes the body to external invasion. The relationship between recent severe physical activity and the appearance of paralysis in poliomyelitis is another case in point. It is well recognized, particularly in tuberculosis, that psychological stresses in the family, at work, and elsewhere seem frequently to be related to the appearance of actual illness (14).

In the mental illnesses, the concept of the single important cause of disease is more difficult to apply. Indeed, one psychiatrist, Dr. Robert Felix, has made the statement—not entirely seriously—that schizophrenia acts like tuberculosis in which the bacillus is absent. He is saying that it is at least possible that schizophrenia is a reaction to complicated, difficult, stressful life situations; that for this disease it is these life situations themselves that are the cause; and that no adjunctive bacterium needs to be present to give the resulting illness a particular character.

The issues of the prevention of psychiatric illnesses are extremely complex. One reason for this complexity is that we tend to think of psychiatric illness as

Reprinted from *Journal of the American Medical Association*, 1956, *162*, 854–857, by permission of the publisher and the author. © 1956, American Medical Association. Dr. Lemkau is Professor of Mental Hygiene, The Johns Hopkins School of Hygiene and Public Health.

a unit, instead of considering the multiple and relatively independent illnesses that are included in that unit. There are some psychiatric illnesses in which the etiology is as clear as it is in the physical diseases in which an invader of external origin is of overwhelming importance. For these psychiatric illnesses, prevention is as easy to consider as it is in connection with typhoid or pneumonia. There are other illnesses, however—and these are the ones that give the greatest difficulty—in which there is no single destructive invasive cause.

Another problem that makes it difficult to think about the prevention of psychiatric illness is the extraordinary fluidity of the field. In the last thirty years, psychiatry has seen the introduction of many new types of treatment. It appears fair to say that research and theory have not entirely been able to keep up with empirical advances in the field. We have gone through a period of innovations in shock therapy using insulin, pentylenetetrazol (Metrazol), and electricity; yet in none of these has the function of the treatment in controlling psychiatric illnesses been completely explained. We have seen the introduction of brain surgery for the relief of psychiatric syndromes, but we are still without an adequate and complete explanation of the effectiveness of these operations in some cases. More recently, there has been the introduction of drugs such as lysergic acid and its derivatives and some of the hormones and hormone-like substances, which, under certain circumstances, induce psychotic behavior in human beings. In addition, the extremely rapid introduction and widespread use of the behavior-regulating drugs, chlorpromazine and the Rauwolfia derivatives, have again produced a therapeutic agent the mechanisms of whose action are not clearly understood. Certainly the relationship of these drugs to, for example, schizophrenia, is far different from the specific relationship of insulin to diabetes mellitus. Yet, it is likely that the length of time it has taken to understand carbohydrate metabolism and the effectiveness of insulin in its regulation resembles the length of the time it will take for psychiatric study and research to solve the problem of the effect of the behavior-regulating drugs on the function of the brain.

In this year of the 100th anniversary of Freud's birth, it is well to recognize also that it has been but 40 or 50 years since the introduction of his concepts of the psychogenesis of the mental illnesses, and that there have been, in that time, numerous corrections and reformulations of his ideas. It is safe to say at the present time that psychiatric research and theory have not, by any means, caught up with the numerous hypotheses he postulated. In other words, psychiatry remains without a completely sound theory of either the causation of the psychogenic mental illnesses or the effect of empirical treatment.

FINDINGS OF EPIDEMIOLOGICAL RESEARCH

There is another aspect of rapid change in the psychiatric field to be accounted for in any discussion of the prevention of psychiatric illnesses. This relates to the findings of epidemiological research. The problem appears in such overwhelming proportions that the need for its control has become perhaps the major issue in the public health programs of the future. Some of these findings are very trite; for example, that half of the hospital beds in our nation are occupied by patients with psychiatric illnesses, most of them chronic. In addition, there are the data concerning the prevalence of psychiatric illness not requiring hospitalization. The two best current studies of this field appear to indicate that psychiatric symptoms severe enough to require treatment may be present in as much as 30 per cent of the population (6, 11). Older studies about the prevalence of psychiatric complaints in the practices of physicians are so well known that their findings need not be repeated here (1).

Epidemiological studies have, however, gone beyond merely pointing with alarm to the large number of cases existing. There are studies that indicate that mental deficiency, epilepsy, cerebral palsy, and certain other illnesses are probably directly related to various obstetric complications, particularly hypertension of pregnancy, eclapsia, and bleeding in the third trimester (10). It appears clear that the prevention of these more or less static conditions that are due to inadequate development, or to direct damage to central nervous system tissue, can be prevented to a considerable degree if the problems of obstetric care can be solved.

Epidemiological studies have gone further than this and have demonstrated that there are certain groups in the population that must be the subject of particular concentration if mental illnesses are to be prevented. It is quite clear that the underprivileged group in the population—underprivileged economically and educationally, probably nutritionally, and certainly in housing opportunities—produces far more of the mental illnesses of all kinds than one would expect if these illnesses were evenly distributed in the total population (9, 12). This leads to the consideration of cultural factors that in some way reduce the threshold for the appearance of mental illnesses in these underprivileged groups.

Thus, in any approach to the problem of the prevention of the psychiatric illnesses, it must be recognized that this group of diseases includes syndromes in which there is an overwhelming cause, for example, encephalitis or brain trauma; illnesses in which there is a nutritional or metabolic disorder, for example, macrocytic anemia and, in a sense, also arteriosclerosis; and illnesses that are exclusively due to chronic reactions to debilitating life circumstances of a personal, as well as of a broader cultural, type.

OPPORTUNITIES FOR PREVENTION

With present knowledge and the rapid extension of theory and laboratory knowledge in this field, what are the present opportunities for prevention? The easiest group of illnesses to deal with is that due to a single cause arising outside the individual. There is nothing new in the concept of the prevention of paresis by the prevention or early treatment of syphilis. If the basic disease, syphilis, is controlled, paresis cannot occur. If there is no tuberculosis, there can be no tuberculoma of the brain, with a consequent behavior disorder, nor tuberculous meningitis, with residua due to destruction of the brain cortex. If there is no traumatic destruction of brain tissue, there can be no post-traumatic psychosis. For the most part, the prevention of this kind of mental illness does not lie in the hands of psychiatrists. It lies directly at the door of public health and, with a few notable exceptions, public health has handled this problem well.

INDIVIDUAL STRESS

The psychiatrist, however, is deeply concerned with the alleviation of the individual and cultural stresses on the person that lower the threshold for the appearance of illness. It must be admitted that in this area the case rests almost entirely at the present time on hypothesis. There is a growing literature on experiments in animals showing that long-continued severe stress upon the individual will cause overgrowth of certain hormone-producing glands. These data make more understandable the precise mechanisms by which the threshold of response, with disease or symptom-reactions, is lowered by long-continued stress. It cannot be said, however, that this mechanism is entirely understood at the present time and, as has been pointed out already, there are undoubtedly many such mechanisms that would have to be considered in order to understand all of the psychiatric illnesses that can be distinguished, even within this field of psychogenic illnesses.

The problem of prevention then becomes the avoidance of stress that is so great that it exceeds the capacity of the individual to deal with it and eventually lowers his ability to withstand the appearance of psychiatric illness (8). At the level of individual stress, it is believed that the best work can be done during the period of rapid structuralization of the personality that takes place in childhood. The newer experiments on the effect of isolation of infants and very young children, which indicate that inadequate stimulation of innate capacities can lead to the atrophy of these capacities, tend to point to the importance of early childhood as an area for preventive work (13). Thus, it would appear that every child, every infant, ought to have a person near to stimulate him to use all of the capacities he has available—capacities to move, capacities to learn, capacities to react emotionally, capacities to love; all these must be exercised lest they atrophy and thus become no longer available for later development. This avoidance of understimulation, both intellectually and emotionally, is not, however, confined to early infancy. It can also be shown that the elderly who are denied social intercourse and stimulation tend to lapse into psychotic disorders more often than those living in better and more stimulating social circumstances (4). In short-term experiments, it can be shown that healthy young adults, if drastically denied any outside stimulation, will quickly react with psychiatric symptoms such as hallucinations and de-lusions (5).

There appear to be many opportunities for the prevention of unnecessary stress on the individual in the parent-child relationship. The study of child development shows that certain types of behavior are normal in children but are also considered bothersome, unhealthy, and embarrassing by many in our culture. For example, many mothers are excruciatingly embarrassed when their children of three throw temper tantrums at a supermarket, and yet it can be safely predicted that 80 per cent of healthy children in most United States environments will throw temper tantrums. In such a circumstance, the acute embarrassment seems rather futile and might well be replaced with an under-standing that during the period of negativism children do have temper tantrums, and that this is a step in the development of mature emotional reactions. In our culture, particularly in middle-class culture, it is well known that a high percentage of children between the ages of two and five will show a great deal of food refusal. Yet there are many mothers and fathers who go through the tortures of the damned trying to get their children to eat food in the amounts they think are necessary during this period. When a reaction such as food refusal is common, it would appear useless to expend so much anxiety about it. Some knowledge on the parents' part not only of the fact that food refusal is all but universal in children during this period but also of the fact that there is probably reduced need for food during this period of slow growth would certainly prevent a great deal of unnecessary anxiety, irritation, and anger.

In adolescence, there is the accelerated maturation of the female as com-pared to the male, so that the 13-year-old or 14-year-old female seeks her companionship from 16-year-old or 17-year-old males. Many parents worry because they fear their daughters are going to be exploited sexually by these "older men," whereas the girl is actually seeking companionship with people of her own developmental rather than her chronological age. Many junior high schools and high schools are deeply concerned by this problem, which includes such questions as, for example, who shall be invited to school dances, since the taller girls will not dance with the shorter boys of their own age. Such problems interfere with a mutually appreciative relationship between parent and child and generally represent useless anxiety based on ignorance of child development, anxiety that knowledge can relieve. To be sure, knowledge itself is frequently ineffective; it must be transmitted in a setting that allows attitudes to mature and change at the same time that the knowledge is being given.

CULTURAL STRESS

In our culture many adults face common problems that are also more than necessarily stressful in the absence of knowledge. For example, most women face childbirth with great stress. Yet it is well recognized that the stress of childbirth is much less if the process is understood and prepared for than if the experience comes with no understanding. Although it cannot thus far be statistically demonstrated, it is believed that proper preparation for marriage tends to reduce postmarital adjustment problems. It has been shown that relatively brief and unsophisticated discussion of such problems as fear, reaction to authority, and homesickness can reduce the incidence of psychiatric illnesses and behavior disorders in inductees entering military service. It has not yet been demonstrated but it is widely believed that preparation for retirement, and anticipation and preparation for the use of leisure time coming after retirement, might well prevent the excessive rates of suicides in older men and, perhaps, also the appearance of senile psychosis in people whose retirement has left them with a vacuum in their lives (8).

The psychiatrist is in a difficult position when he addresses himself to the findings of epidemiology that indicate the high concentration of illnesses in the underprivileged social classes. Here one rapidly approaches the problems of welfare, housing, and public recreation, which are so heavily loaded politically that the physician hesitates to take a stand. The full implications of the World Health Organization definition of health have not yet been worked out. This statement defines health not only as the absence of disease but as physical, mental, and social well-being. In general, medicine is not yet prepared, theoretically or empirically, to deal with these broad, economically tinged problems of social health, nor can one foresee what developments will come as this far-seeing definition begins to affect medical practices more and more. There are certainly germs of ideas for the prevention of psychiatric illnesses coming from these studies. It remains extremely difficult as we presently see "through a glass, darkly" the means of bringing these germs into flowering programs for the prevention of illness.

There is, however, one cultural fact that must indeed give pause. This is the recurring finding that half of the medical and welfare services available to all the community are expended upon a relatively small segment of the population, the now famous "6 per cent" (2). The whole concept of the clustering of diseases of all kinds—psychiatric, physical, and social—in a relatively small group of the population must be considered, for, if some rehabilitation program could be made to succeed for this 6 per cent of the population, we could, in all likelihood, prevent 50 per cent of our social, psychiatric, and physical illnesses. The methods of doing this have not yet been formulated, but they represent one of the most inviting areas for research.

SUMMARY

In considering the prevention of psychiatric illnesses, it must constantly be kept in mind that we are not dealing with a single scheme of prevention but rather with a multitude of illnesses, many of which have specific preventions applicable to them alone. I refer primarily to the mental illnesses secondary to the destruction of central nervous system tissue. On the other hand, there is a large group of psychiatric illnesses that appear to be related to chronic, severe stresses—individual stresses or cultural stresses. It may be possible to reduce individual stresses through education and changing attitudes, particularly in the area of child-parent relationships. There is an approach, not yet fully understood, for the prevention of psychiatric illnesses through the relief of broad cultural stresses playing upon large groups of individuals.

Presently, we are able to work quite exactly in the prevention of brain damage. The relationship between cause and effect is clear and predictable. In the area of the prevention of excessive stress upon the individual, the data are much less exact and the multiple factors have as yet defied final and clear-cut predictability from hypothesized cause to realized illness. It is these two areas, however, where most effective work with present knowledge can be done. We must address ourselves to the future for methods that can be effective in dealing with the third area, the relief of stress playing upon particular groups within the culture—the stresses themselves having their origin, to some extent at least, within the practices of the culture.

REFERENCES

1. Bremer, J. Social psychiatric investigation of small community in northern Norway. *Acta psychiat. et neurol.*, 1951, supp. 62, pp. 1–161.
2. Buell, B., et al. *Community planning for human services.* New York: Columbia University Press, 1952.
3. Dubose, R. J. Unsolved problems in study and control of microbial disease, *J. A. M. A.* 1955, 157:1477–79.
4. Gruenberg, E. M. Epidemiology of mental disease. *Scient. Am.,* 1954, 190:38–42.
5. Hebb, D. O. Significance of neurophysiologic theory for psychiatry. Read before the Annual Meeting of the American Psychiatric Association, St. Louis, May 6, 1954.
6. Leighton, D. Distribution of psychiatric symptoms in small town, *Am. J. Psychiat.,* 1956, 112:716–23.
7. Lemkau, P. V. Epidemiological study of mental illnesses and mental health. *Am. J. Psychiat.,* 1955, 111:801–9.
8. Lemkau, P. V. *Mental hygiene in public health.* 2d ed. New York: McGraw-Hill, 1955.
9. Lemkau, P. V., Tietze, C., and Cooper M. Mental hygiene problems in urban district: I. Description of study, *Ment. Hyg.* 1941, 25:624–26: II. Psychotics: Neurotics, *ibid.* 1942, 26:100–119; III. Epileptics and mental deficients, *ibid.* 1942, 26:275–88; IV. Mental hygiene problems in children seven to sixteen years of age, *ibid.* 1943, 27:279–95.

10. Lilienfeld, A. M., and Pasamanick, B. Association of maternal and fetal factors with development of epilepsy, *J. A. M. A.* 1954, 155:719–24.
11. Rennie, T. A. C. Studies in urban mental health. Read before the Annual Meeting of the American Psychiatric Association, Atlantic City, N. J., May 10, 1955.
12. Rennie, T. A. C., Srole, L., Opler, M. D., and Langer, T. S. Urban life and mental health. Read before American Psychiatric Association, Chicago, May 3, 1956.
13. Soddy, K. *Mental health and infant development.* New York: Basic Books, 1956.
14. Wittkower, E. *Psychiatrist looks at tuberculosis.* London: National Association for the Prevention of Tuberculosis, 1949.

21

Primary Prevention of Mental and Emotional Disorders: A Conceptual Framework and Action Possibilities

ELI M. BOWER

MAGIC and science have had a curious and interesting alliance in the history of human societies. One specific kind of science-magic which man has developed over the years is that of word power. It is illustrated by fairy or folk tales in which discovering or using an appropriate word enables the hero or heroine to gain power over a natural, supernatural or human enemy. *Ali Baba and the Forty Thieves* and *The Story of Rumpelstiltskin,* for example, utilize such magic words to move mountains and solve a complex personal problem. Folklore and myths also exemplify the solution of a problem by abstention from or disuse of an appropriate word or name. In Grimm's *The Wild Swans,* the sister's power to help her seven brothers is gained by her ability not to utter a single word. Odysseus in his adventure with the Cyclops gains power over the giant Polyphemus by telling him his name is "Noman." When Polyphemus is attacked by Odysseus he cries out, "Noman is killing me by craft and not by main force." His brother Cyclops, somewhat dismayed, answers, "Well, if no man is using force and you are alone, there's no help for a bit of sickness when heaven sends it." Odysseus continues, "With these words away they went and my heart laughed within me to think how a mere nobody had taken them all in with my machinomanations (18, p. 108)."

In the twentieth century our "open sesame" to the solution of problems has been the word "prevention," which has found some of its magical fruition in many of man's relationships to viruses, bacteria and protozoans. The "magic bullet" and the newer "miracle drugs" are still part of the "abracadabra" of man's relationship to microbes. Dubos observes,

> The common use of the word "miracle" in referring to the effect of a new drug reveals that men still find it easier to believe in mysterious forces than to trust to rational processes. . . . Men want miracles as much today as in the past (9, p. 132).

Smallpox, however, *is* prevented by a nick on the arm and polio by several shots. The magic of prevention as a word, idea or myth remains a twentieth-

Reprinted from *American Journal of Orthopsychiatry,* 1963, *32,* 832–848, by permission of the publisher and the author. © 1963, American Orthopsychiatric Association. Dr. Bower is a Consultant, National Institute of Mental Health.

231

century Rumpelstiltskin in all branches of man's activities, except one. Little in the way of magic words, incantations or mystical emanations exist for the prevention of the emotional and behavioral disorders of man. Indeed, one would be hard-pressed to divine the kinds of conjurations and "answers oracular" a contemporary John Wellington Wells might dream up to get the job done.

Thus it appears that the lack of creativity and action in the prevention of mental and behavioral disorders originates in forces too powerful for either magic or science. We do not need a Sherlock Holmes or an Arsène Lupin to perceive that there may be more to this conceptual and research abyss in prevention than a lack of imagination and interest. Indeed, one could make a good case for the existence of explicit and implicit cultural resistances to the prevention of emotional and behavioral disorders. Perhaps a necessary first step, then, in any preventive program is to examine the antagonism realistically, and plan strategies of action that take into account the probabilities of success in light of an understanding of the opposition (8).

COMMUNITY ANTAGONISMS TOWARD PREVENTION

A common conception of prevention often obfuscates thinking and action, namely, that little can be accomplished short of major social overhaul. Prevention of mental and emotional disorders is seen as the exclusive result of the abolition of injustice, discrimination, economic insecurity, poverty, slums and illness. To seek less is to attempt to fell a giant sequoia with a toy axe. Any effort, therefore, that is not aimed directly at major social change is viewed as an inadequate and inconsequential attack at the problem. A corollary of this notion is that prevention involves wheels within wheels within wheels. Thus, any possible action is perceived as if it were a combined luncheon check presented by an inexperienced waiter to a group of women at the end of an *a la carte* meal. The alleged magnitude of the complexities and the ungeared wheels within wheels perceived are also major deterrents to biological and social scientists who can, with little effort, find more digestible problems to define and solve. Other scientists who see some value in pursuing this kind of "elusive Scarlet Pimpernel" search in vain for something akin to Archimedes' lever with which the whole of the problem can be moved. Many believe one should concentrate on immediate needs such as the care, treatment and rehabilitation of mental patients. Such problems are real and specific. If one means to do anything in this field, "they" say, let's start with this problem. Small beginnings, however, need to be made on many fronts. Farnsworth, for example, notes, "Both the treatment of mental illness and the promotion of mental health are necessary in any well-conceived community program designed to reduce crippling emotional conflict. To throw up our hands and stop promoting mental health programs because we cannot define mental health or can portray results only inexactly is to show both lack of common sense and lack of courage (11)." There is a *need* and there is a *problem*. The need to care and treat the ill is our major concern, yet it is fairly obvious that all the king's horses and all the king's men will have little effect on the problem—how to reduce or curtail the development of the illness in the first place.

A second and related phenomenon that influences preventive efforts in the mental health field is the high, often impregnable, fortress of personal privacy —the right and privilege of each person, and family, in a free society to mind his own business and have others mind theirs. If prevention of any kind includes early effective intervention in the lives of persons in the population at large, then the intervention must take place prior to such time as the person is singled out for special help. Where it can be shown that such intervention is necessary, indeed, mandatory for the common good, as it is in automobile use, school attendance and physical hygiene and sanitation, acceptance may be given. Yet, in polio inoculations and water fluoridation, invasion of personal privacy is still a major issue in families or communities that decide to accept or reject these preventive programs.

"At present," Bellak writes,

> the governing of men and the raising of children seem to be among the very few occupations in civilized society for which no training or certified ability are required—and for fairly sound reasons. Imposition of laws on either activity could constitute a serious invasion of personal freedom (1, p. viii).

Laws providing sanctions for intervention by an agency or person in the private life of an individual are, therefore, clearly and with sound reason limited to situations that endanger the life or health of the person or his neighbors. In essence, one can only stop minding one's own business and become one's brother's keeper when "brother" is in pretty sad shape. Nevertheless, few persons would be prepared to sacrifice the values of a free society on any nebulous, preventive altar.

Yet, some primary institutions are actually mobilized and authorized to help the family in a positive and potentially preventive manner. For example, the well-baby clinic and the public school are given informal and official sanction to interfere and meddle—the former, in relation to the child's health, the latter, in terms of the child's educational progress or lack of it. However, these institutions must also be alert to the dangers inherent in such sanctions. The school must find its leverage in its assigned task of educating children and carefully define and demonstrate the role of auxiliary services such as health examinations, psychological testing and mental health consultation as necessary in carrying out this assignment. The health and educational progress of children represent to most parents important and highly significant achievements; almost always, there is a strong motivation to do whatever is necessary to work with the school or well-baby clinic in enhancing their child's health or educational success.

Another major social resistance to prevention, pointed out by Ruth Eissler, lies in the realm of the reduction of criminal and antisocial behavior:

. . . modern society, with all its dazzling technological progress has not been able to protect itself from individual or mass aggression against property or life. Must we assume that this helplessness is accidental and has no psychological basis? If we take the standpoint that society needs its criminals in the same way as the mother of my delinquent patient needed his delinquency, then we understand the existence of two general tendencies. The first is the seduction of individuals into criminal acting-out. The second is the interference with or the prevention of anything which promises to prevent delinquency (10, p. 228).

One explanation advanced for this phenomenon is related to cultural values in which success lies with virtue and failure with sin. In a free society each person has equal opportunity with his fellows to show his mettle as a conscientious, hard-working and, therefore, successful citizen. If he chooses not to be conscientious and hard-working, he has only himself to blame for the consequences. Such competition in games, school work, business and life can only be perceived as successful for all when it is unsuccessful for some. As Don Alhambra sings it in *The Gondoliers,* "In short, whoever you may be/To this conclusion you'll agree/When everyone is somebodee/Then no one's anybodee."

To a great extent, the ritual of the TV-Western, in which good wins over evil fair and square, celebrates this notion at least once or twice each evening. On the other hand, increasing clinical and research evidence supports the notion that those individuals who find positive satisfactions and relationships in family, neighborhood and school also find these satisfactions and relationships as adults; and that those who find frustration, failure and defeat in these primary institutions also tend to be defeated in adulthood. This unconscious sponsorship and enhancement of defeat and alienation in and among groups of children and adolescents is often spelled out in terms of pseudo-Darwinian theory (17). Yet the idea of equalitarianism is in our historical bones. How have we come to place equality for all and excellence for all as one-dimensional opposites? Gardner states the question more succinctly: "How can we provide opportunities and rewards for individuals of every degree of ability so that individuals at every level will realize their full potentialities, perform at their best and harbor no resentment toward any other level? (14, p. 115)."

WHO BELLS THE CAT?

As a specific activity, prevention still has the major problem of interesting and involving members of the professions dealing with mental illness, most of whom are involved in individual relationships with patients. Clinicians trained in treatment, rehabilitation and adjunctive therapies in a one-to-one relationship naturally find this more rewarding than they find plunging into the misty arena of prevention. The physician is responsible for the health of his patient, particularly when such health is threatened. As Fox points out,

Curative medicine has generally had precedence over preventive medicine: people come to the doctor to be healed, and most practicing physicians still think of prevention as subsidiary to their main task—which is, to treat the sick. Though they subscribe, intellectually, to prevention, they really feel more at home when the disease has "got going" (12, p. 16).

Often, the mental health worker, be he psychiatric technician, nurse, psychologist, social worker or psychiatrist, is deeply impressed by the mountainous obstacles to effecting positive, healthful changes in mental patients and, consequently, finds it difficult to comprehend how other less intensive types of experiences might have prevented the illness.

Yet, one is often surprised by the range, variety and quality of human experiences and human relationships that can and do produce significant changes in personality. Sanford's experience and research lead him to conclude that marked and profound changes do occur in students during the college years.

"Some students," he writes,

> undergo in the normal course of events changes of the same order as those brought about by psychotherapy. Not only may there be expansion and reorganization in the ego, with increased sophistication, broader perspective, increased flexibility of control but, also, there may be changes in the relations among the ego, the id, and the super-ego. The question is, what makes these changes occur and what can be done deliberately to bring them about. There is a common notion that changes so profound as to involve the relations of id, superego, and ego can be brought about after adolescence only by means as thoroughgoing as psychoanalysis or deep psychotherapy. I'm suggesting that changes of a pretty fundamental kind can be brought about by regular educational procedures or by events occurring in the normal course of events, provided we know enough about what makes changes occur (30, p. 8).

In bringing prevention into the ken of the psychiatrist, clinical psychologist, or social worker, one may need to recognize and deal with the minimization or depreciation of change processes other than a depth peeling of defenses. Stevenson, in his study of direct instigation of behavioral changes in psychotherapy, finds that some patients often improve markedly when they have mastered a stressful situation or relationship and that by helping such patients manage a day-to-day problem, change is brought about (31). In the early relationships of the mental health professions and the parents of retarded children, it was often assumed that being a parent of a retarded child necessitated intensive psychological help or mental health counseling. Yet, many such parents were more puzzled and distressed by a lack of information and skill in basic home management of the child, and were often best helped by simple instruction in how to help retarded children learn to feed and dress themselves.

It is possible, as Sanford suggests, that our overemphasis on individual therapy as a major community resource retards to some degree our interest in or our giving priority to prevention. The fact is, primary prevention is the concern of all the mental health professions, but the responsibility of no one group. Much preventive gold can be mined from clinicians and therapists by encouraging them to translate their clinical experiences and knowledge into programs with preventive possibilities. Such translations, however, must be within a framework of what is operationally feasible within one of the "key integrative systems" of our society. Gardner Murphy may well be right:

> The ultimate keys to the understanding of mental health will come, not through exclusive preoccupation with the pathological, but with the broader understanding of the nature of life and of growth. Perhaps the understanding of resonant health and joyful adaptation to life will help us to understand and formulate the issues regarding the prevention of mental disorder (24, p. 146).

PREVENTION OF WHAT?

Lastly, there is the knotty problem of defining the goals of prevention. Do such goals include the development of individuals who can more easily be helped by community resources; a reduction in hospitalized schizophrenics; or making persons more amenable to psychotherapy? If our purpose is the promotion of emotional robustness, what exactly does this mean and how can this goal be translated into specific, positive and, hopefully, measurable objectives of health? Dubos notes,

> Solving problems of disease is not the same thing as creating health. . . . This task demands a kind of wisdom and vision which transcends specialized knowledge of remedies and treatments and which apprehends in all their complexities and subtleties the relation between living things and their total environment (9, p. 22).

The lack of specificity as to what constitutes mental illness, plus the changing character of such illnesses, make this baseline difficult to define or use in evaluating programs. Yet, where living is equated with and therefore measured by degrees of illness rather than health, one can easily perceive the world as a giant hospital peopled by patients whose only health lies in discovering how sick they are. Nevertheless, reliable measures or indexes of health or illness of a community are the *sine qua non* of any preventive program.

A FRAMEWORK FOR PRIMARY PREVENTION

No single problem in primary prevention has a solution deserving of greater priority than the development of a platform or position from which one can begin to organize and act. One cannot exert leverage on any field of forces except from some fixed position. Without such a theoretical framework little can be done in developing hypotheses, testing them and further developing or, if need be, abandoning them.

Primary prevention of mental and emotional disorders is any specific biological, social or psychological intervention that promotes or enhances the mental and emotional robustness or reduces the incidence and prevalence of mental or emotional illnesses in the population at large. In this framework, primary preventive programs are aimed at persons not yet separated from the general population and, hopefully, at interventions specific enough to be operationally defined and measured.

Measured how—along what dimensions and by what value system? To be sure, some types of primary prevention can be specified in relation to specific diseases or impairments. In such illnesses as phenylketonuria or pellagra psychosis, an appropriate diet initiated at an appropriate time may prevent some of the serious complications of the illness. Other types of mental illness, however, may come about as the cumulative effect of a myriad of interacting social and biological causes and be relatively uninfluenced by any single intervention. Yet, if one assumes that emotional robustness is built on the interactive elements of a healthy organism with enhancing life experiences, one must consider how one could increase those social forces in a community that help the population at large to cope with normal problems, rather than to defend against them, to deal with stress effectively, and to be less vulnerable to illness, including the mental illnesses.

There is, of course, a basic assumption about human behavior and mental health in these propositions, namely, that those social, psychological and biological forces which tend to enhance the full development of the human characteristics of man are desirable and preventive of mental illness; those factors which tend to limit or block such development have greater illness-producing potential and are, therefore, undesirable. By human characteristics, the full development of which are sought, I mean the ability to love and to work productively (Freud's *Lieben und Arbeiten*). In this framework one might support those social and biological forces that tend to make man an effectively functioning organism with maximum ability to adapt to his own potential as well as to the potential of his environment. One can, therefore, hypothesize that forces which increase or enhance the degrees of freedom of man's individual and social behavior are mentally healthful, whereas, those which reduce such freedom are unhealthful.

What, specifically, is meant by degrees of behavioral freedom? Behavioral freedom may be regarded as the ability of the organism to develop and maintain a resiliency and flexibility in response to a changing environment and a changing self; operationally, such freedom may be defined as the number of behavioral alternatives available in a personality under normal conditions. Such behavioral freedom is not unlike that of a sailboat that can take full advantage of changing winds and currents by changing sails and direction, but is bound by the nature of the craft and the strength and direction of the forces driving it.

We say of a boat skimming the water with light foot, "How free she runs," when we mean how perfectly she obeys the great breath out of the heavens that fills her sails. Throw her head up into the wind and see how she will halt and stagger, how every sheet will shiver and her whole frame will be shaken, how instantly she is "in irons" in the expressive phrase of the sea. She is free only when you have let her fall off again and she has recovered once more her nice adjustment to the forces she must obey and cannot defy (33, p. 43).

In thinking of preventive action as increasing or enhancing man's behavioral degrees of freedom, one must refer to Kubie's restless pursuit of this notion in differentiating normal behavior from neurotic behavior. His contention is that socially positive behavior can be the consequence of either healthy or neurotic processes, but that there is a basic difference in organismic elasticity or homeostasis between the normal and neurotic. This elasticity manifests itself in the individual's freedom and flexibility to learn through experience, to change and to adapt to changing external circumstances.

Thus, the essence of normality is flexibility, in contrast to the freezing of behavior into patterns of unalterability . . . that characterize every manifestation of the neurotic process whether in impulses, purposes, acts, thoughts, or feelings. No single psychological act can be looked upon as neurotic unless it is the product of processes that predetermine a tendency to its automatic repetition (21, p. 183).

In brief, the neurotic is like the magic broom in "The Sorcerer's Apprentice"; he cannot change or curtail actions and becomes overwhelmed by the consequences of repetitive behavior. In its beginnings repetitive behavior represents an economic and ecological solution to a problem or conflict faced by the organism. Because the essence of the solution is only dimly perceived by the individual, the pursuit becomes more and more relentless and recurring. Since such goals are basically symbolic and highly masked to the individual, the chances of crossing the goal line and moving on to new patterns of behavior are slim.

Considerable clinical evidence supports the view that fixed or rigid patterns of behavior are derived from the unconscious components of personality. Despite the possibility that behavior primarily motivated by unconscious forces may be useful and valuable in maintaining the health and personality integration of the individual, such behavior is relatively unresponsive to changing environmental conditions. On the other hand, behavior resulting from forces at a level of relative awareness is most often directed at goals that are reasonably attainable and, subsequently, reduces the need to continue the same pattern of behavior. The degrees of freedom or the number of behavioral alternatives available to an individual are therefore enhanced to the extent to which his behavior is the result of preconscious or conscious forces in the personality.

One might well question the assumption, as does Redlich (28), that acts determined by conscious or preconscious forces move the individual in a more healthful direction than acts determined by unconscious forces. For example, are not unconscious defense mechanisms health-producing and health-oriented in their adaptive and ego-protective goals? To the extent to which the organism needs ego defenses to maintain himself and mediate noxious forces in his environment, such defenses are health-producing. Yet, the increased use of such unconscious defenses will, in the long run, render the organism less and less able to choose alternative modes of behaving and weave into the personality an inflexible and repetitive behavior pattern (22). It is also true, however, that repetitive, inflexible types of behavior can produce benefits in some relationships, particularly in specific vocations or jobs. Neurotic processes in individuals can and do result in *culturally defined* successful behavior, just as one can be a blatant failure without benefit of personality defect or neurosis.

The concept of degrees of behavioral freedom as differentiating between health and illness is utilized by Murphy (25) and Bruner (6) in their discussions of the differences between coping and defending. *In coping with problems,* one enhances and expands the resiliency and resources of the organism; *in defending against problems,* developmental blocks and distortions develop, reducing the resiliency and resources of the organism and depriving it of the freedom to act in new ways. Coping can be conceived of as integrative to personality, defending as disintegrative. Bruner points out that there is always a mixture of coping and defending in dealing with problems, but it is highly important that one distinguish sharply between the two processes, which can best be made in terms of learning effectiveness. "Let me suggest," he writes,

> that effective cognitive learning in school—in contrast to the gratification-demanding, action-related, and affect-infused earlier learning—depends upon a denaturing process, if I may use such a fanciful expression. This involves at least three things. It requires, first, the development of a system of cognitive organization that detaches concepts from the modes of action that they evoke. A hole exists without the act of digging. Secondly, it requires the development of a capacity to detach concepts from these affective contexts. A father exists without reference to the thinker's feeling of ambivalence. It demands, moreover, a capacity to delay gratification so that, figuratively, each act of acquiring knowledge is not self-sufficiently brought to an end either by success or failure, and whatever happens can be taken as informative and not as simply frustrating or gratifying (6, p. 8).

In a defensive, neurotic pattern of behavior, inflexibility or illness would reduce the effectiveness of the organism's functioning, especially as a constructive social being. Thus, one index of the health of a community or a society could be the ways people choose to spend their time, especially their uncommitted time. Meier (23) sees the possibility of compiling an index representing the variety of life in a society—specifically, ways in which people *choose* to spend their time. He proposes that an increase in variety almost always reflects an enhancement in social integration and that human hours have allocation properties which are not dissimilar from those applied to land. Time like land can only be consumed or wasted. There are only trivial exceptions to this rule. Yet, intuitively, we have the general impression that time can be conserved. Like money income, it can be invested. Schooling and the acquisition of skills are examples of such investments of human hours. The return on the investment is not more time but an increase in the range of choice in gainful employment and in social activities. Thus, we arrive at a significant index for social progress—variety in the pattern of life (23, p. 29).

One could, therefore, conceive of *degrees of behavioral freedom* in terms of operational social indexes that would reflect changes in variety and patterns of life and could be used as a method of evaluating preventive programs. For example, one might examine the allocation of time of persons with personality disturbances or a mentally ill group in a hospital as compared to various other persons and communities.

A FRAMEWORK FOR PREVENTION

The zonal classifications of people and services in Fig. 1 presents a framework and a functioning methodology for prevention. Primary prevention can be considered medical, social or psychological action within Zones I and II, which reduces the need for the services and institutions of Zones III or IV. The goals of such action, with respect to the institutions and services of Zone I and Zone II, are threefold:

1. To increase the biological robustness of human beings by strengthening those institutions and agencies directly involved in prenatal, pregnancy and early infant care.

2. To increase the flexibility of the agencies serving persons of Zones I and II, so that such agencies may encompass and affect a greater variety and number of persons in the general population. For example, the extension of school services for retarded or emotionally disturbed children may make it possible for a child usually needing Zone III or IV services to remain in Zone II. The utilization of prenatal medical or nursing advisory services for lower-class pregnant mothers may be significantly influenced by placing such services close to neighborhood shopping or laundry centers. Or the presence of a counseling center for workers may make the difference for a number of individuals in maintaining employment and family economic support.

3. To assist primary institutions in planning individual and social techniques by which stress immunity or manageability can become a natural outcome of their relationship to children and their families.

It is evident that, in this scheme of primary prevention, the preventive forces will be those affecting the operation, accessibility, adaptability and modifiability of the institutions and agencies found in Zones I and II. Partic-

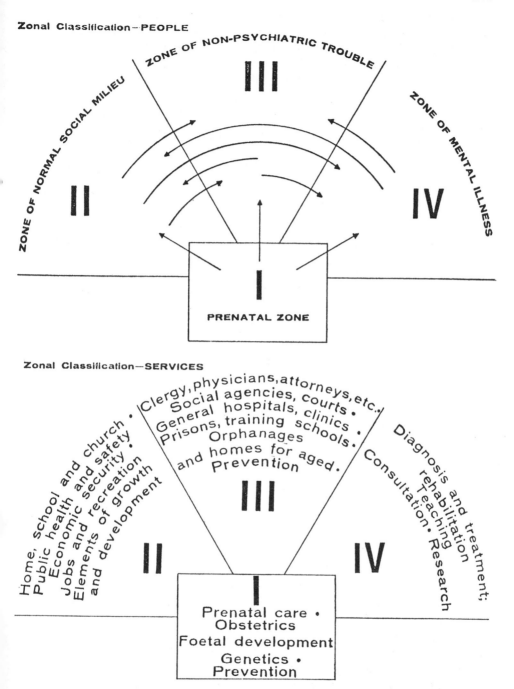

Fig. 1.—Zonal Classifications of People and Services. These are indicative, rather than inclusive. (From Daniel Blain, M.D. Copyright, The American Psychiatric Association. Reproduced by permission.)

ularly, one needs to determine: (a) which specific social and community forces tend to push Zone II persons into requiring Zone III or IV services; (b) how present medical, genetic and biological information can be translated into social action so as to reduce the number of Zone I infants entering Zones III or IV; and (c) how Zones I and II agencies and institutions can be reinforced, modified or developed to lessen the need for Zones III and IV services.

The institutions and agencies in Zones I and II can be denoted as the front-line defenses of a community. If such institutions and agencies cannot adequately serve individuals in their field, Zones III or IV services are required. Some of the forces moving people into Zones III or IV are the number and character of the emotionally hazardous situations and crises the individual has been required to mediate and manage, and how mediation and management were accomplished. The key, therefore, to movement from one zone to another lies in the quality of the mediation (coping or defending) of the emotionally hazardous situation or crisis. Klein and Lindemann (20) define an emotionally hazardous situation as any sudden alteration in the field of social forces affecting an individual so that the individual's perception and expectation of self and others undergo change. In each instance an emotionally hazardous situation or crisis is a normal life occurrence that is temporarily upsetting, not always in an unpleasant sense, but one that necessitates rapid reorganization and mobilization of an individual's personality resources. Such life situations as birth of a sibling, death of a loved one, school entrance, school failure, marriage, job promotion, divorce or inheritance of a large sum of money from a dead uncle's estate are examples of emotionally hazardous situations. The hazard in these situations is that the individual may find himself unable to manage the increased stress in a healthful way. Yet, such hazards and hurdles are part of the normal process of living and are, in large part, the cutting edges that sharpen and crystallize personality development and integration.

Whether for good or bad, emotionally hazardous crises have these aspects in common: (a) They cause a rise in inner tension and uneasiness; (b) they cause some disorganization in normal functioning; and (c) they necessitate some internal change in self to manage the situation. In baseball parlance, an individual in an emotionally hazardous situation is said to "stand loose at the plate," that is, the individual is lightly balanced to be able to move quickly in any direction. During this period of relative instability, minimal forces have their greatest effects, much like the effect of a one-gram weight at one end of a delicately balanced teeter-totter. Such a gram of weight would have little effect if the forces governing the organism were relatively stable.

The implications of the emotionally vulnerable situation or crisis as a fulcrum for preventive action is clear. To the extent to which such situations can be identified and the "crisis" institution or agency prepared and strengthened to make the most of this opportunity, to that extent can it place grams of force on the side of health and personality growth. In primary prevention one is focused on the emotionally hazardous situation that occurs in the context of the operation of each of the services or agencies in Zones I or II. Such institutions and agencies are often aware of some crises and do a great deal to help individuals deal effectively with them. Sometimes, however, the agency or service may fail to recognize relevant crises, or fail to take advantage of the health-producing potential of the situation. For example, the school may well be aware of the effect of the birth of a child on his siblings but, as an institution, it is seldom in a position to obtain and use this information systematically. Such an important and natural event in the lives of children may be sufficiently upsetting to the sibling to warrant some attention by the school. To capitalize on this emotionally hazardous situation, teachers may need to plan opportunities for the sibling to be recognized, to be helpful, to be successful—in short, to help the child, within the structure and role of the institution, to manage and mediate the crisis. In some cases, the child may need no more than an extra pat on the back from the teacher. In others, a planned conference with parents may be of some help. What is critical is the recognition by the institution of the emotionally vulnerable position of the child and a readiness to act positively upon it.

Table 1 lists some services and institutions of Zones I and II, along with some emotionally hazardous and enhancing situations or crises that occur in relation to each institution, with some possibilities for preventive action in each case. Neither the services, hazards, nor action possibilities listed are intended to be comprehensive or exhaustive. However, this conceptualization may help provide a fulcrum for the development of pilot and experimental studies and other preventive programs that can be delineated and evaluated. For example, the first emotional hazard under "family" is that of loss of father through death, divorce or desertion. With few exceptions, the burden for breadwinning is thrust upon the mother who, in turn, finds it necessary to depend upon child-caring services for her children. In part, such services are provided by relatives, friends, nursery schools, foster homes and child-care centers. In California, child-care centers were initiated during World War II to increase the labor force, and have since continued in operation to serve one-parent families of modest incomes and some families of teachers and nurses. Such a child-care facility usually serves preschool children all day and cares for school children part of the day.

There is sufficient evidence to support the hypothesis that one-parent families are more vulnerable to stress and emotional hazards than are intact families. The child-care facility, properly staffed and oriented, would then be a potentially preventive force in developing and maintaining some type of assistance and support for the mothers and children utilizing this service. Such assistance could be provided by a psychiatric social worker or another professional person hired to work with the child-care staff or families. In theory, the child-care center as a primary institution would be reinforced as a preventive agency by enlisting trained personnel to work with parents or child-care staff on the normal problems of people who are bringing up children but who are obliged to work at the same time.

Or, let us take the emotional hazard of pregnancy and birth. One of the

TABLE 1

Zone II service	*Normal emotional hazard*	*Possibilities for preventive action*
1. Family	Loss of father through death, divorce or desertion	Reinforcement of child-care services for working mothers
	Loss of mother	Reinforcement of foster-home services
	Adolescence	Increase in staff and professionalization of high school counselors, deans, and vice-principals
	Birth of sibling	Pediatric or well-baby clinic counseling
	Death	Management of grief—religious or community agency worker
2. Public health	Phenylketonuria	Detection and diet
	Childhood illnesses	Vaccination, immunization
	Stress caused by children —economic, housing, etc.	Reinforcement of well-baby clinic through mental health consultation to staff
	Pregnancy	Adequate prenatal care for mothers of lower socioeconomic status
3. School	Birth of sibling	Recognition of event by school and appropriate intervention
	School entrance of child	Screening vulnerable children
	Intellectual retardation	Special classes and assistance
	Teacher concern and anxiety about a child's behavior	Consultation by mental health specialists
	School failure	Early identification and prevention through appropriate school program
4. Religion	Marriage	Counseling by clergy
5. Job or profession	Promotion or demotion	Opportunity to define role through services of a mental health counselor
6. Recreation	Appropriate and rewarding use of leisure time	Active community and city recreational programs
7. Housing	Lack of space—need for privacy	Working with architects and housing developers

points made by Wortis (34), Pasamanick (19, 27), Freedman (13) and others is that adequate prenatal and natal care is a significant and far-reaching measure in the prevention of neuropsychiatric disorders in children. In most cases, such care is available. Yet, significant numbers of mothers in lower socioeconomic neighborhoods are not normally motivated to seek medical care during pregnancy. Ordinarily they will use medical assistance only as a last resort. Many such mothers would take advantage of preventive medical services if such services were present somewhere along the paths they normally travel, or if they could be motivated to detour a few blocks for them. For example, space in empty stores near laundromats or markets could be rented for health department personnel and manned by nurses who could spend time with a mother while she was shopping or waiting for her load of wash. Such a program could be evaluated by comparing rates of premature births, birth injuries or other birth difficulties before and after the service, or with rates in neighborhoods where no such service exists.

FULCRA FOR PREVENTION

It is increasingly evident that there are three basic interrelated ingredients in primary prevention: (1) a healthful birth experience, (2) a healthful family experience, and (3) a successful school experience. Healthful birth experiences are largely the result of early medical care and advice that help prospective mothers obtain and use preventive medical care. Although the evidence is far from complete, Bowlby (4), Brody (5), and Ribble (29), to name only three, have emphasized the primacy of family relationships and their effect on the mental health of children. Bowlby summarized numerous studies from various countries that illustrated the emotional impact on children of early separation from their parents. Ribble and Brody studied the pivotal relationship of mothering and personality development, and Caplan (7) pointed out how a neighborhood health center can be a preventive force in enhancing and strengthening family resources for the child. Goodrich (16), at the Bio-Social Growth Center of the National Institute of Mental Health, studied the emotional hazard of early separation of the child from the mother in a nursery school setting. He found this crisis a potentially manageable staging area for research in primary prevention and suggested some areas of developmental influences that effect how a child or family manages a crisis. Early separation anxieties in a child often mean the possibility of greater problems later on with school entrance or bereavement.

The school has become increasingly primary to a child's personality growth. Consequently it can be the prime mover for alerting parents whose children need additional help or support within the school or, in some cases, additional services outside the school. In essence, the role of the school as a preventive force is realized to the extent to which it is able to make the educational experience a successful learning experience for all children. Two studies from widely disparate sources illustrate the intertwined threads of successful school experience and primary prevention. In a 30-year follow-up study of children who had been referred to a municipal clinic because of problem behavior, the investigators included students from the files of the public schools who matched the patients in age, sex, IQ, race and residence. In addition, this group was selected on the basis of having no school record of behavior or discipline problems. Although the investigators were not studying the health of the control group, they were struck with the fact "that the simple criteria used to choose the control subjects—no excessive absences, no full grades repeated, no disciplinary action recorded and an IQ of 80 or better—have yielded a strikingly healthy group (26, p. 968)." This was particularly striking since the control group was drawn largely from disadvantaged classes and a history of broken homes was found in one-third of the cases.

The other link of evidence relating school success and primary prevention is found in Ginzberg and his associates' monumental study of the ineffective soldier of World War II. They found that, while poverty, racial discrimination and lack of industrialization could help explain higher rates of emotional instability for individuals who came from certain sections of the country, each of these factors was also related to the differentially low educational achievement of the region. The study demonstrated that, although a higher level of educational attainment was no safeguard against emotional disorders, the lower the educational level, the higher the incidence of emotional disorders. As to cause, Ginzberg noted, "A disturbed childhood is likely to be reflected in learning difficulties; children who do poorly in school are likely to develop emotional problems (15, p. 118).

If the school is to become an effective preventive force, it must develop ways to identify early the children who are or are becoming learning problems, so that school and community resources can help such children most effectively and economically. The potential learning difficulty may be related to intellectual, emotional or family-centered problems; even so, the problem may first manifest itself in the school, which can, if it recognizes the problem, pave the way for early help through parent conferences, counseling or psychological or remedial service (2, 3).

In job situations, the hazards seem to be just as numerous for going up the ladder as down. A person moving up in a large industrial or governmental agency may find it difficult to accept his new role or recast his loyalties with a particular group. He may have greater responsibility for men or production than he is able to manage. A staff-related mental health counselor in industry or work organization may provide some source of help for emotionally hazardous situations of this type.

Wilner and Walkley (32) and others have mapped out preliminary steps for studying the interrelationships of housing and mental health. In studying the mental health of families in relation to their housing, including such things as the extent of plumbing leaks or the number of rats, the general impression of these investigators based on preliminary short-term evaluations is that moving from poor to good housing does not, on the average, result in measurable improvement in the mental health of the family. In the matter of housing and related social economic problems, one must be continually reminded of the large body of research describing the high, positive relationship between the indicators of social class and the many kinds of human illnesses. As Wilner and Walkley point out,

The list of pathologies so related is long, beginning with early studies on crime and delinquency. Other examples are alcoholism, broken homes, and divorce (Beverly Hills notwithstanding), syphilis, tuberculosis, and childhood communicable diseases. New entries are being made as time goes by: Reading disability has entered the lists, as has the incidence of narcotics use among teenagers, as well as the incidence of mental illness.

Housing, by and large, shows a marked negative relationship with most illnesses so that, in general, as housing deteriorates, illnesses rise. Psychoses have been found to increase with housing deterioration; neuroses, on the other hand, seem to increase with improved housing.

WHITHER PREVENTION?

Prevention is, at present, a high-status, magic word generally applicable to almost all professional endeavors in mental health. The term is applicable to newer and more effective treatment methods for schizophrenia, preventive hospitalization of suicidal patients or the use of drugs for quieting patients, or, in vague or general terms, to improved housing, better human relations, better schools, more staff, and so on. This lack of specificity in the term prevention is especially critical in a field that already has a large element of vagueness and expansiveness. If, as Freud noted, thinking is action in rehearsal, it behooves individuals interested in preventive action to get into rehearsal ideas that are primarily preventive, specific enough to be replicated in more than one locality and operational enough to be evaluated within one's lifetime. Also, it must be kept in mind that the preventive battlegrounds are the primary institutions or agencies of a society. We must determine the specific interventions or modifications these institutions can make to reduce the stress vulnerability or enhance the personality resources of the human organisms they serve.

Prevention has to do with the quality of the interactions and the degree of effectiveness of the primary institutions of a society in providing each person with increments of ego strength and personality robustness for coping with the "slings and arrows" of life. The nature of these interactions and experiences would be considered preventive to the extent to which such experiences enhance the degrees of psychological freedom of an individual to select behavioral alternatives and to act upon them. This preventive model and point of view was succinctly illustrated by an old Cornish test of insanity related by Woodward. The test situation comprised a sink, a tap of running water, a bucket and a ladle. The bucket was place under the tap of running water and the subject asked to bail the water out of the bucket with the ladle. If the subject continued to bail without paying some attention to reducing or preventing the flow of water into the pail, he was judged to be mentally incompetent. Similarly, any society that attempts to provide more and larger buckets to contain the problems of that society, without simultaneously attempting to reduce the flow, might be equally suspect. Treatment, rehabilitation and incarceration are our necesary buckets to contain the flow. Prevention, however, deals with the tap, the sources of flow and the leverages needed to turn the faucet down or off.

REFERENCES

1. Bellak, L. *Schizophrenia: A review of the syndrome*. New York: Logos Press, 1959.
2. Bower, E. M. *Early identification of emotionally handicapped children in school*. Springfield, Ill.: C. C. Thomas, 1960.
3. Bower, E. M. Primary prevention in a school setting. In G. Caplan (Ed.), *Prevention of mental disorders in children*. New York: Basic Books, 1961. Pp. 353–377.
4. Bowlby, J. *Maternal care and mental health*. Geneva, Switzerland: World Health Organization, 1951.
5. Brody, S. *Patterns of mothering*. New York: International Universities Press, 1956.
6. Bruner, J. S. On coping and defending (mimeo).
7. Caplan, G. A public health approach to child psychiatry. *Ment. Hyg.*, 1951, 35:235–49.
8. Cumming, E. and Cumming, J. *Closed ranks*. Cambridge: Harvard University Press, 1957.
9. Dubos, R. *Mirage of health*. New York: Harper, 1959.
10. Eissler, R. Scapegoats of society. In K. R. Eissler (Ed.), *Searchlights on delinquency*. New York: International Universities Press, 1955.
11. Farnsworth, D. L. The provision of appropriate treatment: hospital and community collaboration. *Ment. Hosps.*, 1961, 12:18.
12. Fox, T. F. Priorities. In *Steps in the development of integrated psychiatric services*. New York: Milbank Memorial Fund, 1960.
13. Freedman, A. et al. The influence of hyperbilirubinemia on the early development of the premature. *Psychiat. Res. Reps.*, 1960, 13:108–23.
14. Gardner, J. *Excellence*. New York: Harper, 1961.
15. Ginzberg, E. and Associates. *The ineffective soldier: Lessons for management and the nation*. New York: Columbia University Press, 1959.
16. Goodrich, D. W. Possibilities for preventive intervention during initial personality formation. In G. Caplan (Ed.) *Prevention of mental disorders in children*. New York: Basic Books, 1961. Pp. 249–64.
17. Hofstadter, R. *Social Darwinism in American thought*. Boston: Beacon Press, 1955.
18. Homer, *The Odyssey*. W. H. D. Rouse, Trans. New York: Mentor, 1949.
19. Kawi, A. A. and Pasamanick, B. *The association of factors of pregnancy with the development of reading disorders in childhood*. Yellow Springs, Ohio: Society for Research in Child Development, 1959.
20. Klein, D. and Lindemann, E. Preventive intervention in individual and family crisis situations. In G. Caplan. (Ed.), *Prevention of mental disorders in children*. New York: Basic Books, 1961. Pp. 283–306.

21. Kubie, L. S. The fundamental nature of the distinction between normality and neuroses. *Psychoanal. Qtly.*, 1954, vol. 23.
22. Kubie, L. S. Social forces and the neurotic process. In A. Leighton, et al. (Eds.), *Explorations in social psychiatry*. New York: Basic Books, 1957.
23. Meier, R. L. Human time allocation: a basis for social accounts. *J. Amer. Inst. of Planners*, 1959, 25(Nov.) : 27–33.
24. Murphy, G. The prevention of mental disorder: some research suggestions. *J. Hillside Hospital*, 1960, vol. 9.
25. Murphy, L. B. Preventive implications of development in the preschool years. In G. Caplan (Ed.), *Prevention of mental disorders in children*. New York: Basic Books, 1961. Pp. 218–48.
26. O'Neal, P. and Robbins, L. The relation of childhood behavior problems to adult psychiatric status. *Amer. J. Psychiat.*, 1958, vol. 114.
27. Pasamanick, B. The epidemiology of behavior disorders of childhood. In *Neurology and psychiatry in childhood*. Baltimore, Md.: William & Wilkins, 1956.
28. Redlich, F. C. The concept of health in psychiatry. In A. Leighton et al. (Eds.), *Explorations in social psychiatry*. New York: Basic Books, 1957.
29. Ribble, M. *The rights of infants*. New York: Columbia University Press, 1943.
30. Sanford, R. N. The development of the healthy personality in the society of today. In *Modern mental health concepts and their application in public health education*. Berkeley, Calif.: State Department of Public Health, 1959.
31. Stevenson, I. Direct instigation of behavioral changes in psychotherapy. *AMA Arch. Gen. Psychiat.*, 1959, 1:99–107.
32. Wilner, D. and Walkley, R. Housing environment and mental health. In *Epidemiology of mental disorder*. Washington, D.C.: American Association for the Advancement of Science. Pp. 143–74.
33. Wilson, W. The new freedom. In Essie Chamberlain (Ed.), *Essays old and new*. New York: Harcourt, Brace, 1926.
34. Wortis, H., Heimer, C. B., Braine, M., Redlo, M. and Rue, R. Growing up in Brooklyn: an early history of the premature child. *Amer. J. Orthopsychiat.*, 1963, 33(3):535–39.

22

The Current Status of Secondary Prevention in Child Psychiatry

LEON EISENBERG AND ERNEST M. GRUENBERG

FACED with endemic diseases whose prevalence, morbidity and disability are high, the public health physician must attempt to develop a program of control. In so doing, he starts from what is known about the illness, adds what seems probable, organizes these elements along recognized public health principles, and proceeds to secure support for community action. Obviously, the sounder the state of knowledge about etiology, transmission and treatment, the more successful will be the program of control. But the history of public health (73) is replete with examples of incompletely understood diseases that have been effectively limited by informed guesses from patterns of distribution as to probable modes of transmission or by the widespread application of empirically founded therapeutic methods.

Mental illnesses prevail endemically, estimates for urban centers in the United States varying from a conservative 10 per cent in one study (64) to the staggering figure of 80 per cent in certain population groups in another study (68). Their cost in human suffering, in time lost from education and work, and in public funds expended for treatment and custodial care is staggering. Thus mental illness constitutes a public health problem of the first magnitude. Clearly, an effective program for control is a critical necessity.

Knowledge of mental illness is incomplete, but this is not a unique challenge in public health. We never know everything we want to know and we are never in total ignorance. The task for each period is to develop as sound a program as current information permits as a guide to effective action and as a focus on what we need to know. While current methods are not likely to produce radical alterations in the prevalence of mental illness, amelioration of the magnitude of the problem can be achieved.

The present paper has been undertaken in the framework of a charge to the Program Area Committee on Mental Health of the American Public Health Association to prepare a manual on the control of mental illness. This paper discusses only one area: secondary prevention in child psychiatry. It

Reprinted from *American Journal of Orthopsychiatry*, 1961, *31*, 355–367, by permission of the publisher and the authors. © 1961, American Orthopsychiatric Association. Dr. Eisenberg is Professor of Psychiatry, Harvard Medical School. Dr. Gruenberg is Professor of Psychiatry, College of Physicians and Surgeons of Columbia University.

may be useful to begin with a consideration of preliminary assumptions and the definition of terms.

A public health point of view differs from a predominantly clinical orientation in that it is concerned with the impact of illness upon the community rather than the individual. From a public health standpoint, the priority assigned to a treatment program is a function of at least three factors: the prevalence of the illness to be treated, the disability and mortality the illness causes, and the effect of available methods of treatment upon its course. In general, the public health worker is concerned with illness in direct proportion to its prevalence and its severity, but a widespread disorder that produces relatively little disability may be less important than one of lower prevalence but greater disability; or again, a highly effective treatment for an uncommon disorder may be given a higher priority than one of uncertain impact on a more common illness.

In order to appraise the relative damage produced by different illnesses, we need biostatistical methods that measure partial disability as well as instances of total breakdown. This is analogous to the necessity to go beyond mortality to morbidity statistics in other illnesses. For example, medicine has successfully lowered neonatal mortality but is only now recognizing the number of handicapping conditions in the infants who have been saved (39). Mortality data alone grossly overestimate medical success in correcting prenatal and paranatal pathology (63). In similar fashion, statistics on mental hospital admissions constitute data of prime importance, but are insufficient in themselves to indicate the burden of mental illness. Available data on outpatient admission rates (2, 3) supplement mental hospital figures in a useful way but there remains an urgent need to sample representative populations in order to detect the mentally ill not now registered as patients.

In approaching the task of collating available psychiatric knowledge, it is important to specify the degree of certainty with which given statements can be made. The highest order of certainty is to be ascribed to findings substantiated by precise scientific observation and experiment. A lower order of certainty, but nonetheless a moderately reliable one, is to be accorded those clinical impressions upon which informed experts are agreed. Finally, it is useful to consider those hypotheses which have logical substantiation and apparent clinical support but upon which there is no general agreement. Control programs need to be flexible so that they can put new knowledge to work as promptly as it becomes available.

It has become customary in public health to distinguish three levels of prevention. *Primary prevention* is centered about steps to obviate the development of disease in susceptible populations. The methods employed include both health promotion and specific protection against disease when this is known. *Secondary prevention* is based upon early diagnosis of illness and prompt treatment in order to shorten duration, reduce symptoms, limit sequelae and minimize contagion; that is, the impact of mental illness upon others in the family and the community. *Tertiary prevention* is concerned with instances of illness that are irreversible; its goals are the limitation of disability to the extent possible and the promotion of the rehabilitation of the individual so afflicted. For example, in the case of the hospitalized patient, tertiary prevention is concerned with preventing or reversing the social chronicity so frequently induced by institutionalization itself (66). We will attempt to summarize current knowledge applicable to programs for secondary prevention in child psychiatry.

We will proceed from those illnesses for which there is (a) *convincing evidence* of the effectiveness of treatment to those in which there is a (b) *reasonable likelihood* of reversibility and finally to those in which it (c) *remains uncertain* as to whether present treatment methods are effective.

DISORDERS FOR WHICH THERE IS CONVINCING EVIDENCE THAT TREATMENT IS EFFECTIVE

1. *Toxic psychoses* in childhood are within the realm of prevention on a secondary level. *Prompt* treatment of early lead intoxication with chelating agents can prevent mental deterioration (15). Psychoses due to atropine or benzedrine intoxication are readily reversible on removal of the exciting agent as are a number of iatrogenic psychoses as complications of pharmacotherapy (ACTH, bromides, etc.). The acute mental symptoms (in toxic, infectious, and metabolic brain syndromes) initially reflect transitional states of cell irritability and cell depression caused both by the noxious agent itself and by cerebral edema. They are reversible to the extent that detoxification occurs before significant tissue loss results. The mental symptoms secondary to cell loss are reversible only insofar as intact areas can asume the function of the destroyed tissue, a compensation which occurs the more readily the less the tissue loss and the younger the organism (7, 46). Moreover, recovery can be facilitated by re-educational techniques (77) and total psychiatric management, a topic to be discussed below.

2. The availability of adequate antibiotic therapy has permitted the effective treatment of certain *infections of the central nervous system,* such as bacterial meningitides and brain abscesses, which previously were almost uniformly associated with complications (33).

3. Galactosemia can be taken as the paradigm of *a metabolic disorder* from which complete control can be obtained by effective management (19). The child with congenital galactosemia is subject to cataracts, mental deficiency, convulsions and death if his disease is not diagnosed and effectively treated. It has been known since the 1930's that the elimination of galactose from the diet of such an infant completely prevents this sequence of events (55). Diagnosis is readily established by specific enzymatic tests which identify a deficiency of red blood cell galactose-1-phosphate uridyl transferase (44). It is possible to detect the carrier state in heterozygous parents (20). The galactosemic individual may develop in later childhood an auxiliary meta-

bolic route by which galactose can be metabolized so that dietary management may not have to be continued throughout life (21).

A second *metabolic disorder* in which amelioration if not complete prevention of untoward consequences can be achieved is congenital cretinism. Untreated, the cretin exhibits severe mental deficiency. With *early* diagnosis and the *prompt* institution of *adequate* thyroid therapy, near normal levels of intelligence can be achieved. Current data suggest that the degree of reversibility may not be total, for the average IQ of such a group of children remains somewhat lower than normal expectancy (75). Nonetheless, treatment has a decisive impact upon course.

A third metabolic disorder with major psychological effects responsive to adequate medical management is phenylketonuric oligophrenia. Most workers (1, 8, 40) have reported that the provision of a diet low in phenylalanine from early infancy will prevent the severe mental deficiency, behavior disorder and convulsions that accompany phenylketonuria. When treatment is not instituted until the child is several years of age, there is some suggestion that behavior can be improved and convulsions diminished but no evidence of a return to normal levels of intelligence has been obtained. Diagnosis is dependent upon the detection in the urine of intermediary metabolites resulting from the inability to parahydroxylate phenylalanine (57, 79). Carrier states in parents can be identified by phenylalanine tolerance tests (41). Pilot programs for routine screening of newborns for the abnormal metabolites with free provision of phenylalanine-low diets have been started by the New York State Department of Mental Hygiene. All siblings of known cases should be followed from birth in order to detect the disease at its first appearance and to institute dietary management.

The recent identification of other types of mental deficiency associated with metabolic abnormalities gives hope that we may in time be able to provide effective methods of treatment for Hartnup disease (5, 42), maple syrup disease (54, 55) and others (76).

4. What can we say of the *psychogenic disorders* of childhood? Impressive documentation exists to the effect that maternal deprivation is associated with (a) reduction in mental capacity, (b) behavior disorder, (c) psychopathic traits, and (d) psychophysiologic derangements (4, 10, 32, 34, 35, 52, 69). If this state of deprivation persists for a number of years, just how many being uncertain, it is the consensus that the disorder is irreversible. However, there are documented case reports of total or almost total recovery when replacement therapy was provided in the second year of life. Engel and Reichsman and Richmond have described severely deprived, developmentally retarded and grossly malnourished infants who responded to psychiatrically oriented nursing care in the hospital (32, 69). Lourie (52) has described a group of children with psychophysiologic disorders, including rumination, vomiting and persistent diarrhea, for which no physical etiology could be established. With the introduction of consistent mothering, remarkable clinical improvement was obtained.

By the early detection of environmental impoverishment and the prompt substitution of adequate mothering care, it should prove possible to return neglected children to a state of near normal function. This would require enriching institutional and hospital care for children, improving foster care programs, extending protective services to multiple problem families likely to be inadequate to meet the needs of their children, and so on.

A number of workers have produced evidence that a specific neurotic disorder of childhood, clinically termed school phobia but probably more adequately described as separation anxiety (43), can be effectively treated during the elementary school period (26, 27, 35, 78). By prompt intervention, cooperating orthopsychiatric and school personnel can help such children to return to class; present evidence indicates that further growth proceeds in a healthy direction (72). If uncorrected, this disorder becomes chronic, with the likelihood of successful cure diminishing in proportion to the duration of the illness and the age of the child. Therapeutic results with adolescents with school phobia are disappointing (17, 72).

DISORDERS FOR WHICH THERE IS REASONABLE LIKELIHOOD OF RESPONSE TO TREATMENT

Let us now turn to those conditions for which the evidence of the treatment effectiveness is suggestive but not definitive. Before considering specific entities, let us ask: Is it necessary or useful to treat the neurotic and personality disorders of childhood? What is the likelihood that a child with a psychiatric disorder of nonpsychotic proportions will be a risk for psychiatric disability in adulthood? The most impressive body of data bearing on this question has been supplied by O'Neal and Robins (61, 62, 70, 71). In a study of the 30-year outcome of a large group of children seen in a court-attached child guidance clinic, they found a significantly higher incidence of major psychiatric disabilities in the adult experience of this group of children in contrast with that of a set of classroom controls. The pediatric patients were classified into three general groups: neurotic disorders; aggressive behavior disorders; and adjudicated delinquents. There were significant differences in the psychiatric disorders in the adult experience of the three groups. Least psychiatric illness was found among the adults who as children had neurotic conditions, though the rates were higher than for controls. The adjudicated delinquents produced the greatest number of adult sociopaths, and the children with aggressive behavior disorders the most adult psychotics. A study by H. H. Morris et al. (60) of children with aggressive behavior disorders revealed a severe behavior pathology in later adulthood.

On the other hand, a report by D. Morris et al. (56, 59) of a group of children who had been diagnosed as shy and withdrawn revealed surprisingly little pathology in adolescent and adult adjustment. Moreover, Lapouse and

Monk (47, 48) found, in a stratified sample of an urban school population, a 10 per cent to 40 per cent prevalence of symptoms frequently regarded as indicative of psychiatric maladjustment.

All research work on treatment for mental disorders in children is difficult and requires painstaking patience. One study in particular illustrates, however, that it can be done. The Cambridge-Somerville Youth Study, inspired and led by Dr. Richard Cabot, evaluated the success of various types of relationship therapy for predelinquents in a masterfully executed study (65). Unfortunately, the reliable finding is that this form of treatment does not reduce the incidence of delinquency in predelinquents.

Most of the large scale studies of the effectiveness of outpatient psychotherapy have been unable to demonstrate a significant difference in adjustment between "treated" and "untreated" cases at the time of a follow-up assessment (50, 51). However, these investigations suffer from methodologic flaws; self-selected drop-outs as "controls"; incomplete reporting; heterogeneous case material; the use of an extensive diagnostic study, itself containing therapeutic implications with the "untreated" controls, and so on (28). It is noteworthy that reported improvement rates cluster with remarkable consistency in the 50 per cent to 70 per cent range in a variety of treatment studies. Whether this represents spontaneous remission or a therapeutic response to some common factor in outpatient treatment cannot be specified at present. The adult psychiatric status achieved by disturbed children in the St. Louis study (62) suggests that spontaneous remission rates may be much lower than the "improvement" rates cited; only 21 per cent of the former child patients were found to be free of psychiatric disease as contrasted with 60 per cent of control subjects. However, inability to compare the diagnostic categories, the clinical severities, and the criteria for change employed in the several studies makes it impossible to draw firm conclusions.

There are several studies which indicate that brief periods of treatment and even diagnostic consultation services result in improvement rates comparable to those reported after more extensive treatment. Cytryn et al. (18) reported symptomatic improvement in 90 per cent of a group of children with neurotic traits six months after five psychotherapeutic sessions. In a second study (31), comparable results were achieved. In both investigations, treatment response was shown to be a function of diagnostic category, neurotic children responding at a significantly more favorable level than hyperkinetic, defective, or sociopathic children. In a study of the effectiveness of a consultation service for disturbed foster children, Eisenberg et al. (30) were able to demonstrate a relationship between favorable outcome and the carrying out of psychiatric recommendations. The diagnostic consultation appeared to have particular value in extending the impact of the psychiatric team through improving the services provided by other child care workers to the children in need of help. Diagnostic consultation and brief psychotherapy merit consideration in programs of secondary prevention since they appear to be able to produce results, at least at a symptomatic level, comparable to those attainable with more intensive (and professionally expensive) methods of treatment.

DISORDERS WHOSE RESPONSE TO TREATMENT IS UNCERTAIN

1. Information on the natural history of psychotic disorders in childhood is beginning to accumulate (6, 22). These reports provide a baseline for a comparison of treatment effects. To the present, there has been no conclusive demonstration of the effectiveness of any therapeutic method in dealing with the psychotic child. This is not to say that treatment is ineffective. Indeed, the problem is one of weak information which does not permit the specification of effectiveness *or* ineffectiveness. The clinician must attempt to use the methods at hand, but progress will depend upon careful and systematic evaluation of proposed methods of treatment.

2. Reading disability, classified as a special symptom reaction in the A.P.A. diagnostic manual, is a widespread disorder with a serious impact upon the school-age population (29). Present evidence indicates that the clinical syndrome may represent a response to one or more of a number of underlying causes, which include understimulation and poor motivation in the socially deprived, subclinical central nervous system damage in a second group and primary emotional disturbance in a third. A logical program of rehabilitation must be based upon diagnostic appraisal. It appears that remedial reading instruction can be quite effective with the emotionally disturbed as part of a total psychotherapeutic program, in contrast with the slow response of the brain-damaged group to the same methods of instruction (67). This emphasizes the importance of special educational techniques designed for each etiologic group. Effective therapy for the socially deprived will have to include efforts at modifying the social environment, altering attitudes toward learning, enriching cultural background, as well as direct reading help. The magnitude of the reading problem and the shattering impact of reading disability on personal and vocational adjustment should accord proposals for its correction a major position in mental hygiene programs.

3. The association of IQ scores with socioeconomic class raises the presumption that cultural enrichment can be a significant factor in preventing what is termed subcultural or familial mental deficiency (16, 74). A number of important studies have demonstrated sizable gains in intelligence test scores among institutionalized children in response to programs which emphasize social stimulation, foster home care, opportunities to participate in community life and so on. Although many of these studies are methodologically inadequate, there is growing conviction among clinicians that such measures as preschool education, improved classroom teaching, casework for multiple problem families, special education for immigrant groups, improved institutional and foster care for borderline "defectives," can make an important

contribution to enhanced intellectual function among many groups of children who currently test at below average levels.[1]

4. Children with chronic brain syndromes are handicapped, not only by the organic symptoms consequent upon brain tissue malfunction but as well by secondary symptomatology which follows upon social rejection (23). Clinical experience suggests that pharmacologic treatment, remedial education and psychotherapeutic management can result in greater stabilization of "driven" behavior, thus enabling these children to achieve a higher level of social adjustment (13, 14, 31, 49). This takes on added significance in view of the clinical observation that the hyperkinesis and short attention span, so disruptive of learning in early years, tend to remit during adolescence (13, 14, 45).

We have thus far reviewed the evidence for the benefits of various treatment procedures. The physician's first duty is to do no harm. Are some of our treatments potentially harmful? Apart from the literature that has accumulated on the toxic effects of pharmacotherapy (12), no unequivocal answer to this question is possible at present. Fears have been expressed that clinic attendance labels a child and alters the way others perceive him to his detriment; that unnecessary or excessively prolonged treatment may foster unhealthy dependence; that inadequate experience by clinicians with the wide spectrum of behavior patterns displayed by normal children may lead to inaccurate diagnosis of illness, and so on. The fact that these criticisms are sometimes voiced by insufficiently informed or indiscriminately hostile critics is no justification for assuming a priori that they are without merit. At the least, they should spur orthopsychiatric personnel to refine their diagnostic criteria, to expand their familiarity with cultural patterns other than their own, to set as precise and attainable therapeutic goals as can be done today, and to recognize the need for systematic evaluation.

IMPLICATIONS FOR CONTROL PROGRAMS

1. It should be recognized at the outset that secondary prevention will be effective only to the extent that it is supplemented by measures for health promotion: the provision of total medical care, adequate housing, and social welfare for the underprivileged; the availability of excellent school programs to foster self-realization for each child and special education for the handicapped; aggressive programs for the rehabilitation of disintegrating communities which constitute almost insuperable barriers to the attainment of total health.

2. The emphasis in secondary prevention upon early diagnosis and prompt treatment implies a need to improve methods of case finding. The studies

[1] For discussion of the pertinent literature, references 16, 25, and 74 should be consulted.

of the St. Louis group in the use of mothers' reports and of teacher screening are promising leads for the future (36, 37). The "multiple problem" family constitutes a reservoir of psychiatric disorder no less threatening to public health than contamination of the water supply by cholera. Traditional methods of agency work have been notoriously ineffective in dealing with this problem area, since such families "lack motivation" and characteristically terminate contact with community resources before rehabilitation is achieved (9). The San Mateo project indicates that vigorous intervention by coordinated community services *can* be effective (11).

3. Existing resources must be amplified and made more efficient. Many communities have no mental health resources; none have facilities sufficient to meet all needs. At the same time that we seek to win support for enlarging present facilities and for creating new ones, we must give attention to the ways in which existing facilities are used. The outstanding implication of the studies we have reviewed is that the local mental health program, to be fully effective, will have to be different from the traditional type of clinic service.

(a) It becomes clear that priority for treatment should, to a much larger extent than is now the case, be based upon an estimate of the problems which can be helped in an important way by current methods. It has been customary in the past few decades to define services in terms of competences and preoccupations of the clinic staff and to gear intake to staff competences and interests. To take an outstanding example, it is not uncommon for child guidance clinics to have an over-all policy of refusing treatment to brain-damaged or mentally defective children. Yet the implications of present information is that perhaps more can be offered certain brain-damaged or defective children than bright but severely neurotic or psychotic children. This is not to suggest that treatment be refused the latter group but that priority for treatment be assigned on the basis of careful review of what treatment can contribute to community health rather than biases against certain clinical entities or predilections for others.

(b) A number of clinics have developed a policy of requiring active cooperation by the families of patients. While there is justification for this in dealing with elective treatment procedures for certain types of neurotic children, this would not appear to be a logical across-the-board policy if the clinic is to have a maximum impact on the mental health of the child population. There are a significant number of children with correctible metabolic disorders and potentially alterable defects of family life, for whom vigorous participation in getting the patient into treatment is mandatory upon the clinic. In essence, what is at issue is the question of active *responsibility* for community health (9).

(c) The lack of definitive proof of the effectiveness of intensive psychotherapy and the tentative demonstration that short term therapy produces equivalent symptomatic results suggests the desirability of increasing the use of time-limited brief treatment, as a method of reaching more families with available personnel. The same considerations apply to extending clinic effectiveness by providing consultations to other health, education and welfare services in the community (24). Consultations regarding the emotional reactions of staff members in public health nursing and school agencies to the emotionally disturbed child are undoubtedly of value. However, our appraisal points to a need to inform staff members of these agencies with regard to the importance of identifying metabolic disorders, correctible brain tissue defects, and emotional deprivation as disorders constituting psychological emergencies which justify active, intensive, and unrelenting efforts at correction.

SUMMARY

Mental illness constitutes a major hazard to public health. Priority must be assigned to the development of effective primary, secondary, and tertiary programs of control. Much remains to be learned about mental disorders, but it is clear that what is now known is not being fully utilized. It is incumbent upon each of the disciplines in orthopsychiatry to reappraise current clinical practices in terms of their impact upon community health. This paper has outlined, in tentative fashion, some of the issues relevant to control programs at the level of secondary prevention of mental disorders of childhood. It will be successful to the extent that it stimulates others to correct, amplify and extend the proposals set forth.

REFERENCES

1. Armstrong, M. D. *Biochemical studies on newborn infants with phenylketonuria.* Montreal: Int. Cong. Pediatrics, 1959.
2. Bahn, A. K., and Norman, V. B. First national report on patients of mental health clinics. *Publ. Hlth. Rep.,* 1959, 74:943.
3. Bahn, A. K., et al. Diagnostic and demographic characteristics of patients seen in outpatient psychiatric clinics for an entire state. *Amer. J. Psychiat.,* 1961, 117:769–77.
4. Bakwin, H. Loneliness in infants. *Am. J. Dis. Child.,* 1942, 63:30.
5. Baron, D. N., et al. Hereditary pellagra-like skin rash with temporary cerebellar ataxia, constant renal amino-aciduria and other bizarre biochemical features. *Lancet,* 1956, 2:421.
6. Bender, L. Childhood schizophrenia. *Psychiat. Qtly.,* 1953, 27:663.
7. Benjamin, P. M., and Thompson, R. Differential effects of cortical lesions in infant and adult cats on roughness discrimination. *Exp. Neurol.,* 1959, 1:305.
8. Bickel, H. *Oligophrenia associated with inborn errors of metabolism.* Montreal: Int. Cong. Pediatrics, 1959.
9. Bloch, D. A., and Behrens, M. L. *A study of children referred for residential*

treatment in New York State. Albany: New York State Interdepartmental Health Resources Board, January 1959.

10. Bowlby, J. *Maternal care and mental health.* W.H.O. Monogr. Series no. 2. Geneva: World Health Org., 1951.

11. Buell, B., et al. Reorganizing to prevent and control disordered behavior. *Ment. Hyg.,* 1958, 42:155.

12. Caldwell, A. E. *Psychopharmaca: A bibliography of psychopharmacology 1952–1957.* Public Health Service Publ. No. 581. Washington: U. S. Government Printing Office, 1958.

13. Chess, S. Diagnosis and treatment of the hyperactive child. Read at American Psychiatric Assoc. Meeting, April 30, 1959.

14. Chess, S. *An introduction to child psychiatry.* New York: Grune & Stratton, 1959.

15. Chisholm, J. J., and Harrison, H. E. The treatment of acute lead encephalopathy in children. *Pediatrics,* 1957, 19:2.

16. Clarke, A. M., and Clarke, A. D. B. *Mental deficiency: The changing outlook.* Glencoe, Ill.: Free Press, 1958.

17. Coolidge, J. C., et al. School phobia in adolescence: a manifestation of severe character disturbance. *Amer. J. Orthopsychiat.,* 1960, 30:599.

18. Cytryn, L., et al. The effectiveness of tranquilizing drugs plus supportive psychotherapy in treating behavior disorders of children. *Amer. J. Orthopsychiat.,* 1960, 30:113.

19. Donnell, G. N., Bergren, W. R., and Cleland, R. S. Galactosemia. *Pediat. Clin. North America,* 1960, 7:315.

20. Donnell, G. N., et al. The enzymatic expression of heterozygosity in families of galactosemics. *Pediatrics,* 1959, 24:418–26.

21. Eisenberg, F., et al. Studies on metabolism of carbon 14-labelled galactose in a galactosemic individual. *Science,* 1957, 125:116.

22. Eisenberg, L. The course of childhood schizophrenia. *AMA Arch. Neurol. Psychiat.,* 1957, 78:69.

23 Eisenberg, L. The psychiatric implications of brain damage in children. *Psychiat. Qtly.,* 1957, 31:72.

24. Eisenberg, L. An evaluation of psychiatric consultation service for a public agency. *Am. J. Publ. Hlth.,* 1958, 48:742.

25. Eisenberg, L. Emotional determinants of mental deficiency. *AMA Arch. Neurol. Psychiat.,* 1958, 80:114.

26. Eisenberg, L. School phobia. *Pediat. Clin. North America,* 1958, 5:645–66.

27. Eisenberg, L. School phobia: A study in the communication of anxiety. *Amer. J. Psychiat.,* 1958, 114:712.

28. Eisenberg, L. Basic issues in drug research with children. In S. Fisher (Ed.), *Child research in psychopharmacology.* Springfield, Ill.: C. C. Thomas, 1959.

29. Eisenberg, L. Office evaluation of specific reading disability in children. *Pediatrics,* 1959, 23:997.

30. Eisenberg, L., et al. Diagnostic services for maladjusted foster children. *Amer. J. Orthopsychiat.,* 1958, 28:750.

31. Eisenberg, L., et al. Effectiveness of psychotherapy alone and in conjunction with perphenazine or placebo in the treatment of neurotic and hyperkinetic children. Read at American Psychiatric Assoc. Meeting, May, 1960.

32. Engel, G. L., et al. A study of an infant with a gastric fistula. *Psychosom. Med.*, 1956, 18:374.
33. Ford, F. *Diseases of the nervous system in infancy, childhood and adolescence.* 4th ed. Springfield, Ill.: C. C. Thomas, 1959.
34. Glaser, K., and Eisenberg, L. Maternal deprivation. *Pediatrics*, 1956, 18:626.
35. Glaser, K. Problems in school attendance. *Pediatrics*, 1959, 23:371.
36. Glidewell, J. C. et al. Behavior symptoms in children and degree of sickness. *Am. J. Psychiat.* 1957, 114:47.
37. Glidewell, J. C. et al. Screening for behavior problems in public schools: The use of mothers' reports of symptoms. Read at American Public Health Assoc. Meeting, Nov. 1957.
38. Goldfarb, W. Emotional and intellectual consequences of psychologic deprivation in infancy. In P. H. Hoch and J. Zubin (Eds.), *Psychopathology of childhood*. New York: Grune & Stratton, 1955.
39. Gruenberg, E. M. Application of control methods to mental illness. *Amer. J. Publ. Hlth.*, 1957, 47:944.
40. Hsia, D. Y.-Y. A one year controlled study of the effect of low phenylalanine diet on phenylketonuria. *Pediatrics*, 1958, 21:178.
41. Hsia, D. Y.-Y., et al. Heterozygous carriers of phenylketonuria detected by phenylalanine tolerance tests. *Acta Genet.*, 1957, 7:189.
42. Jepson, J. B. Indolylacetyl-glutamine and other indol metabolites in hartnup disease. *Biochem. J.*, 1956, 64:14.
43. Johnson, A. M., et al. School phobia. *Am. J. Orthopsychiat.*, 1941, 11:702.
44. Kalckar, H. M. Biochemical mutations in man and micro-organisms. *Science*, 1957, 125:105.
45. Kanner, L. *Child psychiatry.* 3d ed. Springfield, Ill.: C. C. Thomas, 1958.
46. Kennard, M. A. Relation of age to motor impairment in man and subhuman primates. *Arch. Neurol. Psychiat.*, 1940, 44:377.
47. Lapouse, R., and Monk, M. A. An epidemiologic study of behavior characteristics of children. *Amer. J. Publ. Hlth.*, 1958, 48:1134.
48. Lapouse, R., and Monk, M. A. Fears and worries in a representative sample of children. *Amer. J. Orthopsychiat.*, 1959, 29:803.
49. Laufer, M., et al. Hyperkinetic impulse disorder in children's behavior problems. *Psychosom. Med.*, 1957, 19:38.
50. Levitt, E. E. The results of psychotherapy with children: An evaluation. *J. Consult. Psychol.*, 1957, 21:189.
51. Levitt, E. E., et al. A follow-up evaluation of cases treated at a community child guidance clinic. *Amer. J. Orthopsychiat.*, 1959, 29:337.
52. Lourie, R. S. Experience with therapy of psychosomatic problems in infants. In P. H. Hoch and J. Zubin (Eds.), *Psychopathology of children*. New New York: Grune & Stratton, 1955.
53. Mason, H. H., and Turner, M. E. Chronic galactosemia. *Amer. J. Dis. Child.*, 1935, 50:359.
54. Menkes, J. H., et al. A new syndrome: Progressive familial infantile cerebral dysfunction associated with an unusual urinary substance. *Pediatrics*, 1954, 14:462.
55. Menkes, J. H., et al. Maple syrup disease. Isolation and identification of organic acid in the urine. *Pediatrics*, 1959, 23:348.

56. Michael, C. M., et al. Follow-up studies of shy, withdrawn children. II. Relative incidence of schizophrenia. *Amer. J. Orthopsychiat.*, 1957, 27:- 331.

57. Mitoma, C., et al. On the nature of the enzymatic defect in phenylpyruvic oligophrenia. *Proc. Soc. Exp. Biol. Med.*, 1957, 94:634.

59. Morris, D. P., et al. Follow-up studies of shy, withdrawn children. I. Evaluation of later adjustment. *Amer. J. Orthopsychiat.*, 1954, 24:743.

60. Morris, H. H., et al. Aggressive behavior disorders of childhood: A follow-up study. *Am. J. Psychiat.*, 1956, 112:991.

61. O'Neal, P., and Robins, L. N. Childhood patterns predictive of adult schizophrenia. *Amer. J. Psychiat.*, 1958, 115:385.

62. O'Neal, P., and Robins, L. N. The relation of childhood behavior problems to adult psychiatric status. *Amer. J. Psychiat.*, 1958, 114:961.

63. Pasamanick, B., et al. Socioeconomic status: Some precursors of neuropsychiatric disorder. *Amer. J. Orthopsychiat.*, 1956, 26:594.

64. Pasamanick, B., et al. A Survey of mental disease in an urban population. *Amer. J. Publ. Hlth.*, 1957, 47:923.

65. Powers, E., and Witmer, H. *An experiment in the prevention of delinquency.* New York: Columbia University Press, 1951.

66. *Proceedings of the Conference on Social Crippling: A by-product of institutional living, September 1958.* National Institute of Mental Health and Department of Mental Hygiene, State of Maryland.

67. Rabinovitch, R. D., et al. A research approach to reading retardation. *Res. Publ. Ass. Nerv. Ment. Dis.*, 1954, 34:363.

68. Rennie, T. A. C., et al. Urban life and mental health: Socioeconomic status and mental disorder in the metropolis. *Amer. J. Psychiat.*, 1957, 113:831.

69. Richmond, J. B. The role of the pediatrician in early mother-child relationships. *Clin. Proc. Children's Hosp.*, 1959, 15:101.

70. Robins, L. N., and O'Neal, P. Mortality, mobility and crime: Problem children thirty years later. *Amer. Sociol. Rev.*, 1958, 23:162.

71. Robins, L. N., and O'Neal, P. The adult prognosis for runaway children. *Amer. J. Orthopsychiat.*, 1959, 29:752.

72. Rodriguez, A., et al. The outcome of school phobia: A follow-up study based on 41 cases. *Amer. J. Psychiat.*, 1959, 116:540.

73. Rosen, G. *A history of public health.* New York: MD Publications, 1958.

74. Sarason, S. B., and Gladwin, T. Psychological and cultural problems in mental subnormality. *Genet. Psychol. Monogr.*, 1958, 57:3.

75. Smith, D. W., et al. The mental prognosis in hypothyroidism of infancy and childhood. *Pediatrics*, 1957, 19:1011.

76. Snyder, L. H. Fifty years of medical genetics. *Science*, 1959, 129:7.

77. Travis, A. M., and Woolsey, C. M. Motor performance of monkey after bilateral partial and total decortication. *Amer. J. Phys. Med.*, 1956, 35:273.

78. Waldfogel, S., et al. A program for early intervention in school phobia. *Amer. J. Orthopsychiat.*, 1959, 29:324.

79. Wallace, H. W., et al. Studies on the conversion of phenylalanine to tyrosine in phenylpyruvic oligophrenia. *Proc. Soc. Exp. Biol. Med.*, 1957, 94:632.

23

Types of Mental Health Consultation

GERALD CAPLAN

IN this paper the term "consultation" is used in a quite restricted sense to denote the process of interaction between two professional persons— the consultant, who is a specialist, and the consultee, who invokes his help in regard to a current work problem with which the latter is having some difficulty, and which he has decided is within the former's area of specialized competence. The work problem involves the management or treatment of one or more clients of the consultee, or the planning or implementation of a program to cater to such clients.

An essential aspect of consultation, as defined here, is that the professional responsibility for the client remains with the consultee. The consultant may offer helpful clarifications, diagnostic interpretations, or advice on treatment, but the consultee will be free to accept or reject all or part of this help. Action for the benefit of the client that emerges from the consultation is the responsibility of the consultee.

Another essential aspect of this type of consultation is that the consultant engages in the activity, not only in order to help the consultee with his current professional problem in relation to a specific client or program, but also in order to add to his knowledge and to lessen areas of misunderstanding, so that he may be able in the future to deal more effectively on his own with this category of problem.

The above definition applies not only to a single consultant dealing with one consultee, but equally to one consultant and a group of consultees, or a group of consultants and a single consultee or group of consultees.

In defining consultation in this narrow way there is no implication that this is the "correct" usage of the term and that other authorities are "wrong" in their different use of it; on the contrary there is the intention to recognize that confusion exists because so many workers legitimately use the term in so many different ways, and the desire to single out one among the various activities for special study and evaluation. A specialist formally or informally

Reprinted from *American Journal of Orthopsychiatry*, 1963, *33*, 470–481, by permission of the publisher and the author. © 1963, American Orthopsychiatric Association. Dr. Caplan is Clinical Professor of Psychiatry, Harvard Medical School.

designated "a consultant" may engage in many types of professional activity that resemble each other to some extent in regard to goals, methods and techniques. These include inspection, administrative manipulation, coordination, supervision, teaching, casework, psychotherapy, counseling, negotiation, liaison, collaboration, mediation and so on. I believe that we will attain a higher level of professional functioning when the specialist is able to differentiate these various activities and employ each of them consistently in relation to his assignment, his professional goals and his understanding of the demands of each situation. In a previous publication I have made a preliminary attempt to differentiate consultation from supervision, education, psychotherapy and collaboration (1). In a forthcoming publication I intend to deal with this topic in greater detail (2).

What has been said so far refers to consultation as a generic form of specialist professional activity. By the term "mental health consultation," we designate the use of this method as part of a community program for the promotion of mental health and for the prevention, treatment and rehabilitation of mental disorders. The reports of the Joint Commission on Mental Illness and Health emphasize the fact that much, if not most, of the work with actual or potential patients in such programs is currently being carried out by professional workers who have no specialized training in psychiatry, psychology or psychiatric social work—namely nurses, teachers, family doctors, pediatricians, clergymen, probation officers, policemen, welfare workers and the like. Recruitment and training possibilities in the mental health professions are such that this state of affairs is likely to continue indefinitely. Consequently, it seems important that a significant proportion of the time and energies of mental health specialists should be focused upon improving the operations of these other care-giving professionals in relation to mental health and mental disorder. Mental health consultation is one of the methods that have been developed to achieve this goal. It provides an opportunity for a relatively small number of consultants to exert a widespread effect in a community through the intermediation of a large group of consultees. In order to be effective along these lines, the amount of time devoted by a consultant to helping a consultee deal with the mental health problems of a current case must be relatively short, and there must be the maximum educational carry-over to the consultee's work with other cases. It is also worth emphasizing that, in a comprehensive program of community psychiatry, mental health consultation should be used in appropriate balance with other community methods, such as education about mental health issues in the preprofessional and inservice training of care-giving agents, and planning and coordination of care-giving agencies.

TYPES OF MENTAL HEALTH CONSULTATION

It is of value to differentiate four fundamental types of mental health consultation, each of which is associated with characteristic technical demands upon the consultant. A consultation may focus upon (A) the consultee's problems in handling a specific client, as contrasted with (B) his administrative problems in initiating and maintaining a program, and a consultant may have the immediate goal of improving the client or the program, as contrasted with improving the insights, skills and professional objectivity of the consultees. The four types have become known as (A1) Client-Centered Case Consultation, (B1) Program-Centered Administrative Consultation, (A2) Consultee-Centered Case Consultation, and (B2) Consultee-Centered Administrative Consultation. In the following brief description of these types of mental health consultation, Type A2 will be discussed in greater detail, because of its special technical interest.

TYPE A1—CLIENT-CENTERED CASE CONSULTATION

In this type of consultation the problems encountered by the consultee in dealing with a professional case are the major focus of interest; the immediate goal is to help the consultee find the most effective treatment for his client. Increasing the knowledge of the consultee so that he may be better able to deal unaided with this client or class of clients in the future is a subsidiary goal. Since the primary goal is to improve the client, the consultant's fundamental responsibility is to make a specialized assessment of the client's condition and to recommend an effective disposition or method of treatment to be undertaken by the consultee. This means that the consultant's attention is centered mainly upon the client, whom he probably will examine with whatever methods of investigation his specialized judgment indicates are necessary to arrive at an adequate appraisal of the nature of his difficulty. On the other hand, the consultant will pay attention to what the consultee says, to ascertain what type of help the latter is requesting—sometimes the consultee may ask for "consultation" when he really wishes to refer a patient for treatment by the specialist, and he will be angry when the patient is sent back with a diagnosis and a prescription for nonspecialist management. Sometimes all he is requesting is help with screening so that he can decide to which specialized agency he should refer the patient. In that event he is not interested in receiving a complicated diagnostic formulation, and the consultant might well spare himself the expenditure of time and effort in working this out. Here, as elsewhere in community psychiatry, energy expended on diagnostic investigation should be no greater than that necessary to answer the questions that will meaningfully affect disposition or treatment.

The consultant will also pay attention to what the consultee says, to learn how to communicate with him. The more the consultant knows about the consultee's language, conceptual framework and ways of working, the better will he be able to formulate his diagnosis in understandable words and to suggest treatment that the consultee can carry out effectively in his professional setting. Too many consultants write reports in which they communicate only with themselves and with their specialist reference group! This would not affect the welfare of the client, if the specialist were carrying out the treatment, but in consultation the treatment is carried out by the consultee, and only messages that improve his operations will help the client. Needless to say, the consultant must make a correct diagnosis and must suggest effective treatment in order to improve the client's condition. The content as well as the manner of the communication is important for success.

TYPE B1—PROGRAM-CENTERED ADMINISTRATIVE CONSULTATION

In this type of consultation the consultant is called in by a consultee, or more often by a group of consultees, to help with current problems in the administration of programs for the prevention, treatment or rehabilitation of mental disorders. The problems may relate to any aspect of the program, including the planning and administration of services and policies governing the recruitment, training and effective utilization of personnel. In response to the needs expressed by the consultees, the primary focus of the consultant is upon making a specialized assessment of the current program or policy predicament, and then recommending a plan of action to resolve the difficulty. As in Type A1, education of the consultees to be better able to deal on their own with such a difficulty is a subordinate goal.

In contrast with client-centered case consultation, the consultant may make much use of the efforts of his consultees in collecting the data about the workings of the institution upon which he will base his analysis of the problem. He will, however, take into account that the consultees will inevitably distort and bias their reports. He will collect some of the essential data himself, using his own specialized methods. And he will cross check the other data, since in this type of consultation the assessment of the problem is his responsibility alone and is not to be shared with the consultees, however actively he may enlist their cooperation in assembling the facts. His reason for the latter is that he will probably need as many agents as possible in collecting the large amount of complicated data necessary to understand the problems of an institution. An important aspect of these problems may involve the interrelationships of the staff, which he can observe in action as he works with them. Also, through his own interactions in this process, he can learn about the language, values and traditions of the institution, so that his recommendations for remedial action will be expressed in understandable words and will be feasible within the current and future reality of the institution.

Administrative consultants will usually be requested to present their analysis of the institutional problems, and their recommendations for solution, in a written report. This will often deal with short-term solutions that are possible with the current staff and in line with the current administrative framework. It will also contain long-term suggestions of an ideal type, which may act as distant goals toward which the institution may strive in the future. The long-term recommendations will be based largely upon the general knowledge and the experience of the consultant in a variety of other programs, as well as upon his professional value system. They will of course also be directed toward the local situation, but in formulating them the consultant will be minimally influenced by the ideas of the consultees.

On the other hand, if the short-term recommendations are to be acceptable and implemented, they must fit closely within the expectations and the capacities of the consultee group. Experienced administrative consultants find that the best way of ensuring the latter is to communicate their developing judgments in their formative stages to the consultee group, and then progressively to modify these recommendations in the light of the reactions of the consultees. The responsibility for the recommendations is not shared with the consultees, and the disagreement of one or more of them with certain of the recommendations will not necessarily persuade the consultant to change them; but the discussions will enable him to see how closely his plan fits the culture of the group, and the working-through process will prepare the consultees to live with his eventual report. When the consultees read the consultant's report, they should find little in it that he has not already discussed with them, and upon which they have not been able to express an opinion as to feasibility.

An interesting variant of this type of consultation deals, not with programs for the promotion of mental health and the prevention and control of mental disorders, but with the mental health aspects of other programs. In this consultation the mental health specialist is asked for help in regard to those problems of administration that may influence the mental health or the interpersonal effectiveness of personnel or of recipients of the program. His specialized knowledge of personality dynamics and interpersonal relationships in social systems is exploited to help administrators behave more effectively and, at the same time, with a greater regard for the human needs of their colleagues, subordinates and clients. Operational efficiency in an institution such as a hospital or a factory can be achieved in different ways. Some of these may frustrate fundamental needs of the participants and may lead to an increased risk of mental disorder. The mental health specialist may be able to help the administrators maintain or raise the productivity of their institution, while also improving the mental health potential of the workers.

TYPE A2—CONSULTEE-CENTERED CASE CONSULTATION

The primary focus of the consultant in this type of consultation is upon the consultee, rather than upon the particular client with whom the consultee is currently having difficulties. True, the problems of this client were the direct stimulus for the consultation request, and they will form the main content area of the consultation discussions. Also, a successful consultation will usually lead to an improvement in the consultee's handling of the current case, with consequent benefit for the client. But in contrast to client-centered case consultation, in which the consultant's main interest is in diagnosing the difficulties of the client, his primary endeavor in the present instance is to assess the nature of the consultee's work difficulty and to help him handle this. Most or all of the consultant's time will be spent talking to the consultee about the client, and little or no time will be spent in specialist examination of the client. The consultant realizes that, because the consultee is having difficulties with the client, his perceptions and understanding of the case are probably distorted, and that a correct diagnosis of the client by the consultant is unlikely if his data are restricted to this information but, since his goal is to improve the consultee's functioning and not to make a diagnosis of the client, this is not important. In fact, in this type of consultation it is the very distortions and omissions in the consultee's report on the client that provide the consultant with his basic material. He does not need to learn the "objective" reality of the client to be able to identify these distortions and omissions. Instead, he appraises them by identifying internal inconsistencies in the consultee's story, and from verbal and nonverbal cues in both the consultee's behavior and that of others in the consultee institution. When the consultant has pinpointed the nature of the consultee's difficulty, he attempts to remedy this through helping the consultee gain a mastery of the significant issue by means of a discussion of the problems of the client and the consultee's contribution to their solution.

There are four major categories of difficulty that interfere with a consultee's ability to deal adequately with the mental health problems of his client and may stimulate him or his administrative superiors to invoke consultation help. These are (a) lack of understanding of the psychological factors in the case; (b) lack of skill or resources to deal with the problems involved; (c) lack of professional objectivity in handling the case; and (d) lack of confidence and self-esteem due to fatigue, illness, inexperience, youth or old age.

Lack of Understanding

In this type of difficulty the consultee either has not learned during his preprofessional or inservice training enough about psychology and psychopathology to realize what factors are operating in this case, or he has learned the general laws of mental functioning but does not see how they apply to the idiosyncratic complexities of this client and his psychosocial milieu. The consultant will try to help the consultee by adding to his cognitive knowledge and by clarifying the data about the client, to enable the consultee to see meaningful connections between parts of the psychosocial pattern. In doing this, it is important for the consultant to know a good deal about the professional subculture of the consultee so that the information he imparts will be consonant with the type and level of psychological understanding of the consultee's profession. Consultants should guard against trying to turn such consultees as nurses, clergymen and pediatricians into "proxy" psychiatrists or "junior" psychologists. This implies the need, not only to use the terminology of the consultee's profession or else words with a nonspecialized meaning, but also to avoid dealing with concepts such as penis envy, castration fears and pregenital fantasies, the proper understanding of which demands the conceptual framework and style of thinking of a mental health specialist.

Mental health consultation on an individual basis is an expensive way of teaching the facts of human behavior to professional workers. When a particular agency or community makes many requests for this type of consultation, consultants would be well advised to consider organizing preprofessional or inservice training courses in mental health, since systematic group instruction is a more economical way to achieve comparable results.

Lack of Skill

The difficulty here is not lack of understanding of the client's problems, but either lack of professional skill on the part of the consultee, including how to make professional use of the self in dealing with the psychological complications of clients, or else lack of knowledge of appropriate specialist resources in the community or of how to invoke their help for the benefit of the client. The consultant deals with this by assisting the consultee to choose a suitable plan of action. He will therefore be sensitive to the consultee's level and rate of professional development, and, as in the previous category of consultation, he will ensure that the various action possibilities, among which he is helping the consultee to choose, are drawn from a range of actions consonant with the consultee's professional subculture and are not plans specific to mental health specialists. To prevent endangering the professional integrity of the consultee, a consultant who uses this technique must have a great deal of knowledge about the details of role functioning in the consultee's profession.

This type of consultation, which fosters the development of professional skills, is rather similar to technical supervision. Many categories of consultees, such as family doctors, clergymen and pediatricians, have no institutionalized system of technical supervision, and in these cases mental health consultation may be the only way of getting help with skill development, although group instruction should always be considered as a useful supplement to individual consultation. Whenever an institution or a profession does provide supervisors, such as in schools, kindergartens and nursing and social agencies, the mental health specialist should avoid suggestions that imply prescriptions for action by line workers; he should substitute methods to increase the knowledge of supervisors so that responsibility for action can remain undisturbed within the system of the consultee agency. In all the care-giving professions the mental health specialist should attempt to influence preprofessional training to insure that these skills are learned more effectively. Any consultant who encounters many instances of lack of skill in consultees should ask himself whether he might not get results more cheaply by thus deploying some of his efforts "upstream."

Lack of Objectivity

Experienced, well-trained and well-supervised consultees will occasionally meet situations that are beyond their knowledge and skills, and may call for one of the two previous categories of consultation; more commonly, when such a person asks for consultation help, it is because he is unable for various reasons to exploit his knowledge and skills with the particular client. This is usually manifested by a disorder in his professional objectivity due to the distortion of his functioning by subjective factors. His professional empathy for the client and other actors in the client's life situation may be replaced by identification and personal involvement leading to partisanship, or he may turn away from the client's situation because it stimulates in him some personal sensitivity. In either case there is likely to be a distortion of perception and judgment and a lowered effectiveness in utilizing professional knowledge and skills.

My colleagues and I at Harvard School of Public Health have for some years been particularly interested in this category of consultation, and we have formulated the consultee's difficulty as being due to the intrusion into his professional functioning of an interfering problem theme. The latter is derived either from some long-standing personality difficulty made salient by a symbolic trigger in the client's case, or from a current situational conflict in the consultee's home life, or from some problem in the work field—either a role conflict of the consultee or a more general social system disequilibrium, acute or chronic, involving the authority structure or communication pattern within the institution or between it and its surrounding community. Whatever the proximate or ultimate underlying causes, the final common path leading to the work difficulty and the request for consultation is usually a so-called theme interference, that is, a symbolic inhibition of free perception and communication between consultee and client and a concomitant disorder of objectivity. This is usually accompanied by some degree of emotional upset in the consultee, ranging from a relatively mild rise of tension, when he thinks about certain aspects of the client's case (which we call "segmental tension"), to a well-marked crisis response, in which the consultee's general professional functioning and emotional equilibrium are temporarily upset. The consultee usually ascribes his current discomfort to his difficulties with the client, onto whose case he displaces feelings of anxiety, hostility, shame and depression, which can be seen by the consultant to be partly or even primarily originating in his personal life or in his involvement with the social system problems of his institution.

The following example illustrates the operation of theme interference:

A teacher spoke with hopelessness about a ten-year-old girl in his class, who he felt was mentally retarded. He had spent much time in vain trying to teach the child to read so that she would not get too far behind the others in the class. He felt that unless he succeeded she would inevitably become an outcast in society and that others would exploit her weakness. The consultant realized that the teacher was identifying with the child, whom he was perceiving in a stereotyped way as a "mental defective" who must inevitably come to a bad end unless "rescued" by him through greatly augmenting her ability to achieve. The teacher was not perceiving the child's assets, namely, that she was quite popular among her peers, and had non-verbal skills that might one day help her make a useful place for herself in society. He was also exaggerating the likelihood that more intelligent people would exploit her because of her backwardness—in fact, he felt this was inevitable.

This teacher was currently worrying about his own ability to achieve in a new school to which he had come after an unsatisfactory experience elsewhere as a principal. He was particularly sensitive in his relationship with the headmaster, a driving man who demanded high standards from his teachers. The theme of "mental retardation" was also important in the teacher's past life, because he had been backward himself as a child, and had only begun to improve at the age of ten.

This example illustrates a general characteristic of interfering themes; they can be formulated as preconscious syllogisms that mould the consultee's expectations. In this case the parts of the syllogism are:

This girl is mentally retarded.

All mentally retarded people inevitably fail in life and are exploited by more intelligent people.

Therefore, this girl is doomed, despite everything I will do to rescue her.

The stereotyped expectation—*all mentally retarded are doomed to exploitation and failure*—applies equally to himself and to the girl, both of whom are defined by him as fitting into this category. In such instances the consultee stereotypes the perception of the client into a symbol having a personal meaning for the consultee, and this leads to a fixed expectation of some sort of doom for the client, which inhibits the consultee's professional efforts because of a feeling of hopelessness.

In handling this type of situation, our approach is to respect the separation of the consultee's personal life from his work difficulty, and not to investigate the causes of the theme interference, but to focus upon defining the nature of the theme by a careful examination of its manifestations in the work context. The consultant then reduces the theme interference by influencing the consultee to adopt a more reality-based expectation for the client.

In effect, the consultee is defending himself against direct confrontation of a personal problem by working with it vicariously in the client. Irrational fantasies, which prevented him from dealing directly with his own problem, are also hampering him in helping the client. He communicates these to the consultant via the latent content of his descriptions of the client's predicament. The consultant attacks the irrational elements in these fantasies by in turn talking about the client in such a way that he conveys a corrective message through the use of the same symbolism as the consultee uses. The result is that the consultant deals with the consultee's problems without interfering with his defenses, and therefore without arousing anxiety and resistance. Because of this, and because he does not need to uncover the personal sources of the theme in the consultee's current or past life, this type of consultation is most economical. Successful cases usually need only two or three sessions.

The effect on the consultee seems to depend upon the degree of his personal involvement with his client. This is evidenced by the degree of interference with his customary professional objectivity and also by the intensity of his emotional upset in handling the difficulties of his client.

As an example of the reduction of theme interference, let us return to the case of the teacher who asked for consultation with the "mentally retarded" girl. In this particular case, the consultant by chance learned enough about the consultee to realize the personal source of the theme interference. This knowledge was not necessary for his consultation, and consultants usually do their utmost to prevent such personal material entering the content of their discussions with the consultee. When the consultee nevertheless does bring such issues into the consultation, the consultant does not comment directly about them, but turns the discussion back to a consideration of some aspect of the client's problem. In this case, the consultant accepted the consultee's contention that the girl was backward, but he then attacked the inevitability of a bad end for her by involving the teacher in a joint examination of those aspects of her current life from which predictions about her future might validly be made. This was not an entirely intellectual process, since the consultant delayed this discussion until he had encouraged the building up of a supportive relationship between himself and the teacher. On the basis of this relationship he was able to influence the latter to pay attention to such items as the girl's nonverbal skills and her social poise and popularity, which introduced some hope that she might not be entirely useless and unhappy in her future life. The crux of the consultation, however, was a message that the consultant conveyed by implication—by the way he spoke about the girl, and by the way he took it for granted that others would deal with her—namely, that even though it might be recognized that she was mentally dull, the more intelligent people in her environment would not necessarily exploit her.

The invalidation of such a fixed expectation about a personally meaningful issue in the client has an effect not only on the consultee's feelings of hopelessness about this client, but also on similar feelings about himself. It also prepares him in the future to be able to handle, with his customary professional objectivity and skill, other clients who may be correctly or incorrectly perceived as fitting into the first part of the preconscious syllogistic proposition. Incidentally, in this type of consultation it is important not to unlink the client from the first statement of the syllogism—in this case, the perception, *this girl is mentally retarded*. Such an unlinking might be possible with the help of the influence of the consultation relationship. For instance, the consultant might have pointed out that the girl's nonverbal skills indicated a higher level of intelligence, and that she was not really mentally retarded, just slow in the use of words, or else that perhaps she had emotional blocks in reading because of certain past experiences. Had the teacher accepted this possibility, his worry about this girl would have dissipated, but he would have come away from the consultation with no reduction in his theme problem, either in regard to himself as mentally retarded or in regard to future pupils who might appear mentally retarded. In fact, he would very likely search for some other child to take the place of the girl as a displacement object for his personal problem.

It is of interest to point out that, had this case been misdiagnosed by the consultant as due not to theme interference but to lack of understanding of the signs and meaning of mental retardation, the consultation might have been conducted in just such a manner.

Lack of Confidence and Self-Esteem

This type of difficulty is usually easily identified. The consultee's functioning is interfered with in a nonspecific way by illness, fatigue or infirmity, or else by lack of confidence due to inexperience or youth. What is demanded from the consultant is nonspecific ego support. The only technical difficulty is that this should be tactfully given so as not to weaken the consultee further by the explicit recognition of his personal difficulties in a context that may lead to a further loss of self-esteem.

Professional workers who have the benefit of adequate technical and administrative supervision will rarely need this type of consultation, but for those who work on their own, mental health consultation may be a useful source of support in times of human need.

TYPE B2—CONSULTEE-CENTERED ADMINISTRATIVE CONSULTATION

As the name implies, the primary goal of this major category of consultation is to help consultees develop an improved capacity to master problems in the planning and maintenance of programs for the prevention and control of mental disorders, and in the interpersonal aspects of the operations of their agencies. As with program-centered administrative consultation, this method is often applied in group situations and is directed toward helping a group of administrators improve their functioning; also it is not infrequently invoked on an individual basis by an administrator. Since a specialist's assessment of the administrative problem by the consultant is not demanded, it is quite feasible to operate with an individual administrator and to restrict consultation help to the circumscribed area of the institutional life that is his province. This type of consultation is very similar to consultee-centered case consultation, with the major exception that few mental health consultants have as thorough a knowledge of administrative problems as they have of the psychosocial complications of an individual client, and they must be careful to restrict their help to those factors in the administrative situation, such as the interpersonal and group dynamic aspects, concerning which they do have special competence. Most mental health specialists who act as administrative consultants make a serious study of administration and social science to augment the traditional knowledge of their own profession. In successful cases the resulting amalgam leads to a "clinical" approach to administrative problems that many administrator consultees find peculiarly helpful, and characteristically different from the kind of help they are accustomed to derive from specialists in their own field.

As with case consultation, individual consultee-centered administrative consultation may be invoked on an *ad hoc* basis to deal with occasional current problems that may necessitate a short block of sessions for their mastery. Because of the great complexity of the administrative situation, consultees will almost always be burdened with some problem, and regularly scheduled meetings with a consultant may be set up on a long-term basis to deal with whatever is uppermost at the moment. With this pattern of operation, consultants must guard against allowing their role unintentionally to slip into one of supervision or nonspecific emotional support, or into psychotherapy.

Consultee-centered administrative consultation in a group setting is a more complicated operation than the above, and its intricacies still await adequate clarification. It is almost invariably carried out in the form of regularly scheduled meetings over a lengthy period. At these meetings the consultees raise for discussion with the consultant any administrative problem of current concern, and this may be the central topic of one or several meetings. The simplest role for the consultant is to help the group clarify the complexities of the problem and for him to contribute to the discussion on the basis of his specialized knowledge of intrapersonal motivations and interpersonal relations, as well as of the human needs of personnel and clients. He may facilitate the acquiring by the consultee group of group dynamic skills, and also help them explore new patterns of action in dealing with administrative complexities. The main technical difficulty is how to handle theme interference when the consultant identifies this in an individual group member, or when it occurs as a group manifestation.

The techniques of theme interference reduction as practiced in case consultation are often hazardous when handling an individual member in the presence of the group, since, if the consultees are psychologically sophisticated, one of the individual's colleagues may realize his subjective involvement and make a defense-destroying interpretation before the consultant can stop it. Such a situation may rapidly slide into group psychotherapy, in which the separation of personal and work problems is set aside, with the usual arousal of anxiety and resistance. To avoid this, the group consultant must structure the ground rules to prevent the airing of personal problems, and he must maintain a tight control over the direction of the discussion, so that he can steer away from a focus upon theme interference in an individual member. Sometimes this is relatively easy because that member is really acting as spokesman for the group, and his individual theme interference is the presenting example of an issue common to the group as a whole. He may have been stimulated by other members to act as their mouthpiece through a process that Fritz Redl has picturesquely called "role suction." In this situation the consultant can actively refocus the issue as a group problem, and he can thus turn the spotlight away from the individual member.

Such a manoeuver raises the technical question of how to deal with theme interference at the group level. In other words, how does the consultant handle the discussion of a program or policy question when he identifies as a major source of difficulty unstated personal conflicts among group members or between the group and other people, usually administrative superiors or high-status figures in some other division of the organization? Are such issues to be opened up for explicit discussion, and if so how does the consultant differentiate such an approach from analytic group psychotherapy? The answer is not too clear, but the differentiation appears to lie in restricting the content of consultation discussions to role conflicts, and minimizing the discussion of private and personal factors. This is not easy, since personality idiosyncrasies and incompatibilities are a frequent source of role clashes. A useful rule of thumb is to avoid discussing the personality of any member of the consultee group, apart from alluding to fundamental aspects of human nature that are common to everyone, the consultant included.

REFERENCE

1. Caplan, G. *Concepts of mental health and consultation: Their application in public health social work.* Children's Bureau Publ. 373. U. S. Department of Health, Education, and Welfare. Washington, D. C., 1959.

24

Mental Health Consultation with Groups

JOHN ALTROCCHI, CHARLES D. SPIELBERGER, AND
CARL EISDORFER

THE growing interest in prevention of psychological disorders and promotion of mental health has led psychologists and other mental health professionals to engage in a wide variety of activities which may be collectively labeled mental health consultation. Developments in consultation theory, however, have not kept pace with practice and have been concerned with interactions between a consultant and an individual consultee (2, 4), with only a few exceptions (7, 9, 11). The aim of this paper is to present a conceptualization of mental health consultation with groups of consultees.

Mental health consultation generally refers to one aspect of a program for the promotion of mental health and the prevention and treatment of psychological disorders. More specifically, mental health consultation is "a helping process, an educational process, and a growth process achieved through interpersonal relationships (11, p. 85)." The goals are to assist the key professional workers of a community to carry out their professional responsibilities by becoming more sensitive to the needs of their clients and associates and more comfortable and adept in their relationships with them. Members of certain professional groups, such as ministers, teachers, public health nurses, and welfare case workers are likely to be called upon by their clients in times of personal and interpersonal crises; it is assumed that such crises provide particularly opportune times for facilitating the client's emotional growth or the converse (4).

Group mental health consultation is similar in some respects to group supervision, seminar teaching, sensitivity training, and group psychotherapy, but it is also discriminably different from each of these other methods, all of which may have a role in a comprehensive mental health program. While this form of consultation closely resembles group supervision in its emphasis upon the consultees' understanding of the general principles and technical procedures essential to working effectively with their clients, group mental health consulta-

Reprinted from *Community Mental Health Journal*, 1965, *1*, 127–134 by permission of the publisher and the authors. © 1965, Behavioral Publications, Inc. Dr. Altrocchi is Associate Professor of Psychology and Medical Psychology, Duke University. Dr. Spielberger is Professor of Psychology, Florida State University. Dr. Eisdorfer is Associate Professor of Medical Psychology, Duke University.

tion differs from group supervision in that the consultant typically enters the consultees' social system from the outside and is often from another profession, and each consultee's supervisor retains the usual administrative control.

In its educational goals and emphasis on discussion methods, group mental health consultation resembles seminar teaching, but goes beyond it in attempting to make use of group processes and the consultees' affective involvement in their work problems. Group mental health consultation shares with sensitivity training for co-workers (3) the use of group process and consultees' personal involvement; it diverges in its degree of structure and the limitation of content focus to work-related problems of the consultees.

A group method of consultation is similar to group psychotherapy in its attempt to increase personal growth, sensitivity, and effectiveness by applying group processes to individual affective and intellectual learning, but is distinct in several important ways: (a) The implicit psychological contract in consultation (4, 9) involves a relationship between professionals in which the consultee is free to apply what he learns or not as he sees fit; (b) the relative emphasis is on educational goals rather than on the modification of a disorder; and, especially, (c) the content focus is on the professional rather than the personal problems of the consultee. The consultees' affective involvements with clients are considered only in their relation to current work problems. For example, as Parker (9, p. 2) has suggested in reference to group consultation with public health nurses, "When an emotional reaction of the nurse destroys her objectivity about some aspect of her job, that reaction is a suitable subject for group discussion, but the intrapsychic conflict which may have helped to generate the reaction should not be considered . . ." Nevertheless, many of the mechanisms observed in group therapy—acceptance, universalization, intellectualization, reality testing, interaction, spectator therapy, and ventilation (5)—may also be observed in group mental health consultation. Thus, while the primary goals of mental health consultation are educational rather than therapeutic, some phases of group consultation resemble some kinds of group psychotherapy and corrective emotional experiences do take place. Although group consultation is not therapy, it may have therapeutic effects.

A CASE SEMINAR METHOD OF GROUP MENTAL HEALTH CONSULTATION

For varying periods since 1958, each of the authors has been engaged in part-time group mental health consultation in one of two North Carolina counties. One of these is rural and the other is a small metropolitan seaport area. The absence of mental health facilities and the considerable interest of a large number of key professionals in each community made group consultation more appropriate for serving the needs of these communities than working with individual consultees or attempting to work directly with clients. Moreover, time restrictions (only one to three scheduled days a month were spent in these distant counties) rendered "on call" response to individual consultee crises impractical. For these reasons, we focused on group consultation and selected a case seminar approach as the principal consultation procedure.

For each case seminar meeting, a member of the group was asked to present a problem case for which he (or she) had responsibility, and was encouraged to select one of general interest to the group. In order to obtain first-hand contact with the client (patient, student, or parishioner), the consultant, whenever practicable, either interviewed or observed the client interacting with the consultee. This served as a safeguard against missing crucial diagnostic information (e.g., suicidal tendencies) of which the consultee was as yet unaware. Observation of the client also provided the consultant with a better basis for discussing the case with the consultee and for helping the consultee prepare the case for presentation in the group. Actual contact with some clients, when used, permitted the consultant to demonstrate interviewing techniques. In such contacts, the consultant's impact on the client was typically supportive and often therapeutic.

We have used the case seminar method with public health nurses, ministers, welfare caseworkers, probation officers, policemen, public housing authority personnel, elementary and secondary school teachers, principals, school guidance counselors, and school speech therapists. In these meetings the etiology and dynamics of the case are discussed in relatively non-technical terms. The interpersonal relations between client, consultee, and other persons involved in the case, e.g., the client's family and professional workers from other disciplines, are considered in detail, as is the relevance of the specific case to the roles of the consultee group in the community. Although there are individual differences among our consultation techniques, the general approach which developed is coherent and communicable.

GROUP PROCESSES

The processes that we have observed in the case seminar method are similar in a number of respects to those more generally observed in the behavior of small groups. During a single session, there are recognizable phases: an introductory phase; a warming up phase; a problem-focused phase; and an ending phase (7). Over a series of sessions, we have repeatedly observed a number of characteristics peculiar to the group consultation process, each of which offers opportunities for fruitful problem-solving discussions involving the reactions of clients and consultees.

1. In the early stages of group consultation, when group members are unsure about consultation and are testing the consultant, bizarre or "impossible" cases are often presented (11). After discussing such cases, reassurance that

the consultee is doing all that is reasonably possible (if this is true—and it usually is) helps to establish rapport with the group and provides considerable support for group members, each of whom has some impossible cases. Indeed, an important facet of the consultant's role is helping consultees to recognize impossible cases and the guilt and anxiety associated with them. When a consultee understands that the investment of inordinate amounts of time with such cases is often unwarranted, he is enabled to make more optimal use of his professional time.

2. Consultees tend to present clients from minority or impoverished groups, especially in the beginning stages of consultation. Because they are different and distant from himself, such cases help the consultee avoid examining his own attitudes and behavior (11). This tendency, like resistance in psychotherapy, needs to be handled carefully. However, the discussion of attitudes toward minority or impoverished groups often provides an appropriate and useful entree for more specific understanding of the personal reactions of consultees toward their clients (9, 10).

3. Those members of professional groups who initially volunteer to present cases, or who are the first to share their reaction, frequently are the least defensive and most competent members of the group. They can be counted on to help move the group into problem solving. Although it is often tempting to move eagerly ahead with them, the consultant must wait until he perceives that the majority of the group can move forward together so as to avoid subgrouping and fragmentation.

4. There are important differences between groups with respect to initial cohesiveness, resistance, and the rapidity with which they proceed from one phase of consultation to the next. Groups with strong cohesiveness and high morale proceed rapidly into the problem-solving phase where they work productively and creatively toward the solution of the problems of individual consultees and their clients. Other groups are simply collections of professionals with similar jobs who may never move beyond the introductory stage of the group consultation process.

DYNAMICS OF GROUP INFLUENCE

In the case seminar method of group mental health consultation, the consultant attempts to arouse and channel peer influences. Peers have close mutual identifications, share sources of data not available to the consultant, and often provide excellent feedback to each other (3). If the consultant has been successful in stimulating the development of a group atmosphere which is generally supportive and nonjudgmental, then group members will feel inclined to share problems anxieties, and guilt. Sometimes this occurs very quickly, sometimes only after a long testing-out period. The sharing of problems establishes meaningful rather than superficial communication between group members and gradually assures each consultee that his problems are not unique. This reduces the consultees' feelings of isolation and inadequacy, permits a more objective evaluation of problems, and leads to the formulation of helpful alternative courses of action. The feedback provided at continuous case seminars also enables group members to observe the practical results of various suggestions made during former sessions.

We have observed that the work requirements of a professional group may dispose group members to develop similar attitudes toward their clients and similar anxieties concerning their professional competence. Also, each profession tends to attract individuals with similar personality characteristics. These factors increase the probability that the problems which come up in group mental health consultation will be shared and work-oriented. In gaining increased awareness of reactions common to the group as a whole, the individual consultee is helped to achieve insight into his own conflicts (10). Occasionally, when there is sufficient group cohesiveness and confidence in the consultant, a non-shared, but still work-connected, personal problem of an individuual consultee may be introduced into the discussion. (For instance, discussion of a child who has been neglected by a working mother may stimulate a public health nurse to share her personal guilt about leaving her young children to be cared for by someone else.) When this occurs, we have observed that the group usually deals with it in an understanding and appropriate manner. With regard to the sensitivity of consultee groups in handling the personal problems of group members, our experiences with a number of different professional groups are consistent with Parker's observation: "In the ten years of my experience as a mental health consultant, not once has a nurse succumbed to the pressure of anxiety and brought before the group personal matters that were inappropriate in kind or degree (9, p. 18)."

Our observations that group members usually handle personal problems with sensitivity and appropriateness contrast markedly with those of Caplan and his colleagues who have focused on mental health consultation with individual consultees. According to Caplan,

> The techniques of theme-interference reduction as practiced in case consultation are often hazardous in handling an individual member in the presence of the group. If the consultees are psychologically sophisticated, one of the individual's colleagues may realize his subjective involvement and make a defense-destroying interpretation before the consultant can stop it. Such a situation may rapidly slide into group psychotherapy, in which the separation of personal and work problems is set aside, with the usual arousal of anxiety and resistance. In order to avoid this, the group consultant must structure the ground rules to prevent the airing of personal problems and must maintain a tight control over the direction of the discussion, so that he can avoid a focus on theme interference in an individual member (4, p. 228).

We believe that the forces of group influence in mental health consultation, like other social forces, can either be feared and restrained, or can be put to use.

ROLES AND TECHNIQUES OF THE GROUP CONSULTANT

The mental health consultant who uses the case seminar approach must function simultaneously in several different roles; teacher, group leader, clinician and facilitator of communication between community groups. As a teacher the consultant does not necessarily attempt to transmit specialized technical knowledge but he does convey general principles and knowledge about those techniques which can be used within the range of the consultees' particular professional background. In this capacity, the consultant may function as a seminar leader, a resource person, and a lecturer; the specific techniques will naturally depend upon his own professional background as well as the qualifications, experiences, and needs of the consultee group. In early sessions formal lecturing on personality development and psychopathology as well as suggestions on interviewing technique are often appropriate. In later sessions he is more apt to function as a resource person and seminar leader. In the early sessions it is particularly important that the consultant be careful to clarify the limits of his ability to resolve questions raised by the consultee and to dispel any omniscience or omnipotence which may be imputed to him. Since the consultant's primary goal is to help the group and the individual consultees to learn to be able to derive meaningful solutions for work problems on their own, he should gratify demands for him to provide solutions only enough to keep the consultation sessions from becoming unduly frustrating to the consultees.

As a group leader the consultant acts as a catalyst to stimulate members of the group to share experiences and to explore together the problems of their clients, and helps to clarify problems, focus the discussion, and conceptualize solutions suggested by consultees. In the roles of group leader and teacher, we have also found it useful to relate the case under discussion to our own clinical experience and to expose to the group our own limitations and continuing efforts to broaden our understanding of human problems. Such personal reflection typically fosters identification with the consultant and emphasizes his humanness and lack of omniscience and omnipotence (1).

An important technical issue has arisen involving the consultant's teaching and group leader roles. Caplan (4) has suggested that consultants should employ supportive reassurance and praise with great caution in order to avoid implying that the consultant is judging the consultee, and to avoid emphasizing status differences between consultee and consultant. Members of professional groups, however, are aware that they are constantly being judged by their supervisors, colleagues, and clients, and that there are implicit judgments in all interpersonal relationships. Furthermore, consultation, by definition, implies unequal knowledge and skills in specific areas and to ignore this is unrealistic. A very crucial task for the consultant is to demonstrate clear respect for the consultee. Only genuine respect, communicated in many subtle ways, can establish a productive, working relationship and is, in our judgment, more important than the avoidance of specific kinds of verbal statements.

The mental health consultant's role as group leader often merges with his role as a clinician, especially during the discussion of the feelings of a consultee toward a client. Considerable clinical sensitivity may be required in deciding when to slow down or deal with affective expression by a consultee. However, as indicated above, we do not concur with Caplan (4) that the consultant should consistently avoid any direct discussion of the consultee's feelings and should interrupt such discussions if they arise spontaneously in a consultation group. Members of professional groups are not as fragile as patients and therefore do not require the same degree of protection, given the existing protection of the work-group setting. We do draw the line when aspects of the historical development of the consultee's personal feelings enter the discussion. On rare occasions, a brief excursion into a consultee's personal problems may be deemed appropriate because of the centrality of the problem to the role of the particular profession group. Such invasions of the consultee's private life should only be pursued if the consultee has the requisite strength to deal with his problems, commands the respect of the group, and provides the initiative for discussiong his personal problems "as a case at point."

As a clinician, the consultant must always be prepared to use his clinical skills and his knowledge of referral resources and procedures in cases of client emergencies. The consultant's experience and ability as a clinician is a particular asset when consultees are interested in "practical approaches" and not merely theoretical approaches to their problems.

Finally, an additional important role of the consultant becomes clear in his interaction with different community agencies. Case presentations often reveal the frustrations of consultees who must work with personnel from other agencies. Complaints range from individual ineptitude on the part of other professionals to red tape, gross obstructionism, and glory seeking. On more than one occasion workers from two agencies competing for the management of a client presented the same case in their respective seminar groups. This presents the mental health consultant with an ideal opportunity for facilitating interagency communication by helping members of different professional groups to appreciate the role of other professionals. Thus the mental health consultant who works with groups on a community wide basis has the role of a facilitator of communication between various community care takers and the professional groups they represent.

A central feature of this method involves clarifying the relationship between the feelings and attitudes of consultees and their work with clients. As Kevin (7) has pointed out, there are three different foci which the consultant may take in working toward such clarification. If the consultant focuses on the mutual interchange of affectively involved problems and solutions by consultees, group movement and breadth of learning are likely to occur, but this focus can be very frustrating for inexperienced group members who feel that they have little to contribute. If the consultant focuses on the interaction between himself and individual consultees, or if the consultant focuses primarily on the feelings and reactions of individual consultees in response to clients, individual learning at depth is possible, but the consultant must be especially alert to the possibility that such procedures may be sufficiently threatening to some group members to cause them to withdraw from group discussions and he must be constantly aware of the important differences between consultation and psychotherapy. Either of these latter two approaches may provide more direct help with specific problems but also tend to increase the dependency of an individual consultee upon the consultant and to generate competition among the consultees. Some consultants may prefer to use one of these three approaches as a primary approach, despite its potential disadvantages; we have found that the use of all three techniques at appropriate times tends to result in meaningful and rapid progression by the group from the early phase of consultation to the later problem-solving phase. Whichever approach or combination of approaches the consultant uses, however, can be over-used and carried so far that it is disadvantageous to the successful growth of the group and the individual consultees who comprise it. The consultant must always appreciate the difference between consultation and meddling in the affairs of the consultee. Not all the consultee's work problems are appropriate for discussion in group consultation and not all of the client's problems are the business of the consultee. It is important that the consultant remember that his long-range goal is to help the consultee to be more self-reliant and independent; the consultee in turn learns to help his clients to become more able to help themselves. In other words, what works for the consultant-consultee relationship ought to work for the consultee-client relationship.

CONSULTATION WITH GROUPS AND CONSULTATION WITH INDIVIDUALS

The choice of group or individual methods for consultation will depend on many factors. Group methods have the advantage of efficiency; they provide more cues and hypotheses for the consultant and more support to group members. A group focus musters the forces of group influence on individual members and helps to break through intra-group and inter-group communication barriers. In group consultation, members of different agencies can be included in the same groups and this often serves to bring about a more complete understanding of a case while contributing to better cooperation between agencies.

On the other hand, group consultation may have a number of disadvantages: (1) attendance at group sessions takes members of the group away from performing their usual services (7) and requires more coordination of consultee's schedules; (2) problems that involve delicate personal matters, or in which the confidentiality of case material is critical, may be more appropriately dealt with in individual consultation; (3) insecure consultees are often unwilling to expose to their peers work problems which they might discuss alone with the consultant; (4) group consultation is not as adaptable as individual consultation for meeting individual consultee-client crises; (5) if group cohesiveness is lacking, the case-seminar method of group consultation may not be effective. For example, in group consultation with the principals of schools scattered over a large rural county, there was a defensive tendency on the part of some group members to regard the problems presented to the group as idiosyncratic to other schools and not characteristic of their own. Consequently, it became necessary for the consultant to focus upon specific informational content rather than on the cases introduced by the group members. Although this resulted in requests for consultant visits to a number of the schools and opened the door for individual consultation with several principals, such initial non-group (or anti-group) spirit might well present a technical limitation to the case-seminar consultation technique.

Individual and group consultation each appear to have particular advantages and disadvantages. A combination of approaches, such as was noted above with school principals, may prove to be optimal for some professional groups. In group sessions, the individual consultee becomes familiar with the professional competence of the consultant, develops respect for him as a person, and learns to trust him. Subsequently, the consultee may seek consultation on problems that he might feel reluctant to discuss in the group. As a function of such individual consultation, the consultee may ultimately become more comfortable in bringing up his special problems within the group context. Creative exploration of a variety of consultation techniques with many different professional groups by consultants with diverse professional backgrounds is needed.

While there is as yet no objective evidence of the effectiveness of mental health consultation either with individual consultees or with groups, there is impressive agreement concerning many aspects of group consultation by those who have compiled and recorded their observations (1, 8, 9, 10, 11). Our own experiences have indicated that group consultation consistently leads to improved communication, group cohesiveness, and morale among consultees, and to their increased sensitivity with respect to the dynamics of interpersonal relations. We have also been impressed with consultees' reports of the beneficial influence of consultation on their relationships with their clients. However, objective data, derived from carefully controlled research, will be required to evaluate the effectiveness and usefulness of group consultation procedures and to establish consultation theory.

REFERENCES

1. Berlin, I. N. Mental health consultation in schools as a means of communicating mental health principles. *J. Amer. Acad. Child Psychiatry*, 1962, 1:671–79.
2. Bindman, A. J. Mental health consultation: Theory and practice. *J. Consult. Psychol.*, 1959, 23:473–82.

3. Bradford, L. P. Membership and the learning process. In L. P. Bradford, J. R. Gibb, and K. D. Benne (Eds.), *T-Group theory and laboratory method: Innovation in re-education.* New York: Wiley, 1964. Pp. 168–89.
4. Caplan, G. *Principles of preventive psychiatry.* New York: Basic Books, 1964.
5. Corsini, R. J., and Rosenberg, Bina. Mechanisms of group psychotherapy: Processes and dynamics. *J. Abnorm. Soc. Psychol.,* 1955, 51:406–11.
6. Glidewell, J. C. The entry problem in consultation. *J. Soc. Issues,* 1959, 15:52–59.
7. Kevin, D. Use of the group method in consultation. In L. Rapoport (Ed.), *Consultation in social work practice.* New York: National Association of Social Workers, 1963. Pp. 69–84.
8. Maddux, J. F. Psychiatric consultation in a rural setting. *Amer. J. Orthopsychiat.,* 1953, 23:775–84.
9. Parker, Beulah. Psychiatric consultation for nonpsychiatric professional workers. *Public Health Monograph No. 53.* Washington, D.C.: Department of Health, Education, and Welfare, 1958.
10. Parker, Beulah. Some observations on psychiatric consultation with nursery school teachers. *Ment. Hyg.,* 1962, 46:559–66.
11. Rieman, D. W. Group mental health consultation with public health nurses. In L. Rapoport (Ed.), *Consultation in social work practice.* New York: National Association of Social Workers, 1963. Pp. 85–98.

25

The Clinical Psychologist as
a Mental Health Consultant

ARTHUR J. BINDMAN

THE clinical psychologist has become increasingly involved in the new area of mental health consultation. However, his is not the only professional discipline in this area, and he shares it with psychiatry, social work, nursing, sociology, and other types of psychology. Each carries on consultation efforts, but a survey of their writings suggests that the approach varies with the background and training of the consultant. There is only meager theoretical thinking to support consultation techniques and even less evaluation evidence to prove that they work. Yet, everyone seems to be racing each other in describing their use, and the federal government has underscored consultation as one of the ten keystones of a community mental health program (26). The basis for this fact seems to lie in the need to work through significant others, the so-called "caretakers," in order to affect behaviors of many more persons in a more efficient manner.

Since the clinical psychologist is most directly involved with mental health concerns, this chapter is limited primarily to conceptions and principles of mental health consultation (i.e., consultation techniques which are aimed at reducing mental illness and enhancing mental health). It draws upon theory and example from other behavioral sciences, but aims primarily at the work and experience of clinical psychologists.

MODELS OF CONSULTATION

Types of consultation have frequently become confused, not only in the minds of those receiving consultation, but also among the various practitioners. There are a number of different models.

A very old model is that of one professional asking another professional to interview or evaluate the former's client in order to make some recommenda-

Reprinted from Abt, L. E. and B. F. Riess (Eds.) *Progress in Clinical Psychology,* 78–92, by permission of the publisher and the author. © 1966, Grune and Stratton. Dr. Bindman is Regional Administrator for Mental Retardation, Massachusetts Department of Mental Health. He was formerly Director of Psychological Services, Massachusetts Department of Mental Health.

tions for problem solution. The consultant acts as a technical specialist to provide some specific knowledge or experience. In the medical model he may even provide a specific problem-solving procedure; in the psychological model this may also be true in some instances, such as providing a specialized testing method and report. He is the "expert consultant (28)."

Another type of consultation which is frequently noted in health and social welfare agencies is the use of consultants from other disciplines to discuss case material, or to assist in thinking about new program development. These consultants are not acting in a supervisory role. Gilbert (31) clearly notes that a consultant in this latter role cannot become involved in administrative or supervisory functions in order to remain a "pure" consultant. Ferneau (28) terms him the "resource consultant." In the long-run, such a psychological consultant can play an important part in increasing the mental health endeavors of these agencies.

A third model is the consultant who works in an administrative position in a particular agency and provides consultation to the agency personnel. This type of consultant is often seen in departments of education, school systems, and public health agencies. They are intramural consultants, in contrast to consultants "from the outside" or extramural consultants. Since this raises many issues concerning the consultant's functioning in diverse roles, he cannot be considered as a "pure" consultant. Clinical psychologists who have shifted to positions within the school system have often run into this difficulty unless they are extremely careful in clarifying the differences between their administrative and consultative functions.

A fourth example of consultation practised by clinical psychologists is one in which the consultant provides counseling to a consultee, whom he views as the client. This example is frequently seen where psychologists have transferred their clinical skills to other settings, such as industry or schools. This would appear to be direct counseling or psychotherapy, rather than consultation as it is so often labeled, even though the "consultant" comes to the client or consultee.

A fifth example is the so-called "process" model. This model is most closely related to the work of Caplan (16–24, 53), Lindemann (39), Klein (37–41), Bindman (7–15), and others (33, 35, 48, 49, 51, 54, 56). It is specifically related to so-called mental health consultation methods, in which efforts are directed toward changes in the consultee-client relationship, which will enable the consultee to solve mental health problems himself and to handle similar problems in the future in a more competent fashion. Mental health consultation stems from crisis theory, particularly as expounded by Caplan (16, 18, 20, 23). It is based upon the assumption that if a consultee asks for assistance while in a state of tension or crisis concerning an interpersonal relationship, then changes can take place more rapidly through consultative intervention. The mental health consultant should not be viewed as a therapist or giver of prescriptive advice if he is to accomplish his goal. Instead, he must assist the consultee to solve problems with mental health implications by dealing with the consultee as a co-professional who already has requisite skills and knowledge but who is blocked in their use. Caplan divides mental health consultation into four categories: (1) client-centered case consultation; (2) program-centered administrative consultation; (3) consultee-centered case consultation; and (4) consultee-centered administrative consultation (22, 23). Consultee-centered case consultation, in which the goal is to effect change in the consultee, is particularly based upon the process model.

A sixth model for consultation by clinical psychologists is a group consultation approach (1, 2, 3, 4, 6, 36, 45, 46, 47, 52). In this method a group of consultees is seen by a consultant on a regular basis to discuss problems that the consultees face in their professional functioning. The method employed is a case seminar approach in which a group member presents case material for discussion by the group. The consultant acts in the role of "consultant-trainer," (32), in which he is a group leader, teacher, clinician, and facilitator of communication among community groups.

The last model for consultation is the approach used by social psychologists in dealing with communities, schools, or industrial entities. Although we are mainly concerned with new roles for clinical psychologists, nevertheless, as clinical psychologists move into community psychology, there is a need to understand the intricacies of consultation of an administrative and program development type. Gibb and Lippitt (29) have edited an important journal issue in this regard in which a number of different case examples are described. The approach is much more within the realm of social psychological and group dynamics theory. The concept of the "change-agent" rather than the consultant is frequently used by writers such as Bennis, Benne, and Chin (5), as well as Lippitt, Watson, and Westley (43).

DEFINITIONS OF CONSULTATION

Rhodes (51) generally defines consultation as "a psychological change technique applied to a problem situation through interpersonal communication between an individual or group with specialized knowledge, skills or awareness in the problem area, and an individual or group with authority and responsibility for action in the problem area."

The consultant acts as a psychological change agent, in which he hopes to affect human behavior, such as perception of a problem, a change in knowledge or awareness as applied to a work difficulty, freeing up of action in a conflict situation or changing feelings about some area of concern. The consultant deals indirectly with the problem, but directly with those involved with the problem, the consultee(s).

Rhodes also sees consultation as having certain special forms: (1) It is focused upon the problem situation and not the intra- or interpersonal process of the consultant and consultee. (2) It is a work-role limited process, i.e., concerned only with the work- or problem-role of the consultee. If the process ventures into other roles of the consultee, it is no longer consultation. (3) It is a content-centered process, i.e., the consultation relationship is built upon the specialized area of knowledge with which the consultant has extensive experience (4). There is specific goal direction; consultation seeks to obtain specific answers to specific questions.

Lippitt (44) defines consultation as a voluntary relationship between a professional helper (consultant) and help-needing system (client), in which the consultant is attempting to give help to the client in the solving of some current or potential problem, and the relationship is seen as temporary by both parties. The consultant is seen as an "outsider," i.e., is not a part of the hierarchical power system in which the client is located.

It is of interest in Lippitt's definition that the term "client" is used instead of "consultee." In most other definitions, the consultant is seen to be helping a consultee around the problems that the consultee faces, namely, the client. This may make for some confusion at times.

Caplan (22, 23) restricts consultation to an interaction between two professional persons—the consultant, who is a specialist, and the consultee, who asks for help in regard to a work problem which he feels falls within the special area of the consultant's knowledge. Caplan further restricts his definition of consultation by stating that the work problem "involves the management or treatment of one or more clients of the consultee or the planning of a program to cater to such clients." The consultee continues to retain professional responsibility for the clients, i.e., the consultee can accept or reject all or part of the consultant's suggestions. Any action for the client's benefit which is related to the consultation is the consultee's responsibility. Finally, Caplan sees consultation as providing an educational carryover, so that the consultee can deal in an effective fashion with similar problems in the future.

Caplan's view of consultation, although somewhat more circumscribed, is perhaps the one which is most closely related to the work of clinical psychologists. In effect, it is specifically aimed at mental health issues between a consultee and client(s). Bindman (8, 12) has distilled out a definition of mental health consultation from some of the earlier writings of Caplan (18), Prosser (50), and Towle (57), as follows:

> . . . mental health consultation is an interaction process or interpersonal relationship that takes place between two professional workers, the consultant and the consultee, in which one worker, the consultant, attempts to assist the other worker, the consultee, solve a mental health problem of a client or clients, *within the framework of the consultee's usual professional functioning.* The process of consultation depends upon the communication of knowledge, skills and attitudes through this relationship and, therefore, is dependent upon the degree of emotional and intellectual involvement of the two workers. A secondary goal of this process is one of education, so that the consultee can learn to handle similar cases in the future in a more effective fashion, and thus enhance his professional skills.

As one goes from Lippitt's to Caplan's and Bindman's definitions, there is increasing emphasis upon the process of consultation. In the definition cited above, stress is placed upon the fact that the consultant does not make a psychotherapist out of the consultee, nor does he aim at providing counseling to the consultee. The consultant utilizes the consultation process to improve the consultee's own professional skills in handling mental health predicaments.

In general, mental health consultation, as practised by clinical psychologists, has derived its theoretical orientation largely from psychoanalysis; the mental health consultant does not, however, "psychoanalyze" the consultee or client. He utilizes knowledge of personality development, group behavior, psychotherapeutic methods, and behavioral dynamics to develop, work through, and terminate the consultation relationship, but he does not get involved in the consultee's personal problems. Klein (41) makes this distinction quite clear in discussing the relationship between a consultant and educator (consultee)— "many consultees tend to wonder whether they are being given sub-rosa psychotherapy. The consultees are partially correct. Their perceptions and reactions both with respect to clients and the consultant are indeed being analyzed. How else could the consultant truly understand the problem through the consultee's eyes; how else could he tailor his own behavior to match the uniqueness of his educational colleague? The distinction lies in the refusal by all but a few consultants to enter into discussion of the consultee's personal problems and pathogenic life history or to counsel the consultee about these matters."

Even as Klein has noted, some consultants do deal directly with the consultee's personal problems and reactions to the client; the majority deal more indirectly with these issues. Altrocchi et al. (4) indicate the dangers involved in more direct confrontation in group mental health consultation, but they feel that this direct method may be used at times by a skilled consultant. Although many of the primary goals of consultation are educational in nature, some phases of mental health consultation resemble therapy, including corrective emotional experiences, which lead to therapeutic-like effects. Klein (41) concludes that there is no hard evidence that the direct or indirect method is better. He favors the indirect method as a safer technique for the majority of consultees.

CONSULTATION AND OTHER INTERPERSONAL METHODS

Consultation techniques do have some relationship to other interpersonal methods, and confusion often arises, especially in the mind of the less experienced consultant. There are differences which can be spelled out between consultation and education, supervision, psychotherapy, administration, and collaboration (7, 8, 9, 11, 12, 20, 22, 23, 34, 35, 48, 49).

CONSULTATION AND EDUCATION

Education generally emphasizes a long-term, formal, fairly systematic approach; the curriculum content is usually planned and given to the student in a somewhat authoritarian fashion; the meetings are frequent and extend over a lengthy period of time, and the focus is upon the acquisition of knowledge and skills; finally, the teacher often serves as an identification or role model for the student. In consultation, particularly with a mental health emphasis, there is no highly structured, pre-planned approach. Meetings may be regular or irregular, and the consultant uses whatever opportunities he can to form relationships with consultees and to focus upon their problems. The consultee usually asks for assistance, and consultation is carried on individually or in a small group. The consultation is related to the work situation and is not merely for the gaining of knowledge. The consultant may become a partial role model for the consultee. Finally, the consultant may advise; but usually he does this in a non-directive fashion, and in no case does he implement the plan for problem solution himself. Caplan (20) suggests that individual and group supervision, a problem centered seminar or individual tutorial may resemble consultation. Plaut (48) states that mental health consultation is like formal education when knowledge-acquisition is emphasized, but when consultation becomes more affectively oriented, it is less like education. In addition, Plaut (48) points out that the psychological consultant does not want to make the consultee into another psychologist, such as in education; he only wants to provide him with some ego support and a partial role model.

CONSULTATION AND SUPERVISION

In supervision, responsibility is taken by the supervisor for the supervisee; the supervisor may direct or evaluate the performance of the supervised individual; the supervisor is usually from the same professional discipline; supervision is offered on a regular basis and may cover a wide range of professional activities. The consultant is not responsible for the consultee's work performance; he is problem-oriented and does not follow through to see if suggestions are utilized. Contacts may be intermittent and non-evaluative. The consultant is often from a different discipline. Finally, the consultee usually initiates consultation, while supervision is initiated "from above." The key feature is that the supervisor deals directly with the supervisee's professional role, while the consultant focuses primarily upon the work problem.

CONSULTATION AND PSYCHOTHERAPY

Psychotherapy is generally on a fixed schedule and often fairly long-term; it is concerned with the intrapsychic and interpersonal problems of a patient or client; the use of the transference and an attack upon defenses are often key processes; there may also be interpretation and other means of handling resistances; the interaction is usually between a professional and a non-professional; and the emphasis is mostly upon affective features, and the therapist is often non-directive. In consultation, the time span is usually short, and the focus is upon a work-problem of the consultee and not upon personal problems; transference is minimized and defenses are supported; the interaction is usually between two equal professionals; cognitive as well as emotional features may be stressed; the consultant rarely interprets, and, if he does, it will be mostly about the client's problems; and the consultant may be fairly active in his role.

Some of the differences are not clear cut. The use of direct confrontation and interpretation by some workers has been discussed previously in defining mental health consultation (see above). Others have also utilized a fairly fixed schedule of meetings, have manipulated the transference, and, in general, have reduced the differences between the methods. Those who follow the school of mental health consultation espoused by Caplan warn against *sub rosa* therapy of the consultee, and emphasize the need to focus upon the client's problems. Bindman (8, 12) points out that if the consultant allows himself to get involved in the intrapsychic problems of the consultee, he is trapped into a therapist-patient relationship rather than a consultant-consultee relationship. Rhodes (51) feels that consultants are often rejected by consultees when they use a therapeutic approach toward the consultee rather than the consultation method that is desired.

CONSULTATION AND ADMINISTRATION

The administrator assumes responsibility for taking specific action, making decisions, promulgating policy, and taking leadership; subordinates are expected to follow the directions of the administrator. Consultation must have a "take it or leave it" characteristic, with the consultant or consultee having the right to withdraw. The consultant does not make decisions, direct policy, assume responsibility for follow-up, or take a leadership role. The consultant may become involved in administrative-related problems or program consultation, but he should not assume the role of administrator when acting as a consultant. The difficulty in maintaining a "pure" consultant role is noted by several writers (12, 31, 48, 49), especially when the consultant is hired on an intramural basis and has certain administrative responsibilities as part of his job description. Mental health consultation appears to be best when the consultant can keep his role free of authority or responsibility, and when he is able to work on an extramural basis.

CONSULTATION AND COLLABORATION

In collaboration, two or more professionals may interact to solve a common problem. As a result of mutual discussion and planning, they may follow through in a joint endeavor. The consultant relationship differs in that a consultee asks for assistance, and a consultant should not be expected to participate in the implementation of needed action.

THE CONSULTATION PROCESS

There are a number of phases in the consultation process; these vary some-what, and are dependent upon the type of consultation that is practised. Gibb (30) has outlined a series of experiences that seem to take place in the consultation process. These are: (1) entry into consultation; (2) diagnosis of the problem; (3) data collection; (4) relationships; (5) boundary agreements about the roles taken; (6) resource development—how and where the consult-ant is a resource; (7) decision-making; and (8) termination. Although Gibb writes more about social-system consultation, this outline applies to other types of consultation as well. Cohen (25) has made good use of this outline in describing experiences of mental health consultants in the South. He raises a number of important issues concerning the problems of entry and the consult-ant-consultee relationship.

Rhodes (51) divides the consultation process into: (1) the appraisal of the situation; (2) review of forces for change; (3) communication barriers; (4) the relationship; (5) consultee motivation; and (6) situational or organi-zational variables. He feels that consultation is in many respects a specific application of counseling, and the consultant must be aware of special features of his role, and yet use a greater number of sociopsychological cues in his work.

Kazanjian, Stein, and Weinberg (35) divide the consultation process into phases. They are: (1) preparatory phase; (2) beginning phase; (3) problem-solving phase; and (4) termination. These phases often overlap and blend with one another. The authors describe how consultation can be initiated, how the contract is developed, and how the problem-solving phase is put into practice. Their monograph also describes a consultation vignette, some explicit guide-lines, and possible pitfalls to avoid.

Haylett and Rapoport (34) use a similar outline in describing the phases of consultation. The preparatory phase is used to tighten up the administrative understanding which led to the development of a consultation service. The consultant develops a relationship with the top administrator of the consultee agency in order to obtain sanction and support for consultants to begin. The administrator most likely will utilize this preparatory phase to introduce the consultant to his key staff personnel for further discussion of possible consulta-tion service development. If agreement is reached, a contract is agreed upon, which can be either verbal or written, outlining the services to be performed and the functions expected from both consultant and consultees.

In the beginning phase, the consultant further develops his relationship with the consultees, and makes various aspects of the contract more explicit. This is frequently a testing-out phase in which consultees will show resistance, anxiety, and various forms of defensiveness. The consultant must redefine his role, begin to understand the consultee's social system, and assess how his entrance into the system affects its equilibrium. Particular care should be taken by the consultant during this beginning phase to help the supervisory staff members feel at ease—otherwise, they may consciously or unconsciously sabotage a consultation program.

The problem-solving phase is the period during which major issues of mental health consultation are discussed. Haylett and Rapoport (34) break these issues down to three types: "(1) the consultee may lack the special knowledge or skill needed to obtain relevant information or to evaluate available information in order that he may attempt to arrive at a solution; (2) administrative factors may limit his efforts in this connection; (3) the personal factors involved may be of sufficient intensity to interfere with his perception and understanding of the problem." In regard to the first type of issue, the consultant acts as a technical expert or assistant, offering various problem solutions or helping the consultee think through his own method for problem resolution. If the problem is involved with administrative policies, the consultant must be aware of administrative procedures in the consultee's agency and not be manipulated into suggestions which are contrary to agency practice. The problem should be solved "within the framework of the consultee's usual professional functioning (8, 12)," and the consultee should not become diverted into new procedures through the misdiagnosis of the situation by the consultant.

It is in the area of personal factors that the greatest amount has been written in describing mental health consultation. Problems such as a loss of professional objectivity by the consultee due to overidentification of the client with persons in the past life of the consultee, or an increase in the consultee's feelings of conflict when the client's behavior triggers off poorly resolved conflict areas are key issues for the mental health consultant. These are generally dealt with in an indirect fashion, in order to aid the consultee in mastering the situation. The consultant does this by focusing primarily upon the client's problems, which, by implication, are the concerns of the consultee. There is no direct discussion of the consultee's feelings; but this implied method reduces the consultee's tensions, which in turn affects the client, owing to their close relationship. Caplan (22, 23) discusses these personal issues of the consultee under the type of consultation that he terms consultee-centered case consultation. He sees the consultee as having four major categories of difficulty: (1) lack of understanding of the psychological factors in the case; (2) lack of skill or resources for dealing with the problems; (3) lack of professional objectivity; and (4) lack of self-confidence and self-esteem. It is under the category of "lack of professional objectivity" that Caplan discusses in detail a method to reduce stereotyping of the client or to handle problems of "theme interference" between consultee and client. Caplan also provides a very lucid discussion of his mental health consultation methods and their various phases.

The final phase, termination, is usually one of mutual agreement between consultant and consultee that a decision about the work problem has been reached. Some consultants develop a regular visitation schedule, while others try to work out a contract based upon crisis. Termination of the first type may be somewhat different from that of the crisis-based consultation. In the former, the consultant may receive feed-back about the presenting situation from time to time as he makes his visits, while, in the latter, there may be no follow-up or even a return unless another crisis occurs and consultation is requested.

Kevin (36) has described the various phases in group consultation. These processes occur in all small groups, but the difference lies in the work-oriented focus. Kevin describes three major phases: (1) involvement of group members; (2) problem-solving; and (3) ending phase. Within the problem-solving phase, there is a sharing of work problems, reality testing by the consultees, problem-solving through identification or advice and suggestions of group members and the consultant, and a final feedback or assessment of accomplishments through this process. Altrocchi et al. (4) and Rieman (52) also describe similar examples of group consultation process.

Administrative consultation phases are not so clearly defined in the literature. Spencer and Croley (55) discuss problems of entrance, the contract, and the need for planning, implementation and evaluation in developing administrative consultation for program development. Caplan (22, 23) divides administratively-oriented consultation into two types—program-centered administrative consultation and consultee-centered administrative consultation. In the former, he describes how the consultant analyzes the problem, develops a report in which recommendations are made, and how he communicates the findings to the consultees. In the latter, the consultant usually works with the consultees in a group to discuss current administrative problems which affect their professional roles. The phases are those often noted in small groups, as described above, plus the issues noted in consultee-centered case consultation.

TRAINING IN CONSULTATION TECHNIQUES

Consultation methods are not exclusively a psychologist's function; it appears, however, that the clinical psychologist in particular would have a strong professional basis for such training. A background in supervised psychotherapy is essential in order that the consultant be experienced in understanding human dynamics, unconscious processes, and other interpersonal factors. Stress should be placed upon the range of so-called normal behavior, rather than pathological functioning. Bindman (9, 12) has suggested that the psychologist should have the following in his background: (1) thorough knowledge and experience in personality functioning and psychodynamics; (2) thorough knowledge and experience is psychotherapy, both individual and group, and sufficient supervision in these methods so that he understands himself and is able to control his relationships with others; (3) thorough knowledge and experience in diagnostic appraisal, especially through the use of secondary cues and behavioral features; (4) some training and experience in various aspects of educational methods, both in a didactic sense and in the use of other educational and promotional methods; and (5) some knowledge of social psychology and especially of social structures, communities, social groups, institutional structures, and community organization. In addition, as the psychologist becomes involved in administrative consultation, he needs training in administrative principles, organization of community resources, mental health education methods, and possibly industrial management methods.

The above serves merely as a background. The next question is: how and where does the psychologist receive training in consultation methods? Cohen (25) noted that psychologists presently do not receive much predoctoral training in consultation techniques. On the other hand, he feels that graduate students should be acquainted with these methods through lectures and some field experences. Libo (42), in a recent paper describing the use of consultants in the New Mexico mental health program, feels that the "case method" of teaching, utilizing community social problems and consultation examples, should be provided to all graduate students. In addition, practicum training, starting from the first year of graduate work, would involve students in community endeavors. Caplan (24) describes his method of training consultants, primarily at the postdoctoral level, utilizing a combination of didactic seminar and field training experiences under supervision. With the increase in literature on consultation, combined with the need to read in related fields, the student has his work cut out for himself. In addition, as community mental health field training centers develop, there will be an increased need for supervisors of consultation from among those who have experienced and developed their own professional functioning in this area.

RESEARCH AND EVALUATION

A review of the literature on consultation reveals only one study which examines the results of mental health consultation. Cutler and McNeil (27) found significant changes in teachers who participated in a mental health consultation program. In addition, these teacher changes appeared to affect the children in a positive fashion. Caplan (23, 24) and Plaut (48, 49) mention a research study in progress in consultation evaluation, but the results are not reported.

Perhaps this is one of the most serious problems facing consultation methods in the future—how do we evaluate results? One cannot deny that this is a formidable task, owing to the presence of so many uncontrolled variables in any consultation encounter.

Rhodes (51) suggests that research on consultation should concentrate on a number of areas: (1) *consultant behavior*—What do various kinds of consultants do while consulting? How does style of consultation affect outcome? What is the influence of the number of consultation contacts and time span involved? (2) *consultee behavior*—What are the motivating factors leading to consultation requests? What are the attitudes of consultees toward the consultant? (3) *organizational and situational variables*—What differences are there in a situation which utilizes extramural as opposed to one in which intramural consultants are used? Does consultation outcome vary when consultation is requested or "imposed from above"?

All these questions are primarily in the formulative stage. The field of consultation cries out for further careful conceptualization, analysis, and research. Psychologists can play a major part in all these endeavors.

REFERENCES

1. Abramovitz, A. B. *Group consultation with teachers.* Madison, Wis.: Wisconsin Board of Health, 1963.
2. Abramovitz, A. B. Methods and techniques of consultation. *Amer. J. Orthopsychiat.,* 1958, 28:126–33.
3. Adelson, D., and Jacobs, S. N. Some aspects of mental health consultation with groups. Paper read in symposium on the role of the consulting psychologist in community mental health. Amer. Psychol. Assoc., Los Angeles, 1964.
4. Altrocchi, J., Spielberger, C., and Eisdorfer, C. Mental health consultation with groups. *Commun. Mental. Hlth. J.,* 1965, 1:127–34.
5. Bennis, W., Benne, K., and Chin, R. *The planning of change: readings in the applied behavioral sciences.* New York: Holt, Rinehart and Winston, 1961.
6. Berlin, I. N. Mental health consultation in schools as a means of communicating mental health principles. *J. Amer. Acad. Child Psychiat.,* 1962, 1:671–79.
7. Bindman, A. J. Some distinctive features of case consultation. In *Conference on consultation for mental health.* Harrisburg, Pa.: Dept. Public Welfare, 1959. Pp. 5–9.
8. Bindman, A. J. Mental health consultation: Theory and practice. *J. Consult. Psychol.,* 1959, 23:473–82.
9. Bindman, A. J. Training in mental health consultation. Paper read in symposium on the psychologist and mental health consultation. Amer. Psychol. Assoc., Cincinnati, 1959.
10. Bindman, A. J., and Klebanoff, L. B. Administrative problems in establishing a community mental health program. *Amer. J. Orthopsychiat.,* 1960, 30:696–711.
11. Bindman, A. J. Mental health consultation. In *Working together for better mental health.* Columbia: So. Carolina Mental Health Commission, 1961. Pp. 20–28.
12. Bindman, A. J. The psychologist as a mental health consultant. *J. Psychiat. Nursing,* 1964, 2:367–80.
13. Bindman, A. J. Bibliography on consultation. *Boston Univ. J. Ed.,* 1964, 146:56–60.
14. Bindman, A. J. The school psychologist and mental health. *Boston Univ. J. Ed.,* 1964, 146:5–10.

15. Bindman, A. J. (Ed.) Roles and functions in school mental health. *Boston Univ. J. Ed.*, 1964, 146:1–60.
16. Caplan, G. Recent trends in preventive child psychiatry. In G. Caplan (Ed.), *Emotional problems of early childhood*. New York: Basic Books, 1955. Pp. 153–63.
17. Caplan, G. The role of the social worker in preventive psychiatry. *Med. Soc. Wk.*, 1955, 4:144–59.
18. Caplan, G. Mental health consultation in schools. In *The elements of a community mental health program*. New York: Milbank Memorial Fund, 1956. Pp. 77–85.
19. Caplan, G. *Mental health aspects of social work in public health*. Washington: U. S. Children's Bureau, 1956.
20. Caplan, G. *Concepts of mental health and consultation*. Washington: U. S. Children's Bureau, 1959.
21. Caplan, G. An approach to the education of community mental health specialists. *Ment. Hyg.*, 1959, 43:268–80.
22. Caplan, G. Types of mental health consultation. *Amer. J. Orthopsychiat.*, 1963, 33:470–81.
23. Caplan, G. *Principles of preventive psychiatry*. New York: Basic Books, 1964.
24. Caplan, G. Problems of training in mental health consultation. In Stephen E. Goldston (Ed.), *Concepts of community psychiatry*. Bethesda, Md.: NIMH, 1965. Pp. 91–108.
25. Cohen, L. *Consultation: a community mental health method*. Atlanta, Ga.: Southern Regional Education Board, 1964.
26. Community mental health centers act of 1963. Title II. Public Laws 88–164, *Regulations*. Wash., D. C.: U. S. Dept. H. E. W., 1964.
27. Cutler, R. L., and E. B. McNeil. *Mental health consultation in schools: a research analysis*. Ann Arbor, Mich.: Univ. of Michigan, n. d.
28. Ferneau, E. F. Which consultant? *Administrator's notebook,* Univ. Chicago, 1954, 2, No. 8.
29. Gibb, J. R., and Lippitt, R. (Eds.) Consulting with groups and organizations. *J. Soc. Issues,* 1959, 15:1–74.
30. Gibb, J. R. The role of the consultant. *J. Soc. Issues,* 1959, 15:1–4.
31. Gilbert, Ruth. Functions of the consultant. *Teach. Coll. Rec.,* 1960, 61:177–87.
32. Glidewell, J. C. The entry problem in consultation. *J. Soc. Issues,* 1959, 15:51–59.
33. Hallock, A. C. K., and Vaughan, W. T. Community organization: a dynamic component of community mental health practice. *Amer. J. Orthopsychiat.,* 1956, 26:691–706.
34. Haylett, Clarice, H., and Rapoport, Lydia. Mental health consultation. In L. Bellak (Ed.), *Handbook of community psychiatry and community mental health*. New York: Grune & Stratton, 1964. Pp. 319–39.
35. Kazanjian, V., Stein, Sherry, and Weinberg, W. L. An introduction to mental health consultation. *Pub. Hlth. Monogr.,* 1962, no. 69.
36. Kevin, D. Use of the group method in consultation. In L. Rapoport (Ed.), *Consultation in social work practice*. New York: Nat. Assoc. Soc. Workers, 1963. Pp. 69–84.

37. Klein, D. C. Training the psychologist in a community mental health center. Paper read in symposium on newer techniques in community mental health programming. Amer. Psychol. Assoc., Chicago, 1956.

38. Klein, D. C. Consultation in the framework of preventive psychiatry. Paper read at Amer. Orthopsychiatric Assoc. Annual Meeting, San Francisco, 1959.

39. Klein, D. C., and Lindemann, E. Preventive intervention in individual and family crisis situations. In Caplan, G. (Ed.), *Prevention of mental disorders in children*. N. Y.: Basic Books, 1961. Pp. 283–306.

40. Klein, D. C. The prevention of mental illness. *Ment. Hyg.,* 1961, 45:101–9.

41. Klein, D. C. Consultation processes as a method of improving teaching. *Boston Univ. Human Relations Center Research Report*. 1964, no. 69.

42. Libo, L. M. Preparing psychologists for multiple functions in community consultation. Paper read at the Amer. Psychological Assoc. Convention, Chicago, 1965.

43. Lippitt, R., Watson, Jeanne, and Westley, B. *The dynamics of planned change: a comparative study of principles and techniques*. New York: Harcourt, Brace, 1958.

44. Lippitt, R. Dimensions of the consultant's job. *J. Soc. Issues,* 1959, 15:5–12.

45. Maddux, J. F. Psychiatric consultation in a rural setting. *Amer. J. Orthopsychiat.,* 1953, 23:775–84.

46. Parker, Beulah. Some observations on psychiatric consultation with nursery school teachers. *Ment. Hyg.,* 1962, 46:559–66.

47. Parker, Beulah. Psychiatric consultation for non-psychiatric professional workers. *Pub. Hlth. Monogr.,* 1958, No. 53.

48. Plaut, T. Theory and purposes of mental health consultation. In *Consultation in community mental health*. Chapel Hill, No. Carolina: No. Carolina Bd. of Hlth., 1961.

49. Plaut, T. Techniques and problems of mental health consultation. In *Consultation in community mental health*. Chapel Hill, No. Carolina: No. Carolina Bd. of Hlth., 1961.

50. Prosser, D. The summary of mental health consultations which seem to emerge out of the four subgroups. *Proceedings of the ninth annual conference of chief social workers in state mental health programs*. Bethesda, Md.: NIMH, 1957.

51. Rhodes, W. C. Training in community mental health consultation. Paper read in symposium on problems of mental health consultation in the schools. Amer. Psychol. Assoc., Chicago, 1960.

52. Rieman, D. W. Group mental health consultation with public health nurses. In L. Rapoport (Ed.), *Consultation in social work practice*. New York: Nat. Assoc. Soc. Workers, 1963. Pp. 85–98.

53. Rosenfeld, J. M., and Caplan, G. Techniques of staff consultation in an immigrant children's organization in Israel. *Amer. J. Orthopsychiat.,* 1954, 24:42–62.

54. Simmons, A. J. Consultation through a community mental health agency. Paper read in symposium on problems of mental health consultation in schools. Amer. Psychol. Assoc., Chicago, 1960.

55. Spencer, Esther C., and Croley, H. T. Administrative consultation. In L.

Rapoport (Ed.), *Consultation in social work practice*. New York: Nat. Assoc. Soc. Workers, 1963. Pp. 51–68.

56. *The elements of a community mental health program*. New York: Milbank Memorial Fund, 1956.

57. Towle, Charlotte. *The consultation process*. Unpublished mimeographed manuscript, 1950.

58. Vaughan, W. T. Mental health for school children. *Children*, 1955, 2:203–7.

26

Recent Advances in Community Psychiatry

ALVIN BECKER, N. MICHAEL MURPHY, AND
MILTON GREENBLATT

THE past decade has witnessed a phenomenal growth of interest in community mental health in the United States. Articles concerning community treatment of the mentally ill were rare ten years ago. In contrast, the recent literature, both professional and lay, is replete with descriptions of new community programs. This decade of heightened interest culminated in President Kennedy's message to Congress (51) in February, 1963, which resulted in the passage, in the following October, of Public Law 88–164, the Mental Retardation Facilities and Community Mental Health Centers Act. The act provides $329,000,000 to help states build community mental-health centers and develop programs related to mental retardation. At the same time, the Department of Health, Education, and Welfare (23) budgeted $4,200,000 to be made available to states on a matching-fund basis for financing comprehensive, statewide mental-health planning. This historic planning for planning (28) gives the nation its first opportunity to review mental-health programs state by state and to draw up comprehensive blueprints focused around community treatment of mental illness.

In 1953 the first major study concerning the need for increased emphasis on community treatment of the mentally ill was carried out by the World Health Organization (22). These investigators reported that the program to provide more beds in mental hospitals was overemphasized to the neglect of the development of services that would reduce the need for admission. Instead of adding beds to already oversized hospitals, they recommended that additional staff be recruited and that one third of the time of a staff person be spent in community activities. The report also emphasized the need for community information services and mental health education for the many potential caretakers of the mentally ill in the community. Outpatient clinics in general hospitals, ex-patient clubs in the community, halfway houses for former patients in mental hospitals and especially day hospitals were advocated as both economical and efficacious. The committee also had specific recom-

Reprinted from *New England Journal of Medicine*, 1965, 272, 621–626; 674–679, by permission of the publisher and the authors. © 1965, Massachusetts Medical Society. Dr. Becker is Director, Home Treatment Service, Boston State Hospital. Dr. Murphy is Assistant Superintendent, Boston State Hospital and Senior Clinical Instructor in Psychiatry, Tufts Medical School. Dr. Greenblatt is Commissioner, Massachusetts Department of Mental Health. He was formerly Superintendent, Boston State Hospital.

mendations for making the psychiatric hospital more of a therapeutic community rather than a custodial institution.

During the years that followed the WHO report, the attention of psychiatrists in this country was called to the pioneering programs of community-based treatment in England, Holland and Canada. Several distinguished groups of American mental-hospital administrators were commissioned to visit Europe and report back on changes that appeared appropriate for translation to American culture (5).

By 1955 dissatisfaction with the treatment programs for the mentally ill in the United States was so widespread that Congress appropriated money to establish the Joint Commission on Mental Illness and Health. This commission, comprising scores of outstanding psychiatrists and mental-health professionals, was asked to study the overall problem of the treatment of mental illness in the United States and to report to Congress on its findings and recommendations. While the Joint Commission was studying the psychiatric scene in this country the tranquilizer breakthrough in the treatment of serious mental illness occurred. These drugs, proved effective in the control of psychotic symptomatology, accelerated the movement of mental hospitals from custodial to therapeutic institutions and made possible the treatment in the community of many seriously disturbed patients. The drugs have also enabled the family doctor to deal more effectively and more comfortably with his patients who are mentally ill (74).

The Joint Commission completed its study in 1960 and reported to the Congress in March, 1961 (37). Later that year President Kennedy appointed a "cabinet-level" task force to study the report and make recommendations for implementation. On the basis of recommendations of this task force, the President constructed his historic message to Congress (51). A major recommendation was that emergency psychiatric services be developed in the community, in an attempt to provide help to the mentally ill before the aggravation of their disturbance made hospitalization mandatory. A whole spectrum of rehabilitative services was envisioned that could be made available to the mentally ill both before and after hospitalization.

This paper reports on recent developments in three segments of community psychiatry. The first section discusses the changes within the mental hospital that have attempted to transform it from a primarily custodial institution into a *therapeutic community*. The second section concerns the development of the *community mental hospital,* including *transitional facilities* that bridge the gap between hospital and community and *programs for prevention of hospitalization*. The third section describes changes within society that bring it closer to the ideal of a *"therapeutic society."*

THE THERAPEUTIC COMMUNITY

Since World War II, and especially in the past decade, there has been a dramatic change in treatment programs within the mental hospitals of this country. Many of these changes have been based on treatment philosophy developed in other countries, particularly England; they represent in a sense a return to the concept of "moral treatment," prevalent in the first part of the nineteenth century. The key element in this philosophy is the reaffirmation of the dignity of the mentally ill person, accompanied by intensified efforts to enhance his feelings of self-worth and self-esteem (33).

The "therapeutic community" is a term used to describe both goals and treatment methods of the modern mental hospital. In contradistinction to the concept of the mental hospital as a custodial institution, it repudiates the punitive features of the social system. Under its banner, locked wards were opened, patients, previously restricted, were allowed freedom of movement, attendants and nursing personnel renounced their "watchdog" roles and became participants with patients in group activities. Wet packs, tubs, sedation, and seclusion, formerly used to control disturbed behavior, were largely replaced by psychotherapy, chemotherapy, social, occupational and work therapy and rehabilitation programs, all conducive to closer staff-patient interaction. New attempts were made to preserve the patient's individuality and afford him privacy during his hospital stay. Hospital administrators learned that patients were capable of a considerable degree of responsibility and initiative, and began to allow them to participate in planning many activities, and in organizing their own ward government. Visiting hours were made more liberal so that the patient's contact with his family increased to daily visits, when indicated. Volunteers, including large numbers of college students, were invited into the hospital. The atmosphere of inactivity and lethargy gave way to one of increased activity and movement of both patients and volunteers. In short, the whole spirit of the mental institution changed from a hopeless custodial one where patients were often herded about and treated like prisoners to one of optimism where patients were regarded as worthwhile, responsible persons with a capacity to grow.

The introduction of the "unit" system, in which the large hospital is divided into smaller divisions, each responsible for a geographic region of the community, has helped to bring the institution into closer working relation with outer society (6, 64, 73). Personnel on such units become more intimately acquainted with care givers of the assigned region, thus mutually fostering aid and cooperation. Unit plans are common in the Veterans Administration hospital system and have been introduced, among other places, in Kansas, Iowa, New York, and Colorado.

THE COMMUNITY MENTAL HOSPITAL

Improvement of the physical and social environment within the hospital has led increasingly to the realization that the internal community depends greatly upon the *outside* community for aid in developing its program. The movement toward open doors, increased visiting hours for relatives, relaxed criteria for patient discharge and utilization in the hospital of all community elements that could possibly make a contribution has recognized this trend. The merging of the inner and outer community, the breaking down of barriers between hospital and the outside, has ushered in a phase in which the mental hospital attempts to become truly a community mental hospital.

TRANSITIONAL FACILITIES

One of the most distinctive characteristics of this phase is the development of *transitional facilities* defined as therapeutic settings that serve the patient as stepping-stones in the path between hospital and community. In the recognition that for many patients the step is too great for easy negotiation, bridging mechanisms such as those described below have been developed.

The Day Hospital

One of the most important developments in community psychiatry, the day hospital (42) to which patients come during the day for a full range of treatment programs, returning to live with their own families at night, was initiated in Russia in 1933. Its first major use in the Western world was in 1946 in Montreal at the Allan Memorial Institute of Psychiatry. Since then many varieties of day hospitals have been developed in a host of different settings. The first day hospitals established in this country were in private institutions—at the Yale Psychiatric Clinic in 1948 and at the Menninger Clinic in 1949. State hospitals, state departments of mental health, the Veterans Administration system and psychiatric services in general hospitals have all initiated day programs suited to specific needs.

The original rationale for the development of the day hospital was the acute shortage of inpatient beds, which frequently led to the discharge of patients before the full benefit of hospitalization had been obtained. Decompensation, necessitating readmission to the hospital, often resulted. If, instead of direct discharge, the patient is routed from the ward through the day hospital, the full range of therapeutic modalities offered to the inpatient are still available to him. Thus, the day hospital enables a gradual transition from ward to community, the frequency of attendance being "titrated" to the needs of the patient. A prerequisite for a successful day-care program is the presence of an interested family, for without the support of an ally in the home, the program often fails.

Besides its effectiveness as a step from hospital to community, the day hospital has proved of value in screening seriously ill patients considered for hospitalization (52, 56). When mental-health personnel observe the patient several hours a day a much clearer picture of the nature and severity of the illness emerges. On the basis of this detailed information, combined with an evaluation of the patient's initial response to medication and to the supportive environment, a more rational assessment of the patient's need for hospitalization can be made. If inpatient care is not required, a program for more extensive day hospital care can then be formulated. Many day centers report that they are able to provide an alternative to hospitalization for 50 per cent or more of patients who appeared destined for hospitalization at the time of their referral.

By averting hospitalization or shortening the period of hospitalization, the day hospital accomplishes a significant reduction in the cost of psychiatric services. One nursing shift suffices, whereas three are required to staff an inpatient ward. Despite the higher staff-to-patient ratio in day hospitals than in wards, the total staff budget remains less. Additional savings accrue because no beds are required and only one meal a day must be prepared. The economy and efficient use of personnel of a day center make it particularly appropriate in communities where there are few psychiatrists and other trained mental-health personnel and funds for psychiatric services are limited.

For the patient the day hospital mitigates the shock of admission, avoids the stigma of mental hospitalization, maintains the patient in his home environment (thus decreasing the chances of his abandonment by the family), actively involves the family in the treatment program (thus preventing abdication of responsibility) and eliminates regression and dependency that may lead to chronicity. Finally, it aids in the education of the community toward greater understanding and acceptance of the mentally ill, by demonstrating that emotionally disturbed people can be successfully treated outside the institution.

The Night Hospital

This facility, like the day center, provides part-time hospitalization for patients who find the one-step transition from full-time hospitalization to community living too burdensome (41). By so doing it diminishes the number of readmissions in the early period after discharge, a problem of vast proportions in recent years. It is also a haven for nonhospitalized patients who are experiencing an acute or subacute crisis. It offers these patients not only respite from a stressful home environment but also a therapeutic milieu with the full range of psychiatric treatments available in the hospital. Working patients can thus be involved in an active treatment program without disruption of their gainful employment.

The night hospital, like its day-hospital counterpart, is economical to both patient and hospital and safeguards against the regression so often attendant on full-time hospitalization.

Night hospitals with formal treatment programs are a development of the past decade. An outstanding example is the unit that has been functioning at the Montreal General Hospital since 1954 (52). With 15 beds, it offers an active program five nights a week from 6:30 to 11:00 o'clock, including psychotherapy, drug therapy, electric-shock therapy, modified insulin therapy and psychodrama.

Halfway House

In the halfway house (71) a group of former hospital patients live together in intimate social association, supervised usually by a house "mother" and "father." A temporary home is thus provided for patients who are ready to move back into the community but who are homeless or for whom the family home is not suitable. The halfway house, in a sense, provides a "family surrogate" especially adapted for patients who need a family-like environment for support during this transitional phase. In these arrangements the patient assumes family chores and participates in housekeeping, setting up meals and arranging recreation and social life. If he is able to work outside gainfully he is expected to contribute regularly to the "family" income.

This model of a halfway house is perhaps true for a majority; some, however, are very loose arrangements corresponding more to the model of hostels rather than families. They differ from so-called therapeutic clubs in that the latter usually have no arrangements for sleeping in. There are relatively few halfway houses in America, and their affiliations, auspices, locations and degrees of autonomy vary widely.

The three halfway houses in Boston serve as examples of the varying patterns. Rutland Corner House (43), for women only, probably the first successful halfway house in America, was started in 1952 by a group of public-spirited citizens whose organization has carried on philanthropic work for over eighty years. Mostly working, discharged patients live here; almost all are given individual therapy by psychiatrists. A house·"mother," closely relating to an active board of directors, is responsible for their supervision. The House has been closely affiliated with the Massachusetts Mental Health Center.

Wellmet, Incorporated (38), was established in 1960 by a group of Harvard and Radcliffe students working as volunteer aides at a local state hospital. Ex-patients from the Metropolitan State Hospital or Boston State Hospital, with a house "mother" and "father," live together with undergraduates in a cooperative arrangement blessed by both the University and the Hospital. Entirely privately supported, it is located in Cambridge, Massachusetts, in a residential neighborhood. The enthusiastic participation of youthful, vigorous students has contributed to an impressive record of rehabilitative successes.

Canterbury House (46), on the edge of the Boston State Hospital grounds, was formerly the residence of the hospital superintendent. The model of patients living with house "mother" and "father," as well as students, is maintained here too, but the house is state owned.

Woodley House, in Washington (17, 70), maintained by private citizens, has no parent hospital but is closely associated with referring therapists, who maintain responsibility for the patients.

Still another pattern is illustrated by a halfway house in Vermont (10). This is closely affiliated with Vermont State Hospital but financed largely by the Rehabilitation Division of the State. Patients from the hospital are transferred in groups, when possible, to maintain ties developed during their hospital stay.

There is something in the close family living, the homelike atmosphere and the intensive personal supervision that motivates the patient to "grow." The rehabilitation record of some of the halfway houses, even with long standing, chronic cases, has been promising. If these results continue, a new modality of social rehabilitation will have proved itself.

Ex-Patient Clubs

The American pioneer venture in ex-patient clubs was the one established in New York City in 1948. Named Fountain House (30), it gave identity and shelter to a band of ex-patients discharged from mental hospital in the New York area. This organization, headed by John Beard, a social worker by training, has flourished over the years and now provides a variety of services such as job finding, home finding, education, recreation and consultation for a large body of ex-patients. The indications are that former patients attached to Fountain House, if they become committed to the program, are far less likely to relapse and suffer rehospitalization than those without such ties.

Many ex-patients' clubs have been formed throughout the country (34); the variations and patterns are legion. Some are totally independent, some are attached to hospitals, and others are members of a large "chain" developed through the inspiration of Abraham A. Low (49). There is little doubt, however, that whatever the format, they are potentially extremely useful to the ex-patient still insecure in his public relations, who is not ready to venture away from those whose experience has been like his own. While providing a psychologic shelter for the timid and the half well, the ex-patient club, like all such bridging facilities, may sometimes be used as a hiding place for patients who find healthy social reality too painful. The availability of guiding professionals is always an advantage, therefore, in these settings.

Family Care

The systematic placement of mental patients in the care of foster families had its origin many centuries ago in Gheel, Belgium (19). The use made of this treatment varies from country to country. In Norway (14), for example, it is prescribed extensively, and about half of all mentally disturbed patients live in the community with foster families. In the United States (40), where there has been a shift away from the land into smaller houses and apartments in the city, its growth has been slower, although impressive developments in some Veterans Administration hospitals have been recorded.

Barton (4) summarizes some of the reasons for the use of family care: life for the chronically ill mental patient is more normal in the family setting than on a mental-hospital ward; it is less costly, and it saves personnel; overcrowding in the hospital is reduced; it provides an opportunity for an adjustment in the community of patients whose families are unable or unwilling to accept them; it serves as a halfway facility for selected patients; and, lastly, it provides a test of the capabilities of adjustment in the community for the older patient.

Family care in Massachusetts began eighty years ago and was defined as follows:

> [the care of] patients who have been placed in the community in private families other than their own under state supervision. The expense of maintenance may be borne by the state or by the local government, the patient's estate, relatives, old age assistance, or some other agency or person (44).

One hundred dollars a year is now allowed each person for clothing, and about $115 monthly is the average payment made to the caretakers. This is sometimes an inducement and an assistance to distant relatives to enable them to provide a suitable home. It should be noted, however, that appointment of relatives as foster caretakers varies from state to state, but, in general, close family relatives are excluded.

The development of a successful family-care program calls for careful selection of both foster family and patient, as well as aftercare once the patient starts to live in his new home. The Veterans Administration Hospital (63) at American Lake, Washington, for example, has been successful in placing more than 700 psychotic veterans in foster homes since 1947. They attribute the success of their foster program largely to sponsor training, and believe that the result has been both better treatment for the patient and better understanding of him by the sponsor. A foster-family-care committee composed of a number of hospital personnel makes arrangements for regularly held sponsors' meetings; they report that an ever increasing participation by both staff and sponsors has resulted from this program.

Aftercare Services

The posthospital phase of a patient's illness presents many problems that are attracting the attention of mental-health workers. Concomitant with the rapidly increasing admission rate and the added efficacy of inhospital treatment, a major increase in the number of discharged patients has occurred. It is essential that these patients, many of whom are still struggling to maintain a precarious equilibrium, have some organized form of aftercare. In the absence of effective programs for such care the readmission rate to state hospitals has soared, in some cases reaching 40 to 50 per cent. The problem is complicated by the fact that many large public hospitals are located at considerable distance from the centers of population they serve. This militates against close follow-up observation. A further complication is that even when aftercare services are available, patients devoid of insight into their illness may lack motivation to utilize them.

Several different approaches are being tried in an effort to overcome this problem. One is to bring in the family doctor as an active member of the treatment team. This is particularly effective when the physician has had a close personal relation with the patient before his hospital stay. For maximum effectiveness, it is essential that the hospital psychiatrist communicate freely with the family doctor, detailing the patient's course and treatment in the hospital and the recommended medication for aftercare, and that he make himself available for consultation.

A second approach involves the co-operation of the community nursing services (16), either the Visiting Nurse Association or the public-health nurses in the patient's home district. In many areas nursing groups have enthusiastically espoused this extension of their traditional role; in others, responsibility is more slowly being accepted. These nurses can collaborate with either the family doctor or the hospital psychiatrist. By making home visits on a regular basis, they can observe the patient's progress and report back to the physician. They can check on the patient's medication and give support to both patient and family as needed. They are also able to reach out to the patients who for various reasons are reluctant to seek follow-up services on their own. Obviously, consultation must be provided for the nurses involved in the program and is done so by psychiatrists or specially trained mental-health nurses.

A third method calls for the establishment by the remote mental hospital of "satellite" aftercare clinics in the centers of population. Ideally, these clinics would be staffed by the same personnel who cared for the patient during his hospital stay. Unfortunately, this is rarely the case; however, if the unit system, which provides administrative decentralization of the large mental hospital on a geographic basis, becomes more prevalent, it may become feasible to have hospital staff spend a portion of time at such satellite clinics.

Home visits made by the psychiatric social worker comprise an important part of the aftercare program in Veterans Administration hospitals. Again, this offers the advantages of reaching out and the opportunity to see the family, evaluate the home environment and offer support to family members.

PROGRAMS FOR PREVENTION OF HOSPITALIZATION

Four principles of modern community care have been outlined by Lewis (47). The first is that, whenever possible, a patient should be kept in his home community and treated there. Secondly, if hospitalization is necessary, ideally it should be short term, and the patient should return for continuing care on an outpatient basis after the acute phase of his illness. Thirdly, facilities should be provided so that the patient can be seen early in the course of his illness, making it possible to avoid hospitalization in many cases. Fourthly, programs that offer "alternatives to hospitalization" should be fostered since they offer a much less expensive and more therapeutic method of treating psychiatric patients. Alternatives to be kept in mind include all those discussed below.

Home-Treatment Services

The prototype of home-treatment services has been functioning in Amsterdam (25, 57) for approximately thirty years. Staffed by psychiatrists and psychiatric nurse-social workers, it is available twenty-four hours a day to evaluate and treat psychiatric emergencies in the city of Amsterdam. Originally set up to ameliorate the psychiatric bed shortage, it has been retained and expanded in its original form. The goal of the service is to give treatment in the home as soon as a call for help is received. The visits are usually short; drug therapy is the treatment of choice, and no psychotherapy is administered by the home-treatment psychiatrists.

In England, with the increasing emphasis on community services, domiciliary visits are made by the psychiatrists in many areas, usually to evaluate the need for hospitalization; rarely are long-term treatment programs carried out in the home.

The first comprehensive home-treatment service established in the United States was set up in 1957 at Boston State Hospital (26, 27) in Massachusetts. Its aim was to determine whether treatment in the home was feasible as an alternative to hospitalization for seriously ill patients. The Psychiatric Home Treatment Service at Boston State Hospital functioned in a research and demonstration capacity for its first five years; in 1962, through legislative support, it was made a permanent facility of the Hospital.

The Community Extension Service at Massachusetts Mental Health Center, originally set up as a demonstration project, published its studies in 1963 (31). Presently, the Walk-in Clinic of that hospital offers emergency care to many patients formerly served by the Extension Service.

The findings of both Boston services are in considerable agreement: that a program of evaluation and treatment in the home can be effective as an alternative to hospitalization for a large number of patients suffering from serious mental illness. At least half of those who would otherwise be hospitalized can be adequately treated by a home-service team utilizing supportive psychotherapy together with psychopharmaceuticals.

The Boston State Hospital's Home Treatment Service has been referred over 1000 patients during the seven years of its existence. By combining availability of service, flexibility of functioning and creative use of personnel and resources, it has provided treatment programs that are more beneficial for the patient, his family, the community and the mental hospital (29). The Home Service staff has been expanded to include two full-time senior psychiatrists, psychiatric residents, two psychiatric social workers, four psychiatric nurses and an occupational therapist, as well as students of nursing, social work and occupational therapy.

Other important goals of the service are to provide training in community psychiatry to mental-health professionals and consultation to the caretakers of the mentally ill in the community. Many believe that such a service is an *essential* facility in all future community psychiatric services, if the mentally ill are to be offered adequate care at each stage of their illness.

The significance of the family in the illness of the patient is highlighted by the experience of the home-treatment service (58). For treatment to be successful, the family must be an ally of the treatment team. Extensive casework with the family is often necessary before therapeutic progress can be achieved. It is important to note that patients seen by the home-treatment service are often unmotivated for treatment or deny their illness and would not ordinarily seek contact with community treatment agents. Thus, the home-treatment service must reach out to these sick patients if it is to help a group that might otherwise be hospitalized.

Admission Screening Services

Simply because a community physician or a patient's relative requests or demands that the patient be removed to a mental hospital for a period of observation does not mean that this is in the best interest of either the patient or his family: It is essential, therefore, to have an efficient admission screening service (18) in which the staff has a clear understanding of what facilities are available so that the best prescription for treatment can be offered the patient at the outset. Warner et al. (68) have emphasized the importance of screening patients carefully to protect them from "well-meaning general practitioners, constituents, parishioners, and friends, who, for various reason, wanted to hospitalize allegedly psychiatric patients." It behooves one to take a long and critical look before subjecting a patient to what is frequently a traumatic experience.

A screening service has been in operation for over a year at Boston State Hospital. All patients who present themselves for admission or advice are evaluated. Where inpatient care is clearly indicated the patient is sent to one of the wards. At other times referral to one of the Hospital's outpatient facilities, such as the After Care Service, Day Hospital or Home Treatment Service, is more appropriate, or the services of a community agency may be requested. In a large number of cases a disposition is not immediately clear, and a more extended evaluation is desirable. For example, the clinical condition of some patients at the time of admission may be in sharp contrast to that seen by the referring physician. With others it is impossible to assess the interest of relatives and their willingness to become members of the therapeutic team in an attempt to avoid hospitalization. With still others there is an acute crisis situation in which rapid resolution seems likely.

The Screening Service has eight beds for such an extended assessment, and the aim is for a maximum stay of seventy-two hours. The patients have their own facilities separate from the regular hospitalized patients and are left in no doubt about the limited duration of their stay on the unit. They are told that, if at all possible, an alternative to full hospitalization will be worked out.

During the first year of operation 549 patients, representing slightly less than one quarter of all admissions, were admitted for extended evaluation. The Screening Service was able to arrange an alternative to hospitalization for 75 per cent of these patients, most of whom would have been admitted to a regular ward if the facility had not been available (54).

Preadmission Screening Services

Closely related to both home treatment and screening are services that provide home visits to evaluate patients being considered for hospitalization. The service is usually limited to diagnosis and referral.

In Philadelphia (68) where such a program has been operating for several years, an average of 150 cases per year were seen at home by psychiatrists. It is clear that this type of service provides the community a means of dealing with certain psychiatric problems that formerly did not fit into any agency's jurisdiction, but fell into a no-man's-land between social agencies and the police.

In San Mateo, California (24) where the development of community services has been outstanding, a preadmission visit program has been available for the past three years. Its importance for the elderly, emotionally disturbed person is highlighted by the fact that 60 per cent of the patients seen at home were over sixty-five years of age. For many of these elderly people the home visit enabled hospitalization to be averted, and alternate treatment programs to be instituted. The savings attributed to this service amounted to scores of thousands of dollars.

Walk-In Emergency Treatment in the General Hospital

In his recent book on community psychiatry, Bellak emphasized that most emotionally troubled persons do not know where to turn for help. Because he believed that these people needed "a place to turn" he established the "Trouble-Shooting Clinic" (8) at City Hospital, Elmhurst, Long Island. The clinic was one of the first organized to provide immediate screening for patients seeking help. An intake officer assesses the patient's problem, and assigns him to treatment at one of the hospital's psychiatric facilities or makes an appointment for him at one of the community's helping agencies. The clinic proved its worth and has continued to provide around-the-clock service to the community.

Caplan (11) has urged the development of similar clinics to meet the long neglected needs of the mentally ill in the community. He criticized the long waiting lists for evaluation and treatment of most standard psychiatric clinics. He stressed that a clinic responsive to the needs of its community must offer immediate evaluation and treatment adapted to the requirements of the individual patient.

Many hospitals have responded to this call for change, and walk-in emergency service is becoming more prevalent.

The Massachusetts General Hospital (12) in Boston has provided twenty-four-hour psychiatric coverage in its emergency ward for many years. Since 1962, however, this service has been enlarged and formalized. Over 5000 patient visits were made in the past year.

In discussing emergency psychiatric treatment at the Bronx Municipal Hospital in New York City, Coleman and Zwerling (13) emphasized the need to have available both immediate psychotherapy and consultative service for social agencies. The Hospital was also actively involved in arranging transportation for the patients, baby sitters on treatment mornings and home care. Normand et al. (55) studied the utilization of psychiatric facilities by people in economically deprived areas and found that even without a community educational program, the walk-in clinic made contact with a significant number of residents of the areas studied.

In summary, there is increasing recognition of the need to provide emergency psychiatric treatment in the general hospital. Such a "place to turn" is frequently all that is required even for acutely disturbed patients. The provision of such facilities does much to prevent admission to a mental hospital.

Suicide-Prevention Services

Suicide-prevention services represent a special subdivision of emergency psychiatric services. The Los Angeles' Suicide Prevention Center (39) was founded in 1958. Telephone calls from potentially suicidal patients are received and screened by an experienced psychiatric social worker, who has a psychiatrist available for consultation. Aware that the main asset available to him is his incipient relation with the patient over the telephone, the social worker strives to keep the patient talking and thus to capitalize on his ambivalence about dying. Obviously, a patient who calls the center has not made his final decision, and his call represents a cry for help. The worker attempts to reinforce the patient's desire to be helped and offers him hope that a solution can be found to his present dilemma. If successful in supporting the patient's will to live, the social worker then arranges a psychiatric evaluation for the patient. The goal of this evaluation is to motivate the disturbed person to seek further help for his emotional problems. Although approximately half the calls sounded over the telephone as if they represented serious suicidal danger, less than 25 per cent were judged serious risks when they were evaluated in person. The percentage of serious danger was much higher in men than in women.

Rescue, Inc., (53) founded in Boston in 1960 by a priest, Father Murphy, represents another attempt to deal wth this problem. A nonsectarian organization, it was organized with the co-operation of the Catholic archdiocese and the psychiatric service of the Boston City Hospital. Telephone calls are taken by a priest, who endeavors to convince callers whose threats seem serious to come in for psychiatric evaluation. Approximately 1000 calls are received each year.

Psychiatric Services in General Hospitals

The past two decades have witnessed an important and dramatic change in the locus of hospitalization of psychiatric patients. Before World War II most psychiatric hospitalization took place in state hospitals, with only a small percentage occurring in private mental hospitals or in general hospitals. Before

1939 only 37 general hospitals and 6 Veteran Administration hospitals had psychiatric facilities, and these were used mainly for short stays for evaluation leading to referral to mental hospitals (48).

The impact of World War II on this situation was great. During the war all military general hospitals contained psychiatric units. These units proved to be both feasible and effective. After the war psychiatric units mushroomed within general hospitals throughout the country. Within a decade the number of hospitals admitting patients to psychiatric services had jumped from 37 to 614, representing 13 per cent of the 4715 general hospitals in the country (48). Since then the number has grown steadily. One important factor in this increase has been the introduction of drugs effective in controlling acute psychotic symptoms. Whereas only patients exhibiting mild to moderate symptoms were previously accepted into the hospital unit, now the psychiatrist could feel more comfortable in admitting patients who were seriously disturbed. Many acutely psychotic patients could be successfully managed by the combination of milieu therapy, drug therapy, psychotherapy and work with the family.

Another factor that augurs well for a continuing rise in the number of psychiatric patients treated in general hospitals is the increasing number of health-insurance policies that covers such treatment in a general hospital. As it is increasingly demonstrated that many patients can be returned within two or three weeks to a level of functioning no longer necessitating hospitalization, and at a cost only slightly exceeding that for an admission for medical illness, it is hoped that nearly all insurance policies will cover at least short-term psychiatric hospitalization.

College Psychiatric Services

The past decade has found an increasing number of colleges providing psychiatric help for their students. Some universities have several full-time psychiatrists on their medical staffs and offer short-term therapy as well as evaluation. Others have part-time or consultant psychiatrists available for evaluations of troubled students. By providing help on campus, the university health services are often instrumental in preventing emotional crises from deteriorating into conditions requiring hospitalization.

THE THERAPEUTIC SOCIETY

In 1956 we wrote:

Dimly envisaged as an achievement of tomorrow's pioneers, it [the therapeutic society] is hinted at today in all considerations of hospital-community relationships. Here we are concerned with large-scale societal change towards mental illness, wherein statesmen and legislative bodies become the chief agents of action, but where far-sighted professionals and men of influence within our ranks may make an important contribution through public education and consultation with policy-making and budgetary bodies. Problems of prevention of mental illness will thus blend with problems of care of the sick (32).

Great steps toward the ideal of a therapeutic society are taken when the President of the United States assumes a personal interest in forwarding legislation in mental illness and retardation, and when the federal government's participation is extended to broad concepts of research, demonstration, training, hospital construction, hospital improvement, delinquency, child development, poverty areas and support of statewide planning for mental health. In education, corrections, religion and urban renewal, in the school and in the home, the new impetus is felt. Indeed, the image of the "Great Society" of necessity signifies a concerted social attempt to allay the fear and darkness surrounding mental illness.

Leadership tasks in the movement toward the therapeutic society will fall upon many individuals and organizations; we mention here several groups merely as examples of the trend.

THE MEDICAL PRACTITIONER

Postgraduate Training

It was only after World War II had vividly demonstrated to thousands of physicians the dramatic effects of the emotions on servicemen that an upsurge of interest in postgraduate training in psychiatry for the practicing physicians occurred (60). Psychiatrists responded to this interest by developing various programs for postgraduate education. A pioneering experiment in teaching psychiatry to practicing physicians was begun in 1946 in Minnesota (72). This intensive two-week, full-time residential course attempted to impart theory, clinical information and training in interviewing technic. In 1949 Tennessee (66) inaugurated a program in which a series of 10 lectures was given in 45 centers throughout the state. Unfortunately, the program was discontinued after two years.

Bálint's (3) success in England in the early 1950's, using small, informal case-centered group discussions, prompted the development of similar programs in this country. Watters (69), in New Orleans, and Pittenger (20), in Pittsburgh, were among the first to follow suit.

In the past decade, several significant organizational efforts have helped stimulate a rapid proliferation of postgraduate programs (61). During this period the American Medical Association elevated its committee on mental health to the level of a council and thus formally recognized mental illness as a critical problem of concern to the *entire* medical profession, not just to its psychiatric segment. In 1956 the American Academy of General Practice and the American Psychiatric Association appointed liaison committees to work toward fostering psychiatric-education programs for the general practitioner. In the following year they jointly established the General Practitioner Education Project supported by funds from the National Institute of Mental Health.

The availability of these federal funds has given great impetus to postgraduate psychiatric education. In 1958 $1,300,000 was earmarked by the National Institute of Mental Health for training programs for the general practitioner. Proliferation of courses, under many auspices, has taken place. Sponsorship is often shared by local medical societies and medical schools, the American Academy of General Practice, mental hospitals and district branches of the American Psychiatric Association. It was recently estimated that well over 150 courses are presently being offered, and the number swells yearly (62). The number of practicing physicians enrolled in postgraduate courses in psychiatry has risen from approximately 1500 in 1959 to an estimated 3200 in 1964 (1).

AMERICAN MEDICAL ASSOCIATION

In recent years the American Medical Association has responded to the challenge of mental illness with increasing interest and awareness of its key role in the battle. In 1961 the Board of Trustees cited the final report of the Joint Commission "as an historical contribution to the promotion of mental health and prevention and care of mental illness and that it be considered as the basis for a program which the AMA can endorse and support."

The Association's First National Congress on Mental Illness and Health was held in October, 1962; general statewide mental-health programming and priorities were emphasized. In early 1963 President Annis stated that ". . . the new emphasis in mental health is towards community centered treatment . . . comprehensive community programs and facilities are the keystone of the AMA's mental health program (2)."

The Second National Congress, held in November, 1964, directed itself to encouraging physicians, particularly those in private practice, and interested community leaders to activate and participate in effective mental-health programs at the community level. It focused on the physician's role in mobilizing and organizing community mental-health services.

These important moves by the Association are key elements in the needed rapprochement of psychiatry and medicine.

In April, 1964, an editorial in the *New England Journal of Medicine* (15) highlighted the increasing interest of organized medicine in working with the psychiatric community to plan the community mental-health center of the future. It is hoped that the establishment of these centers will at once bring psychiatry back into the community and allow the practicing physician to play an ever increasing role in ministering to the emotional ills of his patient.

THE CLERGY

Pastoral Counseling and Training Seminars

As the monograph, *Americans View Their Mental Health* (35) points out, 42 per cent of people who have sought professional help for personal problems first consulted clergymen, 29 per cent physicians in general, 18 per cent psychiatrists or psychologists, and 10 per cent social agencies or marriage clinics. Thus, clearly, the clergyman is place in a crucial position in screening the emotional problems of his parishioners. As this fact has emerged there has been a rapid expansion in the emphasis placed on training in pastoral counseling within the seminaries. A recent survey (21) revealed that there are about 350 programs offering special training in mental health and that 4 per cent of all clergymen active in pastoral work have had some special training in pastoral counseling. Although there has been considerable debate about the depth to which a clergyman should go in his counseling it is generally agreed that the goal of this function is the maintenance of the mental health of his parishioners, in contrast to the clinician, who endeavors to heal the mental illness of sick patients. Every pastoral counseling center surveyed by McCann (50) stressed the importance of referral for psychiatric treatment of all persons whose problems represented major mental illness.

Recently, psychiatrists have collaborated with clergymen in creating courses of advanced training in mental-health principles for interested clerics. Examples of such courses and seminars are those in Boston (7), Elmhurst (8), Syracuse (61), and Dallas (65).

GOVERNORS' CONFERENCE ON MENTAL HEALTH

For more than a decade, the governors of the several states have been profoundly concerned over the inadequacy of care and treatment of the mentally ill, and as early as 1954 convened a special National Governors' Conference on Mental Health. Within a few months of the final report of the Joint Commission (37), a second Governors' Conference on Mental Health was called. This conference commended the Joint Commission on its excellent study, accepted the finding that much remained to be done and endorsed the concept that federal, state and local governments, as well as private and voluntary efforts, were needed to achieve the goals set.

The Second Governors' Conference made recommendations for improvements in 12 areas of service; many of the recommendations echoed those contained in *Action for Mental Health* (37).

This conference also stimulated many governors to explore the needs of their states. In Massachusetts, in May, 1962, a Conference on Action for Mental Health was convened by the Governor to focus the attention of the citizens of the Commonwealth on the report and its implications for the further development of the mental-health program in Massachusetts.

NATIONAL ASSOCIATION FOR MENTAL HEALTH

Founded in 1909, the National Association for Mental Health is the leading citizens' organization in the mental-health field. There are now associations for mental health in nearly all the 50 states, manifesting the widespread interest in this movement. One major goal is to further public understanding of mental illness. The Association cosponsors the Joint Information Service with the American Psychiatric Association (9). Hundreds of thousands of copies of its pamphlet, *How to Handle Your Tensions,* have been distributed to interested laymen (45). Another goal is to help lay groups organize support for the development of community psychiatric facilities. The Association is also active in the support of legislation essential for the development of needed mental-health programs.

VOLUNTEERS

Although volunteer services have long been successfully utilized by mental hospitals founded by the Society of Friends, it was not until the 1940's that a women's volunteer organization was formed in Massachusetts (36). Such organizations are now commonplace in most state hospitals and are invaluable in breaking down the barriers between the hospital and the community.

Student contacts with mental patients came later, and pioneer work in this regard has been carried out by undergraduates from Harvard and Radcliffe, supplemented later by students from 7 other colleges and universities in the Boston area (67). These volunteers work with patients with chronic mental illness in the Metropolitan State Hospital, Boston State Hospital, Wellmet (a halfway house), and Walter E. Fernald State School for the mentally retarded. The importance of such a program is not only in the service offered both the patients and the hospital but also in the stimulating effect of bringing the social problem of mental illness into the thinking of the university communities. Initial anxieties that contact with patients might have adverse psychologic effects upon the students have proved groundless. Many are eager to develop long-term relations with patients with the most chronic forms of mental illness, in contrast to the attitude of the average community volunteer, who is often afraid of deteriorated patients and would rather work in the periphery of the hospital than on the wards.

SUMMARY AND CONCLUSIONS

Recent advances in community psychiatry may be viewed from three vantage points, the first of which is development of the therapeutic community within the hospital. Here, efforts have been directed primarily toward eliminating punitive, restrictive methods of management, closing the gap between patient and staff, encouraging patient participation in the therapeutic program and breaking down the barriers between hospital and community. The second is development of the community mental hospital, characterized by merging of the inner and outer communities in a combined effort to assist the mentally ill. The community mental-health center of the future, as outlined in recent legislation, calls for a mental hospital surrounded both by transitional facilities and by programs for prevention of hospitalization. The former includes day hospital, night hospital, halfway house, ex-patient club, family care and aftercare program; the latter comprises facilities for community management, home-treatment services, preadmission screening services, walk-in clinics and psychiatric units in the general hospital. Developments have been speedy and impressive in this domain, and many regard this phase as most characteristic and illustrative of recent social psychiatric progress. Thirdly, progress toward a therapeutic society outside the hospital, once a wildly impractical dream, is today beginning to be felt as a reality. A sufficient change in public attitudes toward mental illness and health is manifested by such events as the President's historic message to Congress, the release of federal funds for more research, demonstration, training, construction, prevention of crime and delinquency, retardation and poverty, and state planning. General practitioners, the clergy and certain categories of volunteers will doubtless have a leadership role here.

Thus, the dream of the "Great Society" surely cannot be realized without major progress toward the "therapeutic society."

REFERENCES

1. American Psychiatric Association. *Psychiat. & M. Pract. Bull.*, 1963, 1:10.
2. Annis, E. R. Changes coming in nation's mental health profile. *J. Indiana M.A.*, 1963, 56:460–66.
3. Bálint, M. *The doctor, his patient, and the illness: Foreword by Maurice Levine.* New York: International University Press, 1957.
4. Barton, W. E. Family care and outpatient psychiatry. *Am. J. Psychiat.*, 1963, 119:665–69.
5. Barton, W. E., Farrell, M. J., Lenehan, F. T., and McLaughlin, W. F. *Impressions of European psychiatry.* Washington, D. C.: American Psychiatric Association, 1961.
6. Beckenstein, N. New state hospital. In L. Bellak (Ed.), *Handbook of community psychiatry and community mental health.* New York: Grune, 1964.
7. Becker, A. Unpublished data.
8. Bellak, L. Comprehensive community psychiatry program at City Hospital. In L. Bellak (Ed.), *Handbook of community psychiatry and community mental health.* New York: Grune, 1964.
9. Blain, D. Organization of psychiatry in U.S. In S. Arieti (Ed.), *American*

handbook of psychiatry: Editorial bd.: Kenneth E. Appel (and others). Vol. 2. New York: Basic Books, 1959.

10. Brooks, G. W. Opening rehabilitation house. In M. Greenblatt and B. Simon (Eds.), *Rehabilitation of the mentally ill, social and economic aspects: A symposium of the Association, cosponsored by the Section on Social and Economic Sciences of the American Association for the Advancement of Science and the American Sociological Society, and presented at the Indianapolis meeting, Dec. 29–30, 1957.* Washington, D. C.: The Association (Publ. No. 58).

11. Caplan, G. *Principles of preventive psychiatry: Foreword by Robert H. Felix.* New York: Basic Books, 1964.

12. Chafetz, M. E. Acute psychiatric services in emergency ward. *Massachusetts General Hospital News,* 1963, no. 22:1–3.

13. Coleman, M. D., and Zwerling, I. Psychiatric emergency clinic: flexible way of meeting community mental health needs. *Am. J. Psychiat.* 1959, 115:980–84.

14. Davis, J. E. Family care of mentally ill in Norway. *Am. J. Psychiat,* 1962, 118:154–58.

15. Dilemmas of mental health. *New Eng. J. Med.,* 1964, 276:853.

16. District of Columbia, Department of Public Health. *Report of mental health followup project.* Washington, D.C.: Government Printing Office, 1963.

17. Doniger, J., Rothwell, N. D., and Cohen, R. Case study of halfway house. *Ment. Hosp.,* 1963, 14:191–99.

18. "Dr. Whatsisname": "No" man at door. *Ment. Hosp.,* 1964, 15:190.

19. Dumont, M. P., and Aldrich, C. K. Family care after thousand years: Crisis in tradition of St. Dymphna. *Am. J. Psychiat.,* 1962, 118:116–21.

20. Enelow, A. J., and Adler, L. M. *Psychiatric Skills and knowledge for the general practitioner: Annual report of the psychiatry in medical practice program of the University of Southern California School of Medicine.* 1962–1963.

21. Ewalt, J. R., and Farnsworth, D. L. Psychiatry and religion. In *Textbook of psychiatry.* New York: McGraw-Hill, 1963.

22. Expert committee on mental health: Third report. *Tech. Rep. World Health Organ.,* 1953, 73.

23. Felix, R. H. Our present prospects and task ahead. *Compr. Psychiat.,* 1963, 4:368–74.

24. Fink, L., Asbury, D. M., and Downing, J. J. *The San Mateo County preadmission home visit program.* San Mateo, California, 1963.

25. Friedman, T. T. *Community psychiatric services in Amsterdam.* Prepared by Boston State Hospital, Boston, Massachusetts, 1960.

26. Friedman, T. T., Becker, A., and Weiner, L. Psychiatric home treatment service: Preliminary report of five years of clinical experience. *Am. J. Psychiat.,* 1964, 120:782–88.

27. Friedman, T. T., Rolfe, P., and Perry, S. E. Home treatment of psychiatric patients. *Am. J. Psychiat.,* 1960, 116:807–9.

28. Glasscote, R., Frazier, C., and Brill, H. Plans for planning. *Ment. Hosp.,* 1963, 14:632.

29. Gold award: Home treatment service. *Ment. Hosp.,* 1964, 15:546–48.

30. Goertzel, V., Beard, J. H., and Pilnick, S. Fountain House Foundation: Case study of ex-patient's club. *J. Social Issues,* 1960, 16(2)54–61.
31. Greenblatt. M. *The prevention of hospitalization: Treatment without admission for psychiatric patients [report on the Community Extension Service of the Mass. Mental Center: Based on the study Prevention of Hospitalization of Psychotic Patients Referred to the Mass. Mental Health Center (Boston Psychopathic Hospital) a research project sponsored by the National Institute of Mental Health: Principal investigators: Milton Greenblatt and others].* New York: Grune, 1963.
32. Greenblatt, M., and Lidz, T. Some dimensions of problem. In M. Greenblatt, D. J. Levinson, and R. H. Williams (Eds.), *The patient and the mental hospital: Contributions of research in the science of social behavior.* Glencoe, Ill.: Free Press, 1957.
33. Greenblatt, M., York, R. H., and Brown, E. L. *From custodial to therapeutic patient care in mental hospitals: Explorations in social treatment.* New York: Russell Sage, 1955.
34. Grob, S. (Ed.), *The Community social club and the returning mental patient.* Revere, Mass.: R. Novin, 1964.
35. Gurin, G., Veroff, J., and Feld, S. *Americans view their mental health: A nationwide survey: A report to the staff director, Jack R. Ewalt.* New York: Basic Books, 1960.
36. Hyde, R. W., and Hurley, C. F. Volunteers in mental hospitals. *Psychiat. Quart.,* 1950, Supp. 24:233–49.
37. Joint Commission on Mental Illness and Health. *Action for mental health: Final report of the Commission, 1961.* New York: Basic Books, 1961.
38. Kantor, D., and Greenblatt, M. Wellmet: Halfway to community rehabilitation. *Ment. Hosp.,* 1962, 13:146–52.
39. Kaphan, M. N., and Litman, R. E. Telephone appraisal of 100 suicidal emergencies. *Am. J. Psychotherapy,* 1962, 16:591–99.
40. Karl, V. C., and Russell, S. B. *V.A. foster home program. Part 3. V.A. field station summary,* January, 1962.
41. Kinder, E., and Daniels, R. S. Day and night psychiatric treatment centers. I. Description, organization, and function. *Am. J. Psychiat.,* 1962, 119:415–20.
42. Kramer, B. M. *Day hospital: A study of partial hospitalizaiton in psychiatry: With a foreword by Milton Greenblatt.* New York: Grune, 1962.
43. Landy, D., and Greenblatt, M. *Halfway house: A sociocultural and clinical study of Rutland Corner House: A transitional aftercare residency for female psychiatric patients.* Washington, D. C.: Vocational Rehabilitation Administration, 1965.
44. Lee, D. T. Family care: selection and prediction. *Am. J. Psychiat.,* 1963, 120:561–66.
45. Lemkau, P. Mental hygiene. In *American handbook of psychiatry: Editorial bd. Kenneth E. Appel (and others).* Vol. 2. New York: Basic Books, 1959.
46. Levine, J., and Wolff, R. Canterbury house: A family setting for resocialization. *Ment. Hosp.,* 1965, 16:21–24.
47. Lewis, F. A., Jr. Community care of psychiatric patients versus prolonged institutionalization. *J.A.M.A.,* 1962, 182:323–26.
48. Linn, L. Some aspects of psychiatric program in voluntary general hospital.

In L. Bellak (Ed.), *Handbook of community psychiatry and community mental health.* New York: Grune, 1964.

49. Low, A. A. *Mental health through will-training: A system of self-help in psychotherapy as practiced by Recovery Incorporated.* Boston: Christopher, 1950.

50. McCann, R. V. *The churches and mental health: A report to the staff director, Jack R. Ewalt.* New York: Basic Books, 1962.

51. *Message from the President of the United States to the Congress relative to mental illness and mental retardation.* United States House, 88th Congr. Washington, D. C.: Government Printing Office, February 5, 1963 (Doc. No. 58).

52. Moll. A. E. Evolution of psychiatry in general hospital and community. *Compr. Psychiat.,* 1963, 4:394–408

53. Murphy, K. B. Special article: Rescue, Inc. *Massachusetts Physician,* 1964, 22:158.

54. Murphy, N. M. Unpublished data.

55. Normand, W., Fensterheim, H., Tannenbaum, G., and Seger, C. J. Acceptance of psychiatric walk-in clinic in highly deprived community. *Am. J. Psychiat.,* 1963, 120:533–39.

56. Peck, H. B. Role of psychiatric day hospital in community mental health program: Group process approach. *Am. J. Orthopsychiat.* 1963, 33:482–93.

57. Querido, A. Early diagnosis and treatment services. In *The elements of a community mental health program: Papers presented at 1955 annual conference of Milbank Memorial Fund.* New York: The Milbank Memorial Fund, 1956.

58. Rolfe, P. Psychiatric team comes to home. In R. H. Felix et al. (Eds.), National Conference on Social Welfare. *Mental Health and Social Welfare.* New York: Columbia University Press, 1961.

59. Sandt, J. Personal communication.

60. Sheeley, W. F. Brief history of psychiatric education for non-psychiatrist. II. Age of reason—and beyond. *Psychosomatics,* 1962, 3:379–89.

61. Sheeley, W. F. Reparative postgraduate psychiatry and physician. *Am. Practitioner,* 1962, 13:16–20.

62. Sheeley, W. F. Treatability of emotional states by practicing physician. *J. Louisiana State M. Soc.,* 1963, 115:365–73.

63. Singer, E. I., and Guilford, E. W. Step by step to foster-family training. *Ment. Hosp.,* 1964, 15:555–60.

64. Snow, H. B., and Bennett, C. L. *Report of the Dutchess County Project: A community psychiatric facility.* Fall, 1963.

65. Stubblefield, R. Personal communication.

66. Townsend, R. P. Pilot program in post graduate teaching of psychiatry to general practitioners. *Am. J. Psychiat.,* 1954, 110:681–86.

67. Umbarger, C. C., et al. *College students in a mental hospital: An account of organized social contacts between college volunteers and mental patients in a hospital community: Prepared with the assistance and supervision of David Kantor and Milton Greenblatt.* New York: Grune, 1962.

68. Warner, S. L., Fleming, B., and Bullock, S. Philadelphia program for home psychiatric evaluations, precare and involuntary hospitalizations. *Am. J. Pub. Hlth.,* 1962, 52:29–38.

69. Watters, T. A. General practitioner and psychiatry. *J. Louisiana State M. Soc.,* 1959, 111:64–69.
70. Wayne, G. J., and Richardson, I. K. Halfway house: How it serves as pathway agency for psychiatric patient. *Psychiat. Quart.,* 1963, 37:67–96.
71. Wechsler, H. Halfway houses for former mental patients: Survey. *J. Social Issues,* 1960, 16 (2):20–26.
72. Witner, H. L. (Ed.), *Teaching psychotherapeutic medicine: An experimental course for general physicians given by Walter Bauer and others.* Cambridge, Mass.: Harvard, 1947.
73. Zubowicz, G. Change to unit system. In *Psychiatric studies and projects.* Washington, D. C.: American Psychiatric Association, Mental Hospital Service, August, 1963. (No. 8.)
74. Zussman, L., and Linn, L. Family doctor's new role on treatment team. *Am. J. Psychiat.,* 1963, 120:553–60.

27

Sociotherapeutic Camping for the Mentally Ill

GLENN V. RAMSEY

BEGINNING in the summer of 1956 and yearly thereafter the Texas State Hospital system has sent sixty mental patients at a time to participate in a camping program. Each year one or two camp sessions have been held, some lasting for one week, others two, and still others for three weeks. In all, a total of 685 male and female patients have participated in the camping program during the past six years. This paper attempts to give a brief description of the camp, present an underlying philosophy, list some operating principles, and cite some of the results achieved by this sociotherapeutic demonstration.

The camping project has attempted to explore some of the therapeutic possibilities of a patient community so designed that its social structure and processes are viewed as principal treatment agents. The operational task has been to structure the community so that its social forces will enhance patient communication, participation, and group identification. The underlying assumption is made that the patient who engages more fully in social and interpersonal activities will register a therapeutic gain. It is further believed that such shifts in a person's overt social behavior will also bring about desirable changes in his attitudes, feelings, and perceptions of self and others.

The sociotherapeutic concept as announced here is decidedly different from traditional psychoanalytic beliefs and procedures that emphasize intellectual or cognitive analyses of the individual's past experiences. In contrast, the camp's approach focuses upon everyday living experiences. The "here-and-now" experiences and feelings become the core of the camp's therapeutic effort rather than the process of uncovering and analyzing mental life and past experiences. Some current sociotherapeutic experiments focus upon a cognitive understanding of a person's social behavior in synthetic or practice groups. The camp project, however, does not concern itself with such an intellectual analysis of either past or present behavior but simply assumes that patient

Reprinted from *Social Work*, 1964, *9*, 45–53, by permission of the publisher and the author. © 1964, National Association of Social Workers. Dr. Ramsey is a consulting psychologist in private practice, Austin, Texas.

involvement and participation in day-to-day activities are in themselves therapeutic.

No inferences are made as to the relative superiority of the camping approach to other means, whether medical, psychiatric, or different social methods of treatment. The camp project is simply viewed as a worthwhile endeavor to explore one possible method of sociotherapeutic treatment for the mentally ill.

SELECTION OF PATIENTS

The responsibility for selecting patients to attend the camp rests in the hands of the superintendent of each of the state's six mental hospitals. Approximately equal numbers of men and women are selected.

The criteria for selection of patients present a thorny and unsolved problem in many ways. In general, medical staff members of each hospital recommend those patients they feel might profit therapeutically from the opportunities and experiences offered by the camp. The selection is based largely on the knowledge physicians have gained from observing therapeutic results attained from previous camp programs.

Some criteria for exclusion from camp have evolved or been adopted. Not accepted for the program are those patients who cannot participate in camping activities because of physical limitations, such as the aged, physically handicapped, epileptics, and those suffering from serious brain damage, cardiac disorders, and other physical weaknesses. Camping experience has also shown that certain types of patients do not seem to profit in any significant way from the design of this particular camp program. On this basis are excluded the mentally defective, chronic alcoholics, the extremely disturbed, and the chronic sociopath.

The following variables do not seem to be closely related to predictable therapeutic outcomes: sex, degree of willingness to come to camp, and type of previous treatment received except for prefrontal lobotomies. Age is not significant except as it limits physical activity. Length of hospitalization seems to be related, as the patients who respond best have been hospitalized only one or two years.

Only four of the 685 patients sent to camp have been returned to their respective hospitals because of an inability to adjust to the camp program. One youth wandered away two or three times the first day of camp and was therefore returned. Another sent back was an 11-year-old who was judged by the staff as not suitable for a program designed for adults. The other two patients were so emotionally and mentally disturbed on arrival that they had to be returned because of their disturbing effect upon other patients. The camp is not equipped with a private room for temporary care of disturbed patients.

FACILITIES AND STAFF

All sessions of the camp have been held at a ranch located in the hill country of Texas. This ranch comprises approximately 2,000 acres and is made available without charge for the project. The actual camp site is on the banks of the Frio River. A permanent group of attractively designed buildings provides quarters for patients, modern kitchen and dining room facilities, large recreation areas, administrative offices, activity rooms, and so on. The patients are housed in cottages, each of which provides beds, storage, and toilet facilities for eighteen persons.

Surrounding the camp buildings are large outdoor recreation areas with space provided for baseball, volley ball, horseshoes, and other games. The many hills, valleys, and streams provide natural facilities for hiking, fishing, and swimming. Since the ranch is a wildlife preserve, it abounds with deer, wild turkey, many kinds of birds, and a great variety of small animals.

The camp site is in steady use throughout the year by various other groups. Not a single change is made in the physical camp facilities or equipment for the patients' program. No doors or windows are ever locked. Maintenance machines and equipment are not removed. The same safety rules that apply for other types of campers using the same site are adopted by the project camp.

The camp staff is composed of six permanent members selected from regular personnel employed in the various state mental hospitals. The camp director works regularly as a rehabilitation therapist and has prior experience as a professional camp director. This dual qualification was considered essential in the successful operation of this camping project. The remaining five permanent staff members were selected because of special skills in recreational and small group activities, outdoor sports, handicrafts, music, nature study, and so on. Four other staff members manage the kitchen and transportation services.

Besides these, there are six ward attendants who accompany each group of sixty patients to camp and become cabin unit leaders while in camp, living in the cabins with the patients. These unit leaders are responsible for the general welfare and safety of the patients at all times, except when the patients are engaged in activities being directed by the permanent staff. The cabin leaders are also responsible for holding nightly cabin discussions, reporting special camper needs to the director, preparing daily evaluation reports on each patient, and similar duties. One general qualification essential to all staff members is a genuine interest in the camping program and a desire to participate enthusiastically in camp activities. In general, younger personnel make better staff members, probably because of their greater physical strength and general adaptability.

The superintendent of a nearby state mental hospital serves as medical director of the camp. While no physician has been in residence at the camp for the past few years, the superintendent, his hospital, and his staff are available at all times if an emergency should arise. No individual or group psychiatric services or treatment are offered at camp. An experienced hospital nurse is always present and has the responsibility of administering whatever pharmaceutical treatment a patient's home hospital physician may have prescribed for the camp period. Consequently, the medical program is a rather constant factor in the patient's treatment while in camp. The nurse also renders first aid services.

The camp director has had sole responsibility for the actual operation of the camp, except for medical services, and has collaborated closely with an outside clinical psychologist assigned to the project and with heads of the medical, psychological, and rehabilitation services of the Texas State Hospital System. Thus the camp's philosophy, goals, and procedures have evolved from the joint effort of several specialists and from the knowledge gained from actual operation of the camp.

Soon after the program was established, it became clearly evident that a precamp workshop for all staff personnel was needed. Consequently, each year an inservice training program has been conducted for staff members, held at the camp site and lasting for three days. The camp director and professional consultants conduct the program.

ACTIVITIES OFFERED PATIENTS

Various lengths of the camping session were tried. The unanimous opinion of the staff was that three weeks is the minimum length for such a program. It takes almost that long to reveal which patients will respond to this type of treatment and to establish some degree of stability in the changes the camp produces. Possibly in an ideal sociotherapeutic program each patient would remain until he had achieved maximum benefits. Furthermore, the staff felt that more custodial-type cases would respond to this treatment if the period were extended beyond three weeks.

During their stay various types of activities are offered to the campers. Outdoor activities provided include swimming, hiking, fishing, nature study, field sports, bus trips, small group cookouts, large group barbecues and fish fries, and campfire events. Indoor or patio activities include dancing, handicrafts, kitchen parties, group singing, camper talent shows, religious services, movies, games, costume and other parties, and so on. No outside talent is brought in to entertain the patients.

The daily schedule follows that of other camps. Times are set for all activities. The campers and staff usually plan and carry out their own religious services. On visitor's day, the campers help plan the reception and the day's events. Sometimes a one-day bus trip is taken to a nearby state park.

Each camper is expected to care for his own bed, clothing, and other personal effects. Each cabin group is responsible for cleaning its own bathroom facilities and the area around its quarters. Daily inspection of quarters is made by a team of campers, but no punitive action is ever taken against a noncooperative camper. Personal hygiene and dress are individual responsibilities. Usually the social pressure of cabin mates or other campers brings the careless camper up to group standards and expectations.

During the morning and afternoon activity periods and the free hour each camper may join any one of the large number of activities offered. An individual camper is free to join any activity at the beginning of any group formation. He may elect not to join a large group but to remain alone or with a small informal group. Pressure is never put upon a camper to participate in a planned activity other than the offering of an invitation to join the group. After the first few days, practically all campers join in some of the group activities. With such an elective or free-choice factor operating, the daily program is highly flexible in order to meet the interests and needs of the campers.

UNDERLYING "DEMOCRATIC" PHILOSOPHY

Often investigators who attempt to explain the underlying philosophy for current sociotherapeutic experiments select the term "democratic" to describe their orientation. This is a good descriptive term for the basic philosophy of the camp project also. However, in spite of the widespread application of the phrase "democratic philosophy" to sociotherapeutic projects, only scattered efforts have been made to explain what this concept means in terms of such a treatment program. Some of the basic tenets that seem inherent in such an approach are as follows:

1. *Every person is to be accepted and treated as having equal human rights.* This implies a fundamental respect for the integrity, dignity, and worth of everyone, including the mentally ill. Incompatible with this philosophy are all beliefs and practices that view the mentally ill as less than the equals of other human beings. Too often in the past mental patients have been viewed as not entitled to the same care, respect, and rights accorded to other persons.

2. *Recognition is given to the uniqueness and individuality of each person.* The mentally ill are, therefore, viewed as persons with individual patterns of needs, wants, and aspirations. Too often in the past they have been treated as so many cases or charges—inmates for whom there must be provided so many meals, treatment sessions, and beds. Under the democratic philosophy the individual patient is never lost in the group. The mental illness of each patient will present unique features that often demand special attention. A good treatment program and recognition of human individuality, therefore, are perceived as inherently going hand in hand.

3. *Each person is to be encouraged to express himself according to his abilities in a way that is personally and socially desirable.* In the treatment of

the mentally ill this means that they, too, are encouraged to become active, productive, creative persons according to their respective capacities, interests, and skills. They should be provided with opportunities to choose, decide, and participate in everyday living activities.

4. *Each person is expected to accept and discharge responsibilities for self and others consistent with his capacities and capabilities.* In the past, once a person was designated as mentally ill he was immediately considered almost totally irresponsible. The project's philosophy is directed by the belief that the mentally ill can accept and discharge a much greater degree of responsibility for both self and social group than has been granted to most patients in the past. Rather than withdrawing responsibility, the camp program makes an effort to encourage the patient to assume as much responsibility as he is able to discharge in a socially purposeful and desirable way.

STAFF RELATIONSHIPS WITH PATIENTS

In addition to these basic tenets the democratic philosophy has certain implications for those who are involved in the care and treatment of the mentally ill. Such workers must have a certain basic faith and trust in human beings. This involves a positive belief in human nature, not a negative one. A hopeful view is held that mentally ill persons may be helped by their own efforts and those who care for them. Another shift this orientation calls for is a focus upon the healthy residuals and potentials within each patient and avoidance of a preoccupation with pathology and disorder. Finally, the staff largely functions through a democratic process of interaction based on their skills rather than by invested authority and power.

This approach demands that those working with the mentally ill have a genuine ability to accept, support, and understand all patients, first as human beings and second as persons needing additional care and treatment because of their illness. This orientation places a great demand upon those who work in a sociotherapeutic program, as they must give of themselves and not merely do something *for* the patients.

The democratic philosophy underlying sociotherapeutic treatment programs can be contrasted with authoritarian philosophy, which supports many of the physical treatment methods of medicine. In this latter approach an expert takes over the patient and the treatment processes. He assumes initiative and responsibility for diagnosis, treatment, and outcomes. In general, he examines, diagnoses, prescribes for, or operates upon the patient. The patient is the recipient.

This model has proved its worth in the treatment of many kinds of illness and disease. A danger arises, however, when the philosophy and techniques of the expert are imposed upon sociotherapeutic endeavors such as that described here. The democratic philosophy inherent in a sociotherapeutic program is incompatible with that guiding the manipulative type of treatment program. This does not mean, however, that the treatment programs growing out of each approach cannot be pursued simultaneously. Such joint approaches simply need to be integrated into an effective treatment program based on the needs of each patient. As stated previously, the sociotherapeutic treatment program is viewed as only one method of attacking the problem of mental illness, and as one that holds sufficient promise for further exploration and development.

OPERATING PRINCIPLES

Translation of the democratic philosophy into a set of operating principles has evolved in the camp project more or less on an empirical basis. Some principles are still rather vague and more implicit than explicit. Still others are viewed as tentative guides for further exploration. The following are some that more or less guide the staff's work in organizing and directing the camp.

1. *The staff carries full responsibility for the over-all care, welfare, and treatment of the patient-campers.*

2. *The camp is perceived as a sociotherapeutic treatment program.* Its goal is to help patients improve. The project is not seen as "something nice to do *for* patients," or as a reward to those patients who have served faithfully as hospital service workers. Every moment is viewed as a potential opportunity to create conditions that may contribute to patient improvement or recovery.

3. *The camp is organized to encourage patient participation and involvement.* The wide range of activities offered or created invites patient participation. These activities are not provided *for* the patients, but are created and carried out by the joint efforts of patients and staff.

4. *An effort is made to delegate as much responsibility to patients as they can carry satisfactorily.* Patients have demonstrated that they can participate intelligently in the establishment and enforcement of safety rules, codes of conduct, personal hygiene and sanitary standards, and other regulatory measures, and can develop and carry out many of the camp activities. Finally, they have shown that they have a genuine concern for other patients whose illness handicaps them from participating in camp life and activities. Often it is the help of a campmate or a camp group that assists some patients to become better-functioning individuals and group members.

5. *The camp is so operated that the patients feel they have a real part in its government and control.* The camp council is a central governing body whose members are elected representatives from the various cabin units. This council meets daily with one or two staff members. Reports are received from the representatives and from the staff on camp life and activities. Problems are discussed, programs planned, rules established, and projects created. Representatives report back to their respective cabin members the feelings of the council, decisions rendered, and other matters that have received attention.

6. *Effort is made continually to encourage free and easy communication between staff and campers and among campers.* No formal channels of communication are established, thus encouraging free, easy conversation. Any patient may talk to any staff member or any other camper. Staff members address each patient by his first name. The staff do not ask to be addressed by job or professional title, and wear sports clothing rather than uniforms. Letters written by patients are sent uncensored, and the patients enjoy this freedom. No limit is set on the number of letters a patient may write. The basic belief is that communication is an essential element in achievement of a more normal and healthy pattern of living.

7. *The staff attempts to exert its leadership through a democratic and personal worth process rather than by authoritative power and decree.* The staff gains recognition and acceptance by the patients through actual contributions to the camp's program. Thus, leadership becomes a functionally defined role. Likewise, campers strive according to their abilities to contribute to camp life, whether by helping with an activity program, seeking an elective office, serving on a committee, or in other ways. Both staff and patients alike strive to gain recognition and group acceptance by contributing to the needs of the camp, rather than by a system of invested authority. Only rarely has the staff had to use its basic authority to carry out its duties and responsibilities. In these cases only verbal requests or commands have been given. Never has physical force or restraint been necessary.

A question that naturally arises is how the staff cared for the few cases when individual behavior became too disturbing or threatening. Success with these persons seemed to rest largely on the fact that all the staff members were experienced in caring for mental patients. They could spot impending trouble and move quickly to help, thus avoiding more serious developments. This help could be a friendly talk with an uncooperative camper, a walk with a restless one, or sitting down with a delusional disturbed person. Direct verbal commands and prohibitions were given at times. Often simply getting the troubled person involved in some camping activity would be all that was needed. This professional interpersonal control was estimated effective in about 90 per cent of the cases.

A second method of control was to increase drug medications to maximum prescribed levels in those cases in which mental or behavioral disturbances appeared threatening. A third control, used but twice, was to return the patient to a mental hospital. With a fourth method, the campers themselves offered considerable personal and group support to members who needed help. Group pride and a set of standards of behavior seemed to emerge that had a strong regulatory and inhibitory effect upon each camper regardless of his degree of illness. Most of the serious problems arose during the first few days of camp and then sporadically after that.

8. *All staff members should have a genuine interest in camping as an activity and should participate in it enthusiastically.* The staff members are participant-observers, never just observers. Consequently, they are active members of every group they are part of. The enthusiastic participation of the

staff seems to spread to the patients, leading to their involvement in camp life and activities.

9. *Freedom of choice in selecting activities is given patients whenever possible.* A few may elect to sit alone, others to talk with friends, play cards, or enjoy some other pastime. Most patients after the first few days usually join some of the larger group activities or programs. Often campers themselves serve as the force that helps a withdrawn patient to become a more active participant.

This freedom of choice is enhanced in several ways by the camp's structure and organization. In the dining room patients are free to sit at any table and with anyone they choose. When going to and from activities patients walk alone or with others as they elect. Never are campers "marched," "lined up," or assigned to group formations when moving about. Also, the degree of participation in activities, programs, or services is entirely an individual matter. Patients are often invited to participate by others, but are never forced. In other words, the camp's structure tries to avoid close regimentation, regulation, and coercion by increasing individual freedom of choice as far as possible without jeopardizing the welfare of the group.

10. *The focus of the camp is upon health and not sickness.* Attention is directed to the normal capacities and healthy residuals in each patient, rather than to pathological conditions and disorders. For example, all patients are called "campers" while in camp. Use of medical and hospital terminology with patients is forbidden. Staff members do not discuss with patients any of their abnormal mental phenomena or attempt to explore etiology. The emphasis of the program is upon creating a healthy daily life structure and set of activities that will invite camper participation. The staff has found that an attitude of expectancy of normality and ability to participate is important in eliciting patient participation. The position is taken that camping is fun and all can enjoy being a part of it.

11. *Camp standards and rules are largely established by staff-patient interaction rather than by authoritative decree.* What little consideration is given to rules and regulations is done by open discussion either at the camp council sessions or at the cabin level. Many of the social controls, however, are evolved without formal consideration. Patients sense what is appropriate and reasonable and conduct themselves accordingly. Actual formulation and statement of rules occupy very little attention of staff or campers. Only rarely has a camper's overt behavior demanded special attention by staff in order to protect the welfare of the group.

12. *The camp endeavors to foster a feeling of group identification and belongingness.* As soon as a patient arrives in camp he is assigned to a cabin group, which is the basic social-living unit of the camp. A staff cabin member helps campers to get acquainted, tells them about camp, holds evening discussions, and does whatever he can to develop a group or family feeling. The cabin members select their own leader, elect their own representative to the camp council, supervise their own cabin cleanup, discuss mutual problems,

and so on. Considerable support is generated for both the individual and the group by this cabin organization.

13. *An attempt is made to have camp life reflect a healthy balance between work and play, somewhat similar to the daily activities of persons outside the hospital.* The camp's program is not perceived as providing a "good time" for patients. Included in their daily schedule are such duties as making beds, washing and ironing clothes, mopping floors, providing dining room services, washing dishes, and the like. The staff looks upon such work as an inherent part of everyday activities in which campers are expected to participate. Usually campers join in the assigned work details and feel this is a necessary contribution to camp life.

OUTCOMES

The empirical results given below are based upon the outcomes of six summer sessions of the camp. This period included nineteen weeks of camping and the involvement of 685 patients. Many of the results cited are often considered significant factors in the assessment of programs designed for the care and treatment of the mentally ill.

1. Not one suicide or attempted suicide occurred, although among the patients were a number who had medical records indicating previous suicidal threats or attempted suicides.

2. No physical altercations occurred among patients or between patients and staff. Only rarely have even verbal clashes or arguments occurred. Many patients in each session remark about the complete absence of conflict among campers. In all, a remarkably smooth and co-operative living pattern has been achieved.

3. No threat or use of physical punishment, restraint, or isolation has ever been used by the staff. Disturbed individuals were helped by emotional and verbal support offered by staff and fellow campers.

4. Not a single patient has ever attempted to run away, even though there are no fences around the site. One Spanish-speaking boy wandered away from the immediate camp grounds several times on the first day of camp and had to be returned to his hospital for safety reasons. Because he spoke only Spanish he could not comprehend camp safety rules.

5. No serious accidents have ever occurred to any of the patients. The nurse's daily report shows only minor first-aid problems.

6. No serious physical illness occurred during the history of the camp. Only two patients have been considered in need of medical attention and one was returned to camp immediately by the physician. The other was withdrawn from the program because of a chronic disorder.

7. No swimming or boating accident ever occurred.

8. No heterosexual or homosexual misconduct has ever been observed or

reported. All program activities are "mixed" and women and men eat together at mealtimes.

9. No patient has ever asked to be returned to his hospital. On the other hand, many patients stated they wished the camp period would last longer.

10. Never was it felt necessary to lock a door or window either day or night. The camp was in every sense a completely "open" care and treatment program.

11. No psychiatric emergency arose that required medical referral or hospitalization.

Each ward physician who had sent patients to the camp in 1961 was later asked to render an over-all clinical judgment as to the effects of the camping experience upon them. The evaluation was made about a month after the patients returned to their respective hospitals. The degree of change estimated by the ward physician was registered on a five-point scale. None of the physicians was involved in any way with the camping project, so their evaluations were independent judgments. The ratings so obtained on 119 patients were as follows: 2 per cent worse, 22 per cent unchanged, 42 per cent some improvement, 29 per cent good improvement, 5 per cent excellent improvement. In general 75 per cent of the patients showed "some" to "excellent" improvement according to the ward physicians.[1]

Another evaluation of the camp's effectiveness was attempted by having the six permanent staff members jointly assess each patient's changes on a five-point scale. This method of evaluation was applied to thirty men and twenty-nine women at the end of the 1961 camp session. The results obtained were: 22 per cent unchanged or worse, 35 per cent some or fair improvement, 25 per cent good improvement, and 17 per cent excellent improvement. The close parallel between the independently derived ratings of the ward physicians and those reported by the nonmedical staff members is certainly remarkable.

Still another evaluation of outcomes was obtained from the permanent staff members on patients in the second 1961 camp session. They were asked to make a pooled judgment as to whether a patient had a chance of being discharged after his return to the hospital. In all, thirty-nine patients were rated and the staff felt that eighteen campers (30 per cent) had recovered sufficiently for discharge. Actual discharge was not a valid criterion, as some who were eligible were not released, since no social placement was possible for them.

[1] The data presented here were obtained independently by Philip Roos, Ph.D., Chief Psychologist, Texas State Hospitals and Special Schools.

28

The Pre-Admission Period and
Precare Programs for the Mentally Ill:
A Review of the Literature

M. GANT CARLTON

IN their recent publication, *Action for Mental Health,* the Joint Commission on Mental Illness and Health (1961) recommended:

> Immediate professional attention should be provided in the community for persons at the onset of acutely disturbed, socially disruptive, and sometimes personally catastrophic behavior—that is, for persons suffering a major breakdown. The few pilot programs for immediate, or emergency psychiatric care presently in existence should be expanded and extended as rapidly as personnel becomes available. . . . The objective of modern treatment of persons with major mental illness is to enable the patient to maintain himself in the community in a normal manner. To do so, it is necessary . . . to save the patient from the debilitating effects of institutionalization as much as possible. . . . (46, pp. xiii–xvii).

The Joint Commission further stated that the number of persistent problems in the field of outpatient care and doubts about the effectiveness of present long-term treatment methods have led to new concepts and programs of treatment. The concept of and trend toward extending treatment services into natural community settings and providing immediate, usually short-term, supportive psychotherapy is cited as one such development.

Actually, the concept of community treatment is far from new. Bleuler (10) recognized over 50 years ago that, in general, it was preferable to treat patients within their familiar surroundings and that the patient should not be admitted to the hospital just beause he suffers from schizophrenia.

There has, however, been increasing interest and development in this country in social and community psychiatry, even to where the American Psychiatric Association's *Mental Hospitals* in June, 1962, became not only the journal of hospital psychiatry but of community psychiatry as well. Immediate short-term treatment programs also have been seen as an aspect of preventive psychiatry. Even the term "crisis psychiatry" has been used (70).

Reprinted from *Community Mental Health Journal,* 1965, *1,* 43–54, by permission of the publisher and the author. © 1965, Behavioral Publications, Inc. Mr. Carlton is Research Social Worker, Program Evaluation Staff, Veteran's Administration, Lyons, New Jersey.

This development in social and community psychiatry has been international in scope. A World Health Organization public health paper by Baker, Davies, and Sivadon (3) stated that all approaches lead to the conclusion that mental illness causes a loss of adaptability and integration with the environment. Treatment, they felt, should not only be aimed at the removal of symptoms, but also at the provision of facilities which will enable the patient to once again develop his relationship with the environment.

> From this concept many of the principles of a psychiatric service and its architectural needs can be deduced. As far as possible, all patients should be treated in the community, and the patient should remain in his usual environment, independent and self-supporting. Should this prove impossible, the next treatment area will be the home. . . . Some treatment can be carried out through outpatient facilities close to the patient's home. Day hospital facilities, with effective domiciliary visiting, enable some families to continue partial care of the patient. Should the family prove unable to help the patient, or if the patient is too disturbed for the family unit to remain reasonably stable, hospital care will be necessary as a temporary measure (3, pp. 10–11).

The growth of community methods of treatment has been greater in Europe than in this country. Some European programs provide immediate or emergency psychiatric care. Berkman (7) found some services offered prior to admission in this country, but indicated they were often "occasional and casual," for the most part, inquiries being answered by factual data about admission policies and procedures.

The purpose of this article is to report on the current literature about programs offering precare or pre-admission services which attempt to fulfill the clinical gap between current outpatient programs and hospital treatment. These include telephone services, walk-in clinics, screening units, and home visiting teams. Related literature about the pre-admission period will also be cited. It is expected that such a review will be helpful in the investigation and planning of these programs which provide, in most cases, alternatives to hospitalization.

REVIEW OF THE PRECARE PROGRAM LITERATURE

TELEPHONE SERVICES

Bartholomew and Kelley (4) describe a personal emergency advisory service operated since April, 1960, by trained volunteers in Melbourne, Australia, under the Victoria Department of Mental Hygiene. A 24-hour service is provided and callers are encouraged to talk at length about their problem. Several courses of action are presented. An appointment within 24 hours (72 hours over a weekend) can be made with a psychiatrist in the department's outpatient clinic. About 39 per cent of the calls were trivial requests for information. However, other calls presented problems which were distributed approximately as follows: emotional—20 per cent; mental illness—10 per cent; family and social problems—10 per cent; alcoholic problems—6 per cent; and general problems, many due to loneliness in the aged—10 per cent. During the first 23 months, over 4,500 calls were received. Contrary to expectations, 53 per cent of the calls were received between 9:00 A.M. and 3:00 P.M. The ratio of female callers to male callers was 2:1.

Although perhaps belonging in a separate category, suicide prevention agencies initially meet the emotional needs of the distressed through a 24-hour telephone service. Dr. Querido, pioneer of the Amsterdam plan, emphasized that an emergency psychiatric service should be started on a small scale and allowed to grow gradually (2). He indicated it would be advisable in the beginning to limit the service to one or two groups of patients such as alcoholics, drug addicts, disturbed geriatrics, or suicidal patients. Since Farberow and Shneidman (30) have adequately reported these suicide preventive agencies no attempt will be made to review them at this time. Among the current organizations listed are: Anti-Suicide Department, Salvation Army; Lebensmüdenfürsorgestelle (Suicide Prevention Agency, Austria); Lebensmüdenbetreuung (Berlin); National Save-a-Life League, Inc.; Rescue, Inc.; The Samaritans; and the Suicide Prevention Center.

WALK-IN CLINICS

General hospitals are beginning to provide immediate psychiatric treatment around-the-clock, often as a function of their emergency room operation. Five programs have given detailed accounts of their service: the Massachusetts General Hospital (20); the Grace-New Haven Hospital, Connecticut (22, 27, 73); The Bronx Municipal "Jacobi" Hospital, New York (23, 24, 25, 78, 85); The Elmhurst Trouble Shooting Clinic, New York (6, 43); and The University Hospitals of Cleveland, Ohio (77). In most programs, psychiatric residents provide the emergency treatment on a rotating basis. The Elmhurst Clinic has a unique arrangement wherein the patient is first seen by a staff psychiatrist and a general practitioner trainee. The general practitioner conducts the next interview with the psychiatrist present, and thereafter alone. The Cleveland service appears limited to early consultation, diagnosis and disposition. Most of the programs offer brief, supportive psychotherapy along with medication and environmental modification. Referrals are made to other psychiatric and social agencies where possible. J. V. Coleman and Errera (22) have enlarged upon the problems and limitations of this type of service and offer further references on the subject of psychiatric emergencies.

Alternatives to hospitalization were recommended in only 43 per cent of the Cleveland emergency cases. The Grace-New Haven service hospitalized approximately 65 per cent of both alcoholics and psychotics, compared to only 12 per cent of both neurotics and non-alcoholic personality disorders. Information about time of visit, race, sex, marital status, age, diagnosis, and disposition were presented by both the Cleveland and Grace-New Haven studies, with the latter also reporting type and duration of the problem, religion, source of referral, personnel accompanying patient, and follow-up. The Bronx service cited five types of patients which showed striking benefits from brief psychotherapy (78).

In Oak Ridge, Tennessee (79), a psychiatrist or psychologist is on call should a psychiatric emergency arrive at the general hospital. A study of intake to a psychiatric walk-in clinic in a deprived area was conducted by the Metropolitan Hospital in New York City (63). Contrary to expectations suggested by several studies, the clinic did make contact with a significant number of residents in the area—equivalent to classes IV and V in the Hollingshead Index. The Neruopsychiatric Institute of the UCLA Medical Center. California (1), reports a 24-hour walk-in service. Their findings on precipitating factors will be reported in a later paragraph.

As an outgrowth of their screening program, the Massachusetts Mental Health Center has developed a walk-in clinic for cases that have to be seen right away and cannot be handled by facilities existing in the community (29, 38).

SCREENING UNITS

Because of overcrowding in mental hospitals, long waiting lists, and the conviction that some psychiatric patients could be treated in the community, several mental hospital systems have established screening units. Other factors behind this move were the feeling that some psychiatric hospitalizations were unnecessary and the effort to provide early treatment to the mentally ill.

Perhaps the most widely known screening programs are the Worthing and Chichester Experiments initiated by Dr. Joshua Carse in England in 1957 (5, 16, 17, 18, 19). No patients are admitted to Graylingwell, the district hospital, without first being screened by the mental health unit. At Worthing, about one third are seen in the clinic of the general hospital, less than a third are seen at the service unit, while the remainder are seen in their homes. Later, after a thorough physical examination including laboratory tests, a decision is reached as to hospital or outpatient treatment. After four years' experience, Dr. Carse states that four out of five patients referred to the service have been able to be treated in the community. It is important to note that in an early report (17), an analysis of admissions revealed that of the 284 patients admitted to the Graylingwell hospital from the Worthing area in 1957, about 50 per cent were diagnosed as having an effective disorder. Only 13 per cent were diagnosed with schizophrenia. The Chichester Experiment attempted to replicate the

Worthing Experiment in a different area of the country. Similar findings of a reduction in admissions are reported.

In this country, two hospitals and the city of Philadelphia have independently organized similar programs. The most research-oriented program began operation in September, 1957, at the Massachusetts Mental Health Center in Boston, and became known as the Community Extension Service (CES). Patients on the MMHC waiting list were studied and offered outpatient treatment. Referrals to community resources were made. Results were reported as "encouraging." Their findings indicate that alternatives were provided for 52 per cent of the 128 persons seen in the first two years, the remainder being admitted to the MMHC for inpatient care. Of the 66 who were able to remain in the community, 62 per cent were diagnosed psychoneurotic, psychophysiologic, or personality disorder, 29 per cent as schizophrenic and paranoid reactions, and 9 per cent were involutional and manic-depressive reactions. B. S. Brown (11) reported on the frequency, attitudes, and practice of the home visiting psychiatrists. An earlier study (48) reported on a number of variables found among patients and their families on the waiting list of this small, short-term, treatment center. The CES study, perhaps the most intensive exploration in the area of precare, has been published in book form (38) and has brought about the development of two permanent psychiatric emergency clinics in the Boston area, with a third currently being created.

The Kings County Hospital, New York (80) began offering immediate psychiatric treatment in the admitting office area in March, 1961. After obtaining a thorough psychiatric history and involving one of the patient's family members or friends, most patients are offered regular scheduled appointments once or twice a week. Daily and round-the-clock appointments are also available. During a six-month period, 392 patients were seen—60 per cent being psychotic. Only 13 per cent were admitted within a four week period of service. About one third of the patients failed to keep subsequent appointments. Of the remaining 236 who were seen, 38 per cent were felt to have shown improvement, while 19 per cent remained unchanged.

Since 1954, the Philadelphia Division of Mental Health has attempted to screen potential hospital admissions and find alternatives to hospitalization (81). A Mental Health Center having four closely cooperating outlets was developed within the city's General Hospital. For those patients unable or unwilling to come to the center, a home evaluation program was organized. From their experience with 600 home evaluations, five specific areas of need were found: the aged person; the slow-suicide; the dangerous patient; the who-is-ill category where—within a family unit—it is difficult to ascertain which individual is mentally ill; and a related group where known individual pathology is affecting others in the family. The Philadelphia Department of Public Health (66) reported that the Reception Center was serving nearly 5000 patients per year, yet hospitalizing only 52 per cent. Some of the factors which contributed to the development and success of the Philadelphia program have been cited by Linden, Appel, Davis and Matthews (52). Warner (81) reports

on the development of criteria for involuntary hospitalization and offers a
rating scale used in reaching the decision to hospitalize.

HOME VISITING TEAMS

Some of the programs already mentioned make home visits to those considered in need of psychiatric hospitalization. However, there are seven which
utilize this method almost exclusively.

Probably the most emulated precare program has been the one developed
30 years ago in Amsterdam, Holland, by Dr. Arie Querido, and known now as
the Social Psychiatry Service (2, 5, 19, 61). Although this city of approximately 850,000 is divided into 22 districts, each of which has a mental health
center, there is central screening and control of all patients being considered
for admission. Records are readily accessible and current. Upon referral, often
within an hour, a mobile team of a district psychiatrist and social worker visit
the home. The psychiatrist attempts a temporary solution at that time, and
both public and private resources are later mobilized for continued care in the
community. About 40 per cent of patients referred have been able to remain at
home. Since Lemkau and Crocetti (50) state that well over 70 per cent of the
emergency calls received do not result in hospitalization, it is evident that a
greater percentage of admissions occur from non-emergent situations. Ling
(53) cites suicide and hospitalization rates, concluding that the Amsterdam
system is more effective than the program in greater London. Ross (70)
reports that financial savings to the community favor the program nine to one
over operating a mental hospital system.

A system of effective links and cooperation between hospital and community, urged recently by Felix (31), appears to be present in the integrated
mental health service of Nottingham, England (5, 19, 56, 57). Much of this
integration can be attributed to the hospital and the local city health service
sharing the same administration and staff, and to the pioneer work of Dr. Duncan MacMillan. About one third of the patients admitted to Mapperly Hospital
come through the Local Health Authority which sends a social worker and
psychiatrist team to the home of a referral. Every effort is made to provide
for home treatment. However, should hospitalization be necessary, it is impressed upon the family that the patient will be admitted to the hospital for a
definite, short-term period; and when he is better, they will be expected to take
him home again. It was found that, when this explanation was made before
admission, the relatives usually cooperated well; but if left until two or three
months after admission, they were often unwilling to take the patients home
again.

Some psychiatric hospitals provide precare home visits more in an attempt
to extend their admission services than to seek alternatives to hospitalization.
Poland (67) reports that social workers at the Alan Memorial Institute of
Psychiatry, Royal Victoria Hospital, Montreal, are making home visits to try

to mobilize early family cooperation in treatment, to prepare the patient for treatment, and to lessen his anxiety and that of his family. Immediate social problems are discussed and the family helped in reaching solutions. Both the patient and the family are informed as to what they may expect from hospitalization. By providing early service when the family is in a state of crisis, the social workers have given evidence of the hospital's interest in the family as a whole. They have also indicated to the family the expectation that they participate in the treatment program. It has been found that, if no contact has been made prior to admission, families offer considerable resistance, both open and hidden, to visiting the hospital and entering into a working relationship toward further planning. In contrast, families have welcomed the suggestion of pre-admission visits with eagerness and relief, and have continued spontaneously to communicate with the hospital.

In Boston, the Psychiatric Home Treatment Service (PHTS) was organized on an experimental and clinical basis in 1956 (35, 68, 78, 83). Three phases of the program are outlined: evaluation, disposition, and treatment. Home visiting is used extensively during the evaluation phase. There are generally three interviews over one or more weeks, after which a dispositional staff conference is held, and the recommendations and decision made known to the referring agent. Initial results were given in the PHTS Progress Report of 1959 based on 48 completed cases out of 70 patients studied during the period October, 1957 to April, 1959. Perhaps the most important findings were the final disposition of the total and closed cases. Sixty-one per cent of the total 70 cases did not require hospitalization. Of these cases, however, 22 were still open and had not had a final disposition. Of those 48 which had been closed 64 per cent had remained in the community. Of the 29 diagnosed psychotic, 34 per cent had been maintained outside of the hospital. The staff found it necessary to convince both patient and family that outpatient treatment was appropriate treatment. Although PHTS was available for limited emergency service, most patients appeared to be the chronic, exacerbated, troublesome cases which other outpatient facilities are not prepared or willing to handle. Preliminary analysis, based upon 46 completed cases, failed to reveal any statistically significant associations between pre-referral urgency (can wait— can't wait) or pre-referral issue of hospitalization (raised—not raised) and diagnosis (psychotic—not psychotic) or outcome (hospitalized—not hospitalized).

To eliminate the unnecessary jail detention of the mentally ill, Washington County in Maryland (13), organized a psychiatric emergency service. In response to a referral, a physician and a nurse promptly visit the patient wherever he is. In three years' experience, nearly 300 emergency calls were handled. Cameron indicates that about one third of the patients referred were found to need no treatment or were able to be treated in the outpatient clinic. In his opinion, they would otherwise have been hospitalized precipitously.

A similar program is now established in Pinellas County, Florida (14). During the first year of operation 1,215 emergency calls were received. Forty-seven per cent of patients who received emergency psychiatric care were able to remain at home, while 44 per cent were admitted to general hospitals and 8 per cent referred to nursing homes. New admissions to state hospitals from Pinellas County were reduced by 15 per cent although the area population increased.

Schwartz, Waldron, and Tidd (72) report a program where home visitation was integrated into the pre-admission evaluation procedure of the UCLA Medical Center in West Los Angeles. The essential purpose was to estimate the value of home visits both clinically and from the standpoint of teaching interns rather than offering a service. After only 11 visits, they concluded that home visits had a definite teaching value and in some cases, a clinical value. The clinical value was seen in three areas: (1) in reaching a decision relative to admission or making alternative plans, (2) in planning the patients' hospital treatment, and (3) in the patients' disposition following hospitalization.

DISCUSSION

The literature describes most of these precare programs as serving three separate functions: diagnostic and screening, therapeutic, and referral to another agency. The third follows when neither hospitalization nor treatment is offered or when aftercare is recommended. Hirsch (43) also has outlined general functions of such a community service and a philosophy of emergency care. Meerloo (60) and M. D. Coleman (23) further amplify upon the theory, techniques, and observations involved in emergency psychotherapy, but J. V. Coleman and Errera (22) point out that there is no agreement on what constitutes a psychiatric emergency.

In about half of the programs, home visits are made, not only by psychiatrists, but by psychiatric social workers and psychiatric or public health nurses. However, there is no general agreement as to who should be the first to visit. Baars (2) and Querido (69) feel very strongly that the first contact with the patient should be made by the psychiatrist. In PHTS, the nurse made the initial visit as it was felt she represented a more "neutral" figure than either the psychiatrist or social worker, and would probably be a more welcomed person where resistance might exist. In the CES program there also were instances where initial visits were made by the nurse, or the nurse and social worker. In any case, there was general agreement that home visits were an important aid in diagnosis and treatment.

In nearly all programs, family participation was felt essential. From the experience at Nottingham and Montreal, it appears that the responsibility of the social worker in encouraging the family to maintain "positive, non-rejecting attitudes" is better met by pre- than post-admission visits.

Role conflicts and anxiety were felt initially by the staff in many programs, but often diminished as the service became established. Some, i.e., PHTS, felt that special skills were required, while others, i.e., CES, found that personnel and procedures needed to provide this type of community treatment were similar to those available in existing clinics and hospitals. While a few of the programs provided staff training, some medical schools (8, 71) felt it necessary to establish special training programs for community psychiatry.

It was reported in seven of the programs offering precare that alternatives to hospitalization were found for 33–80 per cent of total referrals. In three programs it was found that only 9–38 per cent of psychotics were able to be treated in the community.

It appears also that these programs providing alternative care in the community are less costly than hospital-centered programs. Hyde and Brennan (45) offer one way of comparing such costs.

REVIEW OF THE PRE-ADMISSION LITERATURE

Before attempting to implement a precare program of immediate psychiatric treatment in which alternatives to hospitalization are to be considered, it would seem important to be aware of what factors are related to hospitalization. Specifically, what are precipitants which lead someone to raise the question of hospitalization? Who is it that seeks hospitalization, and to whom do they turn? What is the nature of the path to the hospital? Are common experiences found in the research of the pre-admission period? Partial answers or implications are found in some recent studies.

FACTORS RELATED TO ADMISSION

Most studies about precipitants have occurred after the hospitalization has taken place. Wolfram, Essey, Pang, and Courtney (86) found the following combination of three factors occurring approximately at the same time to precipitate hospitalization in 34 men: change in the husband's employment pattern, a change in the wife's health, and the onset of different behavior. Whitmer and Conover (84) suggest that hospitalization is sought by a family for one of its members primarily because of behavior and circumstances rather than because of recognition of the pathological symptoms of mental illness. Such a generalization supports Yarrow, Schwartz, Murphy, and Deasy (89) in their finding that situational factors tend to lead wives to seeing their husband as mentally ill. They felt immediate, serious and direct physical threats or the influence of others may be the deciding factor. Using a modification of the Critical Incident Technique, Whitmer and Conover (84) cite loss of reality contact, somatic or seizure complaints, and aggressive or threatening behavior among the most frequent incidents leading to hospitalization. Grad and Sainsbury (37) also found that bodily complaints were an aspect of the patient's behavior which occurred most frequently prior to admission. However, threatening the safety of others occurred only in 12 per cent of the families studied. Likewise, Linn (55) found patients with physical complaints more likely to be hospitalized, but added that families tend to react to the totality of symptoms rather than to any particular type of behavior.

Two studies (58, 87) seem to suggest that hospitalization is "motivated, goal-directed behavior" and an "end in itself over and above the question of getting help with symptoms." Mahrer and Katz (58) found a high negative correlation—contingency coefficient was $-.33$—between number of symptoms checked and number of previous hospitalizations. Linn (54), in his study of pre-admission symptoms, found they were not associated, for the most part, with education, occupation, marital status, religion or other characteristics of patients.

Precipitating factors of a psychiatric emergency service are reported by Adler and Bunn (1). Marital status and chronicity were reported to be significantly related to category of stress—interpersonal, intrapersonal, and no apparent stress. The mean age of chronic cases, 43 years, differed significantly from the acute cases, 34 years.

Kalis, Harris, Prestwood, and Freeman (47) stated that explicit attention to the question of what leads a person to apply for psychiatric help can provide a perspective to the nature of the patient's current difficulties and his expectations from treatment.

AGENTS OF HOSPITALIZATION

There have been many studies indicating who seeks hospitalization and to whom they first turn for help (21, 34, 41, 44, 51, 59, 62, 84, 86, 87). Greenblatt et al. (38) found it was usually the family, rather than the patient, family physician, or community source that initiated the search for psychiatric treatment; but most of the other studies suggest that it is usually someone other than the family who finally makes the referral for treatment. Thus, for many, the source of help becomes the source of referral or the significant agent of hospitalization.

Although some studies (34, 41, 44) have indicated that very few patients or families make use of existing outpatient psychiatric agencies prior to hospitalization, most of these and other studies have found that some type of non-psychiatric help was sought. Mandell and Cromack (59) found in their study that 34 per cent of patients and 46 per cent of patient and/or family had been known to at least one of a group of selected health and welfare agencies within a community within a three-year period prior to admission. Their findings also appear to support the Hollingshead and Redlich (44) finding that use of sources of help is related to social class. Landy and Albert (48) state that 57 per cent reported using community resources prior to hospitalization.

In nearly all the previously cited studies, the general practitioner is found to be the person to whom most families turn for help. Lemere and Kraabel (49) in a survey of 600 general practitioners found they reported 24 per cent of their practice as "predominantly psychiatric."

THE GENERAL PRACTITIONER

Whether the general practitioner is willing and able to meet the needs of the mentally ill at the point where the question of hospitalization is raised, or whether there needs to be another means to fill the clinical gap between current outpatient programs and hospital treatment is a question to be considered in view of the following problem areas. Peterson, Spain, Andrews and Greenberg (65) found only 17 per cent able to recognize and treat emotional problems with sufficient competence; 54 per cent were able to recognize emotional problems, but did not attempt psychological treatment or treated physical aspects of the complaints only; and 29 per cent did not generally recognize emotional problems or attempt to treat them. That some doctors do not want to treat psychiatric patients or they find it quite overwhelming has been recognized by Gunderson (39). Lemere and Kraabel (49) further cite reasons general practitioners are reluctant to refer their patients to psychiatrists, and Cammer and Tarail (15) discuss some of the problems involved for a general practitioner in making a psychiatric referral. However, lack of communication between the general practitioner and the psychiatrist can be attributed in part to the psychiatrist. Garber (36) in a survey of 2,640 general practitioners found that 57 per cent reported that state and county hospitals usually do not refer their patients back to them, 41 per cent said Veterans Administration Hospitals usually do not, and 32 per cent said private hospitals do not. It seems also significant to note here that of 125,450 surveys circulated through the Smith, Kline and French publication *Consultant,* only 2,640 replies (2 per cent) were reported received. Taylor (76), in a study of the treatment practices of general practitioners and psychiatrists, cites the differences he found in their approach to the mentally ill. Efforts to increase the participation of general practitioners in community care of the mentally ill have been described (6, 74, 80, 88); and it has been predicted (28) that they will eventually provide all emergency care. It is evident some general practitioners are attempting to meet this challenge (42).

PATH TO THE HOSPITAL

Hollingshead and Redlich (44) indicate that there are four "milestones" each person must pass before reaching the psychiatrist. There first has to be an occurrence of "abnormal" behavior. Secondly, this behavior must be appraised as "disturbed" in the psychiatric sense. Next, a decision must be reached that psychiatric treatment is indicated. Finally, this decision must be implemented. Yarrow et al. (89) have indicated the problems involved in appraisal; while Clausen and Yarrow (21) have pointed out that the reaching and implementing of a decision is a path beset with obstacles, trauma and discontinuities. Two studies (51, 86) show that the path is a circuitous one, involving on the average three different sources of help.

That the use of "paths" by two writers (21, 44) should change to "roads" by more recent authors (38, 86) is reflective of what Freeman and Simmons (33) have called the major problem in the field of mental illness—the rehospitalized patient. It thus appears that the "path" has become the "beaten path" and that the "closed door," which gave way to the "open door," has now become the "revolving door." It was recognized (75) over twenty years ago that an increase in the institutional recovery rate would be attended by a corresponding increase in the return rate. This return rate was estimated (9) to be from 20–40 per cent of patients released. Recent research (12, 40) has found similar return rates for the first year out to be from 32–46 per cent. Free and Dodd (32) also report similar return rates in a five-state study. They also found that organized aftercare reduced the rehospitalization rate about 50 per cent. The importance of drugs on the return rate has been indicated by Engelhardt, Rosen, Freedman, Mann, and Margolis (26). Although Greenblatt et al. (38) felt that the prevention of a re-admission might present different problems than a first admission, most of the programs described in this review dealt with both situations.

Since several studies (48, 64, 87, 89) indicate that admission is often delayed for months, even years, two questions arise. Why is hospitalization delayed and what effect does this delay have upon the family? Overprotection, neglect, and the psychosis not being recognized are probable reasons cited by Ödegaard (64) in his study of delayed admissions. Whitmer and Conover (84) and Yarrow et al. (89) suggest similar and other reasons. As to what effect delayed admission has upon the family, Ödegaard (64) concludes that the burden has often been very heavy upon the relatives. Landy and Albert (48) and Lewis and Zeichner (51) give more specific information. Yarrow et al. (89) point out that a defensive normalizing process of a husband's neurotic and psychotic symptoms will provide momentary attenuation of this burden. The question may be raised as to what burden is placed upon a family by a community treatment program, which in a sense could be delayed admission. Grad and Sainsbury (37) compared the effects upon the family of a community-care service and a hospitalization service and found that the burden on the family a month after referral was not reduced significantly more in one service than the other. Admission to the hospital by itself, it was felt, did not necessarily solve the family's problems. What did seem important was that, in both services, either contact with the psychiatrist, or awareness that help is now available and something is being done, helped to reduce the family burden by the end of the month.

WORDS OF CAUTION

Several points have been raised that require that prudence be exercised in establishing a precare program. M. S. Schwartz and his associates (46) wonder if treatment pursues the patient rather than vice versa, how can the patient's rights to privacy and his right to live with his emotional burdens and refuse help be protected. Finally, Ewalt, Alexander, and Grinspoon (28, p. 13) advise ". . . that we examine each of our new techniques to make certain that the new plan is not really motivated by rejection of the patient by the staff, or entered into with substantial elan because it is 'new' and will bring a momentary touch of glamor to a particular hospital or program."

REFERENCES

1. Adler, R. H., and Bunn, D. R. Precipitating factors at a psychiatric emergency service. *Psychiat. Stud. and Projects,* 1963, No. 3.
2. Baars, C. W. The Amsterdam plan. *Ment. Hosp.,* 1959, 10 (5):18–19.
3. Baker, A., Davies, R. L., and Sivadon, P. *Psychiatric services and architecture.* Geneva: World Health Organization, 1959.
4. Bartholomew, A. A., and Kelley, M. F. The personal emergency advisory service. *Ment. Hyg., N. Y.,* 1962, 46:382–92.
5. Barton, W. E., Farrell, M. J., Lenehan, F. T., and McLaughlin, W. F. *Impressions of European psychiatry.* Washington: American Psychiatric Assoc., 1961.
6. Bellak, L. A general hospital as a focus of community psychiatry. *J. Amer. Med. Assoc.,* 1960, 174:2214–17.
7. Berkman, T. D. *Practice of social workers in psychiatric hospitals.* New York: American Association of Social Workers, 1953.
8. Bernard, V. W. A training program in community psychiatry. *Ment. Hosp.,* 1960, 11 (5): 7–10.
9. Black, B. J. The workaday world: Some problems in return of mental patients to the community. In Greenblatt, et. al. (Eds.), *The patient and the mental hospital.* New York: Free Press, 1957.
10. Bleuler, E. *Dementia praecox or the group of schizophrenias.* New York: International University Press, 1950 translation.
11. Brown, B. S. Home visiting by psychiatrists. *Arch. Gen. Psychiat.,* 1962, 7:98–107.
12. Brown, G. W., Carstairs, G. M., and Topping, G. Post-hospital adjustment of chronic mental patients. *Lancet,* 1958, 2:685–89.
13. Cameron, W. R. How to set up a county psychiatric emergency service. *Amer. J. Publ. Hlth.,* 1962, 52 (Supp. pt. 2): 16–19.
14. Cameron, W. R., and Walters, V. The emergency mental health service: An important contribution to preventive medicine. Paper read at Southern Medical Assoc., Memphis, Tenn., November, 1964.

15. Cammer, L., and Tarail, M. The private practitioner and the psychiatric referral. *Ment. Hosp.*, 1962, 13:19–21.

16. Carse, J., Panton, N. E., and Watt, A. A district mental health service: The Worthing experiment. *Lancet*, 1958, 1:39–41.

17. Carse, J. *The Worthing experiment: A report*. Chichester, England: Graylingwell Hospital, 1959.

18. Carse, J. Community care and treatment of the psychiatric patient. *Practit.*, 1961, 187:672–78.

19. Casey, J., Rackow, L. L., and Sperry, A. W. *Observations on the treatment of the mentally ill in Europe*. Washington: Government Printing Office, 1960.

20. Clark, E. Round-the-clock emergency psychiatric services. *Soc. Wk. Pract.*, 1963, 44–57.

21. Clausen, J. A., and Yarrow, M. Paths to the mental hospital. *J. Soc. Issues*, 1955, 11 (4):25–32.

22. Coleman, J. V., and Errera, P. The general hospital emergency room and its psychiatric problems. *Amer. J. Publ. Hlth.*, 1963, 53:1294–1301.

23. Coleman, M. D. Methods of psychotherapy: Emergency psychotherapy. In J. H. Masserman and J. L. Moreno (Eds.), *Progress in psychotherapy*. New York: Grune & Stratton, 1960. Pp. 78–85.

24. Coleman, M. D. Problems in an emergency psychiatric clinic. *Ment. Hosp.*, 1960, 11 (5):26–27.

25. Coleman, M. D., and Zwerling, I. The psychiatric emergency clinic: A flexible way of meeting community needs. *Amer. J. Psychiat.*, 1959, 115:980–84.

26. Engelhardt, D. M., Rosen, B., Freedman, N., Mann, D., and Margolis, R. Phenothiazines in prevention of psychiatric hospitalization. *J. Amer. Med. Assoc.*, 1963, 186:981–83.

27. Errera, P., Wyshak, G., and Jarecki, H. Psychiatric care in a general hospital emergency room. *Arch. Gen. Psychiat.*, 1963, 9:105–12.

28. Ewalt, J. R., Alexander, G. L., and Grinspoon, L. L. Changing practices: A plea and some predictions. *Ment. Hosp.*, 1960, 11 (6):9–13.

29. Ewalt, J. R., Zaslow, S., and Stevenson, P. How non-psychiatric physicians can deal with psychiatric emergencies. *Ment. Hosp.*, 1964, 15:194–96.

30. Farberow, N. L., and Shneidman, E. S. (Eds.) *The cry for help*. New York: McGraw-Hill, 1961.

31. Felix, R. H. Presidential address: The hospital and the community. *Ment. Hosp.*, 1961, 12 (2):1–4.

32. Free, S. M., and Dodd, D. F. Aftercare for discharged mental patients. *Ment. Hlth. Va.*, 1961, Summer issue, 1–6.

33. Freeman, H. E., and Simmons, O. G. Treatment experiences of mental patients. *Amer. J. Publ. Hlth.*, 1961, 51:1266–73.

34. Freeman, H. E., and Simmons, O. G. *The mental patient comes home*. New York & London: John Wiley, 1963.

35. Friedman, T. T., Rolfe, P., and Perry, S. E. Home treatment of psychiatric patients. *Amer. J. Psychiat.*, 1960, 116:807–9.

36. Garber, R. S. The hospital, the family doctor, and aftercare. *Ment. Hosp.*, 1963, 14:214–15.

37. Grad, J., and Sainsbury, P. Mental illness and the family. *Lancet*, 1963, 1:544–47.

38. Greenblatt, M., Moore, R. F., Albert, R. S., and Solomon, M. H. et al. *The prevention of hospitalization.* New York: Grune & Stratton, 1963.
39. Gunderson, R. The G. P. as a psychiatrist. *SK&F Psychiatric Reporter,* 1962. Sept.–Oct., 9–10.
40. Gurel, L. Release and community stay criteria of mental hospital effectiveness. Paper read at Eighth Annual Conf. of the Cooperative Studies in Psychiat., Kansas City, Mo., March 25–27, 1963.
41. Gurin, G., Veroff, J., and Feld, S. *Americans view their mental health.* New York: Basic Books, 1960.
42. Gwartney, R. H., Auerback, A., Nelken, S., and Goshen, C. E. Panel discussion on psychiatric emergencies in general practice. *J. Amer. Med. Assoc.,* 1959, 170:1022–30.
43. Hirsch, J. Suicide, part 5: The trouble-shooting clinic. *Ment. Hyg.,* 1960, 44:496–502.
44. Hollingshead, A. B., and Redlich, F. C. *Social class and mental illness: A community study.* New York: John Wiley, 1958, Pp. 171–93.
45. Hyde, R. W., and Brennan, M. J. Cost of alternatives to hospitalization. *Ment. Hyg.,* 1960, 44:197–205.
46. Joint Commission on Mental Illness and Health. *Action for mental health.* New York: Basic Books, 1961.
47. Kalis, B. L., Harris, M. R., Prestwood, A. R., and Freeman, E. H. Precipitating stress as a focus in psychotherapy. *Arch. Gen. Psychiat.,* 1961, 5:219–26.
48. Landy, D., and Albert, R. S., Waiting for hospitalization. *Arch. Gen. Psychiat.,* 1959, 1:519–29.
49. Lemere, F., and Kraabel, A. B. The general practitioner and the psychiatrist. *Amer. J. Psychiat.,* 1959, 116:518–21.
50. Lemkau, P. V., and Crocetti, G.M. The Amsterdam municipal psychiatric service: A psychiatric-sociological review. *Amer. J. Psychiat.,* 1961, 117:779–83.
51. Lewis, V. S., and Zeichner, A.M. Impact of admission to a mental hospital on the patient's family. *Ment. Hyg., N. Y.,* 1960, 44:503–9.
52. Linden, M. E., Appel, K. E., Davis, J. E., and Matthews, R. A. Factors in the success of a public mental health program. *Amer. J. Psychiat.,* 1959, 116:344–51.
53. Ling, T. M. The prevention of mental illness: Some lessons from Holland. *Lancet,* 1954, 1:1127–28.
54. Linn, E. L. The association of preadmission symptoms with the social background of mental patients. *Arch. Gen. Psych.,* 1960, 3:557–62.
55. Linn, E. L. Agents, timing, and events leading to mental hospitalization. *Human Organ.,* 1961, 20 (2):92–98.
56. MacMillan, D. An integrated mental health service. *Lancet,* 1956, 2:1094–95.
57. MacMillan, D. Mental health services of Nottingham. *Int. J. Soc. Psychiat.,* 1958, 4:5–9.
58. Mahrer, A. R., and Katz, G. K. Psychiatric symptoms at admission to hospitalization. *Psychiat. Dig.,* 1963, 24 (2):23–30.
59. Mandell, W., and Cromack, I. Pre-hospitalization contacts by community health and welfare agencies with individuals having major mental illnesses. *Ment. Hyg.,* 1958, 42:511–20.

60. Meerloo, J. A. M. Emergency psychotherapy and mental first aid. *J. Nerv. Ment. Dis.*, 1956, 124:535–45.
61. Millar, W. M., and Henderson, N. J. The health service of Amsterdam. *Int. J. Soc. Psychiat.*, 1956, 2:141–50.
62. Nilsson, G. L., and Kurland, A. A. The general practicing physician as a resource for the mentally ill. *Ment. Hyg.*, 1960, 44:103–4.
63. Normand, W., Fensterheim, H., Tannenbaum, G., and Sager, C. J. The acceptance of the psychiatric walk-in clinic in a highly deprived community. *Amer. J. Psychiat.*, 1963, 120:533–39.
64. Ödegaard, Ö. A clinical study of delayed admissions to a mental hospital. *Ment. Hyg.*, 1958, 42:67–77.
65. Peterson, O. L., Spain, R. S., Andrews, L. P., and Greenberg, B. G. An analytical study of North Carolina general practice, 1953–1954. *J. Med. Educ.*, 1956, 31:41–42.
66. Philadelphia Department of Public Health, Division of Mental Health *Annual report.* Philadelphia: Author, 1960.
67. Poland, P. Preadmission visits encourage positive attitudes. *Ment. Hosp.*, 1961, 12(7):8–9.
68. Psychiatric Home Treatment Service. *A progress report.* Boston: Author, 1959.
69. Querido, A. Early diagnosis and treatment services. In Milbank Memorial Fund, *The elements of a community mental health program.* New York: Author, 1956. Pp. 158–81.
70. Ross, M. Holland's social psychiatry service. *Ment. Hosp.*, 1963, 14:375–76.
71. Ruesch, J. Research and training in social psychiatry in the United States. *Int. J. Soc. Psychiat.*, 1961, 7:87–96.
72. Schwartz, D. A., Waldron, R., and Tidd, C. W. Use of home visits for psychiatric evaluation. *Arch. Gen. Psychiat.*, 1960, 3:57–65.
73. Schwartz, M. D., and Errera, P. Psychiatric care in a general hospital emergency room: Diagnostic features. *Arch. Gen. Psychiat.*, 1963, 9: 113–21.
74. Smith, J. A., Strough, L. C., Wittson, C., and Mansfield, E. A program for the psychiatric training of general practitioners while utilizing their offices as an outpatient facility. *Amer. J. Psychiat.*, 1958, 115:539–42.
75. Sullivan, H. S. Socio-psychiatric research: Its implications for the schizophrenia problem and for mental hygiene. *Amer. J. Psychiat.*, 1931, 87: 977–91.
76. Taylor, J. B. The psychiatrist and the general practitioner. *Arch. Gen. Psychiat.*, 5:1–6.
77. Ungerleider, J. T. The psychiatric emergency. *Arch. Gen. Psychiat.*, 1960, 3:593–601.
78. Vaughan, W. T., and Downing, J. J. Planning for early treatment psychiatric services. *Ment. Hyg., N. Y.*, 1962, 44:486–97.
79. Wachtel, A. S. A comprehensive community clinic. *Ment. Hosp.*, 1962, 13:653–55.
80. Waltzer, H., Hankoff, L. D., Engelhardt, D. M., and Kaufman, I. C. Emergency psychiatric treatment in a receiving hospital. *Ment. Hosp.*, 1963, 14:595–600.
81. Warner, S. L. Criteria for involuntary hospitalization of psychiatric patients in a public hospital. *Ment. Hyg.*, 1961, 45:122–28.

82. Warner, S. L., Fleming, B. A., and Bullock, S. C. The Philadelphia program for home psychiatric evaluations, pre-care, and involuntary hospitalization. *Amer. J. Publ. Hlth.,* 1962, 52(1):29–38.
83. Weiner, L., and Bergen, B. J. Psychiatric home treatment: Problems of innovation in community psychiatry. *Intl. J. Soc. Psychiat.,* 1963, 9: 200–207.
84. Whitmer, C. A., and Conover, G. A study of critical incidents in the hospitalization of the mentally ill. *Soc. Wk.,* 1959, 4(1):89–94.
85. Wilder, J. F., and Coleman, M. D. The "walk-in" psychiatric clinic: Some observations and follow-up. *Int. J. Soc. Psychiat.,* 1963, 9:192–99.
86. Wolfrom, E., Pang, L., and Courtney, B. Roads to the mental hospital. *Ment. Hyg.,* 1963, 47:398–407.
87. Wood, E. C., Rakusin, J. M., and Morse, E. Interpersonal aspects of psychiatric hospitalization—the admission. *Arch. Gen. Psychiat.,* 1960, 3:632–41.
88. World Health Organization, Expert Committee on Mental Health. *The role of public health officers and general practitioners in mental health care.* Geneva: Author, 1962.
89. Yarrow, M. R., Schwartz, C. G., Murphy, H. S., and Deasy, L. C. The psychological meaning of mental illness in the family. *J. Soc. Issues,* 1955, 11(4):12–24.

29

Paid Employment as a Rehabilitative Technique
in a State Mental Hospital:
A Demonstration

HERBERT J. HOFFMAN

REMUNERATIVE work as a technique of therapy and rehabilitation for the hospitalized mentally ill has received relatively little emphasis in the United States. The extensive use of work programs in Europe and in England, as an integral part of the treatment process, is in marked contrast to the lack of its use on this continent.

This is also in marked contrast to the emphasis on purchasing power and material possessions as measures of esteem and success in this highly industrialized society. Approximately 50 per cent of the mental hospitals in England have factory type buildings and settings in which patients are productively occupied and prepared for return to the community. This is a picture duplicated in Belgium, the Netherlands, across the continent, and into the U.S.S.R.

The scope of this paper is the presentation of the history, problems, mechanics, administration and results of a particular paid employment program unique in its time—the Sheltered Workshop at Metropolitan State Hospital in Waltham, Mass. While other programs for the institutionalized mentally ill existed prior to this one, e.g., at the Veterans Administration Hospitals in Bedford and Brockton, Mass., the Metropolitan State Hospital program represented the first time that a community voluntary agency, a state hospital and a state rehabilitation commission cooperated on such a venture in the United States. As the details of this partnership unfold, it will become clear that certain beneficial advantages not originally anticipated have accrued to the patients that otherwise may never have been possible, as a consequence of this collaboration.

It may seem that a "cookbook" for the establishment of a paid employment program in a state hospital is being outlined, but this is not the intent of this paper. Certainly one goal of telling the story of this project is the hope that it will stimulate the development of similar programs in other institutions.

Reprinted from *Mental Hygiene*, 1965, *49*, 193–207, by permission of the publisher and the author. © 1965, National Association for Mental Health. Dr. Hoffman is Assistant Professor, Florence Heller Graduate School for Advanced Studies in Social Welfare, Brandeis University.

ROLE OF THE VOLUNTARY AGENCY IN THE PAID EMPLOYMENT PROGRAM WITHIN A STATE INSTITUTION

The impetus for a paid employment program at Metropolitan State Hospital arose from the concern of the president of the Brookline Association for Mental Health, who observed on the wards indigent but able-bodied men and women engaged in purposeless or no activity. Her observations, in 1960, of workshop programs in European hospitals where patients were productive, purposeful and being rehabilitated led her to ask the Commissioner of Mental Health in Massachusetts why such a program could not be instituted in this hospital. The superintendent of Metropolitan State Hospital, who had toured mental hospitals in Europe in 1959 and was favorably impressed by the work programs he observed, was receptive to the concept of a paid employment program in his hospital when approached by the Brookline Association for Mental Health (BAMH).

At this point, the BAMH enlisted the support of the Commissioner of Mental Health to proceed with the exploration of methods for establishing a paid employment program and gained the approval of a hospital superintendent to house such a program. The means by which this was to be implemented had to be worked out, since the Department of Mental Health was unable to staff such a project at that time. A committee was set up by the BAMH to develop a means for transforming the idea into a reality; that the committee served to establish effective channels of communication with key individuals and agencies from the very early stages played, and continues to play, a significant role in the realization of an idea and the support of that realization. Serving on this Advisory Committee were members of the BAMH, and representatives of the Department of Mental Health, Metropolitan State Hospital, Massachusetts Rehabilitation Commission, the State Employees Association and the Boston Labor Council.

Among the relevant questions considered were: the manner in which a paid employment program is therapeutic and/or rehabilitative; and how it differs from the traditional work programs of hospital industry and occupational therapy. The key to the value of such a program is the role of money as a motivator. The receipt of a regular wage for work produced serves as a concrete reminder to the patient that what he does has value and is valued. For him it is a first step back into the market place of society; no longer are his productions worthless and his level of self-esteem is raised.

In the workshop, an atmosphere similar to a factory setting is produced, which is different and distinctly apart from the regular hospital milieu and routine, thus distinguishing it on another level from occupational therapy and, to a lesser degree, from hospital industry. The expectations in terms of productivity, quality of work, reliability, capacity to work under supervision and constructively with others, can be higher in the workshop because the goals are not principally therapeutic in the more traditional context of resolution of intrapsychic conflict. The goals are ego-directed with the aim of bringing about a rapprochement between the patient and society that will allow him to resume a place in it.

The recommendations of the Advisory Committee were as follows:

1. The establishment of a Sheltered Workshop, a facility licensed by the Wage and Hour and Public Contracts Division, U. S. Department of Labor, for the purpose of providing training and employment service to carefully selected patients.

2. Metropolitan State Hospital would provide space, utilities and patients. It had no money or staff to allocate to this program.

3. The Massachusetts Rehabilitation Commission would utilize the workshop for evaluation and training of its clients, and a per diem fee for each client would be paid to the Brookline Association for Mental Health.

4. The Brookline Association for Mental Health would operate the workshop and solicit and maintain contracts. It would also assume responsibility for the bookkeeping, clerical duties and staffing.

These recommendations set into motion an administrative arrangement for the operation of a Sheltered Workshop (in a state hospital by a voluntary agency) that was unique in the United States. Although such a three-cornered arrangement, i.e., two governmental agencies and a voluntary agency, had many potential drawbacks and pitfalls, it was not without precedent in Massachusetts. It is possible to consider it an extension into the state hospital of the community partnership program for the operation of mental health clinics sponsored by the Department of Mental Health, whereby local citizen groups cooperate with the state to bring direct clinical services to their community (2).

THE SHELTERED WORKSHOP

The paid employment program at Metropolitan State Hospital opened its doors on May 15, 1961, as a licensed Sheltered Workshop. This permit grants exemptions from the Minimum Wage Law by allowing a lower minimum rate, as well as exemptions from Social Security taxes and insurance coverage under Workmen's Compensation. Although the minimum wage is lowered, the "workshop must use its tax-favored and community-supported position fairly in competing with labor and for markets with private enterprise."

From an initial start in a corner of an O.T. shop and one contract, one patient and one foreman, the shop has grown steadily. Five months after its inception, because the workshop had outgrown its quarters, the hospital found new space in the basement of the male dormitory. The area, approximately 800 square feet, was painted and new lighting and wiring installed. As the project developed, more contracts were secured and additional patients employed; a second expansion, one year later, was necessary and the adjoining room added to the workshop doubled its floor space.

The workshop is equipped with benches, tables, chairs, a large variety of tools (primarily for maintenance), a typewriter and the machinery necessary for production. In many instances it has been possible to secure machinery and equipment on a loan basis from those firms who have subcontracted, but the absence of such a loan arrangement has not deterred the acceptance of a contract if there was a reasonable balance between the cost of equipment and the projected length of the contract. Therefore, the Brookline Association for Mental Health has purchased capital equipment and machinery, and has on occasion rented equipment for the production of items under short-term contract.

Early in the workshop's history, a one-year grant by the Permanent Charity Fund sustained the project during a critical period of growth and served as a "pump primer" to a more permanent funding arrangement with the Massachusetts Rehabilitation Commission.

ADMINISTRATIVE STRUCTURE

1. The BAMH employs a foreman, business agent and consultant. Its executive director and volunteer workshop director are responsible for overseeing the administration of the workshop.

The foreman is employed full-time. He operates the workshop; i.e., assigns the work, teaches the operations, maintains quality control, keeps the time and production records for each employee, maintains receiving and shipping records. The capacity to work with patients and to have patients work *with* him are the most important criteria for this position. While knowledge of and experience in factory operation are desirable, mechanical ability and capacity to conceptualize and master new operations brought in on subcontract are even more relevant.

The business agent has been engaged on a part-time basis to date, but expansion to a full-time basis is anticipated in the near future. The major responsibilities of the business agent are to acquire new contracts and maintain and develop established contracts. He is also responsible for the movement of work both into and out of the shop, as well as the maintenance of production schedules for each contract. This latter responsibility places him over the foreman in the line of authority. Ideally, this position should be filled by an individual with considerable business experience and a flair for selling, someone who can talk to the manufacturer on his terms and in his language. The business agent must be active and persistent. The particular area of previous business experience does not appear to be important.

The consultant, at the present time, is the social worker assigned by the hospital to the Continued Treatment Group (chronic hospital population) from which most of the patients have been drawn. This is a "piece-work" position which is done on the worker's free time, and the unit of pay is the completion of an application form required on each patient in order to be considered as a client by the Massachusetts Rehabilitation Commission.

The workshop volunteer director has the responsibility for the over-all supervision of the workshop, including the financial structure. His duties include preparing the weekly payroll, maintaining payroll records with duplicates for the BAMH office, maintaining close contact with the foreman and business agent, and acting as "trouble shooter." He also initiates and negotiates business contracts and supervises the daily balance of work and patient production scheduling. This man is employed as a high-level executive in a large corporation and contributes his time and efforts to the workshop program.

The executive director of the BAMH has the responsibility of overseeing the entire operation of the Sheltered Workshop, one part of the total program of the BAMH, including the maintenance of proper records, the filing of various legal documents and forms as required, and the hiring of new personnel. This portion of the BAMH program takes up, on the average, a little less than one-tenth of the executive director's work week. The present director, a qualified clinical psychologist, also conducts a biweekly group meeting of all patients in the workshop; the content of this meeting is centered about work problems and developing motivation to leave the hospital.

2. *Metropolitan State Hospital* (MSH), since late 1962, has assigned one social worker (who is also the consultant) to work with the patients in the workshop as part of her regular duties. This social worker is the only hospital staff person deeply involved in the program, although many others do come into peripheral contact when initiating a referral or evaluating the progress of a patient.

There are no aides or hospital staff present in the workshop during the work day. The absence of aides, along with the current location, appears to be a boon in the sense that the workshop is both physically and emotionally set somewhat apart from the institution of the hospital, and it begins to approach the institution of the society "outside."

The involvement of the social worker as a consultant brings her closer to the workshop operation and, therefore, helps her in the effective utilization of this resource in her capacity as the only social worker for 1,250 patients. It also helps to focus the worker's attention on one of the few direct service programs available to the "chronic" patients.

3. *Massachusetts Rehabilitation Commission* (MRC) initially assigned a psychiatric rehabilitation counselor one day per week to the MSH, and his major efforts were directed toward clients placed into the workshop. With the growth of the program and its increasing importance, the Commission has assigned a counselor to the hospital five days a week and a psychiatrist one-half day a week. The major role of the counselor has been that of evaluation of clients and potential clients. Time devoted to vocational planning and job placement has been limited, these areas being filled in by the social worker, the executive director, and BAMH volunteers.

4. *Committee meetings* designed to keep this multiagency arrangement operating smoothly and to develop methods and plans for improving the rehabilitative process are held on a regular basis.

a. A committee composed of the BAMH executive director and president (a volunteer), consultant social worker, rehabilitation counselor and occupational therapists meets biweekly to discuss prospective applicants to the workshop, evaluate the progress of patients in the workshop, and make plans and set goals for the future of these patients. On occasions when patients are not deemed eligible by MRC (or once in training, their eligibility is withdrawn), this committee may make the determination to maintain the patient in the work setting if there are compelling reasons for doing so. In such cases administrative costs are assumed by the BAMH.

b. A larger committee, including the above members as well as psychiatrists, heads of hospital departments, and high-level administrators of the MRC and MSH, is chaired by the hospital superintendent, and meets once every six to eight weeks. This committee serves the very important functions of evaluating the program, maintaining communications among the cooperating agencies, maintaining and developing effective and administrative policies, and developing plans for improving the rehabilitative process.

THE PATIENTS

Selection and Evaluation

Referrals from the wards usually originate with attendants, nurses, occupational therapists, psychiatrists, social workers and volunteers. When a referral has been originated and channeled through the ward physician to the consultant social worker, she, in turn, arranges for completion of MRC forms by social service, ward physician and occupational therapy. The social worker prepares the patient for evaluation interviews by the psychiatric rehabilitation counselor and the MRC psychiatrist, who determine eligibility for vocational rehabilitation services. Once eligibility is determined, the patient is placed in the workshop for work evaluation, personal adjustment training, or vocational training, as indicated by the patient's condition and under the terms of the contractual arrangement mentioned above.

There is another category of patients employed in the workshop. These are patients who are not eligible for MRC services, usually because of severity of symptoms, but those who the workshop committee feels could benefit from the experience. Since this group of patients is not a source of training or evaluation fees which are necessary to run the shop, only a very limited number can be employed at a time.

Work Conditions

Compensation is on a piece-rate basis and each patient is encouraged to maintain a record of his daily production. (The shop foreman keeps his own daily work sheets which provide the basis for the computation of the payroll.) Each week a pay check is deposited directly to the hospital account of the patient, and the patient receives a receipt indicating the amount of earnings. Each patient is provided with a notebook for keeping a record of earnings and withdrawals and is encouraged to utilize it for this purpose. The hospital rules governing withdrawals, i.e., maximums of two weekly and $3 per withdrawal, apply, but supervising personnel are instructed to provide withdrawal permission without restriction upon a reasonable request by a workshop employee.

CONTRACTS

The acquisition of new contracts, maintenance and development of old contracts, and the pacing of work are the very heart of any program such as the one described in this paper. If there is no work, there is no paid-employment project! If the work program must be cut back to fewer than five days a week, or if workers must be temporarily laid off, the risk of losing therapeutic and rehabilitative gains is increased.

Over 20 firms have contracted with the Sheltered Workshop with a range from a one-spot job lasting a week to regular work from the first firm to subcontract. This latter firm has increased the number and type of jobs as well. The major portion of these contracts has been initially landed via direct acquaintance between a firm member and a BAMH volunteer or staff person. The name of somebody who "sent me" has been the next most successful means of entrée to a firm. Approaching a firm "cold" has proved to be entirely unsuccessful to date.

Although this type of project has an impressive story to tell and an important impact on almost every citizen, experience indicates that a prospective subcontractor is motivated primarily by economic benefits. The fact sheet presented to prospective subcontractors covers the advantages of utilizing a Sheltered Workshop facility (see Appendix B).

The piece rates are set by the subcontractors and are based on their average in-shop cost. Those jobs on which there is no basis for establishing a rate are assigned rates based on time studies completed in the workshop. The individual patient's pay varies in relationship to the amount of time he works and the skills he develops. All the receipts for work completed are applied to the payroll. Thus, the patient gets the entire benefit of the work produced without any percentage deducted for overhead.

While it would be desirable to determine the occupational and training needs of each patient and select contract work on the basis of the skills required, this is impossible, and the workshop is thankful whenever a contract is procured. Nevertheless, the shop has always aimed at diversification of tasks, and a variety of levels and types of skills required to produce the work. To these ends, fortuitously and by design, the shop has been relatively successful.

Among the more than 30 different contracts completed during the first two and one-half years of the workshop's operation are the following tasks: packaging (from simple to complex, collating, reclaiming bent metal frames, assembling camera lenses, stapling, wiring and soldering radio switches, wire-stripping, sewing, cloth-cutting, inserting a rubber washer onto an electronic component, and many others. The workshop's record has been excellent, with minimum spoilage of material and very few rejects of finished products. In many instances the quality of the output has received generous praise from the manufacturers. Also noteworthy is the fact that no time has been lost in the workshop as a result of an accident on the job in the more than two and one-half years of operation.

RECORD-KEEPING

The secretarial force of the BAMH maintains the records pertinent to the workshop. All the bookkeeping, billing and paying is done from this office. The shop foreman forwards shipping and receiving records as well as the daily worksheets to the BAMH office. The workshop volunteer director provides the office with duplicates of the payroll records.

GOALS

The basic goals of the paid employment project are to:

A. Provide a supportive atmosphere for the development of healthier social relationships.

B. Enable patients to learn to work productively with each other and under supervision.

C. Provide a meaningful work experience which would teach skills and prepare the patients for employment outside the hospital.

D. Enable patients to earn a wage for work produced and thus provide an opportunity for them to have cash savings upon leaving the hospital.

RESULTS

A total of 108 patients, 56 women and 52 men, have been placed in the Sheltered Workshop in the period from May 15, 1961, to December 31, 1963. Of the 89 patients who had completed their training by the end of 1963, 54 are out of the hospital, representing a discharge rate of 61 per cent from the workshop. Forty-one patients (76 per cent), are gainfully employed, many for the first time in years, and of the remaining 13 patients out of the hospital, some are housewives, others are living at home and the status of two is unknown. The average stay in the workshop is approximately six months, and the weekly wages range from $12.00 to $20.00, with an average of $15.00.

In 1963, wages paid to patients employed in the workshop amounted to $10,000.

Of the 34 patients in this group still hospitalized, 4 have been out of the hospital for periods up to one year, but have been readmitted; 2 have been transferred to Veterans Hospitals, and their present status is unknown; 9 are active in hospital industries. One patient died of natural causes before she completed her workshop experience.

A summary of the above data is given in Table 1.

TABLE 1. SUMMARY OF RESULTS

| | DISCHARGED | | | | HOSPITALIZED | | |
	Employed	*At home*	*Escape*	*Workshop*	*Ward*	*Deceased*	*Totals*
Males	16	6	1	10	19	0	52
Females	25	5	1	9	15	1	56
Totals	41	11	2	19	34	1	108

A more detailed study of the first 84 patients entering the workshop was undertaken. On December 31, 1963, 56 per cent (45 patients) of this group had been discharged from the hospital. This figure may represent a more stable rate than the 61 per cent noted for the total group of 108 patients, since six months had passed from the time of entrance into the program of the 84th patient to calculation of the discharge rate. Thus there had been a longer time for the correcting factor of readmissions to operate.

The discharge rate from the Sheltered Workshop of 56–61 per cent compares very favorably with the results of the Harvard Volunteer Program reported by Beck, Kantor and Gelineau (1). In their survey of 120 chronic patients "treated" by college volunteers, 31 per cent were able to leave the hospital. When contrasted to Brown's finding (3) that after 4 years of hospitalization only 3 per cent of patients will ever be discharged, it was concluded that the Harvard program was successful. The workshop patients were drawn from the same wards in the same hospital as the Harvard patients, and had similar characteristics along the measured dimensions.

Summarized in Table 2 are the data (averages) on a number of selected criteria for describing the group of 84 patients. The summary is dichotomized along the male-female dimension and the hospitalized-discharged dimension.

The average patient described by the tabled figures is moving into the middle-aged category (the woman almost seven years older than the man), has completed the sophomore year in high school, has had multiple mental hospital admissions, and the average male can document an illness of almost 6 years duration while the average female has been ill more than twice as long. For the male, the probability of his last recorded diagnosis being some form of schizophrenia is better than 7 out of 10 chances, while the female's chances are almost 6 out of 10.

The average patient who has left the hospital from this group differs rela-

TABLE 2. SUMMARY OF SELECTED CRITERIA
TOTAL GROUP (N = 84)

Average	Males	Females
Age	35.6	42.4
No. admissions	3.1	3.5
Age at 1st admission	27.9	30.3
No. years of education	10.0	10.5
Chronicity*	5.8	12.8
Modal diagnosis (schizophrenia)	72%	59%

DISCHARGED (N = 45)

	Males	Females
Age	33.9	39.3
No. admissions	3.2	3.5
Age at 1st admission	30.7	29.3
No. years of education	10.0	11.5
Chronicity*	5.6	10.9
Modal diagnosis (schizophrenia)	61%	50%

* Chronicity refers to the number of years from first admission to a mental hospital to date of last discharge, or December, 1963, for those still hospitalized.

tively little along these dimensions. He or she is somewhat younger than the total group (males by 1.7 years, females by 3.1 years). She averages a year more schooling and almost 2 years less illness than the total group of females. (This latter figure appears to be a relatively insignificant difference inasmuch as it deals with a chronicity measure of greater than 10 years duration.) The male schizophrenic appears to have had a less successful outcome on the average than the female schizophrenic.

The important indices of duration of illness, i.e., number of admissions and chronicity, are not different for the total group and the discharged group, thus indicating that the latter group was not selected on the basis of, nor does it represent a "most likely to succeed" group. These results indicate that a significant proportion of even the "hard-core chronics" in a mental hospital can be rehabilitated to the point of being able to return to the community and enter into a more productive and meaningful existence.

PAYMENT OF EARNED WAGES

Patients who have been hospitalized a long time frequently find it difficult to leave the hospital because of lack of good clothing and funds to provide food, lodging and transportation until the first pay check is received. A major purpose of the program is to enable patients to accumulate adequate funds in order to leave the hospital, with the additional security provided by banked savings.

During the first 18 months of operation, wages in the form of checks were paid directly to the patient each week. There was no ambiguity about the mean-

ing of money in hand when the payroll was passed out. It was a tangible nego-
tiable return for the energy and effort that had been expended. Such an experience was not otherwise duplicated in the hospital. Nevertheless, the Workshop
Committee too often found patients ready to leave the hospital with no more
than $10 or $15 in savings. Close investigation revealed that some patients
were spending their earnings unnecessarily on semiluxury items and on food.
Others were secreting their money on the wards and some thefts had taken
place. Only a few were systematically depositing a portion of their wages.

It was obvious that something had to be done, but the most therapeutic
decision was not obvious. The ideal solution would have been to continue
direct payment of wages and to have each workshop client meet regularly
with a counselor for guidance in the management of money. The ideal solution, however, was not possible because of the lack of staff and staff time available for such purposes. It was with reluctance that the committee decided to
change the method of payment to the one described in an earlier section, involving depositing wages directly into the patient's hospital account. The decision was based on the consensus that the positives accruing as a consequence
of direct payment were outweighed by the negatives resulting from poor management of funds.

To communicate this policy change, a group meeting led by the BAMH
executive director was held in the workshop. The immediate response by almost
every patient was one of anger, e.g., "You trying to treat us like babies?"
Patients were allowed to express feelings and present counterarguments. A
follow-up meeting was held a few weeks later, and while there was still some
hostility, the beginning of a change in attitude was evident. One patient pointed
out that it was a much better system, "Nobody on the ward can bum dough off
me," thus resolving a problem which had placed a great pressure on a number
of patients, but one not anticipated by the committee. Subsequent group meetings enabled patients to work through feelings regarding the policy change and
it was well-accepted in a relatively short time.

Patients now leaving the hospital from the workshop do have substantial
savings and the policy change is considered successful. Nevertheless, if personnel were available for individual counseling, direct payment would add an
additional dimension to the patient's workshop experience.

GROUPS

The experience during the period of "payroll policy change" of working
with the patients in a problem-oriented group convinced the members of the
Workshop Committee that such a group should be conducted on a regular
basis. The BAMH executive director has led a workshop group on a biweekly
basis dating from that time.

The major goals for the group are: (1) a "gripe" session to provide
opportunities for expression of feelings and gathering of information; (2) a

forum for announcing administrative changes in the operation of the work-shop as they affect the workers; (3) a source of factual information regarding questions about their hospitalization or workshop experience; (4) a motivator for patients to look forward to discharge and outside employment; (5) an opportunity to share experiences and thoughts associated with job-seeking.

The response to these meetings has been generally good to excellent. It varies, as one would expect, with the number of times the patients have met as a unit (at times workshop turnover is high, thus substantially changing group composition between sessions). A large number of issues have been discussed in the group, including institutionalism, ambivalence over discharge, being truthful on work application forms, the role of good grooming, and excessive drinking.

The group has served well as a "safety valve" at times when feelings were running high over one matter or another and appears to have played a role in keeping relationships within the shop as smooth as they are (there have been no fights, heated arguments, physical destruction, or other symptoms of marked interpersonal difficulties during working hours). Often, members of the group have been therapeutically supportive of fellow patients who are experiencing particularly anxious moments. From time to time, the group has alerted workshop administrators to potential areas of difficulty and thus helped to solve and avert problems before they come into full blossom.

CONTRACTS

The acquisition and maintenance of contracts constitute the life blood of a paid employment program. Without contracted work there can be no program. Although contracts have been discussed in some detail in an earlier section of this paper, additional problem areas should be noted.

A workshop cannot afford to be completely dependent on contracts from a single source, because if the one source of work should fail, the whole work program fails as well. Therefore, initial attempts should focus on gaining more than one contract which can be counted on to provide steady work. Having acquired these contracts, any kind of contract can be considered realistically without too much concern for length or quantity of work.

During periods when new work is slow in coming and there is limited work on the floor, it is important to pace, if possible, the amount of daily production in such a way so as not to exhaust the work. It is better to maintain the shop in continuous operation, perhaps on a shortened work day, than to be forced to close down temporarily or lay off patients because of lack of work.

It is imperative that lines of communication and direct contacts be maintained on a continuing basis with those firms subcontracting to a workshop. A contract once acquired cannot be relied upon to sustain itself without any more attention than inspection in the shop of the finished product. A number of occasions have arisen when contracts were about to be terminated because of misunderstandings or disinterest on the part of the management in the firms subcontracting. The workshop volunteer director has been the major "trouble shooter" for this workshop, and has been effective not only in preserving contracts but also instrumental in developing additional contracts from the same firms. Perhaps the lesson learned is that all contracts are to be regarded on a marginal status and therefore must be treated with tender, loving care. This follow-up care of contracts may be done by someone employed by the workshop on a paid or volunteer basis, but it must be done continually in order to keep work flowing and contractors happy.

VOLUNTEERS

A major reason that this workshop has been able to operate successfully with limited staff is the very substantial amount of time contributed by volunteers from the community. The volunteer director's duties have been outlined, and it is clear that he holds a key position in the effective operation of this program. Volunteers have worked effectively with hospital and rehabilitation staff in moving workshop patients out of the hospital and into the community. Volunteers have developed employment opportunities, solved housing problems, and provided the type of support that has enabled the patient to bridge the gap successfully between hospital and community. A great deal of volunteer time is given in the various planning and policy meetings involving the workshop program, and there was even an instance in which volunteers have moved heavy equipment from plant to hospital on a Saturday morning in order to develop a new contract.

The volunteers have made it possible to operate a well-functioning, smoothly operating, and substantial rehabilitation facility in a state hospital on a very modest budget. Not only do the patients and state benefit directly from this program, but the experiences and involvements of the volunteers in this program have a positive effect on attitudes toward the mentally ill in the communities in which they reside.

Although a number of volunteers are involved in the program, the major responsibilities have been assumed by the president of BAMH and the workshop volunteer director, both of whom have contributed substantial time and thought on a continuing basis.

SOME CONCLUSIONS

The results of this project after two and one-half years of operation exceed the expectations of its founders. The close co-operation and working relationships developed among the Massachusetts Rehabilitation Commission, Metropolitan State Hospital, and the Brookline Association for Mental Health to provide an effective service program can well serve as a prototype of the highest order for other projects. The out-of-hospital percentage of 61 for those patients having completed the Sheltered Workshop experience, while impressive on its own merit, takes on additional significance in the light of the chronic condition of the patients involved. Equally impressive is that 76 per cent of those patients who have left the hospital are gainfully employed in the community.

The Sheltered Workshop has brought to Metropolitan State Hospital a facility that it would not otherwise have had. This has been accomplished without increasing the hospital's budget. Initially, this program was received with concern by many hospital staff people since it represented an intrusion into the established order by an outside agency and was viewed as possibly more burden than help, but the workshop has now become fully integrated into the hospital and is regarded as a highly valuable resource. There is reason to believe that it has helped to lift the morale of staff assigned to those chronic wards served by the workshop as a consequence of its activity and results.

The experience of the MRC in working with the Sheltered Workshop has helped to solidify the concept within this agency that the hospitalized mentally ill have rehabilitation potential and can be helped.

The shared experience of working together productively has developed an *esprit* among the patients in the workshop that is almost tangible. Meaningful, mutually supportive, mutually respectful relationships emerge among these patients, the quality of which is rarely seen on the wards. These attitudes are also reflected on the ward as the workshop employees tend to relate better to other patients, have a better sense of responsibility, and are better-groomed. Interest has been awakened among the patients not in the "project," as the workshop is called, into getting into the workshop. Among some patients the hope of earning money and retaining self-esteem has replaced apathy and dejection.

The workshop experience has, in some instances, resulted in reawakening the interest of families in patients who had been neglected for long periods. It has helped the families to realize that their relatives are once again capable of being productive and self-supporting and would not be a financial burden if they returned home.

The workshop program has made an impact on industries in the Greater Boston area. It has helped demonstrate to manufacturers, many of whom were very skeptical, that the mentally ill can be productive and are able to do quality work comparable to that produced in their own plants. Although only a few of these same manufacturers are now willing to employ known ex-mental patients, there is evidence that the contact with the workshop is influencing change in their attitudes toward the mentally ill. There is also what may be termed a "rippling out" effect as a consequence of the contact these firms and individuals have with mental patients that otherwise would not have taken place. Changes in their attitudes are frequently communicated, in turn, to those firms and colleagues with whom they do business. Thus, a single point of positive contact with mental patients is responsible for far-reaching changes in attitude toward the mentally ill.

The utilization of volunteers in new and creative ways has been a hallmark of the paid employment program from its inception. The workshop volunteer director is a business executive who stated that he never would have become involved with the mentally ill had not his particular talents been needed. He, in turn, with a similar appeal, has interested other businessmen in working for the mentally ill.

The effectiveness of the BAMH hospital volunteers has been increased through their involvement with workshop patients from the time they enter the program until they are ready to leave the hospital, and after. Planning living arrangements, developing employment leads, and providing social support when the patient has returned to the community are some of the significant ways in which these volunteers work with and assist professional staff. The volunteers, in helping return the patient to self-supporting community living, concentrate on the strengths displayed in a work situation and "soft-pedal" the history of mental illness.

A paid employment program gives to the patient about to leave the mental hospital the only positive feature in an otherwise negative history of hospitalization, insofar as industry is concerned. Industry is little concerned with the fact that an individual is significantly less pathological after "X" months of treatment when compared to condition at time of admission. Industry is far more concerned with the skills, work habits, and capacity to work with and for people that an individual brings to a job. The Sheltered Workshop experience can provide the concrete answers to industry's concerns.

A paid employment program for the hospitalized mentally ill should not be construed as the only effective rehabilitative program in a mental institution, nor are these conclusions meant to imply this. It is one segment, one of the final segments, of a therapeutic and rehabilitative complex of services and programs designed to return the hospitalized mentally ill to a state of health and adjustment that will make possible their return to community living.

NEW DEVELOPMENTS

The successful progress of the Sheltered Workshop, as it met the needs in a number of areas, pinpointed or created needs in other areas. The BAMH has already moved into new programs as a consequence.

It was noted early that a number of patients who were ready for release from the hospital could not leave for want of a therapeutic living arrangement. These were individuals who were beyond the "half-way house" stage, but not yet ready for truly independent living. In an effort to meet this need, the BAMH opened a "cooperative apartment" for four female ex-patients in October of 1963. Although there is no onsite supervision, a few volunteers, in conjunction with the professional staff of the Brookline Mental Health Clinic, provide the type of community support that has maintained these women in the community, working productively and improving their level of adjustment. The demonstrated effectiveness of this program has led to the demand for the establishment of similar living arrangements for males and adolescents as well.

The search for appropriate employment openings for patients inevitably presents problems and frustrations. Although the workshop patients have good work histories to "sell," finding an employer who is willing to "buy" continues to be difficult. The BAMH, in its efforts to open up job opportunities, has been instrumental in developing formal arrangements with two major department stores in downtown Boston for the employment of selected workshop graduates. Four patients have already been successfully employed, and the stores are pleased with the program. As this arrangement becomes more widely publicized in the business world, it is anticipated that it will result in more job opportunities for the ex-mental patient.

The workshop offers training opportunities for students in rehabilitation counseling. This facility has already been utilized by the placement of two students enrolled in the Harvard University Medical School Psychiatric Rehabilitation Internship Program at the Metropolitan State Hospital. It is anticipated that arrangements with other university programs will develop in the future.

REFERENCES

1. Beck, J. C., Kantor, D., and Gelineau, V. A. Follow-up study of chronic psychotic patients "treated" by college case-aid volunteers. *Amer. J. Psychiat.*, 1963, 120:269–71.
2. Bindman, A. J., and Klebanoff, L. B. Administrative problems in establishing a community mental health program. *Amer. J. Orthopsychiat.*, 1960, 30:696–711.
3. Brown, G. W. Length of hospital stay and schizophrenia: A review of statistical studies. *Acta Psychiatrica et Neurologica Scandinavia*, 1960, 35:414.

ACKNOWLEDGMENTS

The program and accomplishments described in this paper were the result of the inspiration, dedication, devotion and perseverance of Mrs. Edna Stein and her husband, Mr. Michael Stein, identified in the body of the paper as president and workshop volunteer director, respectively, of the Brookline Association for Mental Health. Both Mr. and Mrs. Stein continue to provide, through their extraordinary efforts, the very lifeblood of this program.

The author wishes also to thank Ludmila W. Hoffman for her assistance in data collection and analysis, and her critical reading of the manuscript. He is also grateful to Edna Stein for her repeated readings and many valuable suggestions. The help and co-operation of the Massachusetts Rehabilitation Commission and the Metropolitan State Hospital, and their respective staff members, Katharine Macdonald and Joel Samuels, is also acknowledged.

APPENDIX A: CONDITIONS OF EMPLOYMENT, SHELTERED WORKSHOP, METROPOLITAN STATE HOSPITAL

1. Employees are expected to be neatly and appropriately dressed.
2. Employees must report to work punctually.
3. Lunch is taken from 12–1, outside the workshop.
4. There are 2 coffee breaks—15 minutes each—10:30 A.M. and 2:30 P.M.
5. Payments for work completed will be made weekly, on time plus piece-work basis. Money will be deposited to the employee's hospital account and a duplicate deposit slip given to the employee for his own record. Money may be drawn from the account according to the established hospital rules.
6. Employees are advised to save as much money as possible toward the time when they may be leaving the hospital.
7. Employees will have an opportunity to meet periodically with a rehabilitation counselor and with a social worker to discuss their progress in the project.

APPENDIX B

The following are some of the more important advantages of our Sheltered Workshop Project to employers:

1. Compliance with Wage-Hour Laws

This workshop is authorized to produce goods for interstate shipment under a special certificate issued by the Wage and Hour Division of the U. S. Department of Labor.

2. Subcontractor Relationship

The relationship of this workshop to its employers is that of a subcontractor. Except for paying the going piece rate for work performed, the employer incurs no other costs or responsibilities, as explained below.

3. Elimination of Indirect Labor Costs

a. *Federal Employer Taxes.* The Internal Revenue Service has furnished us with a written ruling that activities carried on within the hospital for the purposes of rehabilitation are exempted from all Federal employer taxes.

b. *State Unemployment Compensation Taxes.* The Commonwealth of Massachusetts, following the lead of the federal Internal Revenue Service, has also given a written ruling that the Sheltered Workshop Project at this hospital does not subject co-operating firms to the Massachusetts Unemployment Compensation taxes.

c. *Workmen's Compensation.* Inasmuch as these people are not employees of the company for which the work is being done, premiums are not required for workmen's compensation.

d. *No Fringe Benefits.* You eliminate the expense of fringe benefits such as hospitalization insurance, pension funds, etc., that may be applicable to employees.

4. Overhead Savings

a. *Rental Equivalent.* The Metropolitan State Hospital furnishes valuable work areas, including heat, light and power for the carrying on of the operation. This reduces the cost of rent or rental equivalent at your plant and may free valuable space for other work activities.

b. *Supervisory Personnel.* The project is supervised by one or more full-time supervisors whose function it is to make certain that patients are trained in good work attitudes and habits as a preparation for a return to the community and outside employment.

c. *Personnel Problems.* Subcontracting with this workshop reduces problems of recruitment, training, record-keeping and labor turnover. It provides a flexible work force which can be expanded or reduced in accordance with your production demands.

d. *Employer Liability.* Inasmuch as these patients are not employees of the company, there is no responsibility for medical care in connection with any injury or accident that might occur to them while in the performance of the work. All necessary care and treatment are furnished by the Metropolitan State Hospital while they are engaged in this rehabilitation activity.

30

The Vocational Rehabilitation
of Ex-Psychiatric Patients

SIMON OLSHANSKY

BEFORE reviewing some aspects of the vocational rehabilitation of former mental hospital patients, I should like to discuss briefly four factors, two encouraging and two discouraging, that tend to shape our work.

The first encouraging factor is that, of all roles, the role of worker is the easiest one for most ex-patients to fill. It is generally the most structured, providing almost all the necessary clues to guide behavior. By way of contrast, how does one define, let alone fill, the role of friend, or parent, or citizen? How does one recognize or begin to measure effectiveness in filling any of these other roles? The second encouraging factor is that even some of the sickest ex-mental patients are able to work—that is, incomplete recovery is not necessarily a bar to working with acceptable effectiveness. Why some chronically sick ex-mental patients are able to work is not clear, and might be a worthwhile area of research. In any case, these two factors make helping ex-mental patients vocationally much less strenuous than we would generally expect.

Offsetting these two encouraging factors are two discouraging ones. The first is that we do not know why a person becomes mentally ill or why he becomes better. In a sense we are often working (and whistling) in the dark. One ex-patient, despite a nearly perfect job, family, and social situation and despite continuing treatment, may suffer relapse; and we cannot often identify any cause for this relapse (2). Contrariwise, another ex-patient may continue to improve despite many adverse circumstances. (However much we may want to forget the fact of our limited knowledge, it continues as a serious obstacle to the helping process and serves to create an atmosphere of overt or covert professional pessimism, though it is recognized that some professionals in this field of vocational rehabilitation find the limited knowledge a source of encouragement: it gives them a freedom and challenge they would not otherwise have.) A second discouraging factor is that we do not need the manpower restored through vocational rehabilitation. This factor is discouraging not only to some professionals, but also to some of the ex-patients.

Reprinted from *Mental Hygiene,* 1968, *52,* 556–561, by permission of the publisher and the author. © 1968, National Association for Mental Health. Mr. Olshansky is Executive Director, Community Workshops, Boston, Massachusetts.

Although it is recognized that our talent to predict the impact of automation on labor market requirements is limited, it would appear that the need for manpower, except for those with stable work histories and high educational achievements, is likely to continue to be uncertain. It is well to remember that, even though 1966 was an exceptionally good year for employment—the best since 1953—the average rate of unemployment was close to 4 per cent. This means that there were, on the average, about three million persons without jobs throughout 1966. The rate of unemployment was more than twice as high for non-whites and almost four times as high for youth. The unemployment rate among non-white youth was estimated to be in the neighborhood of 25 per cent. Of the 150 labor markets in the United States, there was not one that reported an over-all labor shortage.

One implication of this is that perhaps we should become less concerned with the work needs of ex-patients and more concerned with their social and recreational needs. We should at least stop pretending that the re-employment of ex-patients is a matter of societal urgency. A second implication is that we shall have difficulty in motivating some professionals and some patients to achieve a goal neither group is convinced is important. Whatever the psychological value of work and however much it may contribute to the maintenance of mental health for individual ex-patients, the fact is that our labor market does not, and is not likely to, need or want much of the manpower restored through vocational rehabilitation. Just as some of us may pretend that we know more about mental illness than we do, others of us may also pretend that the labor market needs every single ex-patient who is able to work. But however long we want to deceive ourselves, ultimately we have to face and deal with reality.

THE EX-MENTAL PATIENT POPULATION

For the purpose of vocational rehabilitation, we may divide the ex-patient population into two groups.

One group, invisible to professionals, leaves the hospital and goes to work (4). If these people do not live happily ever after, in large measure they are able to handle and solve their occupational problems with little or no help. They are invisible to professionals because they melt into the labor force and more or less resume their normal lives. Within industry they also become invisible because they are able to "pass" (6) and to shed their unwanted identity as ex-patients. To a considerable extent, ex-patients with good prognoses tend to exclude themselves from post-hospital help (1).

A second group, visible to the professionals, leaves the hospital and continues unemployed or intermittently employed. Many of this visible group are unemployable in the normal labor market. These are the patients who are generally referred to state vocational rehabilitation agencies. But, try hard as we can, we do not know how to make these unemployable ex-patients employable. Some of them want to work, but lack the capacity for regular work; others have the capacity, but lack the will; a few have neither the will nor the capacity.

THE MYTH OF TRANSITIONALISM

This visible population of ex-patients who challenge, harass, and frustrate some of us professionals has stimulated many misperceptions.

One of the misperceptions is that many ex-patients require a network of transitional facilities within the community to restore them to normal participation in the labor market. Some of the transitional facilities considered necessary are sheltered workshops, social clubs, and halfway houses.

Now, I would not deny that a part (perhaps 25 per cent) of this visible group might derive some benefit from such transitional facilities. However, I would insist, on the basis of the available, though limited, evidence, that it is only a small part.[1] By far the largest part of this visible group requires these facilities not as transitional, but as long-term, facilities that would permit many of them to stay out of the hospital, or to improve their performance while in the community. In a sense, these patients are too well for continued hospitalization but not well enough, or likely to become or stay well enough, to meet the rigors of regular work.

It is rather ironic that plans for helping ex-patients are often based more on the needs of professionals who are wedded to the notion of transitionalism than to the needs of the ex-patients seeking help. It would seem that some professionals are responding more to the cues provided by their training and interests than to the cues emerging from the observation and study of ex-patients.

One assumption underlying the myth of transitionalism is that of "sequential development," i.e., that many ex-patients have to pass through certain

---

[1] J. F. Wilder, after reviewing many follow-up studies, estimates that the rehabilitation needs of all released psychiatric patients are as follows: about 40 per cent to 50 per cent do not require any special help; about 10 per cent to 20 per cent might benefit from transitional services; about 40 per cent to 50 per cent require long-term services. (*See* his "A Case for a Flexible Long-Term Workshop for Psychiatric Patients." Paper presented at workshop meeting on "Industry in the Mental Hospital" in New York City, April 22, 1965. Washington, D.C., Veterans Administration.)

Many studies of thousands of released schizophrenic patients, the largest subpopulation, show that between 35 per cent and 40 per cent are readmitted within one year of release and about 65 per cent, within three years. Of a sample of 3,248 patients discharged from twelve Veterans Administration hospitals, 67 per cent worked less than one month during the six-month period following discharge. Readmission rates are consistently high across the country. The evidence would suggest, furthermore, that patients discharged from well-staffed hospitals with a high reputation do not do much better in the community than those released from less adequate hospitals. (*See* Kelley, ref. 2.)

stages of psycho-social development to achieve employability. These ex-patients, it is assumed, have to be "resocialized" in order to accept themselves, their peers, and authority figures. They have to learn to tolerate increasing amounts of frustrations. They have to learn the "give-and-take" of everyday life. Like children, they have to be led carefully and patiently up the steepening staircase to social maturity.

Although there is little question that this assumption of sequential development is valid for some ex-patients, it is not valid for the larger part of the visible population. Some ex-patients who are unemployed and unemployable are sufficiently socialized whereas others who are working regularly are, by comparison, poorly socialized. The capacity of many ex-patients for compartmentalizing work abilities and social skills, though not clearly understood, is apparent to many professionals who have worked with released patients. However impeccable the logic of sequential development, it has not been empirically verified except for a small number of ex-patients.

Some professionals will resent and resist this interpretation of the post-hospital needs of ex-mental patients and will continue to make their greater investment in transitional services, on the basis of their perceptions of the needs of only a small part of the visible ex-patient population. If they do, I would urge that their efforts be attended with continuing research to demonstrate that ex-patients do need transitional services more than they need long-term services.

Again, it should be pointed out that there is no reason why long-term services cannot be organized and structured with many revolving doors so that ex-patients can come, go, return, or stay, depending on their changing or unchanging needs. Moreover, there is need for some experimental work designed to try out new and better methods of reducing the number of ex-patients who need long-term services.

To a society on the "go" such as ours, and committed to the fiction that all problems are quickly solvable, it is bitter medicine to have to think of planning for the long-term needs of some ex-patients. But bitter as it may be, it is medicine we have to take if we are to meet the needs of those ex-patients who seek our help.

Of course, professionals may say that, in the past, transitional services were not always effective because they were poorly organized and poorly run. In response to this allegation, what can one say? With the continuing and growing shortage of professional personnel and with the great amount of job-shifting [2] of professionals in and out of the field of psychiatric rehabilitation, is the quality of transitional services likely to improve?

---

[2] Though there is no easy way of reducing job turnover, we should become more sensitive to the psychological costs to ex-patients who have to learn to deal with new helpers at frequent intervals. Moreover, some of the ex-patients are subjected to unintended trauma as new helpers learn about psychiatric rehabilitation through unavoidable trials and errors. Fortunately, many ex-patients are sturdy enough to endure most of these trials and errors.

EMPLOYERS AS SCAPEGOATS

Many professionals are unwilling to accept the fact that, despite their great and often selfless efforts on behalf of the small and visible population of ex-patients, many of these ex-patients continue unemployed. How frustrating to invest so much on some ex-patients to achieve their employability only to find them still unemployed!

Could it be that these ex-patients are unemployable?

"No," answer some of these professionals. They are, or would be, employable if only we could eliminate employer discrimination (3). The enemy is the employer, not our lack of rehabilitation "know-how." The prescribed remedy is to educate the employer even if he feels no need for education and, in fact, feels quite satisfied with his hiring practices.

But educate as long and as much as we can, few employers could be persuaded to hire and retain ex-patients who were unable and/or unwilling to work. Most employers are unwilling to function as quasi-therapists and to turn their work places into extensions of the psychiatric outpatient clinic; nor should we expect them to assume this role.

Ex-patients are, by and large, more realistic about employers than are some professionals. They know through their own experiences that employers prefer to hire non-disabled persons. They know that mental illness is a source of stigma and would create resistance to their employment. Why not accept the traditions of the labor market and circumvent as best one can any obstacle to employment? Why not withhold information regarding their history of mental hospitalization?

Whether we like it or not, passing is the road followed by most ex-patients who want to work. And, in pragmatic terms, it works. It is not suggested that passing is the ideal road to travel, or that it is without psychological costs to those who pass. But what are the alternatives? And would these alternatives work as well in helping ex-patients secure the acceptance of employers and fellow workers?

In addition, ex-patients also know what some professionals tend to forget: that to get a job is generally less difficult than to hold a job. There is no way of assuring the latter except to perform in a consistently satisfactory way.

In short, the available evidence suggests that almost all ex-patients able and willing to work are working. Those who are not working are generally unemployable within the normal labor market. Though employers have many prejudices against the ex-patient, these prejudices do not account for their unemployment. The ex-patient's value in the labor market varies directly with his work history and his work skills. Some ex-patients would be unemployable even if they had never been hospitalized.

Generally, the best predictor of future employment success for an ex-patient is his pre-hospital work record. A history of mental hospitalization, although it does interfere with one's getting jobs, does not create an insuperable obstacle to employment if the ex-patient is able and willing to work.

THE MEANING OF WORK

Why do ex-patients work (5)? Why don't they seek public welfare? What satisfactions do they secure in exchange for their work dissatisfactions?

First, they acquire some self-esteem in their identification as workers and in functioning in an approved adult role. Becoming self-supporting is important in a culture that places a low value on dependency.

Second, work provides a way of shedding one's patienthood. In our society, idleness has to be explained. By working one can avoid the issue of past hospitalization.

Third, work provides a means of denying one's illness and avoiding the threat of rehospitalization. As long as one continues to work, one's normality will be accepted by oneself and by significant others. Work becomes a visible measure of normality—in fact, there are few other visible means available to the ex-patient to "prove" his wellness.

Fourth, work provides an opportunity to be busy and have something to do. This need to do something is especially important for persons with limited internal resources and limited interest in leisure-time activities.

What would be the alternative to working? The fact is that many fear idleness because without work they would "feel lost," "go crazy," "feel useless," or "feel bored." Many would not know what to do with their time. Idleness would confront them with themselves, which many would find intolerable. For some, work is their central life activity and only interest; and, if work is taken away, for whatever reason, they are face to face with a real crisis (7).

It is very important that all disabled persons wanting to work should have appropriate opportunities for paid work. Very likely, these opportunities may have to be planned and subsidized by non-profit and governmental agencies.

In summary, I should like to stress the following points:

Many ex-patients need little or no help in finding work.

A small number among the visible population of ex-mental patients can be aided by transitional services.

Most of the visible population of ex-patients require long-term services if they are to avoid rejection and regression.

Colette has said that we should look for a long time at what pleases us and longer still at what pains us. I would ask that we look long and hard at those points which may pain us and with which we may disagree and determine by further research the extent to which the points of disagreement can survive such research.

REFERENCES

1. Freeman, H. E., and Simmons, O. G. Treatment experiences of mental patients and their families. *Amer. J. Publ. Hlth.*, 1961, 51:1266.
2. Kelley, F. E. Research in schizophrenia: Implications for social workers. *Social Work*, 1965, 10:32.
3. Olshansky, S. Employer receptivity in rehabilitation of mentally ill. Washington, D.C., American Association for the Advancement of Science: 1959.
4. Olshansky, S. et al. Survey of employment experiences of patients discharged from three mental hospitals during period 1951–1953. *Ment. Hyg.*, 1960, 44:510.
5. Olshansky, S., and Unterberger, H. The meaning of work and its implications for the ex-mental hospital patient. *Ment. Hyg.*, 1963, 47:1.
6. Olshansky, S. Passing: Road to normalization for ex-mental patients. *Ment. Hyg.*, 1966, 50:86.
7. Walker, R. Mistreatment of the mentally ill. *Amer. J. Psychiat.*, 1964, 121:215.

IV

WHERE DO COMMUNITY MENTAL HEALTH ACTIVITIES TAKE PLACE?

IN ATTEMPTING to discover where community mental health activities take place, this section covers individuals at work, in hospitals, at community mental health centers, in schools and in other related agencies, such as settlement houses, health departments, and family service agencies. Since the school plays such a large part in the socialization process, special attention has been given to presenting a fairly broad viewpoint in that area.

Problems change in time responding to environmental factors. Although this section deals only with a few areas, they are part of the trend toward integration of programs and the linking of mental health issues with the increasingly intensified urbanization of this nation. Dealing with mental retardation is an integral part of the comprehensive mental health program, and with rising rates of alcoholism. Delinquency and crime in the cities present a major concern. Aged populations are swelling as a result of the advances of medical science. Poor people have always been with us but now they are more visible and the subjects of considerable health and welfare programs. Suicide, at certain age levels, constitutes a great portion of the causes of death. Children as a specific group require specialized mental health approaches.

Brown notes that the state mental hospital provides the major source for care of the mentally ill in the United States. However, the tide of events is forcing the state hospital to become a more conscious part of a larger system. A major issue concerns itself with whether the state hospital is to be replaced by community mental health centers or whether a new adaptive role can be formulated to make the most effective use of the existing system of care.

In their review of the relation between the community and the community mental health center, Smith and Hobbs examine the broad scope of an intensive program. Their article includes the elements of community control, range of services, reaching those who need help most, innovation, manpower, train-

377

ing, evaluation, research, and the need for variety, flexibility, and realism. A total picture of the many facets of a local community mental health program is presented and related to the community and its needs.

Schools and colleges offer particularly suitable community mental health settings for educational psychiatrists to divert young people from illness to health. Differences between work in these surroundings versus ordinary psychiatric practice are delineated by Farnsworth. Specific attention is given to the first college years and to the problem of college dropouts.

Caplan identifies the goals of primary prevention of mental disorders in children, noting efforts to ensure adequate basic physical, psychosocial, and sociocultural supplies. From that point, he proceeds to discuss activities involving preventive intervention, anticipatory guidance, teacher training, collaboration, and research, with particular emphasis on the emerging role of the school psychologist as a focus for such services.

An early nursery center program for preschool mentally retarded children is described by Bindman and Klebanoff. The development of the program and its achievements are noted. Relations between policies and programs are spelled out and the problems encountered are detailed.

Plaut discusses the magnitude and impact of problem drinking, the low priority of services to problem drinkers, the nature of current services, the role of helping agencies, and the role of community mental health programs. These issues should be dealt with in developing and planning community services for persons with drinking problems.

Providing improved mental health services to the poor raises some special factors for consideration. Hersch enumerates the magnitude of the task—since the poor have a high rate of psychiatric and social impairments, disengagement from the existing services, and alienation. He notes the requirement for a spirit of innovation and the need to mold techniques to problems, rather than vice versa.

An effective community mental health program for urban disadvantaged areas requires techniques derived from social action as well as the more traditional services. Peck, Kaplan, and Roman describe the small-group approaches and the use of nonprofessionals in neighborhood storefront centers. Some of the basic dilemmas raised include the resistance to change, centralized planning and decentralized functions, political "hot potatoes," and action research.

Occupational medicine has moved from emergency surgery and compensation cases to the realization that about half of the case load is made up of people with emotional problems. In reporting on occupational mental health as an emerging art, McLean traces historical influences, discusses current activities, surveys selected publications, and considers possible implications for future development.

Two great enemies of sanity in older people must be conquered: enforced uselessness and enforced aloneness. James calls for improving urban mental health services by recognizing the problems that keep patients from getting care, by integrating mental and physical care, by binding the splinters of medical care systems, and by concentrating on the family and the home.

Advantages and disadvantages of treating moderately to severely disturbed children and families using a home therapist are noted by Egan and Robison. Preliminary observations suggest that the technique is helpful in treating behavior problems, the less severely psychotic and borderline psychotic child, school phobics, and other antagonistic symbiotic problems.

31

The Impact of the New Federal Mental Health Legislation on the State Mental Hospital System

BERTRAM S. BROWN

I AM tempted to entitle this speech, "A horse, a horse, my kingdom for a horse. . . ." One of the first things a federal employee learns, however, is "Don't stir up anybody's constituency." I am sure you are all wondering what I would imply by such a title. "What does he mean? birth? death? or reincarnation?" Let me explain. Whereas King Richard was in dire need of a horse— we have one. For it is clear that the state mental hospital is the major horsepower for the care of the severely mentally ill in the United States.

Everyone teases or neglects this work horse while he bravely pulls a major portion of the load. Aristocratic ponies with long pedigrees (children only, neurotics only, suburban residents only) prance around flipping their outpatient tails and stealing the limelight. Intellectual verbal horses standing on the podium of a couch preach the psychoanalytic psychodynamic doctrine so loudly that they drown out the tired sighs of the still ever-plodding work horse. It was not until the doctoring of the horse with tranquilizing drugs in the 1950's and the better paving of the roads by improved community attitudes that the work horse began to find the load lighter over the last ten years; but while the weight of the load decreased, the slope of the hill became steeper. In other words, as everyone here is too painfully aware, we have succeeded in decreasing the resident patient load in the face of a rising admission rate.

Still the work horse plods along, taking care of the greater number of the seriously mentally ill. And now comes the latest challenger, the community mental health horse—I mean "center."

I am sure I would convince no one if I tried to claim that I am not, in some sense, a representative part of this new animal. Which end, I leave to your judgment. Let me assure you, however, that it is not my function either to praise or to bury the state mental hospital. I would like to persuade you that the development of new approaches and new resources has given all of us the opportunity to significantly relieve the load of the state mental hospital and to constructively alter its functions.

Reprinted from a speech given at the Northeast State Government's Conference on Mental Health, Hartford, Connecticut, 1964, by permission of the author. Dr. Brown is Deputy Director, National Institute of Mental Health.

The new Community Mental Health Centers Program, or perhaps better put, the new community mental health center thrust or approach, would supposedly eliminate the state mental hospital as it is known today. Focusing on elimination or obliteration is really a misplaced emphasis, for the issue is not elimination or abolition, not civil war or revolution, it is evolution or change; for the state mental hospital is changing as part of a long, historical process.

There are dramatic, interesting, and important shifts taking place in the population of the state mental hospitals. Looking at the trends of the past ten years, and recognizing the distinctive differences between certain characteristic groups of patients classified by age, sex, and diagnosis, what changes can we expect during the coming ten years?

In the age group 35–44 years, a 41 per cent reduction can be expected. Why? There needn't be any mystery. This is the group now receiving rapidly increasing amounts of community care in general hospital psychiatric services and in outpatient facilities. For example, in the brief three-year period 1959–62, the utilization of outpatient facilities by persons in this age group increased by over 34 per cent.

It is evident that intensive community services made available and utilized by other age groups may have a similar dramatic impact. For example, consider children and adolescents. If we take the number of resident patients in a state mental hospital and group them by age and look at changes from 1950 to 1951, we see that in every age group there has been a decrease in the number of resident patients, except for two—age 10 to 14 and age 15 to 24. The increase in the youngest, those under 15, is dramatic—from under 1,000 in 1950 to over 4,000 in 1962. This increase in the adolescent population in the state mental hospital has been recognized for some time and again reflects the need for community programs. This subject was one of the themes of recent efforts by the leaders in the field of child psychiatry in preparing a soon to be released document on planning psychiatric services for children and youth.

You may ask—haven't the adolescents been receiving an increasing amount of outpatient care as well as the adults? The answer is a yes, *but* that care was mainly diagnosis and evaluation for other agencies, and not treatment. A recent study, presented just last month at the American Public Health Association meeting, showed that of 53,000 adolescents served in outpatient departments in 1962, two-thirds received no therapy at all.

From these very simple descriptions it is abundantly evident that the size and composition of the state mental hospital patient population is increasingly interdependent on the size and type of community service.

Dr. Morton Kramer of the Biometrics Branch of the National Institute of Mental Health has extensively analyzed these trends in the state mental hospital population. He has looked at these results in juxtaposition to the statement found in President Kennedy's Special Message on Mental Illness and Mental Retardation: "If we launch a broad new mental health program now, it will be possible within a decade or two to reduce the number of mental patients now under custodial care by 50 per cent or more." Dr. Kramer considers it can be done *if,* and it is a big if, appropriate hospital and community programs for treatment, care, and rehabilitation are developed to make possible:

1. the placement of many patients now in these hospitals in community facilities more appropriate to their needs than the public mental hospital;
2. the reduction of admissions to these hospitals; and
3. the rapid turnover of patients who must be admitted to these institutions.

HISTORICAL BACKGROUND

How does a statement like the one just quoted get into the President's Message?

A brief review of some historical highlights may place into perspective the scope and content of the new federal programs and perhaps shed some light on the likely impact of these new programs on the state mental hospital system.

We are all aware of the Joint Commission on Mental Illness and Health. Like all extensive reports, one can find what he wants somewhere in the manuscript of the final document—"Action for Mental Health." But I think it is fair to say that a main emphasis of the report was on the upgrading of the state mental hospital system to a therapeutic level. The maximum number of beds for any mental hospital was recommended as 1,000. These hospitals were to have intensive treatment, supplemented by a vast array of small outpatient clinics, perhaps one for each 50,000 of the general populations. The clinics would provide aftercare and rehabilitation services. This proposal would have required about 5,000 fully staffed clinics by 1980 on a somewhat smaller scale than those now proposed under the Community Mental Health Centers Program. There were no specific proposals regarding the road one would travel to get intensive treatment in the state mental hospital. Massive federal support in inservice training and similar programs was clearly implied.

Even before this final report was finished, voices of dissent were raised. I need only remind you of Dr. Harry Solomon's presidential address to the American Psychiatric Association in 1958 when he said, "The large mental hospital is antiquated, outmoded, and rapidly becoming obsolete. We can still build them but we cannot staff them; therefore we cannot make true hospitals of them."

Nevertheless, the final report was delivered to the Congress, to the governors, to the Surgeon General, to the nation, in the spring of 1961.

President Kennedy played a vital role in the subsequent history of this report—which some feel distorted the good in the Joint Commission Report—and which others feel improved the recommendations.

President Kennedy appointed a Secretarys' Committee consisting of Secretary Ribicoff, Secretary Goldberg, Commissioner of Veterans Affairs Gleason, with representatives from the Bureau of the Budget and the Council of Economic Advisors. They were to review the Joint Commission Report and propose Presidential action. After a year they emerged with the community mental health center as the bold new approach.

The debates that went on during that year, the work of all of us at the National Institute of Mental Health who served en masse as staff to the committee under Bob Felix's leadership, and the final pulls, pressures, controversies that occurred as the various proposals percolated through the stratified membranes of the bureaucracy—all these are matters of history yet to be written.

I was privileged to be present during the final confrontation of opposing points of view as the Secretarys' Committee report was reviewed by the President's staff at the Bureau of the Budget and the White House before final Presidential approval.

The issues were clear. Let me quote from a table developed by the White House staff during January, 1963, a table entitled, "Appraisal of Underlying Issues Raised by Proposals for National Action for Mental Health":

Issue I. Should the emphasis be on comprehensive mental health centers as a substitute for State mental hospitals?

Issue II. What is to be the future role of the State mental hopital?

Issue III. Who will run the comprehensive community mental health center?

Issue IV. How can the operating cost of the community mental health center be financed?

Issue V. What is to be the relationship of community mental health centers to general hospital and other resources of the community?

Issue VI. Will manpower be available to achieve the goal of 500 centers by 1970 and possibly 2,000 centers by 1980?

The clarity of the statement of the issues speaks for itself. Extensive analysis of the often conflicting but sometimes similar approaches of the Joint Commission on Mental Illness and Health and the recommendations of the Secretarys' Committee were done by the White House staff.

The end result of these issues, insofar as the President's Message and his legislative proposals are concerned, you well know.

Let me highlight first the direct approach to the state mental hospital system itself.

HOSPITAL IMPROVEMENT AND HOSPITAL INSERVICE TRAINING PROGRAMS

While the community mental health center emerged as the major thrust, the state mental hospital was not neglected. The words of the Message itself speak clearly:

Until the Community Mental Health Centers Program develops fully, it is imperative that the quality of care in existing State mental institutions be improved. By strengthening their therapeutic services, by becoming open institutions serving their local communities many such institutions can perform a valuable transitional role. The Federal Government can assist materially by encouraging State mental institutions to undertake intensive demonstration and pilot projects, to improve the quality of care, and to provide inservice training for personnel manning these institutions.

This should be done through special grants for demonstration projects, for inpatient care, and inservice training. I recommend that ten million dollars be appropriated for such purposes.

Clearly, the state mental hospitals were seen as transitional.

The Hospital Improvement Program and the Inservice Training Program have fared well, and in general, have been enthusiastically received.

For the Hospital Improvement Program, Congress authorized 6 million dollars in September, 1963. By December, 1963, a total of 188 applications had been received from 48 of the 54 states and territories. Six million dollars for 80 institutions, one-fifth of the total institutions in the United States, was approved.

For the Hospital Inservice Training Program, 3.3 million dollars was appropriated in September, 1963, and by December applications were received for twice that amount; 3.3 million dollars was appropriated for one-third of the total institutions.

I will not belabor the details of these programs. One can look upon them as large or small according to varying perspectives. For the two regions represented here, over one million dollars for this year is involved. For the nation, three to six years from now, these programs should involve 50 million dollars, approximately 5 per cent of the budgets of the state mental hospitals, and it is clear that all state mental hospitals and institutions for the retarded are eligible. But in terms of possible impact, they are certainly significant and concrete illustrations of the new federal legislation's relationship to and awareness of the state mental hospital.

The use of these funds is one where the result depends to some extent on the goals, directions, stipulations, hurdles, red tape, and so forth, placed on the funds by the federal government. But to a greater extent it depends on how the state mental hospital itself utilizes these funds. In essence, the impact will be dependent not only upon the financial feeding of the state mental hospital, but also upon how it responds and utilizes the funds.

Evidences of the creative utilization, and indirectly the focusing on areas of special need by the state mental hospital, is indicated by a review of the nature of the projects approved.

The majority focus on special age or diagnostic groups such as children, adolescents, the aged, and chronic patients. A surprising number, seven out of 48, focus on special education in mental illness. Well over one-fifth of the projects focus on organization of services for continuity of care and strengthening hospital-community relationships—most involving a unit or catchment area to be served. Other projects are a veritable catalogue of creativity ranging from administrative concerns such as patient records, through use of volunteers, to a plethora of transitional and rehabilitative services including day-night hospitals, halfway houses, sheltered workshops, and many more.

In my estimation, one of the most vital aspects of these Hospital Improvement Programs is the attempt to integrate the individual institution's program into an overall statewide approach. The state agency under which these institutions are administered must approve the project before submitting it to the federal government.

PLANNING

The role of the state agency in the Hospital Improvement and Inservice Training programs serves as a useful transition to another major aspect of the new federal program, planning—comprehensive, confused, or otherwise. There are so many planning programs today—mental health planning, mental retardation planning, alcoholism planning, planning for the children and the aged, economic planning, and, of course, the hallmark of repetitive redundancy —plans for planning—that it seems as if we as a society have finally matured from the so-called age of anxiety to the age of planning.

Clearly, the 8.4 million dollars appropriated by congress for planning purposes will have an important impact—not only on the state mental hospital, but on all mental health programs, not only on mental health programs, but on all types of welfare programs, and perhaps not only on all social welfare programs, but at least on the careers of a new group—the planners themselves. One measure of this impact is the straightforward fact that over half the states at this point have a distinctive permanent planning unit or planning office in their mental health departments which have sprung into being as a result of this planning effort.

Planning for human beings has become such an important business that it is beginning to have impact upon, and to utilize our defense and technological knowhow. Let me illustrate.

The bureaucracy of our more sophisticated state governments has finally been overwhelmed by a bad case of information-gathering indigestion. I just reviewed a document dated October 1, 1964, by the Department of Finance of the State of California. I quote:

To Prospective Bidders:

The State of California is interested in having a study program performed in order to provide guidelines for the design of a statewide information system relating to the special needs of the people. Further, it is the intent of this request for a proposal to elicit responses from large aerospace systems managers having extensive research and development experience in the design and management of major military systems.

At a different point in the document the work summary states:

A general study will be undertaken to outline the development of a State information retrieval and data processing system embracing information about persons and the needs of the general population. This system would be designed to assist the State in planning and accomplishing actions to meet these ends and needs. The study should draw heavily on the experience and advanced information technology system for planning and management in those industries which have solved large-scale complex systems problems.

Description of tasks. In performance of the tasks the contract will consider the following categories of information for possible inclusion in any system:

1. Health and safety
2. Public welfare and services
3. Education
4. Employment
5. Economic conditions
6. Social and residential conditions
7. Law enforcement
8. Administration of justice
9. Licensing and regulation

I could go on at length, but what does this all mean for the state mental hospitals? It means that the state mental hospital, as one of the largest participants in state programs and services for people, is and must become part of a larger network or system. The state mental hospital has been the major system for care of the severely mentally ill in the past. It is becoming an important component of a larger system caring for the severely mentally ill—a system that, for example, cares for the mentally ill in outpatient settings and in general hospital psychiatric services, and in new settings such as day and night hospitals. It must become a working partner to sister systems attempting to prevent mental illness and to promote mental health through activities such as consultation and education to various caretaker groups in the population who have contact at key stress points in the life cycle.

This emphasis on organization is clearly necessary. There is no choice. *The tide of events is forcing the state mental hospital to become a more conscious part of a bigger system.*

One set of events already discussed that is forcing the state mental hospital in this direction is the Hospital Improvement Program, the Inservice Training Program, and the planning grants. Another major event is the community mental health centers legislation.

By part of a system I mean many things, but to be practical and pragmatic one might examine the state mental health administration rubric in which the state mental hospital functions.

ADMINISTRATIVE SHIFTS

Since 1951 there have been 16 major shifts of the mental health authority relative to state mental hospital systems, that is in fully one-third of the states. These changes have been in the direction of the establishment of new comprehensive departments of mental health in 8 of the 16 states. There is only one state which has a department of mental health that includes the mental hospitals but not the mental health authority responsible for community programs. In the general battle between public health and mental health at the state level, mental health is winning. Into this evolving process comes the new Community Mental Health Centers Program with its request for the governor to designate a single state authority to administer or supervise the administration of the program. This has heightened the controversy in many states. During the heat of battle one hears the public health community-oriented health department advocate talking in a derogatory way about the state mental hospital folks as having an "institutional mentality"—and knowing nothing about the community. In contrast, one hears the state mental hospital people talk about the fact that they are experienced in the care of the severely mentally ill, and anyhow the health department and local people have never really been interested in mental health. The state mental hospital people feel that they will set up the precare and aftercare programs and really have an impact.

In the controversy it matters little who wins administratively. What does matter is whether more consciously designed comprehensive programs, or to return to our earlier analogy, more comprehensive systems of prevention, treatment, and rehabilitation, are established.

FINANCIAL PROBLEMS

As we have gradually plunged into the deeper, darker layers of controversy and strife, let us get down to the tap root of all evil—money.

What about the financial prospects of the state mental hospital system?

The state system is the overwhelming fact in the financing of mental health services, accounting for well over 50 per cent of the total direct expenditures, approximately one billion out of the 1.8 billion we can identify for mental health services.

Over the last ten years states have nearly doubled their expenditures to maintain patients in these institutions. The $5.51 per-patient-day expenditure for the half-million people in these institutions is still woefully inadequate when contrasted with $35 to $40 per-patient-day expenditure in general hospitals or $14 per day in Veterans Administration neuropsychiatric institutions, but the improvement is dramatic.

In looking at the financing of state mental hospital systems, it is interesting to note what has happened to expenditures for additions and improvements, that is, capital construction. In 1956, which is roughly the period when the decline in patient populations began, the expenditure for additions and improvements was about $84 million annually. In 1962 this figure had declined to 70.3 million. Thus, what apparently has happened, is that states were able, through the decline in patient resident populations, to put a higher proportion of their funds into patient services without adding to the number of beds. It is quite a tribute to the states that they have continued to increase their patient service expenditures in the face of declining populations, because the tendency of many budgeteers would be to cut funds for services in proportion to the cut in resident patients. This decline in capital expenditures varies considerably from state to state and it is interesting to note that while California, with a rapidly growing population, has decreased its annual capital expenditures for state institutions from $9.6 million a year to $2 million a year in the seven-year period since 1956, New York, with a lesser rate of population growth, increased its capital expenditures from $15.8 million to $19.4 million over the same period.

As you know, federal support for community mental health centers, requested by the President, totaled three-quarters of a billion dollars for both construction and initial operation of these centers. What emerged was a bricks and mortar program in terms of its funding; in terms of its regulations, hopes, and aspirations it maintains a heavy component in the program direction. The Community Mental Health Centers Act of 1963 authorizes appropriations of $150 million over three fiscal years, with this year's appropriation being $35 million.

It goes without saying that this program will have a significant impact on the direction of mental health services, not to mention the budgets of states and localities. The average annual figure of $100 million for this program, including the nonfederal share, compares favorably with the $70 million currently being spent for additions and improvements to the state hospitals. On the other hand, the sums available are in no sense adequate to achieve the goals of the President's Message. The chief problem is, clearly, in the level of the ability of communities to finance the operation of centers.

Assuming the acceptance of the goal of community-based mental health services, what will this mean to the budgets of state and local governments?

One should remember that while state budgets for mental health services, that is, principally the state mental hospitals, have increased markedly, particularly on a per-patient basis, this increase has not kept pace with the even more rapid growth in total state and local budgets. Indeed, the tendency since 1956 has been for the maintenance of patients in state mental hospitals to decline as a proportion of total state expenditures. However, when allowance is made for the growth in state support of community mental health programs, we have a situation where total mental health activities have probably remained a fairly constant 1.5 per cent of total state and local budgets.

We must remember that three states, New York, California, and Illinois, account for well over half of the 100 million dollars expended in community mental health services. Thus, for many of the northeast states represented here tonight the proportion of total state and local budgets expended for mental health purposes has been declining over the past decade.

The dilemma of the financial crystal ball is briefly as follows: We need to double our expenditures in the next decade in order to meet reasonable estimates of decent mental health services. Assuming a continuation of the current growth of total state and local budgets, and that mental health continues to hold the same proportion, 1.5 per cent, we find ourselves with a deficit of perhaps a half a billion dollars. And furthermore, the expected one-half to one billion dollar increase can clearly be utilized by the state mental hospital system alone, with little left over for expanded community services.

My colleague, Bob Atwell, has studied this financing situation in some depth. This is not the time or the place to belabor statistics or hard-to-digest data. Getting to the heart of the financial analysis, we see that the state mental hospital will continue to be the work horse for the seriously mentally ill unless we develop a significant amount of new means of financing community mental health services and programs. Whether this comes through federal help, new revenues at the local level, a change in the willingness of states to put money into mental health, or through the development of psychiatric voluntary insurance is a key question for the future decade.

CONCLUSION

The state mental hospital is at the crossroads. Shall it walk the last mile toward the beckoning image, or is it a mirage, toward adequate, effective community mental health service for all? Or shall it stand stubbornly and proudly, maintaining that it has survived a century of futile threats and empty gestures. Shall it go on as before, changing its name but not its function? Shall it call itself a regional mental health center for a population area of over a million, or shall it like the amoeba split into smaller pieces, decentralizing into several subunits each attached to a community and each calling itself a community mental health center?

Part of the answer lies in the hearts and minds of the men and women who run our state mental hospitals. But it is my conviction that the bigger part of the answer lies within the hearts and minds of men and women all over the nation in our local communities. If they truly want care for the mentally ill close to home, with continuity and compassion, early enough rather than too late, then they will find ways and means to achieve these ends. Through their elected representatives at the local, state, and federal levels, through private effort and voluntary insurance, through charity and taxes, they will be willing to pay for mental health services. They will also want a part of the mental health system to take care of those whom we do not know how to help and who cannot be kept in a local facility, or for especially difficult cases that need specialized, prolonged care. This last system may be the state mental hospital as it changes in the future. My hope is that the state mental hospital will lead actively as well as respond passively to the new federal legislation; that all the programs become part of a cohesive system, effective and dedicated to improving the mental health of our people.

32

The Community and the
Community Mental Health Center

M. BREWSTER SMITH AND NICHOLAS HOBBS

THROUGHOUT the country, states and communities are readying themselves to try the "bold new approach" called for by President John F. Kennedy to help the mentally ill and, hopefully, to reduce frequency of mental disorders. The core of the plan is this: to move the care and treatment of the mentally ill back into the community so as to avoid the needless disruption of normal patterns of living, and the estrangement from these patterns, that often come from distant and prolonged hospitalization; to make the full range of help that the community has to offer readily available to the person in trouble; to increase the likelihood that trouble can be spotted and help provided early when it can do the most good; and to strengthen the resources of the community for the prevention of mental disorder.

The community-based approach to mental illness and health attracted national attention as a result of the findings of the Joint Commission on Mental Illness and Health that was established by Congress under the Mental Health Study Act of 1955. After 5 years of careful study of the nation's problems of mental illness, the Commission recommended that an end be put to the construction of large mental hospitals and that a flexible array of services be provided for the mentally ill in settings that disrupt as little as possible the patient's social relations in his community. The idea of the comprehensive community mental health center was a logical sequel.

In 1962, Congress appropriated funds to assist states in studying their needs and resources as a basis for developing comprehensive plans for mental health programs. Subsequently, in 1963, it authorized a substantial Federal contribution toward the cost of constructing community mental health centers proposed within the framework of state mental health plans. It appropriated $35 million for use during fiscal year 1965. The authorization for 1966 is $50 million and for 1967, $65 million. Recently, in 1965, it passed legislation to pay part of the cost of staffing the centers for an initial period of 5 years. In

Reprinted from *American Psychologist*, 1966, *21*, 299–309, by permission of the publisher and the authors. © 1966, American Psychological Association, Inc. Dr. Smith is Professor of Psychology and Chairman of the Psychology Department, University of Chicago. Dr. Hobbs is Director, John F. Kennedy Center for Research on Education and Human Development, Peabody College and Provost, Vanderbilt University.

the meantime, 50 states and three territories have been drafting programs to meet the challenge of this imaginative sequence of Federal legislation.

In all the states and territories, psychologists have joined with other professionals, and with nonprofessional people concerned with mental health, to work out plans that hold promise of mitigating the serious national problems in the area of human well-being and effectiveness. In their participation in this planning, psychologists have contributed to the medley of ideas and proposals for translating the concept of comprehensive community mental health centers into specific programs. Some of the proposals seem likely to repeat past mistakes. Others are fresh, creative, stimulating innovations that exemplify the "bold new approach" that is needed.

Since the meaning of a comprehensive community mental health center is far from self-evident, the responsible citizen needs some guidelines or principles to help him assess the adequacy of the planning that may be under way in his own community, and in which he may perhaps participate. The guidelines and discussion that are offered here are addressed to community leaders who face the problem of deciding how their communities should respond to the opportunities that are opened by the new federal and state programs. In drafting what follows, many sources have been drawn upon: the monographs and final report of the Joint Commission, testimony presented to Congress during the consideration of relevant legislation, official brochures of the National Institute of Mental Health, publications of the American Psychiatric Association, and recommendations from members of the American Psychological Association who have been involved in planning at local, state, and national levels.

The community mental health center, 1966 model, cannot be looked to for a unique or final solution to mental health problems: varied patterns will need to be tried, plans revised in the light of evaluated experience, rigidities avoided. Even as plans are being drawn for the first comprehensive centers under the present federal legislation, still other bold approaches to the fostering of human effectiveness are being promulgated under the aegis of education and of economic opportunity programs. A single blueprint is bound to be inadequate and out of date at the moment it is sketched. The general approach underlying these guidelines may, it is hoped, have somewhat more enduring relevance.

Throughout, the comprehensive community mental health center is considered from the point of view of members of a community who are seeking good programs and are ultimately responsible for the kind of programs they get. The mental health professions are not to be regarded as guardians of mental health, but as agents of the community—among others—in developing and conserving its human resources and in restoring to more effective functioning people whose performance has been impaired. Professional people are valuable allies in the community's quest for the health and well-being of its members, but the responsibility for setting goals and major policies cannot be wisely delegated.

COMMUNITY INVOLVEMENT AND COMMUNITY CONTROL

For the comprehensive community mental health center to become an effective agency of the community, community control of center policy is essential. The comprehensive community mental health center represents a fundamental shift in strategy in handling mental disorders. Historically, and still too much today, the preferred solution has been to separate the mentally ill person from society, to put him out of sight and mind, until, if he is lucky, he is restored to normal functioning. According to the old way, the community abandoned its responsibility for the mental patient to the distant mental hospital. According to the new way, the community accepts responsibility to come to the aid of the citizen who is in trouble. In the proposed new pattern, the person would remain in his own community, often not even leaving his home, close to family, to friends, and to the array of professional people he needs to help him. Nor would the center wait for serious psychological problems to develop and be referred. Its program of prevention, detection, and early intervention would involve it in many aspects of community life and in many institutions not normally considered as mental health agencies: the schools, churches, playgrounds, welfare agencies, the police, industry, the courts, and community councils.

This spread of professional commitment reflects in part a new conception of what constitutes mental illness. The new concept questions the appropriateness of the term "illness" in this context, in spite of recognition that much was gained from a humanitarian viewpoint in adopting the term. Mental disorders are in significant ways different from physical illnesses. Certainly mental disorder is not the private misery of an individual; it often grows out of and usually contributes to the breakdown of normal sources of social support and understanding, especially the family. It is not just an individual who has faltered; the social systems in which he is embedded through family, school, or job, through religious affiliation or through friendship, have failed to sustain him as an effective participant.

From this view of mental disorder as rooted in the social systems in which the troubled person participates, it follows that the objective of the center staff should be to help the various social systems of which the community is composed to function in ways that develop and sustain the effectiveness of the individuals who take part in them, and to help these community systems regroup their forces to support the person who runs into trouble. The community is not just a catchment area from which patients are drawn; the task of a community mental health center goes far beyond that of purveying professional services to disordered people on a local basis.

The more closely the proposed centers become integrated with the life and institutions of their communities, the less the community can afford to turn over to mental health professionals its responsibility for guiding the center's policies. Professional standards need to be established for the centers by federal and state authorities, but goals and basic policies are a matter for local control. A broadly based responsible board of informed leaders should help to ensure that the center serves in deed, not just in name, as a focus of the community's varied efforts on behalf of the greater effectiveness and fulfillment of all its residents.

RANGE OF SERVICES

The community mental health center is "comprehensive" in the sense that it offers, probably not under one roof, a wide range of services, including both direct care of troubled people and consultative, educational, and preventive services to the community. According to the administrative regulations issued by the United States Public Health Service, a center must offer five essential services to qualify for federal funds under the Community Mental Health Centers Act of 1963: (*a*) *inpatient care* for people who need intensive care or treatment around the clock; (*b*) *outpatient care* for adults, children, and families; (c) *partial hospitalization:* at least day care and treatment for patients able to return home evenings and weekends; perhaps also night care for patients able to work but needing limited support or lacking suitable home arrangement; (*d*) *emergency care* on a 24-hour basis by one of the three services just listed; and (*e*) *consultation and education* to community agencies and professional personnel. The regulations also specify five additional services which, together with the five essential ones, "complete" the comprehensive community mental health program: (*f*) *diagnostic service;* (*g*) *rehabilitative service* including both social and vocational rehabilitation; (*h*) *precare and aftercare,* including screening of patients prior to hospital admission and home visiting or halfway houses after hospitalization; (*i*) *training* for all types of mental health personnel; and (*j*) *research and evaluation* concerning the effectiveness of programs and the problems of mental illness and its treatment.

That the five essential services revolve around the medically traditional inpatient-outpatient core may emphasize the more traditional component of the comprehensive center idea somewhat at the expense of full justice to the new conceptions of what is crucial in community mental health. Partial hospitalization and emergency care represent highly desirable, indeed essential, extensions of the traditional clinical services in the direction of greater flexibility and less disruption in patterns of living. Yet the newer approach to community mental health through the social systems in which people are embedded (family, school, neighborhood, factory, etc.) has further implications. For the disturbed person, the goal of community mental health programs should be to help him and the social systems of which he is a member to function together as harmoniously and productively as possible. Such a goal is more practical, and more readily specified, than the elusive concept of cure, which misses the point that for much mental disorder the trouble lies not within the skin of the individual but in the interpersonal systems through which he is related to others. The emphasis in the regulations upon consultation and public education goes beyond the extension of direct patient services to open wide vistas for imaginative experimentation.

The vanguard of the community approach to mental health seeks ways in which aspects of people's social environment can be changed in order to improve mental health significantly through impact on large groups. Just as a modern police or fire department tries to prevent the problems it must cure, so a good mental health center would look for ways of reducing the strains and troubles out of which much disorder arises. The center might conduct surveys and studies to locate the sources of these strains; it might conduct training programs for managers, for teachers, for ministers to help them deal with the problems that come to light. By providing consultation on mental health to the governing agencies of the community, to schools, courts, churches, to business and industry, the staff of the center can bring their special knowledge to bear in improving the quality of community and family life for all citizens. Consultation can also be provided to the state mental hospitals to which the community sends patients, to assist these relics of the older dispensation in finding a constructive place in the new approach to mental health. Preferably, revitalized state hospitals will become integral parts of the comprehensive service to nearby communities.

In performing this important and difficult consultative role, the mental health professionals of the center staff do not make the presumptuous and foolish claim that they know best how the institutions of a community should operate. Rather, they contribute a special perspective and special competencies that can help the agencies and institutions of community life—the agencies and institutions through which people normally sustain and realize themselves—find ways in which to perform their functions more adequately. In this endeavor, the center staff needs to work in close cooperation with other key agencies that share a concern with community betterment but from different vantage points: councils of social agencies, poverty program councils, labor groups, business organizations, and the like. To promote coordination, representatives of such groups should normally be included in the board responsible for the center's policies.

Communities may find that they want and need to provide for a variety of services not specifically listed among the additional services in the regulations issued by the United States Public Health Service: for example, a special service for the aged, or a camping program, or, unfortunately, residences for people who do not respond to the best we can do for them. The regulations are permissive with respect to additional services, and communities will have to give close and realistic attention to their own needs and priorities. For many rural areas, on the other hand, and for communities in which existing mental health services are so grossly inadequate that the components of a comprehensive program must be assembled from scratch, the present regulations in regard to "essential services" may prove unduly restrictive. Communities without traditions of strong mental health services may need to start with something short of the full, prescribed package. So long as their plan provides for both direct and indirect services, goes beyond the traditional inpatient-outpatient facility, and involves commitment to movement in the direction of greater comprehensiveness, the intent of the legislation might be regarded as fulfilled.

Many of the services that are relevant to mental health will naturally be developed under auspices other than the comprehensive center. That is desirable. Even the most comprehensive center will have a program that is more narrowly circumscribed than the community's full effort to promote human effectiveness. What is important is that the staff of the center be in good communication with related community efforts and plan the center's own undertakings so as to strengthen the totality of the community's investments in the human effectiveness of its members.

FACILITIES

Facilities should be planned to fit a program and not vice versa. The comprehensive community mental health center should not be thought of as a place, building, or collection of buildings—an easy misconception—but as a people-serving organization. New physical facilities will necessarily be required, but the mistake of constructing large, congregate institutions should not be repeated. The danger here is that new treatment facilities established in medical centers may only shift the old mental hospital from country to town, its architecture changed from stone and brick to glass and steel. New conceptions are needed even more than new facilities.

Small units of diverse design reflecting specific functions and located near users or near other services (such as a school or community center) might be indicated and can often be constructed at a lesser cost than a centralized unit linked to a hospital. For example, most emotionally disturbed children who require residential treatment can be effectively served in small residential units in a neighborhood setting removed from the hospital center. Indeed, there is the possibility that the hospital with its tense and antiseptic atmosphere may confirm the child's worst fears about himself and set his deviant behavior.

Each community should work out the pattern of services and related facilities that reflects its own problems, resources, and solutions. The needs and resources of rural areas will differ radically from those of urban ones. Every state in the nation has its huge mental hospitals—grim monuments to what was once the latest word in treatment of the mentally ill, and a major force in shaping treatment programs ever since. It should not be necessary to build new monuments.

CONTINUITY OF CONCERN

Effective community action for mental health requires continuity of concern for the troubled individual in his involvements with society, regardless of awkward jurisdictional boundaries of agencies, institutions, and professions. A major barrier to effective mental health programing is the historical precedent of separating mental health services from other people-serving agencies— schools, courts, welfare agencies, recreational programs, etc. This is partly a product of the way of thinking that follows from defining the problem as one of illness and thus establishing the place of treatment and the professional qualifications required to treat it. There are thus immense gaps in responsibility for giving help to people in trouble. Agencies tend to work in ignorance of each other's programs, or at cross purposes. For example, hospital programs for emotionally disturbed children often are operated with little contact with the child's school; a destitute alcoholic who would be hospitalized by one community agency is jailed by another.

Current recommendations that a person in trouble be admitted to the total mental health system and not to only one component of it fall short of coming to grips with the problem. The laudable aim of these recommendations is to facilitate movement of a person from one component to another—from hospital to outpatient clinic, for example, with minimum red-tape and maximum communication among the professional people involved. Such freedom of movement and of communication within the mental health system is much to be desired. But freedom of movement and of communication between systems is quite as important as it is within a system.

No one system can comprise the range of mental health concerns to which we are committed in America, extending from serious neurological disorders to include the whole fabric of human experience from which serious—and not so serious—disorders of living may spring. Mental health is everyone's business, and no profession or family of professions has sufficient competence to deal with it whole. Nor can a mental health center, however comprehensive, encompass it. The center staff can and should engage in joint programing with the various other systems with whom "patients" and people on the verge of trouble are significantly involved—school, welfare, industry, justice, and the rest. For such joint programing to reflect the continuity of concern for the individual that is needed, information must flow freely among all agencies and systems. The staff of the center can play a crucial role in monitoring this flow to see to it that the walls that typically restrict communication between social agencies are broken down.

REACHING THOSE WHO MOST NEED HELP

Programs must be designed to reach the people who are hardly touched by our best current efforts, for it is actually these who present the major problems of mental health in America. The programs of comprehensive community mental health centers must be deliberately designed to reach all the people who need them. Yet the forces generated by professional orthodoxies and by the balance of public initiative or apathy in different segments of the community—forces that have shaped current model community mental health programs—will tend unless strenuously counteracted to restrict services to a favored few in the community. The poor, the dispossessed, the uneducated, the poor treatment risk, will get less service—and less appropriate service—than their representation in the community warrants, and much, much less service than their disproportionate contribution to the bedrock problem of serious mental illness would demand.

The more advanced mental health services have tended to be a middle-class luxury; chronic mental hospital custody a lower-class horror. The relationship between the mental health helper and the helped has been governed by an affinity of the clean for the clean, the educated for the educated, the affluent for the affluent. Most of our therapeutic talent, often trained at public expense, has been invested not in solving our hard-core mental health problem —the psychotic of marginal competence and social status—but in treating the relatively well-to-do educated neurotic, usually in an urban center. Research has shown that if a person is poor, he is given some form of brief, mechanical, or chemical treatment; if his social, economic, and educational position is more favored, he is given long-term conversational psychotherapy. This disturbing state of affairs exists whether the patient is treated privately or in a community facility, or by a psychiatrist, psychologist, or other professional person. If the community representatives who take responsibility for policy in the new community mental health centers are indignant at this inequity, their indignation would seem to be justified on the reasonable assumption that mental health services provided at public expense ought to reach the people who most need help. Although regulations stipulate that people will not be barred from service because of inability to pay, the greatest threat to the integrity and usefulness of the proposed comprehensive centers is that they will nonetheless neglect the poor and disadvantaged, and that they will simply provide at public expense services that are now privately available to people of means.

Yet indignation and good will backed with power to set policy will not in themselves suffice to bring about a just apportionment of mental health services. Inventiveness and research will also be indispensable. Even when special efforts are made to bring psychotherapy to the disturbed poor, it appears that they tend not to understand it, to want it, or to benefit from it. They tend not to conceive of their difficulties in psychological terms or to realize that talk can be a "treatment" that can help. Vigorous experimentation is needed to discover ways of reaching the people whose mental health problems are most serious. Present indications suggest that methods hold most promise which emphasize actions rather than words, deal directly with the problems of living rather than with fantasies, and meet emergencies when they arise without interposing a waiting list. Much more attention should also be given to the development of nonprofessional roles for selected "indigenous" persons who in numerous ways could help to bridge the gulf between the world of the mental health professional and that of the poor and uneducated where help is particularly needed.

INNOVATION

Since current patterns of mental health service are intrinsically and logistically inadequate to the task, responsible programing for the comprehensive community mental health center must emphasize and reward innovation. What can the mental health specialist do to help people who are in trouble? A recent survey of 11 most advanced mental health centers, chosen to suggest what centers-in-planning might become, reveals that the treatment of choice remains individual psychotherapy, the 50-minute hour on a one-to-one basis. Yet three minutes with a sharp pencil will show that this cannot conceivably provide a realistic basis for a national mental health program. There simply are not enough therapists—nor will there ever be—to go around, nor are there enough hours, nor is the method suited to the people who constitute the bulk of the problem—the uneducated, the inarticulate. Given the bias of existing facilities toward serving a middle-class clientele, stubborn adherence to individual psychotherapy when a community could find and afford the staff to do it would still be understandable if there were clear-cut evidence of the superior effectiveness of the method with those who find it attractive or acceptable. But such evidence does not exist. The habits and traditions of the mental health professions are not a good enough reason for the prominence of one-to-one psychotherapy, whether by psychiatrists, psychologists, or social workers, in current practice and programing.

Innovations are clearly required. One possibility with which there has been considerable experience is group therapy; here the therapist multiplies his talents by a factor of six or eight. Another is crisis consultation: a few hours spent in active intervention when a person reaches the end of his own resources and the normal sources of support run out. A particularly imaginative instance of crisis consultation in which psychologists have pioneered is the suicide-prevention facility. Another very promising innovation is the use under professional direction of people without professional training to provide needed interpersonal contact and communication. Still other innovations, more radical in departure from the individual clinical approach, will be required if the major institutional settings of youth and adult life—school and job—are to be modified in ways that promote the constructive handling of life stresses on the part of large numbers of people.

Innovation will flourish when we accept the character of our national mental health problem and when lay and professional people recognize and reward creative attempts to solve it. Responsible encouragement of innovation, of course, implies commitment to and investment in evaluation and research to appraise the merit of new practices.

CHILDREN

In contrast with current practice, major emphasis in the new comprehensive centers should go to services for children. Mental health programs tend to neglect children, and the first plans submitted by states were conspicuous in their failure to provide a range of services to children. The 11 present community programs described as models were largely adult-oriented. A recent (1965) conference to review progress in planning touched occasionally and lightly on problems of children. The Joint Commission on Mental Illness and Health bypassed the issue; currently a new Joint Commission on Mental Health of children is about to embark upon its studies under Congressional auspices.

Most psychiatric and psychological training programs concentrate on adults. Individual psychotherapy through talk—the favored method in most mental health programs—best suited to adults. What to do with an enraged child on a playground is not normally included in curricular for training mental health specialists. It would seem that our plans and programs are shaped more by our methods and predilections than by the problems to be solved.

Yet an analysis of the age profile of most communities—in conjunction with this relative neglect—would call for a radically different allocation of money, facilities, and mental health professionals. We do not know that early intervention with childhood problems can reduce later mental disorder, but it is a reasonable hypothesis, and we do know that the problems of children are receiving scant attention. Sound strategy would concentrate our innovative efforts upon the young, in programs for children and youth, for parents, and for teachers and others who work directly with children.

The less than encouraging experience of the child guidance clinic movement a generation and more ago should be a stimulus to new effort, not an occasion for turning away from services to children. The old clinics were small ventures, middle-class oriented, suffering from most of the deficiencies of therapeutic approach and out-reach that have been touched upon above. A fresh approach to the problems of children is urgently needed.

We feel that fully half of our mental health resources—money, facilities, people—should be invested in programs for children and youth, for parents of young children, and for teachers and others who work directly with children. This would be the preferable course even if the remaining 50 per cent would permit only a holding action with respect to problems of adults. But our resources are such that, if we care enough, we can move forward on both fronts simultaneously.

The proposal to place the major investment of our mental health resources in programs for children will be resisted, however much sense it may make, for it will require a thoroughgoing reorientation of the mental health establishment. New facilities, new skills, new kinds of professional people, new patterns for the development of manpower will be required. And new and more effective ways must be found to reach and help children where they are—in families and schools—and to assist these critically important social systems in fostering the good development of children and in coming to the child's support when the developmental course goes astray. This is one reason why community leaders and other nonprofessionals concerned with the welfare and development of people should be centrally involved in establishing the goals of community mental health centers. They can and should demand that the character of the new centers be determined not by the present habits and skills of professional people but by the nature of the problem to be solved and the full range of resources available for its solution.

PLANNING FOR PROBLEM GROUPS THAT NOBODY WANTS

As a focus for community planning for mental health, the comprehensive center should assure that provision is made to deal with the mental health component in the problems of various difficult groups that are likely to fall between the stools of current programs. Just as good community programing for mental health requires continuity of concern for the troubled individual across the many agencies and services that are involved with him, so good programing also requires that no problem groups be excluded from attention just because their problems do not fit neatly into prevalent categories of professional interest, or because they are hard to treat.

There are a number of such groups of people, among whom problems of human ineffectiveness are obvious, yet whose difficulties cannot accurately or helpfully be described as mainly psychological: for example, addicts, alcoholics, the aging, delinquents, the mentally retarded. It would be presumptuous folly for mental health professionals to claim responsibility for solving the difficult social and biological problems that are implicated in these types of ineffectiveness. But it would also be irresponsible on the part of persons who are planning community mental health programs not to give explicit attention to the adequacy of services being provided to these difficult groups and to the adequacy of the attack that the community is making on those aspects of their problems that are accessible to community action.

Recently, and belatedly, national attention has been focused on the mentally retarded. This substantial handicapped group is likely to be provided for outside the framework of the mental health program as such, but a good community mental health plan should assure that adequate provision is in fact made for them, and the comprehensive center should accept responsibility for serving the mental health needs of the retarded and their families.

Some of the other problem groups just mentioned—e.g., the addicts and alcoholics—tend to get left out partly because treatment by psychiatric or psychological methods has been relatively unproductive. Naturally, the comprehensive center cannot be expected to achieve magical solutions where other agencies have failed. But if it takes the approach advocated here—that of focusing on the social systems in which problem behavior is embedded—it has an opportunity to contribute toward a rational attack on these problems. The skills that are required may be more those of the social scientist and community change agent than those of the clinician or therapist.

In planning its role with respect to such difficult groups, the staff of the center might bear two considerations in mind: in the network of community agencies, is humanly decent care being provided under one or another set of auspices? and does the system-focused approach of the center have a distinctive contribution to make toward collaborative community action on the underlying problems?

MANPOWER

The present and future shortage of trained mental health professionals requires experimentation with new approaches to mental health services and with new divisions of labor in providing these services. The national effort to improve the quality of life for every individual—to alleviate poverty, to improve educational opportunities, to combat mental disorders—will tax our resources of professional manpower to the limit. In spite of expanded training efforts, mental health programs will face growing shortages of social workers, nurses, psychiatrists, psychologists, and other specialists. The new legislation to provide Federal assistance for the staffing of community mental health centers will not increase the supply of manpower but perhaps may result in some minor redistribution of personnel. If adequate pay and opportunities for part-time participation are provided, it is possible that some psychiatrists and psychologists now in private practice may join the public effort, adding to the services available to people without reference to their economic resources.

The manpower shortage must be faced realistically and with readiness for invention, for creative solutions. Officially recommended staffing patterns for community mental health centers (which projected nationally would require far more professionals than are being trained) should not be taken as setting rigid limitations. Pediatricians, general medical practitioners, social workers other than psychiatric ones, and psychological and other technicians at non-doctoral levels should be drawn into the work of the center. Specific tasks sometimes assigned to highly trained professionals (such as administrative duties, follow-up contacts, or tutoring for a disturbed child) may be assigned to carefully selected adults with little or no technical training. Effective communication across barriers of education, social class, and race can be aided by the creation of new roles for specially talented members of deprived groups. New and important roles must be found for teachers, recreation workers, lawyers, clergymen. Consultation, in-service training, staff conferences, and supervision are all devices that can be used to extend resources without sacrificing the quality of service.

Mental health centers should find ways of using responsible, paid volunteers, with limited or extended periods of service. There is a great reservoir of human talent among educated Americans who want to contribute their time and efforts to a significant enterprise. The Peace Corps, the Vista program, Project Head-Start have demonstrated to a previously skeptical public that high level, dependable service can be rendered by this new-style volunteer. The contributions of unpaid volunteers—students, housewives, the retired—can be put to effective use as well.

PROFESSIONAL RESPONSIBILITY

Responsibility in the comprehensive community mental health center should depend upon competence in the jobs to be done. The issue of who is to be responsible for mental health programs is complex and is not to be solved in the context of professional rivalries. The broad conception of mental health to which we have committed ourselves in America requires that responsibility for mental health programs be broadly shared. With good will, intelligence, and a willingness to minimize presumed prerogatives, professional people and lay board members can find ways of distributing responsibility that will substantially increase the effectiveness of a center's program. The tradition, of course, is that the director of a mental health center must be a psychiatrist. This is often the best solution, but other solutions may often be equally sensible or more so. A social worker, a psychologist, a pediatrician, a nurse, a public health administrator might be a more competent director for a particular center.

The issue of clinical responsibility is more complex but the principle is the same: competence rather than professional identification should be the governing concern. The administration of drugs is clearly a competence-linked responsibility of a physician. Diagnostic testing is normally a competence-linked responsibility of a psychologist; however, there may be situations in which a psychiatrist or a social worker may have the competence to get the job done well. Responsibility for psychotherapy may be assumed by a social worker, psychiatrist, psychologist, or other trained person. The director of training or of research could reasonably come from one of a number of disciplines. The responsible community member, to whom these guidelines are addressed, should assure himself that there is a functional relationship in each instance between individual competence and the job to be done.

This issue has been given explicit and responsible attention by the Congress of the United States in its debates and hearings on the bill that authorizes funds for staffing community mental health centers. The intent of Congress is clear. As the Senate Committee on Labor and Public Welfare states in its report on the bill (Report No. 366, to accompany H. R. 2985, submitted June 24, 1965):

> There is no intent in any way in this bill to discriminate against any mental health professional group from carrying out its full potential within the realm of its recognized competence. Even further it is hoped that new and innovative tasks and roles will evolve from the broadly based concept of the community mental health services. Specifically, overall leadership of a community mental health center program may be carried out by any one of the major mental health professions. Many professions have vital roles to play in the prevention, treatment and rehabilitation of patients with mental illnesses.

Similar legislative intent was established in the debate on the measure in the House of Representatives.

Community members responsible for mental health centers should not countenance absentee directorships by which the fiction of responsibility is sustained while actual responsibility and initiative are dissipated. This is a device for the serving of professions, not of people.

TRAINING

The comprehensive community mental health center should provide a formal training program. The need for centers to innovate in the development or reallocation of professional and subprofessional roles, which has been stressed above in line with Congressional intent, requires in every center an active and imaginative training program in which staff members can gain competence in their new roles. The larger centers will also have the self-interested obligation to participate in the training of other professionals. Well-supervised professional trainees not only contribute to the services of a center; their presence and the center's training responsibilities to them promote a desirable atmosphere of self-examination and openness to new ideas.

There should be a director of training who would be responsible for: (a) in-service training of the staff of the center, in the minimum case; and, in the larger centers, (b) center-sponsored training programs for a range of professional groups, including internships, field placements, postdoctoral fellowships, and partial or complete residency programs; and (c) university-sponsored training programs that require the facilities of the center to give their students practical experience. Between 5 per cent and 10 per cent of the center's budget should be explicitly allocated to training.

PROGRAM EVALUATION AND RESEARCH

The comprehensive community mental health center should devote an explicit portion of its budget to program evaluation. All centers should inculcate in their staff attention to and respect for research findings; the larger centers have an obligation to set a high priority on basic research and to give formal recognition to research as a legitimate part of the duties of staff members. In the 11 "model" community programs that have been cited previously, both program evaluation and basic research are rarities; staff members are commonly overburdened by their service obligations. That their mental health services continue to emphasize one-to-one psychotherapy with middle-class adults may partly result from the small attention that their programs give to the evaluative study of program effectiveness. The programs of social agencies are seldom evaluated systematically and tend to continue in operation simply because they exist and no one has data to demonstrate whether they are useful or not. In this respect the model programs seem to be no better.

The whole burden of the preceding recommendations, with their emphasis on innovation and experimentation, cries out for substantial investment in program evaluation. Only through explicit appraisal of program effects can worthy approaches be retained and refined, ineffective ones dropped. Evaluative monitoring of program achievements may vary, of course, from the relatively informal to the systematic and quantitative, depending on the importance of the issue, the availability of resources, and the willingness of those responsible to take the risks of substituting informed judgment for evidence.

One approach to program evaluation that has been much neglected is hardheaded cost analysis. Alternative programs should be compared not only in terms of their effects, but of what they cost. Since almost any approach to service is likely to produce some good effects, mental health professionals may be too prone to use methods that they find most satisfying rather than those that yield the greatest return per dollar.

All community mental health centers need to plan for program evaluation; the larger ones should also engage in basic research on the nature and causes of mental disorder and on the processes of diagnosis, treatment, and prevention. The center that is fully integrated with its community setting will have unique opportunities to study aspects of these problems that elude investigation in traditional clinic and hospital settings. That a major investment be made in basic research on mental health problems was the recommendation to which the Joint Commission on Mental Illness and Health gave topmost priority.

The demands of service and of research are bound to be competitive. Because research skills, too, are scarce, it is not realistic to expect every community mental health center to have a staff equipped to undertake basic research. At the very least, however, the leadership in each center should incorporate in its training program an attitude of attentiveness to research findings and of readiness to use them to innovate and change the center's practices.

The larger centers, especially those that can establish affiliation with universities, have an obligation to contribute to fundamental knowledge in the area of their program operations. Such centers will normally have a director of research and a substantial budget allocation in support of research, to be supplemented by grants from foundations and governmental agencies. By encouraging their staff members to engage in basic studies (and they must be sedulously protected from encroaching service obligations if they are to do so), these centers can make an appropriate return to the common fund of scientific and professional knowledge upon which they draw; they also serve their own more immediate interests in attracting and retaining top-quality staff and in maintaining an atmosphere in which creativeness can thrive. As a rough yardstick, every center should devote between 5 per cent and 10 per cent of its budget to program evaluation and research.

VARIETY, FLEXIBILITY, AND REALISM

Since the plan for a comprehensive community mental health center must allocate scarce resources according to carefully considered priorities tailored to the unique situation of the particular community, wide variation among plans is to be expected and is desirable. Since decisions are fallible and community needs and opportunities change, provision should be made for flexibility and change in programs, including periodic review of policies and operations. In spite of the stress in these guidelines on ideal requirements as touchstones against which particular plans can be appraised, no single comprehensive center can be all things to all men. Planning must be done in a realistic context of limited resources and imperfect human talent as well as of carefully evaluated community needs, and many hard decisions will have to be made in setting priorities. In rural areas, especially, major alterations in the current blueprint would seem to be called for if needed services are to be provided. As a result, the comprehensive community mental health centers that emerge should be as unique as the communities to whose needs and opportunities they are responsive. This is all to the good, for as it has been repeatedly emphasized, there is no well-tested and prefabricated model to put into automatic operation. Variety among centers is required for suitability to local situations; it is desirable also for the richer experience that it should yield for the guidance of future programing.

The need for innovation has been stressed; the other side of the same coin is the need for adaptability to the lessons of experience and to changing requirements of the community. Flexibility and adaptiveness as a characteristic of social agencies does not just happen; it must be planned for. The natural course of events is for organizations to maintain themselves with as little change as possible, and there is no one more conservative than the proponent of an established, once-radical departure. Plans for the new centers should therefore provide for the periodic self-review of policies and operations, with participation by staff at all levels, and by outside consultants if possible. To the extent that active program evaluation is built intrinsically into the functioning of the center, the review process should be facilitated, and intelligent flexibility of policy promoted. Self-review by the center staff should feed into general review by the responsible board of community leaders, in which the board satisfies itself concerning the adequacy with which the policies that it has set have been carried out.

This final recommendation returns once more to the theme, introduced at the outset, that has been implicit in the entire discussion: the responsibility of the community for the quality and adequacy of the mental health services that it gets. The opportunities are now open for communities to employ the mechanism of the comprehensive mental health center to take major strides toward more intelligent, humane, and effective provision for their people. If communities rise to this opportunity, the implications for the national problem of mental health and for the quality of American life are immense.

33

Concepts of Educational Psychiatry

DANA L. FARNSWORTH

YOUNG people of today have an uncertain future. Although men have made enormous technological advances in the last few decades, little progress has been made in the understanding and controlling of themselves. As a result there fate is dependent in large part upon those who have the means of nuclear attack. For the first time in history man can destroy himself and others by a force which he has loosed, in contrast to previous threats from forces alien to himself. If security is to be achieved, it must come from an internal development; certainly there is no security outside. Achieving inner security is an awesome and complicated task, one that is not inborn but has to be learned. Even when learned it can be self-deceptive, and constant comparison with reliable opinions and attitudes of other trusted people is necessary for its maintenance. Inner security may not be equivalent to maturity, but they certainly are related.

The educational psychiatrist is acutely interested in encouraging these qualities, whether through education or psychotherapy. The latter is, of course, a very specialized educational technique. The psychiatrist works by helping the sick resolve personal problems, by aiding any person or groups caught in crisis situations, and by working with those who are helping young people toward the goals of satisfaction and effectiveness. He tries to encourage trust, friendliness, warmth in personal relations, and self-understanding, while minimizing hostility, suspicion, unwanted isolation, and self-centeredness.

Psychiatric practice, at least as it has been developing during the last few decades, has tended to concentrate on understanding the psychopathology of those who come to psychiatrists for treatment. This is perfectly reasonable and proper. But it is not enough. There has been a noticeable tendency to concentrate on what is wrong with the individual to the detriment of a proper understanding of his capacities for solving his problems and doing creative work. Principles of behavior important to everyone are derived from the psychiatric study of disturbed persons. It is possible to make some major contributions to the solution of social problems by the appropriate use of those

Reprinted from *Journal of the American Medical Association*, 1962, *181*, 815–821, by permission of the publisher and the author. © 1962, American Medical Association. Dr. Farnsworth is Henry K. Oliver Professor of Hygiene, Harvard University and Director of the Harvard University Health Services.

principles. Slowly, but effectively, psychiatric thinking has added to our understanding of such matters as juvenile delinquency, the effects of unfair segregation, the nature of responsibility in the criminal, and mental retardation. It has also led to a better understanding of relations between ministers and their parishioners, lawyers and their clients, teachers and their students, and physicians and their patients.

If psychiatric knowledge is ever to be used effectively in the prevention of mental illness and in the improvement of living conditions, then it should certainly be applied in our educational institutions. More than one-fourth of our 186,000,000 people are in school, either as students or as teachers. More than 4,000,000 persons are engaged in our colleges and universities. The most promising prospect for improving both teaching and learning lies in a realization of the importance of the emotions. The potential contributions of psychiatry to education will not be a burden on teachers or students if it frees their energies for the work they wish to do. It should help those working below their capacity to attain or regain the full use of their abilities. Perhaps this idea sounds both presumptuous and naïve. Much depends upon the basic attitudes of psychiatrists who work in this area. If they work quietly, preferably through others when practicable, promise no spectacular results, and influence their colleagues to give appropriate recognition to the importance of motivation and feeling in their students, they will do much toward improving the educational process. If they confine themselves to treating disturbed students only and do not share their findings with the faculty, with administrators, and with the students themselves, then they might as well remain in their private offices and have those students who need help come to them there.

In this discussion the major emphasis will be placed on the work of psychiatrists in colleges and universities, but many of the principles involved are applicable at any level of schooling. Psychiatrists are relative newcomers to this field. Clinical psychologists and a variety of professional counselors have made great contributions to the improvement of teaching and learning which are gratefully acknowledged. College psychiatrists seek to supplement, not compete with, their efforts. Collaboration sometimes becomes difficult because of personality needs or qualities of the individuals concerned, but there is no theoretical bar to working together with mutual satisfaction.

WORK OF EDUCATIONAL PSYCHIATRIST

The work of an educational psychiatrist is demanding but very different from that of the private practitioner or from the duties of a staff member in a mental hospital. Most psychiatrists work under circumstances in which illness is in the foreground and regaining health the goal; whereas the educational psychiatrist spends his time in an environment in which health is assumed and deviations from it are to be recognized and dealt with or prevented if possible. When not interviewing disturbed students or faculty members, he is representing a discipline or point of view which is, in a sense, competing for usefulness and significance with psychology and all the other social sciences, the humanities, and the natural sciences. Since psychiatry is based on or can learn from all of these disciplines, the individual psychiatrist has to be on guard lest he assume knowledge that he does not have. He must also take care not to lapse into psychodynamic formulations for all the behavior he observes. If he does, he may appear naïve or narrow or obsessed with dogma. In working with students and faculty he shares quandaries with those of many of his colleagues from other disciplines, but with the added complication that his specialty is often characterized by authoritarian practices appropriate or even necessary in the practice of medicine or surgery but usually not applicable to psychiatric practice. He must, therefore, be on guard against a natural tendency to advise a particular course of action before all opinions and facts are available. In brief, a college psychiatrist should continually study his own and other institutions of higher learning, while he helps the people in them to achieve solutions to their personal problems and while he applies his knowledge to the general task of improving those institutions.

Much can be accomplished in raising the level of awareness of how the emotions affect learning by working with those who are involved in conflicts. Even more can be done in the thousands of personal but nonprofessional encounters between the psychiatrist and his colleagues in informal or social situations. A psychiatrist who is comfortable only in the one-to-one relation with patients would not enjoy college psychiatry.

Psychiatrists who work in a college or university have a peculiar advantage not shared by those of their colleagues who work in mental hospitals or who are engaged in private practice. The college psychiatrists see a much wider range of emotional problems. They are to be sure, consulted by many sick students, but they also see many youngsters temporarily handicapped by emotional problems who need not be classified as mentally ill. Ordinarily these students would get no help or, perhaps, advice from well-meaning friends or counseling from teachers or occasionally from professional counselors, but they would not be sent to a psychiatrist unless their symptoms had become alarming, dramatic, or possibly disabling.

If the only purpose for having psychiatrists on the staff of a college health service were to treat those persons who become mentally ill, then they might as well not be there. Colleges could carry out their responsibilities by referring sick students to private psychiatrists. Even if the college paid the bills, it would be more economical than paying the salaries of psychiatrists. The presence of psychiatrists in a college health service is justified more because they learn about the institution, become familiar with the pressures encouraging or inhibiting maturity and independence, and thus become able to consult with faculty members and administrators in a constructive manner about any matters in which abnormal behavior is an issue than because they treat disturbed students.

In many institutions of higher learning, emphasis on the emotional maturation of students has little meaning. No one person, except possibly the dean of students, can have a realization of how widespread is the emotional turmoil with its resulting inappropriate, often destructive, behavior. When some individual becomes psychotic, it is usually assumed that the tragedy was inexplicable or unavoidable. His removal from the community gives everyone a sense of relief. When acute disturbances occur, indicative of unresolved psychological tensions, some overly simple explanation may be accepted, often preventing the learning of the real causes of the upheaval. People generally proceed on the theory that if students can be kept busy between their academic obligations and a few extracurricular activities their emotional growth and development will proceed automatically. Vandalism in the library, cheating in the classroom, plagiarism in preparation of term papers, stealing books and records in the local stores, experimentation with drugs, excessive use of alcohol, underachievement in marked contrast to ability, and preoccupation with anti-intellectual activities in various campus organizations—all may seem unrelated. Perhaps they are too complicated for a systematic attack on them. It is, indeed, a formidable task to convince logical people of the logic of apparently purposeless or destructive behavior. The psychiatrist or psychologist who does so opens himself to the criticism that he is trying to find excuses for the offending student's behavior and that he is basically undermining the morals of his patients and weakening the authority of college administrators. Understanding a student's behavior is equated with condoning it, if it be antisocial. It is difficult for many people to see that a young person has a much better chance of developing self-control if he and those who influence him can be helped to understand the reasons for asocial behavior.

Up to now no college has committed itself to giving extensive psychotherapy to any of its students as a part of its health program. To do so would be practically impossible and probably theoretically inadvisable. After all, the business of a college is teaching, learning, and doing research, not furnishing medical treatment. Any health program should be predicated upon the notion that it exists for the furtherance of these three functions, not as an end in itself. Therefore, one of the chief functions of a college psychiatric service is to use brief psychotherapy. It serves as the most effective medium for applying psychiatric principles to the educational needs of the institution.

BRIEF PSYCHOTHERAPY

Brief, or short-term psychotherapy, is peculiarly appropriate to college students because they are usually not yet so dependent upon inappropriate defenses that they cannot change readily. They are intelligent and hence can usually profit from insights into the origins and nature of their difficulties. They usually have a strong wish to improve. In addition to these advantages the psychiatrist in an educational institution has a better opportunity than in most other situations to see all aspects of a student's environment.

Blaine (1) has admirably outlined the chief elements in brief psychotherapy as practiced at Harvard University. These involve: (1) ventilation or allowing the student to express his emotions, (2) giving information, (3) utilization of transference or serving as an example to the student (replacement), (4) developing insight, (5) aiding in reality testing, (6) environmental manipulation (to be used sparingly), (7) preparing a patient for intensive therapy when indicated, (8) goal-centered group discussions, and (9) judicious use of sedatives and tranquilizers.

College students caught in emotional conflicts need help in self-expression, help in being themselves, and help in freeing their impulsive life within the confines of responsibility. They emphatically do not want to be molded to a pattern based on someone's preconceived notion as to what they should be. As Blaine points out, when therapy is offered in this spirit, young people may be deflected from illness and resume their advance toward maturity.

Among those students who requested psychiatric help, disturbed relations with their parents are very common. Whether they are more common in this group than in any other similar number of persons is not clear. Nevertheless, it seems apparent that no factor is so important in the development of a strong and resilient personality and sound character as a closely knit family life. Children have certain fundamental needs which can hardly be met under any other social arrangement thus far developed. These include genuine love and affection, warmth in their interpersonal relations, firm discipline from respected sources, good role models for emulation (with enough consistency in their behavior for children to learn how to act appropriately in any given circumstance), adequate space and freedom for their motor activities, and continual expectations of performance somewhat above their present levels. When these are not met, the possibility of emotional disturbances is greatly increased. In brief psychotherapy the student must learn to understand the effects of parental attitudes on himself. This will also help him become a good parent.

SPECIAL PROBLEMS

There are a number of special problems in connection with college psychiatric practice that should be understood by students, parents, teachers, and administrators if optimum usefulness of psychiatry is to be gained. These have to do with maintenance of confidence, with the use of psychiatric records for screening purposes, and with the divided responsibility of the psychiatrist to his patient and to the institution he serves.

It is vitally important that nothing a student says to a college psychiatrist in confidence, be divulged to any one without the patient's permission. Of course, if a student is overtly psychotic, suicidal, or homicidal, the safety of the individual and people in the community must take precedence over maintaining confidence, but in such instances the patient is told what needs to be done and the reasons for it. Even parents are not necessarily notified that their son or daughter has sought help from the college psychiatrist unless the patient requests or permits this to be done or unless there is a compelling reason for doing so. The necessity for this rule seems obvious to the college health officials; without it, students simply would not come for help. To parents, however, the rule may seem harsh, unjustified, and unreasonable. Some even threaten reprisals on the college for permitting their children to get psychiatric help, feeling that in some way this reflects on them.

After long and vexatious experience the opinion is rapidly gaining ground that psychiatric records of college students should not be used for screening purposes, that is, to help college officials decide upon qualifications for entrance to graduate schools, nor should they be made available to governmental agencies even for eliminating security risks. According to this point of view, psychiatric records should not be so given out even when patients give written consent, since they may be forced to do so by conflicting pressures over which they have no control. If students knew that their records were being so used, they would be showing good judgment and appropriate self-interest by staying away from college psychiatric services. Thus, they would be depriving themselves of help when perhaps they need it most. When students who have received psychiatric help have been transferred to other institutions, their records then become available, with their written consent, to the psychiatric service of these institutions, or abstracts of pertinent findings may be sent to other physicians who will become responsible for their health.

These considerations do not imply that undergraduate colleges should not help graduate schools in the onerous task of selecting those students best qualified for graduate work. Nor do they indicate that psychiatrists are disinterested in national security. They do mean, however, that material gained in a strictly confidential relationship with students may not be used in ways that may harm the individual. This is a situation where the welfare of the person takes precedence over the demands of any organization, thus, in the long run, furthering the welfare of both. If any student is irresponsible or so impaired by illness that he cannot perform his tasks effectively, signs of these defects usually become manifest to sources that are not confidential.

How to handle authority poses a special problem for large numbers of college students. Many of them are still in the process of achieving independence from their parents and in forming an identity of their own. They are still in rebellion against many of the customs or opinions about which they have had strong feelings earlier in life. Displacement of negative feelings from their parents to the college or to some of its officials is quite common. Their attitudes toward the college's use of authority remains ambivalent; although they expect limits to be set on their behavior, they resent their application. If discipline is lacking or if the enforcement of authority is done inconsistently or with favoritism, the psychiatrist's task is greatly complicated. A basic goal of psychotherapy should be to free the individual from crippling inner conflict by inculcating the kind of honesty, sincerity, and integrity in him that will enable him to act with confidence and a sense of competence. In situations involving inappropriate response to authority, such consultations between college officials and psychiatrists have great value.

In a society which has evolved effective controls over nature and considerable freedom from dependence upon the whims of weather and business cycles, many students have little awareness of the value of money or the need for cultivating the character traits which their ancestors are said to have valued. Adapting to the circumstances in which they live has consisted much more of learning how to manipulate people or their opinions than in developing well conceived, long-range goals, followed by measures designed to realize them. In such situations, learning how to please others takes precedence over satisfying one's self. A young person may do the "right" thing because it seems to bring him esteem or prestige, rather than because such conduct is intrinsically proper. Such a person is also likely to do the "wrong" thing if it brings him approval and notoriety. Short cuts and compromises which bring quick results have high priority and are often undertaken despite the fact that in the process ethical and moral boundaries become blurred. Every college has more than its share of "manipulators," and the task of developing in them an integrity which is conducive to effective functioning of the institution is a difficult one.

As academic standards are being raised due to a variety of pressures, ranging all the way from the increasing numbers of young people wishing to go to college to competition with educational practices in the Soviet Union, there is a danger that the quantity of work assigned or required may be increased at the expense of its quality. If students are merely required to do more and more reading, the time will come, and has already come in some instances, when no one will be able to complete all the assignments. The smarter ones will then devise ways to make it seem that they have done the work. Others, more methodical but highly conscientious, will be severely frustrated. Gamesmanship will tend to take precedence over thoughtfulness, with a resulting lowering of standards of integrity. Grades will be more highly prized than the satisfaction of solid intellectual accomplishment. Unless our faculty members display as much concern with the development of character and integrity in their students as in their intellectual development, their efforts are going to be frustrated.

Every good student in our culture is expected to complete a stated amount of work each year, graduating from college at approximately age 22. There is no disapproval, possibly even increased prestige, when a student skips a year or two and advances to a higher class. When a student drops out of college, however, he may feel and his family practically always does feel that he has been a failure.

DROPOUTS FROM COLLEGES

The drop-out rate from American colleges is very high, averaging in the neighborhood of 50 per cent. The causes of this attrition include, among many others, academic difficulty, lack of motivation, marriage (particularly among girls), and conflicts in values between the students' homes and the college. Summerskill has recently reviewed the available literature on this subject and has shown that in most studies "the student is classified rather than understood" (3).

In institutions that have a high degree of selectivity in choosing their students the drop-out rate should be less than the general rate for all colleges. At Harvard College about 88 per cent of all entering students receive their degrees within 5 years of the expected date, and about 75 per cent are graduated on schedule. What occurs among the nearly 13 per cent who are delayed in obtaining their degrees? Is dropping out of college a year or so necessarily undesirable? These questions call for intensive research in a variety of institutions.

Our experience at Harvard suggests that if a student does drop out for whatever cause, he should stay out for at least a year, a period long enough for him to have made some significant achievement. This may be a job in industry, travel, psychotherapy, or 2 or 3 years in military service. Those who return in a few months or before they have worked through the issues which brought about their leaving college generally do rather poorly.

It is a common assumption of most psychiatrists that patients must make some financial sacrifice if they are to be motivated to get the most out of psychotherapy. For students who receive brief psychotherapy under prepaid medical care programs, this source of motivation is absent. Yet, they generally do quite well; the absence of the fee-for-service principle is apparently no handicap. Of course, they have many other reasons for trying to profit from treatment—saving their own time, making a better academic record, and relieving their own anxiety, not to mention the pleasure they get from doing a better job.

Some of my colleagues have said, "We treat patients here that we would not be seeing at all in private practice." This might be interpreted by critics of psychiatry as an indication that such students should work out their own problems or talk them over with friends or with their instructors. I prefer to believe that such students are getting help in learning how to devise better methods of solving emotional conflicts than they otherwise would before these conflicts have become so overwhelming as to produce a real psychiatric illness.

No psychiatrists working in colleges want to convert the schools into institutions primarily devoted to psychotherapy. We hear again and again, "A college is not a sanitarium." True enough, but colleges should not be so organized and administered as to increase the need for psychotherapy in its students or to interfere with it when needed. It is quite essential that teachers, administrators, counselors, and psychiatrists work together so that the frequent emotional conflicts of late adolescence and the early adult period can be worked out early in their course, rather than waiting for them to become organized into the traditional forms of neurosis and psychosis which call for more intensive, individual treatment.

As we attempt to encourage teachers to take the personality characteristics of their students into consideration as a means of increasing their effectiveness, we do not mean to imply that they should become amateur psychiatrists or psychologists. A teacher's efforts should remain centered on methods of facilitating learning. While he may be aware of those internal or unconscious factors which inhibit learning, he should not focus his attention primarily upon them. That is the function of the psychotherapist. Sensitive collaboration between psychiatrist and teacher may enable a student to solve some of his own quandaries by himself which otherwise might be perpetuated to the point of causing him lasting distress and disability.

FIRST COLLEGE YEARS

The first few years of college is the time for many students to throw off the restraints of parents and society and to experiment with new and often seemingly inappropriate ways of behaving. Many of them want all of the advantages of independence without giving up any of the advantages of dependence on their parents. They may discard many of the customs to which they have been accustomed and which seem necessary to polite and considerate relations with neighbors and colleagues. In their place they substitute noisy and boorish manners, carping criticism of anything already established, or studious neglect of their parents. Their sanitary and esthetic habits may deteriorate; they affect unusual mannerisms in clothing or personal care; and in general they seem to do just those things which will reduce their parents and those who love them most to excruciatingly painful helplessness and frustration. When college students undergo these exasperating changes in their behavior a few weeks or months after going to college, what could be more natural than that parents should blame the college for these changes? Yet, neither the anguished protests of parents nor angry outbursts of proctors, deans, or house mothers have much effect in improving such patterns of behavior.

A few students trying to work out their emotional conflicts in these dramatic and mildly antisocial ways may give rise to the idea that college officials are either uninterested in or unable to maintain discipline. Yet, no college approves behavior which is destructive to the reputation of the students indulging in it or to that of the college itself. What college officials strive for is an environment in which its students may learn how to acquire mature habits of thought and behavior, develop whatever creativity may be potentially in them, and learn to be independent without being unnecessarily offensive to those who may not agree with them. The limits beyond which students may go are clearly defined, but they are applied with restraint and thoughtfulness, not with impulsive anger..To apply sanctions in a punitive manner at this period of development only perpetuates the undesirable behavior and makes the rebellion more intense, more painful, and more prolonged. It seems to justify the young person's resentment and to postpone or prevent the acquisition of self-control. It is in just such situations that conferences between psychiatrists and those who are more intimately concerned with student behavior have their greatest usefulness. A college should be a place in which students try out new ideas and forms of behavior, but there should be safeguards to keep them from destroying their careers in the process and also from making public nuisances of themselves.

Herein also lies a trap for the unwary psychiatrist, especially if he is not intimately familiar with the college in which he is consulting or if he is inexperienced in the special characteristics of late adolescence and early adult behavior. He may consider the reactions he encounters more psychopathological than they are, frighten those to whom he reports, and advise hospital treatment when it is not really necessary. No psychiatrist can hope to escape criticism from college officials, parents, or his own colleagues. Yet experience with young adults in college brings with it a confidence that spreads to those with whom he deals. It is unfortunate that very few training centers exist as yet where a young psychiatrist may obtain such experience under supervision.

The fact that a college psychiatrist has a responsibility to the institution as well as to his patients bothers some psychiatrists in private practice a great deal. It is seldom difficult, however, to reconcile these two apparently conflicting demands. Those deans and other officials who feel that they must know everything that goes on on their campuses will be uncomfortable in having a psychiatrist as a colleague since he knows many things about the students which they do not know. The wise officials realize that they cannot know everything about everybody and are pleased to have someone whom they can trust working in this hitherto murky area of impulsive actions, unconscious motivation, and symbolic behavior. Deans and psychiatrists must either work together with mutual confidence or else the psychiatrist had better withdraw, since American colleges seemingly cannot operate without deans.

PREVENTIVE PSYCHIATRY

The task of developing a preventive psychiatry in education is a particularly challenging one for college psychiatrists. The paradox of preventive medicine is that if we do prevent some disorder we destroy the evidence that we have done so. In estimating the effectiveness of psychiatric treatment and other activities, a variety of indirect indices, all of them somewhat crude, is available. For example, the annual number of persons hospitalized for mental illness may change. The number of suicides may vary. Opinions of college administrators regarding the helpfulness of a psychiatric service may be important, but these cannot be considered statistically significant. At Harvard University, with a relatively large as well as recent service, the number of persons hospitalized yearly has reduced and the number of suicides has decreased. Whether these improvements will be sustained cannot be predicted.

If psychiatrists working in college expect to reduce the incidence of emotional disorders in young people, it seems evident that they will have to use educational devices rather than rely on psychotherapy alone. It is all right to drain the water out of a flooded cellar, but it might be better to stop the holes in the roof or repair a leaking faucet.

A promising but quite idealistic approach to preventive psychiatry is that of attempting to portray to students who are themselves soon to become parents, or perhaps already are, the essential conditions in family living which the present state of our knowledge suggests are necessary if they are to have the best chance of bringing up their children with good characters. The emotional needs of children have already been summarized. Helping parents or prospective parents to learn how to meet those needs involves far more than just giving them intellectual awareness of them; such forms of teaching still await development.

CONCLUSIONS

From all these considerations regarding the professional activities of a psychiatrist in a college setting, a few clear conclusions emerge:

1. Many college students need professional help in resolving their emotional problems, probably about 10 per cent each year, but only a few of these students need be described as emotionally ill according to existing diagnostic categories.

2. Students who consult a college psychiatrist should not automatically label themselves as sick but should look upon the psychiatrist as a special tutor in emotional growth and development, an area not heretofore considered of primary concern to educators.

3. Early treatment combined with consultations with significant persons involved in students' development serves to divert many of them from illness to health. Clinical psychologists, deans, chaplains, and skilled faculty counselors may all have an important part to play in augmenting the psychiatrist's efforts in psychotherapy.

4. The problem of developing optimum conditions for emotional maturity in a college is much too large to be left to the efforts of any one group alone. Psychotherapy for the emotionally handicapped is not enough, necessary as it is.

5. What is learned about the problems of those college students who seek psychiatric help should be organized and made available to those who plan the curricular and extracurricular life of the college. Such facts can be of help to the healthy as well as the sick.

Collaboration between teachers, deans, psychologists, psychiatrists, and counselors of all types is most desirable. To be of most use to the institution, a psychiatrist working in a college should spend as much time working with teachers, administrators, and parents as he does with the students themselves.

The goals of college and university psychiatric services are gradually becoming clearer as experience accumulates. These include: (1) Treating sick students or those who may become so if their conflicts are not mitigated. Similar aid to faculty members is provided in some institutions, with gratifying results. (2) Changing attitudes of students, faculty, and employees toward emotional problems from aversion, fear, or denial to understanding, tolerance, and cooperation in their management. (3) Improving relations between students and college staff to the end that learning be enhanced. (4) Freeing the intellectual capacity of students to do creative and satisfying work. (5) Identifying and counteracting anti-intellectual forces which impede or prevent learning. (6) Creating a complex network of communication among all people in the institution to enable early discovery of those persons showing signs of disabling conflict. This must be done without creating the impression that there is a spy system, even though established for benevolent purposes. (7) Coordinating and integrating of all counseling services in the institution, not with a view to domination or control but to see that all available resources are open to anyone needing them.

The prevention of mental illness and the promotion of mental health are both important aspects of a college psychiatrist's work. The management of acute disturbances contributes directly or indirectly to these ends. Every college psychiatrist should be working toward the ultimate ideal of making his professional help unnecessary in that setting.

We are now on the threshold of new and far-reaching efforts designed to bring the energy of society to bear on the solution of some of the age-old problems of mental disease, thanks to the favorable reception that has been accorded the recent report of the Joint Commission on Mental Health and Illness (2). Through appropriate utilization of opportunities in our colleges and universities, psychiatry can make important contributions to improving the climate for teaching and learning and thus enhance the public welfare.

REFERENCES

1. Blaine, G. B., Jr. In Blaine, G. B. and McArthur, C. C. (Eds.), *The emotional problems of the student*. New York: Appleton-Century-Crofts, 1960. Pp. 232–48.
2. Joint Commission on Mental Illness and Health. *Action for Mental Health*. New York: Basic Books, 1961.
3. Summerskill, J. In Sanford, N. (Ed.), *The American college*. New York: John Wiley & Sons, Inc., 1962. Pp. 627–57.

34

Opportunities for School Psychologists in the Primary Prevention of Mental Disorders in Children

GERALD CAPLAN

"PRIMARY prevention" is a public health term denoting measures to reduce the incidence of a disorder in the community; namely, to lessen the rate of new cases of this disorder occurring during a specified period of time.

In contrast to "secondary prevention," which aims at lowering the frequency of sick persons at a particular time by successful treatment of established cases prior to that time—so that the duration and therefore the number of old cases is reduced—primary prevention focuses not upon persons who are sick but upon those factors which lead to sickness.

At the present time we do not know the etiology of many mental disorders, but we do have some plausible assumptions regarding factors which are conducive or inimical to mentally healthy functioning, and based upon these it is possible to develop programs which may lower the risk of persons reacting to life experiences in a mentally unhealthy way.

In the field of mental health a conceptual model borrowed from the field of physical nutrition is helpful in clarifying some basic issues. We can conceive of healthy personality development and the avoidance of mental disorders as depending upon the provision to the individual of adequate supplies—physical, psychosocial, and sociocultural—which are appropriate to his successive phases of growth and development.

Underprovision or overprovision of these supplies in relation to his current needs constitutes a pathogenic influence which may lead to an immediate mental disorder, because the individual can find no healthy, reality-oriented way of coping with the stress, and he is forced to deal with it by the magic of neurotic symptoms or by separating himself from the burdensome world of reality through some alienating psychotic response. It may also lead to a weakening of personality through the development of a pattern of evading the issue, which may be successful on this occasion but may break down in the face of some future difficulty.

On the other hand, many individuals will master the current pathogenic

Reprinted from *Mental Hygiene,* 1963, *47,* 525–539, by permission of the publisher and the author. © 1963, National Association for Mental Health. Dr. Caplan is Clinical Professor of Psychiatry, Harvard Medical School.

influence, because adequate supplies in the past have given them psychological strength and resilience, and because they make active use of alternative sources of supply in the present.

Primary prevention of mental disorders has the long-term goal of ensuring continually adequate physical, psychosocial, and sociocultural supplies, which both avoid stress and increase the basic capacity to withstand future stress; and also the short-term goal of providing current help to individuals wrestling with life difficulties so that they may find healthy ways of mastering them.

The long-term goals and the short-term goals can be conceptually linked by using the theory of *crisis*. This theory focuses upon the phenomena which are regularly manifested when an individual struggles with a current life stress, related either to the loss or threat of loss of his basic supplies, or to a novel situation which challenges him beyond his current capacity.

A period of cognitive and emotional upset ensues for the individual, whose previous equilibrium of behavior is disorganized by burdens and demands which he has no ready way of escaping or mastering. He is said to be in a state of personal crisis; he is usually confused, and he suffers from a rise of tension and from a variety of negative feelings, such as anxiety, depression, anger, shame, guilt and frustration.

The most characteristic manifestation of a crisis is that it is self-terminating; after a relatively short period of a few days to a few weeks, the tension dies down, the negative feelings dissipate, and the individual achieves a new equilibrium. This occurs as a result of a complicated series of changes, both in the psychological structure of the individual, and in his relationships with his environment. These adjustments and adaptations suffice to deal with whatever problem precipitated the crisis.

Important for the current or future mental health of the individual is the pattern of his coping behavior during the crisis. Studies (4, 5, 10) have shown that some individuals, during such a crisis, struggle with their problems in an effective way and achieve a reality-based, culturally acceptable pattern of adjustment and adaptation.

These individuals emerge to a new equilibrium which is healthier than their previous state. During the crisis they added to their previous repertoire of defenses and problem-solving methods some novel responses which have increased their capacity to master new stresses successfully in the future. They are less likely than previously to be forced to deal with such situations by magical, regressive, or alienating mechanisms, which lead to mental disorder.

Other individuals show the opposite picture. They do not cope adequately with the crisis problems. They do develop novel responses, but these are ineffectual; that is, they evade the issues or they make use of magical or regressive defenses. They emerge to a new equilibrium which is mentally less healthy —either an overt disorder, or an increased likelihood of future disorder— because they have incorporated new neurotic or psychotic defenses into their problem-solving repertoire.

The previous history of a mentally healthy individual shows that he has passed through a succession of crises, some of them associated with expectable transitions in his biological development or in his psychosocial role—the so-called biopsychosocial developmental crises, such as the socialization crises of early childhood, becoming a school child, becoming an adolescent, getting engaged and married, becoming a parent, etc.—and some associated with accidental happenings, such as personal illness, death of a loved one, natural or social disaster, etc. At each of these crises a more or less significant development of his personality occurred. The improvement in his capacity to deal with life in healthy ways has occurred in a series of spurts, and during each crisis a personality enrichment took place.

In contrast, the history of a mentally unhealthy individual shows a series of crisis way stations, at each of which wrong paths were taken, so that his personality developed more and more significant weaknesses until a "straw broke the camel's back," and he emerged from a particular crisis with an overt illness. Looking back at his life, it can be conceived that on a number of occasions it might have been possible for him to have chosen different coping mechanisms and to have taken a healthier path in his life trajectory.

This idea raises the question of what differentiates the group of effective copers, who emerge from crises with improved mental health, from the group of inadequate copers, who emerge with worsened mental health. Are crises states during which those with healthy personalities inevitably get stronger and those with unhealthy personalities get weaker?

Some light is thrown upon this question by attempts which have been made, mainly in the armed services, to predict from personality studies how individuals are likely to react during and after particular crises. Such studies, carried out with much energy in a number of countries, and using a variety of personality tests, have been uniformly unsuccessful in making accurate predictions, except in extreme cases. It is clear that an individual's reaction during crisis is influenced by the personality with which he enters the situation, and by all his past experience; but studies of crisis show that his coping patterns and the crisis outcome are also influenced both by the vicissitudes of the life events during the crisis period and their personal significance to him, and, in addition, by the details of his social interactions during the crisis.

A person rarely faces crisis on his own. He is usually involved during that period in relationships with his family and friends, and with professional and nonprofessional members of his community. As his tension rises during a crisis, he usually tries to elicit help from these people, and the signals of distress which he emits usually stimulate the latter to intervene on his behalf, a complementary pattern which has primitive biosocial roots. Moreover, during the disequilibrium of a crisis an individual is more susceptible to influence by others than during his customary psychological steady state.

This means that the failure of personality tests to predict crisis response is due to the outcome being influenced to a major degree by the details of the developing crisis situation and by the nature of the material and psychological assistance derived from significant others during the crisis period.

Direct studies of the reactions of individuals during crisis have corroborated this. The way a mother copes with the crisis of the birth of a premature baby is much influenced by the reactions of her husband and other relatives, as well as by the behavior of the hospital nurses and doctors, and by the help she receives from public health nurses and pediatricians when she takes the baby home (4). The way a patient handles the crisis of a surgical operation can be modified by the assistance he receives from doctors and nurses (9). The way a bereaved person handles the crisis of the removal by death of a loved one is influenced by the reactions of his family and social group and by the ministrations of his priest or clergyman (12).

This leads us to the realization that since life crisis involves not only the danger of provoking mental disorder but also an opportunity for improved mental health, an important aspect of basic biopsychosocial supplies is training in crisis coping, and also the provision of services so that during inevitable crises individuals will receive appropriate material and psychological help to assist them to cope adequately with the current situation, and to improve their capacity to withstand future stress.

IMPLICATIONS FOR PRIMARY PREVENTION IN SCHOOLS

ENSURING ADEQUATE BASIC SUPPLIES

Physical Supplies

Mens sana in corpore sano is an accepted slogan in most schools in this country, and there is little need to dwell here on this issue, which lies more in the province of the athletic coach, the school nurse, and the school doctor than in that of the psychologist.

It may be relevant, however, to emphasize that those focused primarily on mental health must collaborate actively with the workers mainly interested in physical health. In such instances as inadequate nutrition of underprivileged children, disorders of vision and hearing, or culturally based prejudice against exercise, psychologists should be alert to invoke the aid of the health workers for the benefit of children who have first come to their attention. It is also necessary to build up satisfactory relationships with the doctors and nurses so that they, in turn, will call upon the psychologist for advice and collaboration in cases of acute and chronic physical illness. The treatment and rehabilitation of a physical defect usually carries with it the opportunity for primary prevention of psychological disorder.

Psychosocial Supplies

The provision of most of these supplies, such as love and affection, a balance between gratification and control of instinctual wishes, appropriate balance between support of dependent needs and the fostering of independence, and provision of personality role models and a primary group as a basis for identity formation, etc., takes place outside the school in the family circle.

On the other hand, especially in kindergarten and the earlier grades, the school acts as an extension of the family group, the teacher being a supplementary parent figure, and the other children being accessory sibling figures who can complement and, if necessary, replace supplies which are inadequately provided at home.

Later on, as children approach adolescence, teachers become important, nonparental role models, and the peer group of children becomes an essential reference group for the development of values which are incorporated as an enrichment of personality. Throughout school life the interchange with teachers and other children provides an opportunity for developing interpersonal skills, and for the consensual validation of a child's feelings about his own identity.

Sociocultural Supplies

The school shares with the family the task of providing most of the basic sociocultural supplies during childhood. Among community agencies, its role in this area is pre-eminent, and although religious and recreational agencies have their part to play, and general neighborhood and community traditions and expectations have an important molding effect on the child's personality, it is the school, as the socializing instrument of the community, which determines to a considerable extent how the child perceives the world and its problems, and how he goes about dealing with them.

The effect of the school on the child is partly cognitive—in developing and patterning his perceptual set and his methods of problem-solving. Many people believe that the basic function of the school is in teaching children how to think, which in turn influences how they act and react.

Ojemann (13) has criticized the content and process of teaching which obtains in many schools in this country. He believes they encourage children to develop what he calls "a surface approach," in which they react in judgmental and stereotyped ways to the manifestations of situations, including the actions of others. He has suggested alterations in the content of teaching materials and in methods of teaching which foster a "causal orientation"; that is, an approach in which the child attempts to understand the causes of the phenomena he perceives, and to choose from among a range of alternatives those reactions which are in keeping with the complicated nature of the presenting situation.

This "causal approach" is not taught as a special course but, as Ojemann has shown, can be integrated in all phases of the school curriculum. He has evaluated the differences in those children exposed to this type of teaching as compared to traditional instruction, and he has shown that the former children are better able to deal with the confusion and ambiguity of a difficult problem, and are more flexible in working out effective solutions—both of which have positive implications for crisis-coping.

Ojemann's work points to a significant role for school psychologists in collaborating with educators, in order to modify teaching materials and methods so that children are better equipped with those problem-solving skills which will help them deal in a mentally healthy, reality-based way with future crisis situations.

The contribution of the school to the personality development of children is, of course, not confined to the cognitive area. Both the inculcation of values, which influence motivation, and the development of skills to master and exploit feeling are an essential aspect of education—the so-called character-building upon which good educators have always placed so much emphasis. In relation to improving a child's capacity to deal in a mentally healthy way with life's problems, particular importance is to be ascribed to training him to withstand frustration and anxiety, to persevere with problem-solving in the face of diffi- culty, to confront his problems actively and maintain them in consciousness despite their unpleasantness, and to be able to ask for help and use it without a weakening loss of self-esteem.

The work of a group of psychologists associated with the Bank Street School in New York, and reported by Barbara Biber (1) is a good example of the contribution of psychology to the understanding of the mental health implications of the total pattern of the educational process and of the school setting (what Biber calls "the 'organized complexity' of total school function- ing") that includes not only intra-classroom processes but also the value system and psychological atmosphere of the school—"the interaction patterns among staff, between parents and school personnel, and between the school and its community."

Biber and her colleagues show how all these factors influence the molding of the child's developing personality, with particular reference to psychological resilience and robustness, which are not only a basis for effective functioning and creativity but also a bulwark against mental disorder.

The work of Ojemann and Biber points to a significant role for psycholo- gists in the school system as participant observers of school life with reference to its general implications for the present and future mental health of the children, and as resource persons who can advise on modifications which may improve the provision of psychosocial and sociocultural supplies.

The primary actors in this process are the school administrators and teachers. They are the people who initiate and maintain the educational pro- gram and determine its setting, in response to their own personalities, training, and professional experience, and to the prescriptions and demands of the community. They have always been interested in the "character building" aspect of their work, and they have developed humanistic traditions to deal with this.

In recent years many educators have become aware of the specialized re- searches and thinking of psychologists and would be interested in exploiting this added resource in developing new approaches to their educational goals.

On the other hand, psychologists must move cautiously in this area; first, because we are relative newcomers in this field and have as yet little scientifically validated knowledge upon which to base specific advice; and second, because mental health, although *our* chief professional goal, is not the primary goal of education, and sometimes must yield precedence to other goals, such as technical proficiency or social conformity, which the community enjoins upon its school system.

Moreover, administrators and educators may feel threatened by the demands of psychologists for changes in traditional patterns, and may be ambivalent and uncertain about possible unfortunate and unexpected side effects of changes which are advocated by those who lack expert knowledge of education.

Nevertheless, psychologists may achieve major mental health goals if they can develop relationships of mutual trust with educators so that the latter will invoke their help in regard to adding a new mental health dimension to their planning and program management. The contribution of the psychologists will occasionally be in the form of specific advice about course or curriculum content and timing, but more often it will take the form of putting forward a point of view about the psychosocial and sociocultural needs of children which the educators may find useful in coming, on their own, to a more sophisticated decision.

This point of view should, wherever possible, be backed by communication of research findings, such as those of Ojemann (13) and Biber (1), and this means that school psychologists should act as channels of information and as interpreters, to the educators, of significant research and professional thinking gleaned from psychological and mental health literature, and from conferences of school psychologists.

Psychologists who are interested in this approach may benefit from certain principles and practices of community organization which have been found useful in community mental health. In this field we have discovered that in order to be optimally effective as professional consultants and expert resource persons, it is important not to campaign actively for our own goals with missionary or reforming zeal. Such behavior tends to arouse resistance among members of other professions with different value systems and traditions. This is particularly unfortunate if they happen to have not only the responsibility but the authority to reject discordant elements.

Instead, we try to make ourselves available to our colleagues and to offer help on their terms in relation to their current felt needs. Little by little, they learn what we have to offer, and begin to respect our competence and our point of view. We take care not to trespass beyond the boundaries of our sanctioned roles; that is, we do not tell *them* how they should manage *their* affairs, and we show our respect for their areas of professional competence by not presuming to judge their functioning. Instead we stay strictly within the limits of what we have been specifically asked to do in the community by virtue of our own professional training and experience.

On the other hand, we do try to arrange for our roles not to become circumscribed so that we get shut off in a corner. Instead, we try and obtain sanction to move relatively freely within the system, so that we can establish proximity with colleagues with whom we can interact and build up the mutually respectful relationship which is the essential prerequisite for being asked for meaningful consultation assistance.

The permission to move around in the system is also important because it provides us with the opportunity to learn at firsthand how our colleagues perceive their problems and deal with them, since this knowledge is essential if we are eventually to understand the inner meaning of the questions they ask us and the nature of those replies which will have significance for them. Probably the most important insight is that gaining the acceptance of members of another profession and learning how they operate within their system is often a lengthy process. It cannot be hurried. It is rarely a smooth process.

We have to develop a common language, mutually acceptable ground rules of interaction and behavioral cues, and free channels of communication. We have to get to know and respect each other, which means that we have to overcome personal and cultural stereotypes that distort our view of each other. This is a two-way process and requires effort and patience on both sides. For instance, many teachers have the stereotyped fantasy that psychologists are mind readers and will ferret out their personality weaknesses and their socially unacceptable instinctual desires. This naturally leads to some anxiety and defensiveness in relating to a psychologist.

On the other hand, many psychologists imagine that teachers who do not share their systematic knowledge of the laws of psychology are ill-equipped to understand and deal with interpersonal matters. This may lead to a belittling attitude of superiority, which they may unsuccessfully try to hide, and which may blind them to the evidence that the teachers have their own conceptual systems for guiding their handling of interpersonal transactions, which may not be so elegantly expressed as the psychologists' but which in many cases may be not less effective as a basis for action.

HELPING CHILDREN TO COPE WITH CRISIS

In contrast with efforts to ensure adequate basic physical, psychosocial, and sociocultural supplies, which are long-continuing and are directed to the entire school community and its effect on all children, the present section deals with short-term activities focused upon specific children or groups of children, who are currently upset, or in whom it is possible to predict upset in the near future.

There is a link between these short-term activities and the ongoing program of ameliorating the school environment, because every individual case should also be considered in relation to its general implications; and repetition of cases of similar types in certain grades or at characteristic times in the school year should always stimulate the consideration of general policy changes which may attenuate the hazards or challenges so that they may be less burdensome. It is not possible or desirable to prevent crisis althogether by obviating threat, loss, or challenge, but if these can be reduced in intensity or sometimes postponed till individuals have acquired greater problem-solving capacity, there is more likelihood that the crisis will be adequately handled and will lead to a healthy outcome.

IDENTIFICATION OF A CRISIS

The recognition of crisis depends mainly upon observing signs of the relatively sudden onset of cognitive and emotional disequilibrium in a child whose previous pattern of functioning was known to be fairly stable. Classroom teachers are in an excellent position to identify crises in their students because of their hour-by-hour and day-by-day observation of their behavior. A child's functioning is not static. He shows minor variations of emotional response and cognitive effectiveness. Some children are more unstable in this respect than others. Teachers, however, learn the expectable and consistent styles of each of their children, and can identify marked deviations when they occur.

It is probable that crises only achieve significance as turning points in personality development when they have a duration of at least several days, and when their intensity is such as to lead to observable rise of tension, lowered effectiveness in learning, and signs of negative feelings, such as anxiety, depression, anger, shame, and guilt, which are not consonant with the current reality situation.

Children in such states of turmoil should not be thought of as emotionally disordered or ill, even though they are cognitively and emotionally disturbed. This disturbance is the sign that they are wrestling with a problem which is, for the time being, insoluble, and it usually does not last longer than four to six weeks.

If a disturbance lasts for a longer period, it probably is not a crisis or reaction to a current problem, but is a true emotional disorder, which represents a stabilized outcome of a crisis. Temporary crisis upsets occur both in mentally healthy and mentally unhealthy children. It is therefore sometimes difficult to differentiate a crisis in a neurotic child from some endogenously provoked exacerbation of his chronic symptoms.

Most psychological screening instruments will not differentiate children in crisis from those with stable emotional disorders, so any systematic screening program, such as that developed in California (2, 3) will screen out not only the emotionally disordered but also those children who happen to be in crisis at the time.

Identification of crisis is facilitated not only by observing the response of a child, but also by knowing that he is currently confronted by the loss or threat of loss of a source of basic biopsychosocial supplies, or by a challenge which burdens his readily available resources. Similar environmental situations will not evoke crisis in all children, since the subjective meaning of the situation will vary from child to child because of his cultural and personal background, and because some children may have learned in the past to handle such a situation with relative ease.

It is possible, however, to identify situations which are likely to provoke crisis in a significant proportion of children, and this enables us more easily to diagnose that certain behavioral upsets are likely to be signs of crisis, and also to predict that when such situations occur, a certain number of children will become upset.

As previously indicated, these hazardous or challenging situations are of two main types—*regularly occurring biopsychosocial transitional points* and *accidental happenings*. The so-called developmental crises occur both in relation to expectable endogenous changes associated with biological and psychological growth and development phases which are more or less linked with chronological age, such as the stages of personality development described by Freud (8), Piaget (14) and Erickson (7), and also in relation to the regular succession of events associated with a child's school career, such as the transition period on entering kindergarten, between kindergarten and first grade, on leaving the early grades (usually during fourth grade), between junior high and senior high, during the last year before college, etc. A survey of a school population should show a number of regularly occurring peaks in the incidence of children in crisis related to the consonance of transitional periods in biopsychological and school career development phases.

Superimposed upon these will be the accidental situations: (a) family problems associated with such events as illness or death of a family member, birth of a sibling, economic insecurity, change of father's job, mother going out to work, change of address to a new neighborhood, etc.; (b) personal illness of the child, which may be hazardous in itself and may be associated with added burdens because he may miss critical learning opportunities which may not be repeated; and (c) problems in school, such as status or prestige change due to academic or athletic failure or success, loss of relationship with a significant teacher or a school friend because of illness or death or because of moving to another class, etc.

The Role of the School Psychologist

The preventive activities of school psychologists in relation to crises in children can be considered under three headings: (1) Direct action (2) Indirect action and (3) Research.

Direct action. Here the psychologist intervenes directly with individual children or groups of children, either while they are in crisis, which is called "preventive intervention," or before a crisis occurs, which is called "anticipatory guidance" or "emotional inoculation."

PREVENTIVE INTERVENTION. The psychologist may intervene in the case of an individual child during a crisis, or he may deal with a group of children, all of whom may be in crisis because of a common hazard or challenge, such as an impending exam or the problems of transition between high school and college.

The essence of preventive intervention is that the psychologist knows enough about patterns of effective and ineffective coping that he can identify among children in crisis those who are using poor coping mechanisms, and with whom he then interacts, so as to influence them to adopt more effective coping patterns. Klein and Lindemann (11) have described some of the techniques involved, and I have discussed certain of the practical issues in my recent book *An Approach to Community Mental Health* (4).

It appears that every situation of hazard or challenge is associated with its own characteristic succession of psychological tasks, which the child must master in the appropriate order in order to deal effectively with the total situation (10). Psychologists are building up a fund of knowledge derived from experience with various crisis situations and the range of reactions to them, and on the basis of this knowledge they are learning to identify unhealthy responses and are working out the details of alternative mechanisms which they influence the children to utilize.

This influence is partly educational and partly psychotherapeutic; it is energized by an ego-supportive relationship between psychologist and child, and the leverage of this is used to direct the child to confront his crisis tasks in a reality-based way. We still do not know much about this process, and there is a need for further research and empirical trial.

In addition to the detailed responses which are specific to each crisis situation, we have reason to believe that there are certain global patterns of coping that appear applicable to most crises (5), and that can be recognized to be adaptive or maladaptive. In general, the psychologist should influence children to confront their crisis problems actively rather than to evade or deny them, which implies maintaining the problem in consciousness, actively collecting information about the factors involved and how to deal with them both by personal observation and thinking and by asking others who have been through the experience or who know of people who have.

The psychologist should influence the children to allow themselves to feel and express the negative feelings associated with the crisis, rather than suppress or deny them. He should counteract any marked tendency to release tension by blaming others or themselves for the difficulty. He should assist the children to master their expressed feelings both by their own efforts, and in interaction with himself and with significant others in their environment. He should help the children become aware of their state of fatigue and manage their coping efforts accordingly, so that they take sufficient rest periods, and yet so that they return to dealing with the problems as soon as they have recovered their strength.

The psychologist should also influence the children in crisis to ask for appropriate help from their families, teachers, and friends, both in handling feelings and in dealing with the material aspects of their tasks; and he should be especially active both in encouraging the children and in influencing their families and friends in those cases where he sees any reluctance to ask for help or to offer it.

Wherever possible, the psychologist should intervene not only with the children in crisis but also with their families, to whom he should offer his support and active guidance (7).

Many of these suggestions for crisis intervention are probably what most psychologists might spontaneously think of doing in offering a human helping hand to an upset child and his family. It is hoped that as we get more experience in this field, and as we subject the process of preventive intervention to further detailed scrutiny, we may refine our techniques. The measures I have suggested are derived from researches we have conducted at Harvard School of Public Health on families dealing with the crisis of the birth of a premature baby (4, 5, 10) from Lindemann's studies on the crisis of bereavement (12), from the researches of Janis on the responses of adult patients to surgical operations (9), and from a study of the reactions of high school students coping with the anticipation of college, carried out by Silber, Hamburg and their colleagues at the NIMH (15).

It will be noted that I do not advocate trying to uncover the causes for poor coping, as one might do in analytic psychotherapy. The essence of preventive intervention is to ameliorate the final common path of the coping mechanisms by "here and now" influence, which alters the child's thinking and behavior, rather than to identify and influence the underlying causes of these mechanisms.

It is important that the child should behave adaptively, and not that we or he should understand why he was previously behaving maladaptively. During crisis his coping is the end result of a multitude of factors pushing and pulling him in various directions. Our minimal intervention brings this balance of forces down in a healthy direction. We are enabled to do so in most cases, despite all the counterbalancing forces in his past experience and personality, because we are intervening at the crucial moment when the iron is hot, and when he is most susceptible to short-term influence. The same influence exerted when the child is not in crisis would have very little effect on his behavior or attitudes.

ANTICIPATORY GUIDANCE OR EMOTIONAL INOCULATION. Identification of regularly occurring hazardous situations in the life of school children allows us to focus our preventive attention on populations of children who, in the near future, will be exposed to the risk of crisis, e.g., children about to enter kindergarten or high school, or children facing the uncertainties of attempting to get into college.

Not all children in the populations will react with crisis, but on the basis of past studies psychologists may be able to predict what proportion of them will suffer. If the rate of crisis is likely to be significantly high, the psychologists may decide to intervene ahead of time in order to prepare the children to cope more adequately with the situation when it arises.

In addition to dealing with predictable hazards by means of this group approach, psychologists may be alert to identify ahead of time stress situations in individual children, such as a child who has to enter hospital for elective surgery, or a child who faces impending separation from a parent—a father who may have to go out of the country on military service, or a mother who may have to enter a tuberculosis sanitorium, etc.

Lindemann has shown that the psychological work of mourning by means of which a bereaved person adjusts to the removal from his life of a loved one, who is a source of satisfaction of his basic psychological supplies, may sometimes be partially accomplished before the death occurs. He calls this "anticipatory mourning" (12). There is some evidence that bereavement is a more difficult crisis to cope with if the death is unexpected, and if anticipatory mourning cannot take place.

Janis (9), studying the adjustment of patients to surgical operations, found that those with the most successful psychological outcome had accomplished a certain amount of active worrying before the operation, so that when the real crisis began they had already achieved some mastery of their feelings of fear and frustration. He suggested the term "emotional inoculation" for active intervention with patients before their operations in order to stimulate them to carry out some anticipatory "worry work."

In public health, anticipatory guidance has long been used, especially in well-baby clinics to prepare young mothers for predictable problems which they will probably have as their babies grow and develop, and in prenatal clinics to prepare pregnant women for the stress of labor and delivery (4).

Psychologists may base themselves upon these and similar studies and practices in working out procedures of focused intervention with individuals or groups of children before a crisis. The essential element in this method is to arouse ahead of time as vivid an anticipation as possible of the details of the predictable hazard or challenge and of the unpleasant emotions and fantasies which are likely to accompany it, while at the same time offering support and guidance in the rehearsal of ways in which these stresses and strains may be handled.

If carried out successfully, the term "inoculation" is a most appropriate name for the process, since what is involved is the introduction of an attenuated stress which stimulates the development of a protective response that subsequently can be used to counteract the greater stress of the real-life crisis situation.

The main technical problem is how to evoke ahead of time a vivid foretaste of the real experience. The further away the crisis is, and the more alien from the child's past experience, the harder this is to do. The use of emotionally toned words and detailed step-by-step descriptions are useful in individual and group discussions, and psychologists who are skilled in the technique may utilize the dramatic impact of role-playing.

Some workers may be concerned about overdoing this type of approach and scaring the children unduly by underlining the gory details, but this is rarely a serious danger, since a competent psychologist will be observing carefully the effect of his efforts on the children, and he will be active in offering support in handling their reactions. Some children, who are excessive worriers, may not be suitable for this procedure, and in their cases it may even be appropriate to reduce their anxieties ahead of time in order to help them achieve the self-confidence to master the crisis problems.

In all cases it is important to help the children gain a realistic view of what is likely to happen and to free them from the exaggerations produced by fantasy elaborations. It is also important to underline the availability of help and support during the crisis itself, and to stimulate a hopeful outlook by discussing the limited nature of the difficulties; that is, by counteracting any tendency to stereotype a possible bad outcome as an inevitably global catastrophe.

The best time to do anticipatory guidance is when some current event is evoking feelings similar to what can be predicted for the main crisis, which means that the feelings are being stimulated by real experience rather than artificially by discussion. For instance, in a recent program of anticipatory guidance for Peace Corps volunteers the feelings of deprivation aroused in them by parting from family and home town friends when coming to their training center provided a realistic foretaste of the more intense feelings of isolation and loneliness they could imagine they would feel when they would go overseas on their assignment. A discussion of the future situation therefore used their current feelings as a meaningful take-off point.

Another strategic time to do anticipatory guidance is in the earliest stages of the crisis, or immediately prior to its onset. At this time the impact of the stress is beginning, but it is not yet overpowering. This is a transitional stage between anticipatory guidance and preventive intervention.

From a certain point of view, all preventive intervention can well be considered anticipatory guidance for future crises, since we must remember that we are intervening currently, not merely to help someone cope with the present difficulty, but also—and perhaps most important—to help him develop healthy coping skills which may enable him to withstand possible greater stress in his future life.

Indirect Action. Here the psychologist attempts to provide emotional support and guidance for children in crisis, not by interacting himself directly with them, but by stimulating and guiding the other school workers to do so— mainly the educators, but also the school nurses, doctors and guidance personnel. He may accomplish this in three main ways, by: (a) teacher training, (b) training of educational supervisors, and (c) consultation and collaboration. In order to save time we will focus only upon the interaction with educators. Similar principles apply to interaction with the other workers.

TEACHER TRAINING. Psychologists should, wherever possible, communicate appropriate knowledge about crisis-coping patterns of children and about methods of preventive intervention and anticipatory guidance to school teachers —both through participation in preprofessional training and also in on-the-job training of school staff. A basic tenet of the community approach is that, wherever possible, preventive work should be carried out by the large number of nonspecialized line workers rather than be restricted to the highly trained specialists who are always too few in number to cover the field.

In the schools, the classroom teachers are the most appropriately placed workers to identify the early stages of crisis in children, and they can often intervene effectively by offering adult support and guidance at the most strategic time. In fact, many teachers do this every day without any special realization of the mental health implications of their help.

Psychologists can introduce some professional self-awareness into this process by sharing with teachers our increasing body of specific knowledge in this field, and by so doing enhance what is currently going on.

In this endeavor there is the possibility of a significant danger which must be consciously avoided. It is important that the psychologists take care not to influence teachers to utilize techniques which are not in keeping with their traditional teaching role. It would be most unfortunate if teachers felt impelled to become psychotherapists, or to act as proxy psychologists. The best safeguard against this is for psychologists to provide teachers with information about the relation of crisis-coping and mental health and about adjustive and maladjustive coping patterns, and leave the working out of techniques of preventive and anticipatory guidance to the teachers themselves.

This approach may be usefully augmented by learning how certain gifted teachers handle these problems, either in the classroom or with individual children, and then communicating this to other teachers as an example of effective preventive work which they may try.

TRAINING OF EDUCATIONAL SUPERVISORS. The approach here is similar to that with teachers. It is singled out for special mention only to emphasize that in order to maximize the effect of his efforts, the psychologist should always try and operate, as it were, "upstream." The supervisory group in the school system must be convinced of the importance of primary prevention so that they will sanction and encourage the teachers to engage in such activity. The psychologist should focus as much effort as possible on adding to their knowledge, so that they in turn can disseminate the information to their teachers.

CONSULTATION AND COLLABORATION. Adding to the knowldge of teachers and supervisors will lead to best results in practice if the psychologist freely offers his services to support, guide, and, if necessary, collaborate with them in implementing their developing insights and skills in relation to specific children. In their early attempts at preventive activity teachers may wish the psychologist to share responsibility for the case in point.

A child or a group of children may be dealt with separately or jointly by both teacher and psychologist. If they work separately, the psychologist should spend a significant part of his time telling the teacher what he is doing, and invoking the teacher's supplementary assistance. With increasing experience the teacher may take over more and more responsibility for future cases, and may work out techniques of his own.

Eventually the teacher may ask only for consultation help when he encounters an especially complicated case, although the psychologist should always offer to "backstop" him by sharing responsibility or accepting all the responsibility for a really difficult problem.

I have discussed techniques of consultation fully elsewhere (6). Although my present paper makes so brief a mention of this technique, I believe that it should be a major focus of effort among school psychologists.

Research. I do not wish to end this paper without making brief reference to the research role of school psychologists in the field of primary prevention. I hope that some school systems will provide the necessary personnel and funds to allow the carrying out of formal projects with adequate research design. I envisage that more commonly the nature of the job demands will be such that psychologists will be operating mainly as practitioners and will have little time or energy for research.

I do believe, however, that alert, interested, and sophisticated practitioners can make major contributions to knowledge by informal studies, or at least by studies which are not rigorously designed. There is, at present, a tremendous need for exploratory investigation in this field, and no group is more strategically placed than school psychologists to undertake this task. This is especially the case in California, where the work of Bower, Lambert, and their colleagues has blazed so important a trail.

I have time only to mention four topics which seem especially appropriate to explore at the present time:—

1. A survey of the types of situation which recur in the school setting as precipitators of crisis, and the characteristics of the children in whom these situations most commonly provoke crisis, in regard to such variables as age, sex, socioeconomic class, and ethnic background.

2. Follow-up studies of coping patterns of children in successive crises of different types, to see whether there are consistent styles of coping, and whether, and under what circumstances, changes in style occur.

3. Development of improved methods of preventive intervention and anticipatory guidance by psychologists and teachers, and definition and description of the techniques.

4. A preliminary approach to evaluating the results of intervention techniques in relation to changes in patterns of coping with future crises, and in relation to changes in general behavior in the school setting.

REFERENCES

1. Biber, B. Integration of mental health principles in the school setting. In G. Caplan (Ed.), *Prevention of mental disorders in children.* New York: Basic Books, 1961. Pp. 323–52.
2. Bower, E. M. Primary prevention in a school setting. In G. Caplan (Ed.),

Prevention of mental disorders in children. New York: Basic Books, 1961. Pp. 353–77.

3. Bower, E. M. *Early identification of emotionally handicapped children in school.* Springfield, Ill.: Charles C Thomas, 1960.

4. Caplan, G. *An approach to community mental health.* New York: Grune & Stratton, 1961.

5. Caplan, G. Patterns of parental responses to the crisis of premature birth, *Psychiatry,* 1960, 23:365–74.

6. Caplan, G. *Concepts of mental health and consultation: Their application in public health social work.* Washington, D.C.: Government Printing Office, 1959. (Children's Bureau Publ. No. 373).

7. Erikson, E. H. *Childhood and society.* New York: W. W. Norton & Co., 1950.

8. Freud, S. Three essays on sexuality. In J. Strachey (Ed.), *Standard edition of the complete psychological works of Sigmund Freud,* Vol. VII. London: Hogarth Press, 1953.

9. Janis, I. L. *Psychological stress.* New York: John Wiley and Sons, 1958.

10. Kaplan, D. M., and Mason, A. E. Maternal reactions to premature birth viewed as an acute emotional disorder. *Amer. J. Orthopsychiat.,* 1960, 30:539–52.

11. Klein, D. C., and Lindemann, E. Preventive intervention in individual and family crisis situations. In G. Caplan (Ed.), *Prevention of mental disorders in children.* New York: Basic Books, 1961. Pp. 283–306.

12. Lindemann, E. Symptomatology and management of acute grief. *Amer. J. Psychiat.* 1941, 101:141–48.

13. Ojemann, R. H. Investigations on the effects of teaching an understanding and appreciation of behavior dynamics. In G. Caplan (Ed.), *Prevention of mental disorders in children.* New York: Basic Books, 1961. Pp. 378–97.

14. Piaget, J. and Inhelder, B. *The growth of logical thinking.* New York: Basic Books, 1958.

15. Silber, E., Hamburg, D. A., *et al.* Adaptive behavior in competent adolescents: Coping with the anticipation of college. *Arch. Gen. Psychiat.,* 1961, 5:354–65.

35

A Nursery Center Program for
Preschool Mentally Retarded Children

ARTHUR J. BINDMAN AND LEWIS B. KLEBANOFF

IN August of 1957, the Division of Mental Hygiene of the Massachusetts Department of Mental Health initiated a nursery center program for preschool mentally retarded children—ages three to seven years—thus paralleling
the increase of institutional beds for preschool retarded with a community
oriented program (9).

This program was made possible by a special act of the legislature, which
provided for the establishment of "nursery clinics" for retarded children of
preschool age. The term "clinic" was used because this program was intended
to be much more comprehensive than a nursery school per se. Funds were
available for salaries of the following: one supervisor for the program, fourteen
nursery center teachers, one principal nursery teacher, four psychiatric social
workers, medical and nonmedical consultants, and clerical personnel. Funds
also allowed for the rental of quarters.

This program was the realization of years of effort on the part of the
Massachusetts groups concerned with retarded children. Formerly, the Division
of Mental Deficiency of the State Department of Mental Health was actively
engaged in a community program for retarded children. This service was
discontinued in 1954 when legislation established a new method of maintaining
special classes for retarded children in the public school systems. One consultant continued to work with local community groups involving small,
privately supported preschool programs for the retarded. This consultant's
services were also used in this new program.

Since the problems with which workers in Massachusetts were faced were
not unlike those faced by Kirk in Illinois, the thinking which lay behind the
Massachusetts program roughly paralleled his (6, 7) with several notable
exceptions. The Masssachusetts program was conceived as a service program
to meet a deeply felt community need to which research interests were, of
necessity, secondary. It was not limited to the educable mentally retarded, as
was Kirk's program.

Reprinted from *American Journal of Mental Deficiency,* 1959, *64,* 561–573, by per-
mission of the publisher and the authors. © 1959, American Association on Mental
Deficiency. Dr. Bindman is Regional Administrator for Mental Retardation, Massachu-
setts Department of Mental Health. Dr. Klebanoff is Deputy Assistant Commissioner for
Mental Retardation, Massachusetts Department of Mental Health and Adjunct Associate
Professor of Special Education, Boston University School of Education.

Plans for the new program included:

1. Services
    (a) to provide more adequte diagnosis and evaluation of these children before their acceptance into these nursery centers, through the use of pediatric, neurological, psychiatric, psychological, and social services, which contribute to a better understanding of each child and of his ability to profit from this program and other training programs in the future;
    (b) to provide a nursery setting for the preschool age retarded child where (under the supervision of a trained nursery school teacher), he will have the opportunity to acquire some basic training and greater socialization in preparation for special class;
    (c) to provide on-going parental counseling for the parents of these children on both a group and individual basis, to aid them in the better understanding of the development and social problems that these children may present.

2. Programming and Policies
    (a) to develop knowledge of the best techniques for aiding preschool retarded children make more adequate social adjustment, and thus become better prepared for special class or other school programs;
    (b) to define and delineate the types of children that will be included in this program, not only on the basis of need, but based on a scientific rationale where possible;
    (c) to develop closer coordination of community resources in order to provide the best possible medical and socio-psychological evaluation of each child who is presented for this program;
    (d) to develop the most efficient and useful method for providing parental counseling, wherein both parents and the total family group will be aided in their adjustment to the problems presented by the presence of a mentally retarded child;
    (e) to develop the best method of publicizing this program so that those parents in need of such services will use them, so that there will be an increasing interpretation of this program and of its benefits to the total community.

3. Evaluation
    (a) to develop methods of determining both the quality and quantity of these services and their impact upon the total problem of mental retardation;
    (b) to develop research methods which can be applied to this population in an attempt to increase our knowledge concerning this age group.

4. Recommendations
    (a) to the Commissioner of Mental Health through the Director of the Division of Mental Hygiene;
    (b) to the Massachusetts Association for Retarded Children and its

affiliated groups in order to enhance their knowledge of programs for retarded children so that they may develop their programs along the most productive lines.

PROGRAM DEVELOPMENT

The personnel provided in this program were to be distributed throughout Massachusetts in a way which would both enhance present programs under the auspices of local associations for retarded children, and also make possible the initiation of new programs. In addition, funds were provided for medical and non-medical consultation and rental of quarters. The consultation funds were to be used to provide pediatric and other specialized assessment of each child. A psychiatric and socio-psychological evaluation was to be made part of the services of the local program of the state and community co-sponsored area mental health centers for children. Four social workers were to be assigned to particular areas of the State. They would be stationed at mental health centers for children in a given locality. Since these centers operate somewhat autonomously and have varying in-take policies, it was expected that this arrangement would facilitate greater participation of the mental health center in mental retardation problems.

Through their local associations, parents of retarded children were expected to play a major role in the development of the program. Not only were they in the forefront in starting nursery programs of their own, but their knowledge of local conditions was expected to be of inestimable value in the development and successful completion of the program. A meeting was called in the early fall of 1957 with 27 presidents of local associations for retarded children, and the executive director of the Massachusetts Association for Retarded Children present. A poll was made and discussion was held concerning the role of the local associations and their preparation for taking part in such a program. A number of local associations had already started small classes of their own, and others were able to give a preliminary estimate of the number of children and families who might take part in this program in their community. After long and careful discussion it was felt that the money for rental of quarters would not be of great value to the program since there was too much "red tape" involved, and each rental had to be approved by at least four different departments of the State. It was felt that quarters that could meet high standards could be obtained for a small fee in local churches or other public buildings. The provision of these quarters then became the responsibility of the local association for retarded children with inspection and acceptance by the Department of Mental Health. The presidents agreed that quarters, supplies, and assistants to the nursery center program would be provided by the local association for retarded children. The Department of Mental Health would provide the nursery center teacher, social work assistance, consultants, and specialized testing equipment which might be needed in the assessment of the children, as

well as the overall direction and supervision for the professional program.
The development of an Advisory Committee for this program which would aid the Department in setting policy, in defining specific aspects of the program, and in providing technical assistance concerning ways of implementing plans, appeared to be essential. A committee was formed including: members of the State Departments of Mental Health and Public Health; representatives of the Massachusetts Association for Retarded Children; representatives of the Massachusetts Conference of Mental Health Associations; and professional persons with experience in the field of mental retardation and nursery training.

Some of the immediate problems, to which the Advisory Committee directed its attention, were as follows:

1. What are the basic standards for such a program?
   (a) Shall the nursery centers be run on a five-day-per-week basis or less?
   (b) What training should teachers have?
   (c) What should the physical setting be?
   (d) What are some of the limitations that should be placed on the nursery center population in terms of chronological age, mental age, degree of physical handicap?
2. How can diagnostic services be best provided as part of the mental health center program?
3. How can counseling services to the parents be best provided through extra social workers, as well as through augmentation of the present programs?
4. How can the diagnostic and nursery center program for preschool retarded children become part of the total community program on mental health, through the closer liaison between an area mental health association and local associations for retarded children?
5. What suggestions, which could be incorporated into the program from its inception, did the Advisory Committee have for research, evaluation, and follow-up?
6. What role could parents of retarded children play in enhancing the effectiveness of this program in relation to the official agencies (2)?
7. What type of curriculum would be best for the children who would be taking part in this program?

Many of these questions are answered below in the description of the program, while others still must be resolved.

PROGRAM ACHIEVEMENTS

The nursery center program for retarded children officially began in August, 1957, but it was not until October, 1957, that the first nursery class for these children was opened. Between October, 1957, and May, 1958, seventeen nursery classes were established in fourteen centers, utilizing the services of fourteen teachers, and involving 160 children. These nursery centers held classes either on a three-morning-per-week basis or on a five-morning-per-week basis with a maximum of 10–12 children per class. Most of the teachers were trained in early childhood education and generally had some experience with handicapped or mentally retarded children. They were hired by the Department of Mental Health and recruited from the local community wherever possible.

In those cases where there were state and community co-sponsored mental health centers for children, the center was asked to participate in the initiation, maintenance, and in such local administrative affairs of the nursery center program as providing diagnostic services or parent counseling services. Mental health center directors were also asked to involve themselves in the determination of the setting for the nursery center and in other matters pertaining to the program. In those instances where there were no community mental health centers for children, the state attempted to provide other consultant services which would take the place of the mental health center services. A general plan was to develop a local committee made up of representatives of the Association for Retarded Children (usually the president or his appointee), representatives from the local mental health center, and representatives from the State Department of Mental Health. There was a continuous effort by the Department to have the community view this program as a cooperative venture, with each doing his part in the development of a nursery clinic.

In general, professional supervision of the teachers came from the Department of Mental Health. Consultants developed their roles through the local mental health center, where such existed, or directly through the Department. The parents' groups were also involved, to some degree, in the screening of teachers and in suggesting names of consultants from the local community. This plan worked fairly well, although in some cases local associations were not well prepared to play their role and take responsibility for their portion of the program. This indefiniteness called for continual interpretation, clarification and discussion between the Department of Mental Health and the local association for retarded children.

The four social workers who were provided in this program were placed in three mental health centers throughout the state, with the fourth worker being assigned to a research project on mental retardation in one community. Most of the budget of this latter project was provided by the U.S. Children's Bureau, but it was felt that if the Department of Mental Health could participate in this research a more useful program could be developed in that community, both in regard to nursery clinic services as well as parent counseling services. Although the social workers were primarily assigned to this program to carry on parental counseling and evaluation of the children, their assignment as extra personnel to mental health centers for children made it incumbent upon the mental health center to provide more complete services for the mentally retarded child. It was later noted that this did increase participation in programming for the mentally retarded, although it was felt that the number of social workers was still inadequate since their services were necessary in many parts of the Common-wealth where there were no mental health centers. There also appeared to be a need to assign the social workers outside of their local mental health center geographical area for work in the field with parents of retarded children. Some local mental health centers began to provide group consultation to parents, and in some areas individual consultation was begun. Counseling organized as group or individual therapy with an orientation to the parents' emotional re-actions to having borne a retarded child met with considerable initial resistance. This resistance took various forms and stemmed from various sources. The old saw, "I don't want anyone to psychoanalyze me," was one form. Another was the feeling that their needs in this respect were being met by the Associa-tion for Retarded Children. This was more or less supported by those associa-tion people who had been filling a counseling role and were threatened by this new program.

The consultation funds for this program were used: (1) to develop the services of local consultants, such as pediatricians, psychologists, speech thera-pists, and others who might be of assistance in the better diagnosis and evalua-tion of the children in this program; (2) to provide therapeutic measures that were needed to give the children better physical care, and that training necessary to future placement in public school special classes. In general, the pediatri-cians provided weekly or bi-weekly consultation to the nursery center in order to aid in the health assessment and other factors which might be entering into the child's adjustment to the nursery class. This was not an altogether satis-factory arrangement for several reasons, the main reason being that there was no clear-cut understanding of what the pediatrician's role should be. Everyone agreed that it was desirable to have pediatricians involved in the program and they were, in effect, sent into the classes to see what would develop. Unfortu-nately, (due to the lack of role clarification) for the most part they could do little. A budgetary cutback in consultant funds for the second year necessitated a sharp reappraisal of this aspect of the program. The feeling remains that pediatric services are important to this program and must be integrated into it.

Speech therapists were also provided to several of the nursery centers ap-proximately once or twice a week. They gave both group and individual speech therapy. An adequate program is still to be developed in this area. Implemen-tation of the planning which is underway, and which is consistent with the material reported by Schneider and Vallon (10) depends on the availability of funds and personnel. The other consultants did psychological testing on a once-or-twice-per-week basis. They also made special studies, such as those in the area of neurology and aphasia, which will be reported more fully below.

PROGRAMMING AND POLICIES

The general policy of the partnership between the local association for re-tarded children and the State Department of Mental Health in developing a nursery center worked out well. Nursery center teachers were supervised by the Department of Mental Health and also received in-service training from the Department. In those cases where the local mental health centers played key roles in developing the program in their communities, this approach to the nursery center program seemed to provide the best type of total mental health and public health assistance to the mentally retarded children and their parents.

An important problem for program development was that of obtaining the services of qualified assistants to the teachers. The policy was formed that each teacher should have some assistance, particularly as the nursery center class became larger. The difficulty in securing voluntary aid was noted throughout the year. In some instances, local mental retardation associations had parents present in an anteroom or close to the class so as to provide assistance in case of emergencies—a practice which has been strongly discouraged at present. In other instances, practice teachers from local educational institutions were utilized. This latter approach served a dual purpose since at least two teachers entered the program upon completion of their training. It also interested the training institutions in the problem of developing nursery teachers to work in the area of mental retardation. Funds were not available from the Department of Mental Health to pay assistants, and few local associations for retarded children could provide money. The Department screened all assistants as to moral background and some minimal understanding of mentally retarded or severely handicapped children. Nevertheless, assistants varied greatly.

Once the program was begun, it was noted that children who entered these nursery centers and who were accepted simply on a basis of "slow mental development," as recommended by the Advisory Committee, were often not well evaluated from a psychological and physical point of view. It was the policy of this program to provide as much service as was necessary to understand the child in the program, and to provide for his training needs along with his social and emotional well being, so that he could make a smooth transition to public school special classes. After a review of a number of case records, it was felt most strongly that these children should have a careful physical and psychological evaluation, and this should be provided either through the utilization of local health services in the community or through development of new services. Careful thought was given to this matter. It was decided that the diagnostic assessment, particularly that of the psychologist, might be carried out through the local mental health center or through consulting psychologists in those communities where there were no mental health centers. The mental health centers or consulting pediatricians were asked to take over the intake records and maintain case records. The Department of Mental Health purchased psychological testing equipment which could be used for examining preschool and handicapped children. This equipment was provided for sixteen mental health centers and consulting psychologists. The mental health center psychological personnel were consulted concerning the type of psychological equipment that was needed. Other consultants were also queried. As a result, the equipment obtained was the best available for examining the young mentally retarded child. Very little testing was done during the initial period; toward the end of the first year some evaluations which were extremely helpful were made. It was expected that psychological evaluation would continue to be of great assistance to a more thorough understanding of these children and their level of functioning.

Standards for the program were developed in the past through the somewhat informal approach of the Massachusetts Department of Mental Health in its work with the nursery classes in the community. A more formal approach to the problem of standards was made by the publication of a booklet concerning day-care standards. This booklet was published by the Massachusetts Department of Public Health in cooperation with many other agencies. The Advisory Committee of this program reviewed the latter booklet and decided that the information contained in the day-care pamphlet, combined with the knowledge that was gained in working with mentally retarded children on a more informal basis, might be integrated to develop a more formalized set of standards for the operation of a nursery center program. A committee is currently at work rewriting these standards for specific application to this program.

If this program were to receive the interest of professional workers, in-service training, both for nursery center teachers and other participants in the program, was necessary. The teachers met almost monthly for discussion of class problems and other matters pertaining to their work. Orientation sessions for new teachers will be held in the future. In addition to visits to state hospitals the sessions will include presentations by specialists in the field of mental retardation. Library material and other educational materials have been ordered to help teachers gain a broader understanding of the problems of mentally retarded children. An institute for other professional personnel is being developed, so as to provide technical knowledge for psychologists, social workers, and physicians in the program, as well as for other participants from local mental health centers. Although there were a number of meetings at the start of the program to acquaint the mental health center directors with the policy and philosophy of the program, a need still remained for more intensive and specific training concerning methods of dealing with the problems of the mentally retarded.

It was noted throughout the year that well-trained professional workers often had unconscious or even conscious antipathy toward the problems of the mentally retarded, and in some instances, completely rejected their role in this program. In another case, however, professional workers in a local mental health center reacted negatively at first, but once they were in contact with the children and their parents, began to feel that this was valuable to the workers as a learning experience, and at the same time, a service to the parents. Continued interpretation, careful and consistent communication, and didactic sessions concerning the problems of mental retardation would seem to be needed in order to develop an interested and well-trained group of professional workers who are willingly concerned with these problems.

The curriculum of the nursery centers varied greatly from one center to another. Some nursery center teachers felt that children could take part in stimulating activity without becoming unduly disturbed or overactive. In other instances, teachers were rigid and concerned with simply "socializing" the hyperactive, or what they felt to be the highly anti-social, retarded child. Much time was spent by the supervisor of the program and by the principal teacher in attempting to help them gain an understanding of each child and the way in which he functions. Also difficult, was the problem of heterogeneity within the class and the psychological implications of dealing with severely brain-damaged or severely disturbed children. Helpful information in this regard was found in outlines by Haeussermann (5), Strazzulla (13) and Wortis (15).

Since the age range was great, and since the children varied greatly in terms of diagnosis, some children were able to gain much from the nursery center program in terms of educational attainment, while others did not. This often resulted in mothers talking among themselves and making a number of comparisons between children which, in the long run, led to misunderstanding and disturbance on the part of some parents. This required the careful interpretation by the nursery center teacher, as she defined what the parents' expectations might be from the child's attendance at the nursery center.

The time of the teacher was divided. Though the major portion was taken up in the nursery center, some was spent on the maintenance of progress reports, home visits and home training of special children, and in intensive work with individual children at the nursery center. The teacher could thus provide some counseling to the parents concerning their role in aiding the child to develop to his maximum capacity. The teachers themselves needed much assistance in understanding parent-child relationships, particularly where this relationship was disturbed. Only through a well-devised in-service program can the nursery teacher be trained to adequately perform her many-faceted role.

Evaluation and research were somewhat slow in getting under way due to the many and varied problems of community organization and program development that first needed to be overcome. This aspect of the total program has begun to develop methods of evaluating both the quality of these services and their impact upon the total problem of mental retardation.

One mental health program began a special research project to evaluate the types of testing that might be used to further aid in the understanding of the child's level of functioning, as well as to offer a new approach in the evaluation of aphasic problems in the mentally retarded. The result of this research has been so interesting and promising that an effort is being made to develop it into a large scale research program in which all of the mentally retarded children in the nursery center program will be involved.

A number of centers have also been interested in the problem of group consultation with parents of retarded children and hope to use this as a basis for research in the very important area of methods for aiding the mentally retarded and their parents.

Another program of evaluation and research is being developed in close coordination with the Massachusetts General Hospital and its Child Psychiatry Unit. The Department of Mental Health has worked closely with the Child

Psychiatry Unit and has obtained the part-time services of a psychiatrist, psychologist, and social worker. This team is housed in a separate unit and plans to screen all the referrals in the Greater Boston area in order to determine how much of an evaluation has already been made, by what agencies or practitioners, and what needs to be done. It is also expected that this will be the basis for research into the various aspects of etiology and prognosis of mental retardation problems. This appears to be a very useful and positive step, in that the relationship with the Massachusetts General Hospital will provide specialized pediatric and neurological techniques which could be most useful for a careful evaluation and study of the children and their parents. In essence, the latter is a service-oriented aspect of the total program but it is also oriented toward research and evaluative techniques.

PROBLEMS

PARENT COUNSELING

As mentioned above, parent counseling services were to be developed through social workers assigned to cover various areas of the Commonwealth. After careful consideration it was decided that a better approach might be the assignment of social workers to a number of mental health centers in which they could either work directly with the mentally retarded and their parents, or have others in the center become active in the provision of these services. However, there were still some geographical areas of the state where parents of young retarded children did not know where to turn in order to resolve the many problems which faced them concerning placement and educational facilities for their children. They often felt frustrated when they did not have individual or group sessions under trained professional leadership for more careful discussion and follow-up of their problems. The Department of Mental Health decided that social workers assigned to this program should give assistance in geographical areas outside of their mental health center area, and that in the future, new social workers would be assigned to each mental health center in the state.

The problem of parent counseling appears frequently in the literature (1, 3, 4, 8, 11, 12, 14,) with no marked unanimity of opinion regarding the best approach. In the Massachusetts program it was felt that the social workers employed should be well-trained and experienced psychiatric social workers. In order to recruit the most able workers and also to involve the entire mental health team in the program, it was thought best to assign the extra workers to a mental health center for general duty, with the director having the responsibility of servicing the nursery center program from among his entire staff. It was hoped that workers who would refuse full time assignments in the area of mental retardation would not too strenuously object to a few hours per week and might indeed, from this exposure, become interested in the problem. This is just what occurred in many instances.

A problem has arisen in this regard which is currently under consideration. Some opinion has been expressed that a psychologist might be a more appropriate extra staff member for this program. It is felt that many parents wish to have their primary working relationships with the person who has examined their child and that this fact provides a ready opportunity for the development of a helpful relationship. It is hoped that it will be possible to offer a choice of personnel to the local mental health center so that they may select whichever discipline would best fit into their program at the particular time.

DIAGNOSTIC SERVICES

Diagnostic services and other evaluative services for the preschool mentally retarded child were not fully developed, although some mental health centers had begun to provide special services of this nature to each child who was a potential applicant for a nursery center. Thus, one mental health center began by having each parent seen individually by a social worker on the staff, and each child tested by the psychologist and given a diagnostic interview by a psychiatrist. This resulted in the initiation of a very good diagnostic program with careful attention and follow-up for both the child and for his parents. In the long run parents were to be seen on an individual and on a group basis by members of the mental health center staff. Diagnosis and counseling with families are closely interrelated. Problems of staffing mentioned above apply here also.

There were still a large number of communities in which nursery centers for retarded children had been established but which did not have local area mental health centers. These communities could rely only on diagnostic services as developed through consulting pediatricians who served as a "clearing house" for the coordinating of medical, psychological and other pertinent information. The question of whether a pediatrician has the time or is the best qualified person for this coordination remained unresolved. It was felt that, in time, local mental health centers would become more involved in the program and would provide additional consulting aid to the nursery centers. Suggestions were made by the Advisory Committee that consultants might be housed in community agencies, such as local community hospitals. This might be one way the Department of Mental Health could support new diagnostic and follow-up services for the mentally retarded, and at the same time provide local hospitals with an added service with very little additional cost to themselves. In the long run, every nursery center should be closely related to a local mental health center, to a community diagnostic and follow-up service in a community setting, or to a local professional person who would act to provide the necessary services through the coordination of other consultants. In general, the Department of Mental Health felt that the best policy would be the provision of services on a local, autonomous basis in order to involve the interest of as many agencies as possible in the problems of mental retardation.

ASSISTANTS

Asssistants in the nursery centers varied greatly although all were screened by the Department of Mental Health. In some cases, they were student teachers from local nursery training institutions; in other cases, they were volunteers with various training in their background; in still other cases, they were partially-trained persons who were paid by the local associations for retarded children.

Various problems arose: (1) Some teachers in the nursery centers felt very strongly that it was important for the assistant to consider herself as a part of the program, and that this could be accomplished more readily if she received some financial recompense. (2) Where adequately trained assistants were not provided, teachers were often inundated by problems of hyperactivity or other control problems on the part of their children, which might have been alleviated by assistants. (3) Because of a lack of funds assistants did not know their important role in the program and frequently did not feel they had to take part on a continuing basis. (4) On many occasions there were no adults to ride with the person who transported the children to provide the additional adult management and protection necessary.

A number of associations for retarded children requested assistants for this program through the use of State funds. They felt that if the assistant and the teacher were provided by the State, both would have their work carefully supervised and controlled through the Department of Mental Health, and each would have a greater stake in the program. As a result, it was strongly recommended by the supervisor of this program that paid assistants be provided on an hourly basis to aid the nursery teachers. It is hoped that in the future this will come about, resulting in a more integrated and better trained nursery center leadership.

TRANSPORTATION

Transportation problems in this program were very great. In some instances, the local association for retarded children did a remarkable job of providing transportation, either through taxicabs or other means, while on the other hand, there were reports of children who were unable to get to the nursery center because of a lack of transportation. Time after time the question arose whether the Department of Mental Health could become involved in providing transportation. Various methods were explored, but it was felt that the Department could not provide transportation for this program because of problems of liability, and further, because of the general policy that this was not the type of function in which the Department could become involved. The Advisory Committee to this program, the Massachusetts Association for Retarded Children, and the Legislative Commission on Mental Retardation were all asked to explore this problem, namely, the tremendous financial burden that is placed upon the local associations for retarded children. It is hoped that in time some reimbursement formula might be worked out in which local associations would receive some assistance in providing a better method of transportation for the children.

SUPERVISORY PERSONNEL

The nursery center program for the retarded child developed very rapidly. By July, 1958, the end of the first year, there were seventeen classes with fourteen teachers. In the fall of 1958, it was expected that there would be as many as 25 classes, and a projected budget for fiscal 1960 suggested there should be as many as 29 nursery center teachers employed, with as many as 35–40 nursery centers. This projection was based upon many contacts with community associations for retarded children, and in most instances, was strongly based on facts about the number of potentially eligible children in the community. There will be need for a large number of well-trained nursery teachers who have had experience with the mentally retarded child. The large number of teachers, consultants, and other participants in this program require continued contact, supervision, and in-service training. It was felt that the Department of Mental Health central office staff could utilize other supervisory personnel, such as an educational coordinator in order to better implement the development of the program and maintain a high level of service. For example, the supervision of the teachers was undertaken by one individual, but it was difficult to maintain continuous contact with the many teachers in the centers, and at the same time to handle the problems of a burgeoning program. As the program rapidly developed, it was felt that intensive liaison must be maintained between the Department of Mental Health, the local mental health center, the local association for retarded children, and consultant personnel. Other important aspects of the program, such as research and in-service training, often had to be placed in the background because of the lack of personnel who would be able to carry out the day-to-day relationships which are so important, particularly in a program of this type. Therefore, it was recommended that at least two to three special supervisory personnel be added to the program's central staff, two of these being educational coordinators for the teachers, and the third being a supervisory speech therapist who might work very closely with the speech therapy consultants in the program. The area mental health center directors who would be assigned extra social workers, would have their work coordinated through the Director of the Division of Mental Hygiene, and through the supervisor of the community mental retardation program. In the long run, as mentioned above, a program of such scope must develop on a local level, with local support and with local assistants, but with technical aid, supervision, and consultation provided by the State Department of Mental Health.

SUMMARY

The first year of the development of a state-supported nursery center program for preschool mentally retarded children has been described. This program had many aims, not the least of which were services for both retarded children and their parents, and an attempt to develop evaluative and research techniques in regard to the preschool mentally retarded child. The following problems remain to be adequately resolved: (1) obtaining necessary professional personnel and assistants, (2) providing transportation, (3) developing community support, (4) obtaining background information about preschool mentally retarded children and their parents, and (5) assisting the many persons involved. Suggestions for improving the program through paid nursery center assistants, more social work services and parental counseling, better methods of diagnosis, more careful supervision and in-service training, and ways to improve transportation are mentioned. The program is expected to continue to develop on a local level with overall technical assistance and standards provided by the State Department of Mental Health.

REFERENCES

1. Begab, M. J. Factors in counseling parents of retarded children. *Amer. J. Ment. Def.,* 1956, 60:515–24.
2. Bostock, N. L. How can parents and professionals coordinate for the betterment of all retarded children? *Amer. J. Ment. Def.,* 1956, 60:428–32.
3. Gordon, E. W., and Uleman, M. Reactions of parents to problems of mental retardation in children. *Amer. J. Ment. Def.,* 1956, 61: 158–63.
4. Grebler, A. M. Parental attitudes toward mentally retarded children. *Amer. J. Ment. Def.,* 1952, 56: 475–83.
5. Haeussermann, E. Estimating developmental potential of pre-school children with brain lesions. *Amer. J. Ment. Def.,* 1956, 61:170–80.
6. Kirk, S. A. A project for pre-school mentally handicapped children. *Amer. J. Ment. Def.,* 1950, 54:305–10.
7. Kirk, S. A. Experiments in the early training of the mentally retarded. *Amer. J. Ment. Def.,* 1952, 56:692–700.
8. Klebanoff, L. B. A comparison of parental attitudes of mothers of schizophrenic, brain-injured, retarded, and normal children. *Amer. J. Orthopsychiat.,* 1959, 29:445–54.
9. Pense, A. W. The problem of the pre-school mentally deficient child. *Amer. J. Ment. Def.,* 1947, 52:168–71.

10. Schneider, B. and Vallon, J. A speech therapy program for mentally retarded children. *Amer. J. Ment. Def.,* 1954, 58:633–39.
11. Sheimo, S. L. Problems in helping parents of mentally defective and handicapped children. *Am. J. Ment. Def.,* 1951, 56:42–47.
12. Stern, E. M. Problems of organizing parents' groups. *Amer. J. Ment. Def.,* 1951, 56:11–17.
13. Strazzulla, M. Nursery school training for retarded children. *Amer. J. Ment. Def.,* 1956, 61:141–51.
14. Weingold, J. T. Parents' groups and the problem of mental retardation. *Amer. J. Ment. Def.,* 1952, 56:484–92.
15. Wortis, J. A Note on the concept of the brain-injured child. *Amer. J. Ment. Def.,* 1956, 61:204–6.

36

Some Major Issues in Developing Community Services for Persons with Drinking Problems

THOMAS F. A. PLAUT

WHAT prompts major American mental health agencies to focus attention on alcohol problems at this time? There is an increasing awareness of the magnitude of these problems and of the very sizable number of persons with drinking problems seen by many agencies—psychiatric as well as non-psychiatric. In addition there is a growing realization that neither mental health programs nor other "helping" services have taken a substantial leadership role in providing care and treatment for these patients.

In recent years psychiatry and allied mental health professions have shown signs of overcoming their traditional lack of concern about alcohol problems. In February, 1965, the American Psychiatric Association issued its first position statement in this area—"Concerning Responsibility of Psychiatrists and Other Physicians for Alcohol Problems." The establishment of a National Center for the Prevention and Control of Alcoholism within the National Institute of Mental Health indicates both an awareness that additional governmental activity is required and that mental health professions (and agencies) should be in the forefront of such activities. This National Center, while administratively part of the National Institute of Mental Health, is to be the focal point for federal programs in the Public Health Service and within the Department of Health, Education and Welfare that bear on alcohol problems. In addition, it is likely to be the principal focus for all federal government activities in this area.

The initial reports of the Cooperative Commission on the Study of Alcoholism will be published in the Fall. This major five-year project, supported by a grant from the National Institute of Mental Health, has undertaken a broad examination of many aspects of American alcohol problems. The policy volume from this Commission will urge that community mental health programs take a major role at the local level in the developing and strengthening of treatment services for persons with drinking problems. Also forthcoming in

Reprinted from a paper prepared for the Surgeon General's Conference with the Mental Health Authorities, Washington, D.C., 1966, by permission of the author. Dr. Plaut is Assistant Chief, National Center for Prevention and Control of Alcoholism, National Institute of Mental Health.

1967 is a report by the Joint Information Service (of the American Psychiatric Association and the National Association for Mental Health) on a study of psychiatric treatment services for problem drinkers.

These varied approaches all emphasize that psychiatric personnel and agencies should mobilize their own resources, and those of other agencies, to deal more effectively with alcohol problems. During the recently-completed nationwide mental health planning activities, twenty-two states established separate alcoholism committees or task forces. However, over half of the states did not administratively identify this as a separate area for study. Even among the twenty-two states singling out this problem, in the majority of instances little or no effort was made to integrate the planning of alcoholism services with that of other mental health services. In too many states the "alcoholism planning" was left to individuals, often narrow in their orientation, who were unable to take advantage of this opportunity to bring the care and treatment of problem drinkers more into the mainstream of psychiatric services and of other community agencies. The recent passage by the 89th Congress of the Comprehensive Health Planning and Public Health Services Amendments of 1966 (PL 89–749) provide another opportunity to overcome the continued isolation and disregard of alcohol problems. Under these amendments the federal government will meet 100 per cent of the costs of statewide health planning activities during the two fiscal years ending June 30, 1968. This comprehensive health planning is to take advantage of and build upon already existing state plans—including the mental health planning activities referred to above. There then is a challenge for all health medical care agencies to ensure that appropriate attention is given to alcohol problems in the development of these state plans—and it is likely that leadership in this regard often will need to be provided by the state mental health authorities.

Six major topics that will be discussed in this paper are listed below. They include a number of issues that should be dealt with in developing and planning community services for persons with drinking problems:

1. Magnitude and Impact of Problem Drinking.
2. Understanding the Low Priority of Services to Problem Drinkers.
3. The Nature of Current Services for Persons with Drinking Problems.
4. Specialized or Integrated Services.
5. The Role of General Helping Agencies.
6. The Role of Community Mental Health Programs.

American attitudes toward drunkenness and toward drinking continue to influence and complicate efforts to develop effective alcoholism programs. These attitudes, including the accompanying ambivalence and residuals of the Prohibition controversy, must be understood and dealt with if progress is to be made in mobilizing professional interest and activity in this area.

THE MAGNITUDE AND IMPACT OF PROBLEM DRINKERS ON PSYCHIATRIC AND OTHER AGENCIES

Large numbers of problem drinkers are in contact with various helping agencies. While these persons often are identified as problem drinkers, in many instances they receive little or no treatment for their drinking problems.

The impact of problem drinkers on major American care-giving agencies is illustrated by the following statistics. In 1964, there were slightly under 70,000 first admissions of male patients to the nearly 300 state mental hospitals in the U.S. Over 15,000 patients, approximately 22 per cent, were given a diagnosis of alcoholism at the time of their admission (12, pt. 2, p. 21). Among women patients the proportion with alcoholic diagnoses was much lower— only 5.6 per cent. Because problem drinkers generally have a short duration of stay in mental hospitals (in California averaging less than two months), the proportion of *resident patients* with an alcoholic diagnosis is far lower— generally under 6 per cent of all patients.

In nine states, alcoholic disorders lead all other diagnoses in mental hospital admissions. Maryland, for example, reports that 40 per cent of all male admissions are for alcoholism (17). There is substantial variation among states in the proportion of male admissions with an alcoholism diagnosis. Some examples of the percentages for different states are: Louisiana 25 per cent, Maine 12 per cent, Ohio 19 per cent, Oklahoma 5 per cent, Pennsylvania 14 per cent, Tennessee 21 per cent, and Virginia 26 per cent (12, pt. 2, p. 21). The majority of these patients are not psychotic, and in many states most are admitted on a voluntary rather than a committed basis. Most still have some ties to their families, and the majority are upper-lower class or lower-middle class.

The number of psychiatric wards in general hospitals is rapidly increasing, and currently more patients are admitted annually to these wards than to the state mental hospitals. The proportion of patients who are alcoholic is virtually identical to the figure for mental hospitals. In 1964, 22 per cent of the men and 5.9 per cent of the women discharged from community-based psychiatric facilities were diagnosed as "alcoholic" (12, pt. 3, p. 41). Here too there was substantial variation from state to state. Some examples of the per cent of all patients discharged from the psychiatric wards of general hospitals who had an alcoholic diagnosis are the following: California 34 per cent, Illinois 15 per cent, Iowa 19 per cent, Minnesota 29 per cent, Michigan 35 per cent, and New York 20 per cent. In these facilities too, the duration of stay for alcoholic patients is short—often lasting for only a few days, i.e., until the "detoxification" is completed.

Over 550,000 adult patients are seen each year in general psychiatric clinics (3). While the proportion of these patients diagnosed as alcoholics is very small, only 3 per cent to 4 per cent, the total number is between 15,000 and 25,000 (2, 3). Here too there is variation between states. In California, for example, where local alcoholism clinics are supported by funds from the

State Department of Mental Health, only 1.1 per cent of the patients admitted to outpatient mental health clinics were diagnosed as alcoholic (4). In Maryland the comparable figure was 7 per cent—with an additional 10 per cent being found to have the "symptoms of excessive drinking," but not having been given an alcoholism diagnosis (1). It is interesting to note that the total number of patients seen annually by the approximately 140 specialized alcoholism clinics probably also is under 25,000.

The impact of problem drinkers on the medical-surgical wards of general hospitals is illustrated by a study in which the extent of drinking problems among one hundred consecutive male admissions to a general hospital was determined. No pre-selection was made in terms of the diagnosis of the patients, and the hospital did not have a psychiatric service. The admitting physicians identified twelve of the one hundred men as problem drinkers, and seventeen additional cases of "probable alcoholism" were uncovered by the researcher, making a total of 29 per cent (13). Case-finding of problem drinkers in this population is then relatively easy.

The relation between economic dependency and drinking problems has been much discussed. However, only a few studies have been made of the incidence of drinking problems in welfare case-loads, and there is little information on the causal relation between the problem drinking and dependency. Problem drinking is found in a sizable proportion—estimates range from 10 per cent to 25 per cent—of the families of welfare recipients (10, 11, 16, 18).

Many arrests involve alcohol-related offenses. The impact of problem drinking on the American police-legal system is graphically illustrated by the following figures. In 1965, out of close to 5,000,000 arrests in the U.S. for all offenses, over 1,535,000 were for public drunkenness (31 per cent). In addition, there were over 250,000 arrests for driving while intoxicated. Another 490,000 individuals were charged with disorderly conduct—which some communities use in lieu of the public drunkenness charge. Thus at least 40 per cent of all arrests are for being drunk in a public place or being "under the influence" while driving (7). Two words of caution must be added here. First, many persons arrested for public drunkenness are no more intoxicated than countless other individuals who escape arrest because they are not exposed and "vulnerable" to police detection as are "skid row" men. The public is more likely to insist on the police removing the unshaven, toothless, poorly clothed men than an equally drunk visiting business man! Second, it is not known what proportion of persons arrested for public drunkenness would be considered as having chronic drinking problems. In any case, it appears likely that various health agencies—including mental health programs—will in the future be asked to take more responsibility for the care of some of these persons—particularly those defined as "suffering from chronic alcoholism." [1]

---

[1] Two court decisions are of particular importance in relation to this question: *Driver vs. Durham, N.C.* (U.S. Fourth Circuit Court of Appeals), January 23, 1966; and *Easter vs. The District of Columbia* (U.S. Court of Appeals for the District of Columbia), March 30, 1966, bar the criminal punishment of alcoholics for the "offense" of public drunkenness.

Professional workers in various helping fields frequently find many problem drinkers among their cases. Public health nurses, social workers in family agencies, welfare workers, physicians in the emergency wards of general hospitals, parole and probation workers, clergymen and lawyers report that problem drinking is one of the most frequent medical-social problems they encounter in their day-to-day work. All—or nearly all—of these problem drinkers need help of one sort or another and most behave in ways that cause concern to others and to some part of the community.

Despite the widespread occurrence of problem drinking, and the substantial contact that most persons in helping positions have with problem drinkers, there has been only very limited provision of adequate assistance to these men and women. The problem drinker often creates bafflement, confusion and other mixed feelings not only in those with whom he is closely associated, but also in those who have some opportunity and responsibility to help him.

LOW PRIORITY OF ASSISTANCE TO PROBLEM DRINKERS

In view of the large numbers of problem drinkers in the U.S. and the extent to which these people are among the clientele of virtually all helping agencies, there has been strikingly little focus on this area by the major professional associations. Psychiatric, medical, social service, or public welfare agencies generally also have not taken the responsibility for ensuring appropriate attention to these patients. For example, despite substantial improvement in recent years, medical care for the acute effects of excessive drinking still leaves much to be desired. The fact that a man's condition is due to the intake of large amounts of alcohol has a great impact on how he is handled by hospitals—or by physicians in private practice. One of the factors influencing the medical care is the appearance and "stance" of patients as they present themselves to the physician (19).

However, the neglect of the behavioral aspects, i.e., the drinking problem itself, is even more striking. Few physicians are interested in or feel qualified to help a patient overcome his drinking problem. The same can be said of psychiatrists, who often believe that problem drinkers cannot be helped by the same methods used for other psychiatric patients. Problem drinkers constitute only a tiny fraction of total case loads in psychiatric clinics. While few clinics have explicit policies excluding problem drinkers, generally the staff felt unable to help these patients, and as a result, most alcoholic patients get "screened out." Other community agencies, often aware of the lack of interest in psychiatric clinics, do not make referrals. Psychiatric wards of general hospitals rarely admit and never seek out alcoholic patients who have been treated for acute illness in these same hospitals. Most mental hospitals are ambivalent in their attitude towards the many problem drinkers admitted to their wards. The short duration of stay and frequent absence of any real treatment for these patients are indicative of this attitude.

Let us compare the reaction of mental hospital staff to three patients. The first is a schizophrenic man admitted to the hospital for the third time in a two-year period. The staff will be concerned about him, will wonder how the treatment could be improved this time. Second is a man admitted for the third time in the same period because of a suicide attempt. Again the hospital staff will be concerned, but also puzzled, perhaps a bit disappointed, and they may consider keeping the man in the hospital longer. The third returning patient is a problem drinker. Here, the reaction is more likely to be one of irritation, anger, and even punitiveness. Comparison with the suicidal patient is particularly instructive, because "self-inflicted" elements also are clearly present in that condition. However, the negative reaction to the alcoholic patient is likely to be far stronger—and less sympathetic.

Until very recently—and it is still substantially true—there were three major stepchildren of the mental health field. Many persons are affected by these three problems and all are areas where psychosocial understanding is needed in care treatment. The three "conditions" are (1) mental retardation; (2) problems of old age; and (3) problem drinkers. And there probably is more potential for interrupting destructive life styles and improving social functioning among problem drinkers than with either of the other two conditions. Thus it is all the more striking that mental health professionals and mental health agencies generally have shied away from giving leadership in the care and treatment of these patients.

UNDERSTANDING THE LOW PRIORITY OF SERVICES TO PROBLEM DRINKERS

Individual and institutional responses to problem drinking cannot be understood without examining certain characteristics of "normal" American drinking practices. Alcohol use in our society is surrounded with many ambivalent attitudes and ambiguous norms. Serving drinks is an intrinsic part of being a good host—in contemporary hospitality patterns. Yet it is unclear how much one should drink, and considerable guilt and discomfort may accompany over-drinking. Drinking is associated with pleasure, with indulgence of impulses in a culture that still retains strong elements of an older ethic stressing the importance of hard work, of self-control, and of personal responsibility. Drunkenness generally is disapproved. Many people react with disgust to it—especially in situations where they feel it is entirely inappropriate. Because most Americans get pleasure from their drinking, and are able to control it adequately, there is a tendency to feel that the problem drinker should also be able to control his drinking. The uncertain reactions to drunkenness point up the lack of clearly defined standards in relation to the use of alcoholic beverages. Less dramatic, but in some ways more significant, are signs of this uncertainty evidenced by the frequent jokes about drinking. Expressions such as "sneak a quick one" and "have a blast" suggest an immaturity or mild guilt feeling which rarely accompanies socially accepted behavior.

The complicated feelings that most Americans have about their own and other persons' use of beverage alcohol probably have delayed the development of more adequate services for problem drinkers. Despite the increasing awareness that problem drinkers need help, there remains a strong belief that the condition is self-inflicted, i.e., that the man could stop his destructive drinking if he "really" wanted to. The heritage of prohibition and the long history of moral and religious controversy about drinking have contributed to the mixed attitudes of laymen as well as professionals towards persons with drinking problems. The polarity between "wet" and "dry" positions still exerts a major influence. Both problem drinkers and those responsible for their care participate to some extent in the deeply-based confusion of feelings about drinking and problem drinking that is characteristic of our culture as a whole.

Further difficulty has been created by the confusion of the medical and behavioral aspects of the condition. Because problem drinkers may require medical attention for immediate (or long-term) consequences of drinking, there is a tendency to stress the importance of medical management to the exclusion of psycho-social management. This is demonstrated in the almost universal isolation, at least in the U.S., of detoxification services from services of a psycho-social nature. Some physicians, as well as laymen, have sought to define alcoholism as a disease or illness in the classical medical sense rather than as a psychiatric problem or behavior disorder. Many members of Alcoholics Anonymous, at least in the past, have been quite reluctant to focus on the emotional and psycho-social aspects of problem drinking.

For many years it was believed that problem drinkers could not be helped; that their recovery was impossible. While there is increasing evidence that this negative view is not justified, strong pessimism still remains about helping problem drinkers. The residual feelings that problem drinking is a self-inflicted condition, that inability to control one's drinking is a sign of moral weakness or inadequacy also influences reactions to "successful" and "unsuccessful" cases. The latter are vividly recalled and the former may be quickly forgotten. The "slips" of problem drinkers are far more likely to be considered evidence of failure than are comparable setbacks of other patients. The setting of unrealistic goals, i.e., expecting almost immediate total abstinence, has added to feelings of pessimism about helping these patients. Further, the cultural ambivalence undoubtedly often has made it more difficult for therapists to develop appropriate "helping relationships" with these patients and this has increased the number of "failures." Finally, many problem drinkers do present difficult therapeutic challenges—this, however, is true also of other psychiatric patients, especially those generally referred to as "character disorders." Some psychiatric workers with experience in treating problem drinkers feel that viewing the drinking problem primarily as a symptom of other underlying psychological difficulties has made more difficult the treatment of these patients. There is, however, no unanimity in this view.

Large numbers of problem drinkers have, of course, been helped by professional agencies, by psychiatrists, by other physicians and by Alcoholics

Anonymous. In addition, there are persons who had serious drinking problems for a number of years and then stopped having difficulty with alcohol, even in the absence of assistance from either A.A. or any professional source of help. Such spontaneous recoveries, of course, are not unknown in the field of general psychiatry either. The continued persistence of pessimistic views about the treatment of problem drinkers, in the face of considerable evidence to the contrary, demonstrates the tenacity of public and professional ambivalence about alcohol use and abuse.

CURRENT SERVICES FOR PERSONS WITH DRINKING PROBLEMS

Emergency Medical Care

There are six principal settings in which the acute consequences of excessive alcohol intake are managed: (1) medical and emergency services of general hospitals; (2) psychiatric wards of general hospitals; (3) special detoxification facilities; (4) mental hospitals; (5) patients' homes or doctors' offices by private physicians; and (6) jails or other "holding facilites." The avoidance of delirium tremens and the treatment of lesser withdrawal symptoms is the objective of such care. Because this emergency medical care is now rather well understood it is all the more shocking that preventable deaths of severely intoxicated persons still occur.

Large numbers of acutely intoxicated persons appear at or are brought to the emergency services of voluntary and municipal general hospitals. Here they may wait long periods of time before receiving care; accident victims and other patients often receive priority. Many hospitals are reluctant to admit intoxicated persons, particularly if they are medically indigent, to the general medical wards unless this is required as a life-saving measure. The treatment provided in general hospitals usually is very limited; rarely are any attempts made to deal with the drinking problem or to develop a plan for the patient's continuing treatment. Referrals to psychiatry or social service departments or to other community agencies—including A.A.—are infrequent.

Patients with alcohol intoxication account for close to 20 per cent of all male admissions in the psychiatric services of many general hospitals. The average duration of stay is extremely short—less than one week. A few patients are transferred to state mental hospitals, but most are released directly to the community without any plans for aftercare or continuing treatment. Patient care usually consists exclusively of sedation and drugs to manage the detoxification and to handle any agitated behavior that might occur. Psychiatric care directed at the underlying drinking problem rarely is provided.

State mental hospitals often admit patients with "alcohol intoxication" as the major diagnosis. In some hospitals such patients account for over 20 per cent of all male first admissions. However, there is great variation both between states and within states in the policy of mental hospitals regarding the admission of intoxicated patients. Some hospital superintendents feel that detoxification is primarily a nonpsychiatric responsibility and should be undertaken by general hospitals rather than psychiatric institutions; others view the mental hospital as the patient's last resource and are more open in their admissions policy. Duration of stay in mental hospitals for these patients is relatively short, except in hospitals with special alcoholism units. (See below) Generally little effort is made to involve the patient in any kind of a continuing treatment program and many leave the hospital almost as soon as the medical crisis has passed. Planning for aftercare and referral to community agencies occurs only very rarely.

More men are "dried out" in jails than in all other kinds of facilities combind. While not all men arrested for drunkenness require medical care, even superficial screening is only rarely provided. Each year most large cities have several deaths of intoxicated persons in the jail. Even if the recent District Court decisions on public drunkenness are applied on a nationwide basis, there will still be an urgent need to provide alternative means of caring for indigent intoxicated persons. The "street-cleaning" function in relation to public drunkenness is likely to remain in police hands for years to come.

The actual medical management of alcohol intoxication, while requiring experience and skill, is not a task of overwhelming difficulty. Some hospitals have treated thousands of cases without any deaths that can be attributed to the alcohol intoxication itself. Most of the deaths occurring in jails and hospitals are preventable: that they nevertheless occur is a severe indictment of both the medical profession and community leaders who permit these conditions to persist. The lack is not in medical or technical knowledge, but in necessary organizational skills and institutional arrangements.

All detoxification services should undertake diagnostic assessment of their patients. Treatment of drinking problems or referral to appropriate community resources should be an integral part of such services. It may be preferable for this type of acute medical care to be offered through general hospitals, but in any case, the care should be closely tied in with these hospitals and with community-based psychiatric services, i.e., community mental health centers.

Inpatient Care

State mental hospitals are the major setting providing residential treatment directed at altering the patient's drinking behavior. Very large numbers of men and women with drinking problems are admitted annually to state mental hospitals. Approximately five times as many men as women patients have such a diagnosis. Nearly half of the patients are between the ages of 45 and 64, and almost half are admitted on a voluntary rather than a committed basis.

While most of the state mental hospitals still provide only minimal treatment, other than medical detoxification, for patients with drinking problems, over 10 per cent of these hospitals now have special alcoholism wards or programs. Some of these programs provide very good care and treatment for problem drinkers. The stimulus for the development of such special programs has been varied—usually the interest of one member of the hospital staff has provided the original incentive; state mental health departments have only rarely taken the leadership role in initiating the alcoholism programs. The three most frequently used "therapeutic approaches" are: (1) didactic lectures, discussions and movies; (2) group psychotherapy; and (3) A.A. meetings. On most wards the staff encourage patients to continue informal discussions about their drinking problems outside of these group meetings. The widespread use of didactic procedures is based on the belief that a problem drinker needs to have an intellectual understanding of the condition from which he suffers: that with such an understanding the patient can consciously exert substantial control over his drinking. These approaches also are seen as a means of increasing the patient's motivation for help.

Therapeutic community and milieu therapy concepts are applied in many alcoholism wards. The morale of both patient and staff often is high—there is a spirit of mutual cooperation and a belief that patients can receive help from the staff and from one another. As is true in most general mental hospital wards, intensive individual psychotherapy is not regularly used. In part this is because of the shortage of personnel, but, in addition, it reflects the professional opinion that individual psychotherapy is not appropriate for many of these patients.

Many of the alcoholism wards use sedatives and tranquilizers during the first days or week of the patient's stay in the unit. Vitamin injections also often are given to help build up the patients physically. Generally, however, the hospital staff seeks to have the patients entirely free of medication long before release from the hospital.

A most serious shortcoming of the mental hospital alcoholism programs is the almost total absence of aftercare and follow-up activities. Rarely are arrangements made for patients to continue treatment with a community agency after their release from the hospital. The hospital staff does not have time for this type of work; it may not even be familiar with the few community resources that do exist. Collaboration with public welfare (and vocational rehabilitation) agencies is increasing. Some units also try to place patients in contact with A.A. groups in their home community prior to release from the hospital.

In many hospitals with alcoholism programs only minimal use is made of the other hospital services—psychology, social service, vocational rehabilitation, occupational therapy, recreational therapy, religious counselling, etc. In addition, psychiatric residents, psychology interns, social work students and nursing trainees often are not assigned to the alcoholism wards. This reflects both the isolation of the alcoholism programs from the rest of the hospital and the relatively low status that these programs have within the total hospital system.

In summary, the alcoholism programs in state mental hospitals represent a significant and major effort to provide inpatient treatment for problem drinkers. However, such programs exist only in a minority of all mental hospitals and even in these hospitals they often serve only a minority of the problem drinkers admitted to the hospital. Despite many shortcomings, such as understaffing, inadequacy of aftercare arrangements, isolation from the rest of the hospital, possible over-emphasis on didactic approaches to the exclusion of others, and some instances of rigidity in treatment ideology, there is much that other mental hospitals and community mental health centers can learn from these programs.

In many respects simliar to mental hospital programs, are the small number of special alcoholism treatment units run under the auspices of state alcoholism programs. While some of these units are better staffed and more adequately funded than the mental hospital programs, they serve only a fraction as many patients as do the mental hospital wards. They are most highly developed in the southeastern part of the U.S., and it is only in this region that further expansion appears likely.

Outpatient (Clinic) Care

The number of alcoholism clinics has greatly increased in recent years. At present there are over 130 such clinics in the U.S., most of which, however, do not operate on a full-time basis. The vast majority of these clinics are psycho-dynamically oriented and the bulk of the actual treatment usually is provided by social workers. Although most alcoholism clinics use group therapy —both for patients and for relatives—the primary therapeutic modality continues to be individual psychotherapy, casework and counselling. This therapy is in many ways similar to that of psychiatric clinics, although alcoholism clinic personnel often are more active and directive in their work with patients.

A striking feature of many alcoholism clinics is their willingness to make at least some provisional contact with the patient right away. Although there often are "waiting lists" for admission to actual treatment, a clinic staff member almost always is available to see the patient at least briefly within a day or two. This type of "crisis-intervention" philosophy is more widespread than in psychiatric clinics. However, only a very small proportion of patients making contact with alcoholism clinics remain for as many as five visits, but this is equally true of general psychiatric clinics. There is a tendency for the less educated, more socially disabled and less motivated patients to drop out before a real treatment relationship is established. Alcoholism clinics, like mental health clinics, tend in a variety of ways, to screen out those patients who appear unable to avail themselves of the particular types of therapy being offered by the clinic. Patients labeled as being poorly motivated and not "sincere" in their desire to do something about their drinking problem often are not accepted for treatment.

Although the alcoholism clinics usually stress to patients that they will have to give up alcohol, many therapists have other goals besides abstinence in mind for their patients. There is concern about overall psychological and social functioning. The drinking problem is viewed in the context of the total personality and attention is directed at helping patients improve their functioning in familial and occupational roles. Most clinics will refer some patients to Alcoholics Anonymous. It is rare, however, for an alcoholism clinic to associate itself directly with A.A., i.e., to provide space for group meetings on its own premises. Also, in contrast to the mental hospital alcoholism units, very few of the clinics have recovered problem drinkers as members of their staff.

Some of the strengths of alcoholism clinics are their ready availability to patients, their work with families, their flexibility in combining traditional psychotherapy with more "reality-oriented" approaches, and their increased use of group methods. Among the major weaknesses are the failure to provide any real treatment for a substantial proportion of the patients making at least an initial contact with the clinic; lack of experimentation in developing new approaches in working with less verbal, lower class patients; the continuing isolation from other agencies, particularly general psychiatric services, mental hospitals and medical detoxification facilities; and the lack of relationship to basic professional training institutions. Probably the most serious shortcoming of all is the very small number of such clinics.

Despite the relatively large number of persons with drinking problems receiving some treatment in general psychiatric clinics these clinics usually prefer not to work with such patients. Some even have explicit policies excluding them. Often the clinic staff does not feel qualified to work with these patients or they question whether psycho-social types of treatment can be effective. Psychiatric clinics are even less likely to receive problem drinkers from emergency medical services or from mental hospitals. As psychiatric clinics become integrated with community mental health programs they will probably be in a better position to work with these patients and to develop collaborative relationships with existing alcoholism clinics.

Half-way Houses

Recent years have seen the expansion of half-way houses (or recovery homes) for problem drinkers. Residents in these facilities are expected to obtain a job as soon as possible and to pay a certain amount weekly for their room and board. The majority of these houses have been developed through the efforts of A.A. members and (a much smaller number) through the efforts of church organizations. Most of the facilities are small, providing care for less than thirty persons.

Although some half-way houses are beginning to work with professional agencies, the only treatment program usually is A.A. meetings. The staff of the houses generally are recovered problem drinkers who work for very little salary beyond room and board. The financial situation of the houses often is quite precarious and a significant proportion of such homes have eventually been forced to close. Despite the name (half-way houses) most residents come directly from the community rather than from a mental hospital or correctional institution. There are strict rules about abstinence in the homes and maintenance of a mutually-supportive "anti-alcohol" culture is an essential character of these houses. The residents often are not Skid Row men, although many have had uneven employment histories and are separated from their families.

The future of half-way houses is still uncertain. They have arisen to fill a critical void in community services for problem drinkers. Existing and future half-way houses should establish better working relationships with other helping agencies and adequate means must be found to place the houses on a sounder financial basis.

SHORTCOMINGS OF TREATMENT SERVICES FOR PROBLEM DRINKERS

1. Medical care facilities, psychiatric agencies, social agencies, public welfare departments, etc., often are reluctant to provide care and treatment for problem drinkers; they tend to neglect and reject these patients.

2. Certain services, generally available to patients with other disorders, often are denied to problem drinkers by policy or practice. These include hospital insurance coverage, admission to general hospitals, assistance by public welfare agencies, voluntary admission to mental hospitals, and participation in most mental hospital aftercare programs.

3. The understanding of the nature of problem drinking and of its management is often very limited in general helping agencies.

4. Where care and treatment is provided for problem drinkers it may be narrow and segmented. That is, adequate assessment of the patient's total problems and potentialities is lacking. Only limited aspects of the patient's life situation and various problems are dealt with. Continuity of care, especially between inpatient and outpatient services and between medical services and behaviorally oriented ones, usually is absent.

5. Agencies serving problem drinkers generally prefer to work with the most motivated, the best educated and the socially most intact patients. Little care and treatment usually is provided to those who do not meet these criteria.

6. The specialized alcoholism services—mental hospital programs, alcoholism clinics, and half-way houses—often are isolated from the other community helping agencies.

CHARACTERISTICS OF ADEQUATE COMMUNITY SERVICES FOR PROBLEM DRINKERS

Below are listed some essential characteristics of services for problem drinkers:

1. A range of different services must be provided—emergency, inpatient, outpatient, and intermediate. These services must be interrelated to ensure continuity of care and optimal utilization. It is not necessary that all such

services be under a single administrative auspice. However, they do need to be properly coordinated and linked with one another.

2. The services must be of sufficient magnitude to meet the need. For example, ten half-way house beds in a city of 500,000 is totally inadequate to the needs for this type of care.

3. Services for problem drinkers should be staffed primarily by personnel skilled in assisting patients with psychological and social problems.

4. Medical facilities serving problem drinkers should be equipped to deal with behavioral as well as medical aspects. Medical treatment of the acute and chronic effects of excessive drinking only rarely influences basic drinking problems.

5. Facilities must serve a wide range of problem drinkers. Different agencies will have to offer services to different types of problem drinkers. Since many agencies currently prefer clients from higher socioeconomic groupings (15), there should be services of equal quality for different social class groups —and each will have to be attuned to the particular characteristics of that subculture.

6. Services for problem drinkers must be coordinated with the major "care-giving" services in the community—mental health, public health, medical care, public welfare, etc. Large numbers of problem drinkers are known to these agencies and it is they who will have to provide much of the help and treatment for these patients.

THE ISSUE OF MOTIVATION

In virtually all facilities providing treatment for problem drinkers, much importance is attached to the issue of motivation (14). Often the key screening criterion is the patient's motivation (or sincerity) in relation to stopping drinking. Few facilities are interested in working with patents whom they define as inadequately motivated. It is assumed that motivation is an all-or-none phenomenon. If present, then the patient can be worked with; if absent, nothing can be done until the patient really wants to stop his drinking. It is almost as though the motivated patient is seen as worthy of assistance and the non-motivated one as not. The earlier attitude of rejecting all problem drinkers has been shifted to an acceptance of those who fit a certain image and a rejection of the remainder. Many workers believe there are clear-cut stages through which problem drinkers pass before becoming "true alcoholics" (9). In some clinics considerable staff time is spent in determining whether patients are "true alcoholics"—even though the treatment implications of such labelling are unclear.

The tendency to place the onus on the patient when treatment fails needs to be replaced by the view that each such occurrence is a challenge for the therapist and the agency to develop better and more effective techniques. If current approaches and techniques are effective with only a certain proportion of the target group, then further study and the development of new methods and approaches are required. Evidence is accumulating that changes in the organization, operation and treatment philosophy of an agency can have a substantial effect on its ability to work with the supposedly unmotivated patient. For example, recent work at the Massachusetts General Hospital (5) has demonstrated that such changes can radically increase the proportion of the referred patients who come into an alcoholism clinic for treatment and who remain in treatment.[2] A similar experiment has been reported in improving the utilization of alcoholism clinic services by women released from a correctional institution (8). Frequently too the use of motivation as a criterion for the screening of patients functions as a way of excluding those from variant cultural backgrounds, particularly persons from lower socio-economic strata who are not comfortable with the whole style of operation of most clinics which are geared to middle class clients. These clinics usually emphasize talking about one's problems, involving other family members in the treatment, and coming in a fixed time every week—all of which may be alien concepts for many lower-class persons.

The necessity of overcoming excessive reliance on a certain type of therapeutic approach is not, of course, restricted to alcoholism clinics. It applies equally to general psychiatric agencies and many other helping services. If mental health centers are to live up to their expectations as true community agencies, they will have to modify and expand the approaches used in the past by most psychiatric clinics and mental hospitals.

IS IT DESIRABLE TO ESTABLISH SEPARATE SERVICES FOR PROBLEM DRINKERS?

It has often been suggested that adequate treatment for problem drinkers can only be provided if a special network of services is established. However, there is increasing agreement that establishing any substantial number of specialized services is neither feasible nor desirable. Many of the services needed by problem drinkers already exist in American communities. The objective should be to ensure that these services are strengthened, supported and made available to problem drinkers on an equal basis with other patients. The establishment of specialized services could weaken rather than strengthen the activities of the key "care-givers" in assisting problem drinkers. There is evidence that some general care-giving agencies will "dump" problem drinkers on

---

[2] Prior to the initiation of the new approach, very few of the patients referred from the emergency services of the general hospital ever appeared at the alcoholism clinic, and none of those appearing remained in treatment for as long as five sessions. The almost universally held belief was that the kinds of patients receiving assistance at the emergency service were not "sufficiently motivated" to make use of the clinic. Under the new arrangement, members of the alcoholism clinic staff were assigned to the emergency service and made contact with the patients at this time. This increased the percentage of patients later appearing for an interview at the clinic to 65 per cent, and the number for staying at least five visits to 42 per cent.

such specialized services. Or, if there is a specialized inpatient unit in a city, general hospitals are even less likely to admit patients with drinking problems.

There is danger that specialized services will operate in isolation from the community helping services—thus weakening the effectiveness of these agencies with problem drinkers and reenforcing the belief that alcoholic patients are very, very different from other patients. The presence of even limited special alcoholism facilities may also create the erroneous impression that much is being done for this patient group, that the problem is being handled.

There also is a danger that persons with drinking problems are seen as having difficulties only in relation to their use of alcoholic beverages. It is unusual to find a person who has only a drinking problem—almost always there are also other problems—physical health, social psychological or economic. There is a striking tendency for problems to "come in bunches." In some instances these other problems can be viewed as antecedents of the drinking problem—perhaps even as "causes." In other cases they have arisen subsequent to the drinking problems, i.e., they may be "consequences."

In the organization of services for problem drinkers there must be an awareness that other problems frequently "co-exist" with the drinking problem. These "other problems" often determine where in the community the person with a drinking problem is seen and what types of immediate and long-term treatment he requires. Persons with drinking problems may be hungry or obese, may suffer from diabetes or cancer, may be unemployed, have a fractured leg, be pregnant or psychotic. Sometimes these nonalcohol problems will need immediate and even continuing attention before the drinking problem can be dealt with; in other instances these problems and the drinking problem will have to be tackled simultaneously. In still other cases no substantial progress can be made until the drinking problem has been dealt with.

There are three major reasons why treatment for problem drinkers should be provided through the basic "helping" services: (1) drinking problems are of such magnitude that sufficient funds and manpower probably could not be mobilized for a special network except by "robbing" other needed programs; (2) drinking problems do not exist in isolation from other social, psychological and health problems. It is inconceivable that any system of specialized facilities could be established to deal adequately with all these associated problems; (3) large numbers of problem drinkers are already known to major caregiving agencies, and often are obtaining some kinds of help from these agencies. The separation of this type of help from assistance for the problem drinking would be unfortunate and possibly even disastrous.

ENSURING APPROPRIATE ATTENTION TO PROBLEM DRINKERS—THE ROLE OF SPECIALIZED PERSONNEL AND PROGRAMS

Until work with problem drinkers becomes fully assimilated into the activities of agencies such as mental hospitals, community mental health centers, general hospitals, welfare agencies, health departments, etc., there will be an important role for special alcoholism staffs. However, such specialists should work primarily in educational, catalytic, supervisory, and consultative capacities, rather than solely in direct treatment relationships with alcoholic patients. These specialists can (1) provide consultation to community care-giving services, and (2) stimulate the development of needed mechanisms for the planning and coordination of programs for ensuring continuity of care.

There must be some means of ensuring proper emphasis in alcohol-related services, lest problem drinkers become lost or "buried" within the larger structure of the agency and the neglect of alcoholic patients continue. The alcoholism specialists seek to bring about social change, to influence agency operations and policy. Their knowledge of the needs of problem drinkers, and about existing services, their understanding of the complex attitudes and feelings about drinking, and their skills in community organization should enable them to assist agencies in providing better services to problem drinkers.

Specialized services for problem drinkers will be needed for certain purposes; to demonstrate that problem drinkers can be helped, to provide a training opportunity for personnel who subsequently will work in other generalized agencies, and to undertake research studies.

THE ROLE OF GENERAL HELPING AGENCIES

While it is a basic thesis of this paper that mental health agencies, especially community mental health centers, can and should have major roles in dealing with alcohol problems they alone cannot provide more than a small fraction of all the care and treatment that is needed. As has already been indicated, a wide range of other community "care-giving" agencies need to be actively involved in community alcoholism programs. There is increasing awareness that psychiatric agencies alone cannot meet the treatment needs in relation to traditional mental health problems—and this is equally true in relation to drinking problems.

Large numbers of problem drinkers are known to different helping agencies. The personnel of these agencies are in an excellent position to provide varying kinds of assistance to problem drinkers. In addition to case-finding and referral (where indicated) they can support and supplement the more specialized help provided to problem drinkers and their families by mental health or specialized alcoholism facilities. In providing assistance to persons with drinking problems such general helping agencies will often need the assistance of the specialized alcoholism personnel referred to in the previous section.

Public health nurses, for example, often are well situated to assist problem drinkers in obtaining help from various agencies. In addition they can work collaboratively with such agencies after the patient has made contact with the more specialized facility. A demonstration program in Boston (at the Massachusetts General Hospital) indicates that public health nurses can supplement the work of an acute psychiatric service by making home visits on cases where the patient has failed to maintain his contact with the service or where other problems are found in the home situation.

Vocational rehabilitation agencies increasingly have expanded their work beyond the traditional areas of physical rehabilitation. Public welfare departments are attempting to shift from an exclusive emphasis on financial support to a greater stress on casework and other social services directed at the numerous social, psychological and health problems frequently found among welfare recipients. Both rehabilitation and welfare agencies can participate actively in community programs directed at drinking problems.

Medical care, emergency as well as other, obviously is required for some problem drinkers. Mental health agencies, including community mental health centers, will not be equipped to provide such care. This makes urgent the development of far more active collaboration between mental health programs and medical facilities, particularly general hospitals, various outpatient medical programs and nursing homes.

Even aside from public drunkenness offenders a very large number of persons convicted of various crimes are known to have serious drinking problems. Correctional agencies—penal institutions, probation and parole departments—need assistance from mental health agencies, as well as from others, in developing programs and training special staff to provide a broad range of services to the men and women who are their responsibility. These programs and this training should include a major emphasis on problem drinking. The drinking problems of Skid Row men—and these persons account for the bulk of arrests for public drunkenness—particularly require the collaborative participation of traditional agencies such as welfare departments, medical care facilities, vocational rehabilitation agencies, mental health agencies and the Salvation Army and also the involvement of newer programs such as economic opportunity and urban development. It is likely that the police-penal system of handling public inebriates will soon be at least partially replaced by other approaches—especially those of a medical and social welfare nature. Some mental hospitals and medical institutions are already beginning to feel the impact of judges' unwillingness to sentence "chronic alcoholics" to penal institutions for the offense of public drunkenness. The interrelated medical, psychological, social, and economic problems found among these persons makes essential cooperation and collaborative planning by numerous agencies—some of which may never before have actively worked together!

Substantial progress will occur only when the numerous general helping agencies begin to take on responsibilities in relation to problem drinkers that they have failed to assume for far too long. Mental health agencies cannot take on this task themselves. They do, however, have unique contributions to make because of resources at their disposal, particularly trained persons in dealing with psychological and social problems. In addition community mental health programs frequently should be able to provide badly needed leadership for the initiation of comprehensive alcoholism activities at the local level.

THE ROLE OF COMMUNITY MENTAL HEALTH PROGRAMS

There are two related but distinct approaches to community mental health. The first emphasizes that mental health services should be *community-based,* i.e., that patients do not have to go long distances to obtain psychiatric care and that various types of services should be located close to their homes. In this approach the emphasis is still essentially clinical, i.e., in the provision of the best possible care and treatment to patients who seek such assistance. The second approach, far more radical in its nature, is heavily imbued with general public health philosophy, i.e., it adds to the clinical dimension a substantially different concern. This view stresses the importance for mental health workers to look beyond individual patients and to ask themselves (and the community) searching questions about mental health problems generally within their area. What are the priority mental health problems of the community? Are there segments of the population in need of treatment who currently are not getting this treatment? Why is such treatment not available to them—or utilized by them? Are there particular points of stress in the community that seem to be accompanied by higher rates of psychiatric disorder? Can anything be done to mitigate and reduce these apparently pathogenic stresses? As is well known this view also stresses the key role of non-psychiatric agencies and institutions in a broad community mental health program. The community mental health program is seen as the focal point, as a kind of catalyst or "conscience" for the community in relation to psycho-social problems.

Understandably only a minority of psychiatric specialists are familiar with and trained to work effectively along the lines of the second approach to community mental health that is summarized above. Many mental health workers remain very skeptical of the scientific bases for this approach—and consequently prefer to function principally as clinicians. Much additional experience is needed with this approach and perhaps quite differently trained personnel will be required before it can be put to an adequate test.

Community programs for dealing with drinking problems require (1) services that are readily accessible to patients and well-coordinated with one another, and (2) a public health-mental health orientation that calls attention to unmet needs, to the role of general helping agencies, to early intervention, to the importance of preventive activities, to the importance of overcoming community resistance to needed action on alcohol problems and to the relation between drinking problems and other social and psychological difficulties. That is, both elements of community mental health programs are applicable to drinking problems. For this reason mental health programs now have a potential for work in the area of alcohol problems that did not previously exist. Locally-based services, a community view of drinking problems and understanding of the psychological and social issues involved in this area are three prerequisites for comprehensive alcoholism programs. Community mental health programs may be alone in meeting these three criteria.

Community mental health programs can use a variety of different administrative and organizational arrangements in developing alcoholism programs. Many of these probably should be tried on an experimental basis in order to learn more about the strengths and weaknesses of each. Certainly no single model can be proposed at this time. Below are listed some examples of how alcoholism services and programs can be integrated into community mental health activities.

1. Complete "integration" of alcoholism services with other activities. Under such an arrangement all services of the program would be open to problem drinkers on an equal basis with other patients. Many psychiatric services state that this is their present policy but, for a variety of reasons, only a few such patients are in treatment with most of these agencies. This arrangement presupposes that staff are sufficiently motivated to work with problem drinkers and that the residual attitudes and prejudices have been overcome. It also assumes that personnel are sufficiently informed and experienced to work effectively with these patients. Such total integration may, however, be quite feasible at some future time.

2. Special alcoholism services or "units" within community mental health centers. Under this arrangement, already in operation in certain centers (and planned for others), the services for persons with drinking problems would be physically located within the center and the staff administratively responsible to the director of the center. But these services would have their own personnel, except perhaps in specialized areas such as vocational rehabilitation, occupational and physical therapy. For example, there might be a separate ward for problem drinkers and/or a special outpatient clinic or day hospital. Ideally trainees from the major mental health professions would rotate through the various services in the center—alcoholic as well as non-alcoholic. Referral of patients and consultation should be relatively easy under such an arrangement.

3. Special alcoholism services or "units" as parts of community mental health programs, but not physically located in a center. This arrangement is similar to the one just described except for the physical distance between major mental health services and those for problem drinkers. Administratively the special services would be responsible to the director of the center. Referral and consultation—as well as sharing of trainees—could occur in much the same fashion as under No. 2, but might be slightly more difficult to work out because of the lack of spatial proximity.

4. Special alcoholism programs not administratively part of the community mental health programs but well coordinated with them. In communities where well established and adequately staffed alcoholism services already exist, formal administrative integration with the mental health program may not be either possible or desirable. However, such "separate" alcoholism services should work collaboratively with the mental health services. Only in this way can appropriate referral and consultation arrangements be developed and implemented. Some "sharing" of staff, or regular joint conferences might also be instituted to ensure better cooperation between the two agencies.

5. Specialized treatment personnel in the mental health program, but no separate alcoholism "units." Under this arrangement certain staff—with particular interest and training—would be designated as "alcoholism specialists." They would be available to work with problem drinkers, but might also treat other patients. There would be no separately identifiable alcoholism services but the bulk of persons with drinking problems might be treated by these workers. In addition they could function as consultants to others on the staff who were giving treatment to problem drinkers. These "specialists" would also establish liaison with those other community agencies who work with problem drinkers. As such they would be important "linkage" persons for the community mental health center and its generic staff.

6. No alcoholism units in mental health programs, but special personnel to function primarily in non-clinical roles. This arrangement differs from No. 5 in that the special personnel would themselves do little or no treatment with problem drinkers. Rather their work would consist primarily of ensuring that problem drinkers received appropriate attention in all the activities of the community mental health programs. In this capacity they might function not only as consultants but also as a kind of "conscience" for both the mental health program and the community in relation to alcohol problems. They could help to stimulate and encourage various activities within the community that bear on alcohol problems. Thus they would act principally as "catalysts," as community organization experts and "change agents" rather than as clinicians or therapists. Overcoming resistance, dealing with stigmatizing attitudes and taking advantage of opportunities to secure greater attention to alcohol problems would be major elements of their work. In line with the second approach of community mental health mentioned earlier, these alcoholism workers would be using the mental health programs as an "operating base" from which to develop broad and comprehensive alcoholism activities within the mental health program, in other agencies and in the community generally.

The type of "coordinating" activity described above is a relatively new innovation in mental health, public health and medical care. There is, however, a growing realization that the complexity of American "helping agencies" requires some such radical steps to ensure better utilization and coordination of various services. Continuity of care, joint planning of programs, and agreement on areas of responsibility are examples of the objectives of such coordination. New York City has sought to achieve better cooperation between its health and welfare agencies by assigning a top administrator from the health department to be in charge of medical care activities within the city welfare department. A similar arrangement has just been developed in Michigan at the state level between the public health and welfare agencies. Vocational rehabilitation counsellors working in mental hospitals, on a full or part-time basis are examples of efforts to overcome the barriers to inter-agency cooperation that frequently arise at the clinical level. The newly established National Center for Prevention and Control of Alcoholism plans to strengthen coordination within the Department of Health, Education and Welfare by having key personnel from other parts of the Department, such as the Welfare Administration, the Vocational Rehabilitation Administration, and the Office of Education assigned to the Center. These individuals would then be channels of communication in relation to alcohol problems between their agencies and the Alcoholism Center. This clearly should be a "two-way" street with the alcoholism staff thereby obtaining a far better picture of the work of the other agencies than would occur in the absence of such an arrangement. Several states have had some limited experience with jobs designated as "alcoholism coordinators"—usually, however, such persons have been attached to state alcoholism programs rather than to general helping agencies. The latter approach might well be equally, if not more, effective in having an impact on general care-givers.

A major difficulty in implementing some of the suggestions made in this paper is the lack of trained personnel. While major professional training institutions undoubtedly should expand their educational activities relating to drinking problems it is likely that many personnel of the type described above will need to have special additional training. Until more programs are developed in which persons can learn from the example of others who are dealing with problem drinking in clinical, consultative and community organization roles it probably will be necessary for agencies to send such trainees for varying periods of time to the few settings in the U.S. where "alcoholism specialists" currently are functioning in roles such as those that have been described. Formally organized short-term training programs as well as brief (or longer) field placements or "internships" are one means whereby some progress might be made in overcoming this manpower "bottleneck." Perhaps the National Alcoholism Center should consider greatly expanding its financial support for such special training programs.

SUMMARY COMMENTS

The magnitude of drinking problems, while not known precisely, is obviously very great and problem drinkers have a significant impact on the work of many helping agencies. There also can be no question about the relative neglect of the needs of problem drinkers by most helping agencies and professions. Neither mental health agencies, nor others, have provided leadership in this regard. However, the last few years have seen increased concern about this problem on the part of many persons, laymen as well as professionals—both inside and outside the mental health field.

Because of the large number of problem drinkers and because other health, psychological, vocational and social problems frequently are found among persons with drinking problems it probably is not reasonable to establish a large separate network of treatment services for these patients. Logistically it would be virtually impossible to do without robbing numerous other agencies of the bulk of their trained and experienced personnel. The need rather is to develop means of ensuring appropriate attention to alcohol problems by a broad range of helping agencies.

There is an urgent need for someone to take on responsibility for this major problem area. Such responsibility obviously would not entail provision of all the needed services by any single agency or administrative unit. Leadership of an organizational and catalytic nature is perhaps of primary importance. A recent report to the House of Representatives on comprehensive health planning and services (6) listed the following principal shortcomings of American health services:

    a. Fragmentation in programs and organizations.

    b. Gaps in service coverage.

    c. Lack of rational comprehensive national planning.

    d. Lack of coordination at state and local levels.

    e. Undue rigidity in financing of federally assisted programs.

    f. Inability to use effectively scarce professional personnel.

These criticisms apply with equal, if not greater, force to alcoholism program activities. In the forthcoming national comprehensive health planning activities—with their new emphasis on non-categorical approaches—mental health authorities and community mental health programs will need to take a major leadership role in ensuring appropriate attention to the area of alcohol problems. The aforementioned Congressional report refers to the role of mental health programs in relation to the "special problem area" of alcoholism (6).

The staff of the National Center for the Prevention and Control of Alcoholism, with the support of the Secretary's Intra-Departmental Committee on Alcoholism and the recently-appointed National Advisory Committee on Alcoholism should provide consultative and other assistance to federal, state and local personnel in the intensive and comprehensive health planning activities that will take place during the next two years. Such collaboration between alcoholism program personnel and general mental health workers can help to ensure that future community health—and mental health—programs deal effectively with alcohol problems.

REFERENCES

1. Bahn, A. K., and Chandler, C. A. Alcoholics in psychiatric clinic patients. *Qtly. J. of Studies on Alcohol,* 1961, 22:411.

2. Bahn, A. K. Outpatient psychiatric clinic services to alcoholics, 1959. *Qtly. J. of Studies on Alcohol,* 1963, 24:213.

3. Bahn, A., et al. Current services and trends in outpatient psychiatric clinics, 1963. *Psychiatric Studies and Projects,* Mental Hospital Service of the American Psychiatric Association, 1965, 3 (7).

4. California Department of Mental Hygiene. Alcoholic patients: California state hospitals for the mentally ill, state-operated outpatient facilities, Short-Doyle programs. *Biostatistics Section,* bull. No. 43, 1964.

5. Chafetz, M., et al. Establishing treatment relations with alcoholics. *J. Nervous and Mental Diseases,* 1962, 134:395.

6. Comprehensive health planning and public health services amendments of 1966, House of Representatives, 89th Cong., 2nd sess., report from the Committee on Interstate and Foreign Commerce, Report No. 2271, October 13, 1966, p. 3.

7. *Crime in the United States—Uniform Crime Reports—1965,* Federal Bureau of Investigation, U.S. Department of Justice, Washington, D.C., 1966.

8. Demone, H. W., Jr. Experiments in referral to alcoholism clinics. *Qtly. J. of Studies on Alcohol,* 1963, 24:495.

9. Jellinek, E. M. *The disease concept of alcoholism.* New Haven, Conn.: College and University Press, 1960.

10. *Massachusetts Mental Health Planning Project Report, Task Force on Alcoholism,* Department of Mental Health, 1965.

11. *Monthly Report Bulletin,* County of Westchester (New York), Department of Public Welfare, 1964, 4 (10).

12. *Patients in Mental Institutions, 1964: State and County Mental Hospitals,* U.S. Department of Health, Education and Welfare. National Clearinghouse for Mental Health Information, Public Health Service Publication No. 1452, Washington, D.C., 1966.

13. Pearson, W. S. The hidden alcoholic in the general hospital: A study of "hidden alcoholism" in white male patients admitted for unrelated complaints. *North Carolina Med. J.,* 1962, 23:6.

14. Pittman, D. J., and Sterne, M. Concept of motivation: Sources of institutional and professional blockage in the treatment of alcoholics. *Qtly. J. of Studies on Alcohol,* 1965, 26:41.

15. Pittman, D. J., and Sterne, M. W. *Alcoholism: Community agency attitudes and their impact on treatment services.* National Clearinghouse for Mental Health Information, National Institute of Mental Health, U.S. Department of Health, Education and Welfare, U.S. Government Printing Office, Washington, D. C., Public Health Service Pub. No. 1273.

16. *Public assistance cases where alcohol is a factor contributing to need, 1965.* Wyoming State Department of Public Welfare.

17. *Statistics newsletter.* State of Maryland, Department of Mental Hygiene, 1965.

18. Wass, D. K. Public welfare and the drinking problem. *Progress,* The Alcoholism Foundation of Alberta, 1964, 6(4):64–68.

19. Wolf, I. Chafetz, M. E., Blane, H. T., and Hill, M. J. Social factors in the diagnosis of alcoholism: II. Attitudes of Physicians. *Qtly. J. of Studies on Alcohol,* 1965, 26 (1).

37

Mental Health Services and the Poor

CHARLES HERSCH

Two great and increasingly intertwined upheavals are at present under way. One of these is within the body of the orthopsychiatric professions, the other within society at large.

In independent papers by Hobbs and by Bellak, the upheaval in the professions has been granted the status of a revolution (3, 21). Both these writers agree that the first revolution in mental health was the introduction of a humane point of view toward the mentally ill, which is associated with the name of Pinel; that the second revolution was initiated by Freud through the establishment and development of psychoanalysis; and that the third and current revolution, while without its established hero, is the increasing orientation toward the community as the locus of professional concern. The essence for Hobbs is that ". . . *the concepts of public health have finally penetrated the field of mental health* (21, p. 823)." For Bellak, the heart of the matter is ". . . *the resolve to view the individual's psychiatric problems within the frame of reference of the community and vice versa* (3, p. 5)." (The italics are theirs.)

The second upheaval, occurring within the total society, derives from the vast stirrings of discontent among the economically, socially, and culturally deprived. Ordinarily without political power, the hitherto silent and invisible poor have begun to find new voices. Like some massive return of the repressed, the disadvantaged portion of the population is breaking through the layers of society's awareness and making its presence known. Among the manifestations are channeled demands for adequate housing, adequate schools, the right to vote, and the right to be treated with decency and respect. But other manifestations are crime and delinquency, street violence, disrupted schooling, financial dependency—in general, the staggering statistics of psychosocial breakdown and welfare economics.

The two upheavals come together in regard to the issue of quantitatively and qualitatively improved mental-health services to the poor (46, 48). At the

Reprinted from *Psychiatry*, 1966, *29*, 236–245, by permission of the William Alanson White Psychiatric Foundation and the author. © 1966. William Alanson White Psychiatric Foundation. Dr. Hersch is Assistant Director and Chief Psychologist, Cambridge Mental Health Center, Cambridge, Massachusetts.

federal level it is the point of confluence of the community mental-health program and the antipoverty program. While the relationship of these two programs is yet to be worked out, it may be said at this point that the application of the public-health perspective is particularly suited to the mental-health disabilities of the poor. The interweaving of social and community problems with individual and personal problems is nowhere more evident than among the poor (18, 49). When Conant, for example, out of his evaluation of education in the slums, warns that "we are allowing social dynamite to accumulate in our large cities (7, p. 10)." It is difficult to separate the community aspects from the individual aspects of the problem. In large measure, this interpenetration of levels provides the framework for understanding the distress of the poor and establishes the guidelines for intervention.

In providing improved services to the poor there are some special factors that have to be considered. One of these is the magnitude of the task, for the poor have a higher rate of psychiatric and social impairment than the other classes in American society. The second factor is the challenge that mental-health services, along with other services, have disengaged themselves from the problems of the poor. The third factor is the alienation of the poor, which prevents them from utilizing available services.

MAGNITUDE

In sheer numbers, the magnitude of the overall task facing the mental-health professions is awesome. The present long waiting lists show how difficult it is even to keep up with the flow of cases that are fortunate enough to have their symptoms recognized as such and referred to an appropriate resource. In the community at large, while there may be disagreement as to the extent of distress and affliction, the available evidence indicates that it is considerable. Lapouse summarizes the prevalence surveys of the fifties:

> That decade gave birth to the Midtown study in which 80 per cent of the population was said to have mild to incapacitating "pathology-denoting" symptoms, and 25 per cent was reported to have seriously impaired mental health. The Stirling County study claimed 65 per cent of the survey population as significantly psychiatrically impaired, and 37 per cent as psychiatric cases needing treatment. The Chronic Disease Commission's study of Baltimore, found that only 10 per cent of the population had sufficient symptoms to justify a psychiatric diagnosis. And the Hunterdon County study found 18 per cent with mental disorders in the survey population (32, p. 140).

The percentages may vary, but it is reasonably clear that there is in the community a significant degree of unattended emotional disturbance.

Regarding children only, the situation is equally serious. At a recent conference on the planning of psychiatric services for children, the following picture was drawn:

> According to a conservative 1962 estimate, there are about 60 million children under 14 years of age, making up 30 per cent of the total population. Of these, from 2,500,000 to 4,500,000 are estimated to be in need of some kind of psychiatric services because of emotional difficulties (1, p. 3).

These unhappy statistics have significance not only in regard to the impaired lives that they represent. They also reveal the discrepancy between the extent of the needs for service and the extent of services available. Of the millions of children estimated to need psychiatric help, it is unlikely that more than 10 percent receive it. One example is reported by Gordon (16). In Middlesex County, New Jersey, a local clinic conducted a mental-health survey of all of the elementary school children. Using teacher ratings based on operational definitions of adjustment, a total of 6,267 children were rated either as poorly adjusted or very poorly adjusted. This is to be compared with the fewer than 600 cases a year that were able to be seen by the combined public and private resources of the community. Here is one instance of what is generally true: the need for mental-health manpower far exceeds the supply. Furthermore, it is not expected that this gap will decrease in the foreseeable future; the reverse is more likely. This inability to meet mental-health needs is the foundation for the increasing swell of voices calling for more imaginative programs of intervention and more strategic deployment of personnel (20, 21, 38, 53).

It is not surprising that these voices are never more forceful than when they speak for the need for improved services to the poor (15, 16, 33, 43, 51). All of the background that I have just presented is by way of highlighting the problem of magnitude as it stands in regard to the impoverished. The evidence is increasing that there is an enormous piling up of mental-health disabilities and related psychosocial disorders among the poor. Harrington states it this way: "The poor are subject to more mental illness than anyone else in the society, and their disturbances tend to be more serious than those of any other class (18, p. 122)."

For example, in the well-known New Haven studies, Hollingshead and Redlich found a heavy concentration of schizophrenics in the lowest socioeconomic group (22). Dunham reported the same finding in his study in Detroit, and he also found that total psychiatric casualties were greater in the lowest class than in those above (11). The increased mental health risk associated with low socioeconomic status was further revealed in the Midtown Manhattan studies, where "the mental health contrast between the top and the bottom strata could hardly be more sharply drawn (52, p. 231)." In Ryan's report on the Boston survey, a recurrent theme was the close relationship between poverty and mental illness (49). Among the findings here was that the disadvantaged areas of the city provided the greatest proportion of patients admitted for psychiatric hospitalization. Ryan also reported that families receiving Aid to Dependent Children showed emotional disturbance and social pathology in greatest numbers and of greatest significance, with their workers estimating that 50 per cent of the families clearly needed professional intervention.

Further evidence for the association between poverty and impaired living may be found in Cambridge. The 1962 study of the Cambridge Planning Board reported on the distribution of a number of psychosocial problems, including delinquency, truancy, and cases of private social agencies (5). Their findings indicate a clear and high degree of correlation between the presence of such problems and low income. A second source of information was a survey done by a local settlement house. The Cambridge Neighborhood House is located within an area of exceptional economic deprivation. Its Director, Elsa Baldwin, did an informal survey of families known to her. This survey was admittedly superficial and also omitted cases of delinquency, in itself a significant problem in the community she serves. She found that over 50 per cent of the families had major disabilities in the mental-health domain that should have been receiving professional attention. A more intensive analysis would certainly have brought the percentage higher, as would have the inclusion of delinquency. It is noteworthy, however, that the 50 per cent figure, referring to those in definite need of mental-health assistance, is similar to that reported by the Aid to Dependent Children workers in the Boston study, and that this is a considerably higher figure than any of those mentioned in the prevalence surveys referred to earlier.

Particular attention should also be paid to the association between poverty and specific aspects of neuropsychiatric disability in children. Ten years ago, at a fairly early point in the history of these studies, Pasamanick and his co-workers reported

> . . . that there are positive and probably etiologic relationships between low socioeconomic status and prenatal and paranatal abnormalities which in turn may serve as precursors to retarded behavioral development, and to certain neuropsychiatric disorders of childhood such as cerebral palsy, epilepsy, mental deficiency and behavior disorder (41, p. 600).

Their subsequent investigations add reading disability and tics in children to the list of disorders that are linked to poverty through the intermediary of abnormalities of pregnancy and birth (40). Recent studies have revealed an associated triad of low economic class, premature birth, and neurological defect (56). Furthermore, among these prematurely born children, the greater the degree of social deprivation for the mother, the greater the possibility of neurological abnormality in the child (55). The late President Kennedy, in his message to Congress on mental illness and mental retardation, placed great stress on the relationship between retardation and poverty (27). The relationship is even stronger for cases without neurological involvement than for those with such involvement. The upshot, as Kennedy indicated, is that in some cities only 1 or 2 per cent of school-age children from the prosperous neighborhoods are considered retarded, while the figure for the slum areas runs as high as 10 to 30 per cent.

Other categories of disability are also linked with poverty. The association between low income and juvenile delinquency found in Cambridge holds generally (13). Impoverished neighborhoods produce an increased incidence of various types of scholastic maladjustment including truancy, learning failure, and school dropouts. In a recent Michigan study, children of nonskilled workers seen at a psychiatric clinic were found to fall into more serious diagnostic categories and were judged to have more malignant symptomatology than children of higher-level skilled workers (35). The list may be expected to grow as further epidemiologic information is gathered. It should also be noted that included on the list are a number of diagnostic groups and symptom syndromes which pose some of the most difficult intervention problems facing the child-guidance effort.

The magnitude of the task is reflected further in the size of the population from which these high-risk candidates are drawn. Although there is some variability in the criteria used, the general estimate is about 20 per cent of the families in the country are living in poverty. The proportion of children is higher than this, since the poor tend to have larger families than do the other classes. The figures for 1961 indicated about 17 million children growing up in poverty, with 3 million belonging to families with incomes of under $1,000 per year. In short, about one-fourth of American children were living under conditions that were financially inadequate to meet their basic needs (6, 54).

Here, then, are some of the things that can be documented. The population living in poverty is large in numbers. For the children, there is inherently a greater risk of disability in their encounter with the school (9, 10, 26; 49, pp. 172–87). For the adults, there are heightened mental-health hazards in the conditions of their work (30, pp. 49–56). They are more vulnerable to the stresses in the circumstances of their living (31). The personal toll wrought by poverty is reflected in the high proportion of social and psychological pathology among the poor, and in the profundity of their impairment. In short, the poverty-stricken present to the mental-health professions a task of staggering dimensions.

DISENGAGEMENT

If mental-health services were organized on a completely rational basis, linking concentration of effort to high levels of need, then the disadvantaged population would have long been a focus of attention. Yet this has not been the case. If anything, the disturbing indications are that the poor, until very recently, have been systematically deterred from obtaining the services they need.

Miller has stated this as follows:

> Insufficient attention has been paid to the poor in America. Richard Cloward has written of social work's increasing disengagement from the poor. Other professions have never engaged or insufficiently engaged themselves with the plight of the poor. Each profession and social service has to confront itself with the issue of how much existing practice is aimed at dealing with the problems of the poor as they presently exist in the United States (37, p. 444; 48, pp. 11–15).

William Brueckner has echoed this concern, commenting on the unfortunate magnitude of the disengagement, and on its existence even among agencies located in low socioeconomic population areas (4).

For this disengagement, the service professions have of late been richly criticized and scolded (16, 49, 51). Obviously not all of the agencies or all of the groups deserve the criticism. Yet, in the overall view, the picture is somewhat disquieting. Here, from varied sources, is what one finds. Services are not geographically situated so as to be readily available to the poor. If the poor do reach the agencies, they do not find the services they expect within a context that is meaningful to them—they are not buying what the agencies are selling, and they do not return after the early encounters. The services are structured in such a way—in terms of procedures, formalized steps, waiting periods, and the like—as to fend off the poor. If they do go through the procedures, they are more readily rejected by the agencies than are those of higher socioeconomic status—there are more breaks in contact initiated by the staffs with the poor than with the classes above them. Those who are accepted for treatment are less often given the type of treatment considered most beneficial by the professionals, treatment choice being class-bound rather than bound to diagnosis. Finally, if they are given the higher-status treatment, it is by less experienced or lower-status personnel.

Within this panorama of systematic deterrence, presumably not too overdrawn, the issue of psychotherapy is particularly interesting. It is a current cliché to state that individual psychotherapy is not a suitable treatment medium for the ills of the poor. It is hard to understand on what basis of experience this cliché is gaining currency. The poor are not seen by therapists in private practice, they seldom reach the stage of therapy in clinics, and they are very rarely indeed seen by the senior personnel who would be best equipped to make the therapeutic enterprise successful. Furthermore, it is just these senior personnel who would be in a position to understand and report on whatever special factors of psychodynamics and therapeutic technique might be involved in treating the emotional disabilities of the poor.

Without such understanding, it seems premature to disqualify the poor from this form of treatment. It may turn out that the problems are insurmountable—that the inherent structure of psychotherapy is incompatible with the personal and cultural characteristics of the poor—but at this point in time, with the experience now available, there is no way of knowing whether this is the case. Perhaps modifications of technique will be required, and this would not be surprising. Psychodynamic psychotherapy has never been a static thing, and has continually altered and grown to encompass new problems. Here, once again, is the necessity for some well-grounded clinical research. Finally, it may be charged that, given the current manpower shortage, advocating further interest in individual psychotherapy is ill-advised. From the overall public-health perspective this may be true. Yet it may also be true that among the poor, as among the other classes, there are psychiatrically impaired people for whom individual psychotherapy is the treatment of choice, perhaps the only treatment that would be suitable to their needs. If at this point decisions are made that result in the denial of psychotherapy to the poor, then one has to ask whether this is being done on rational grounds, or whether it is another instance of the process of disengagement.

Care must be taken not to further this process in even the most progressive steps in the planning of services. The exciting new development in the mental-health field is the concept of the comprehensive community mental-health center (2). This type of facility is aimed at providing a range of services, offering continuity of care to the individual psychiatric patient, as well as consultative and educational programs to the rest of the community. The plan is to provide for localization and coordination of heretofore geographically and administratively scattered services. Yet should such plans develop so as to establish a centralization of functioning within the larger community, it would create an undesirable distancing from local neighborhoods that would particularly affect the adequacy of services provided to the poor. In spite of the express mandate that such centers serve the poor, without adequate safe-guards there is the danger that they also will find themselves disengaged.

What is the historical background of the disengagement from the poor? The reasons are subject for speculation.

One likely factor is that the particular plight of the poor was not adequately recognized by the mental health professions until the third revolution in psychiatry brought with it a conscious orientation toward community, social class, and demographic variables. The hard evidence that poverty is a major epidemiological factor bearing on individual and family breakdown, and that there are clear associations between poverty and a number of specific psycho-pathological conditions, waited for the introduction of public-health viewpoints and methodologies to be brought to the fore. Prior to that point, professional thinking was dominated by what Riessman and Miller have called the psychiatric world view, which interpreted virtually all problems, whether psychological, social, political, educational, or medical, in essentially individual, psycho-dynamic terms (47). The emphasis on intrapsychic factors—which Hobbs refers to as an obsession with the world inside a man's skull (21)—provided profound insights and a firm foundation for all subsequent growth, but obscured the larger context of psychopathological development and contributed to the insufficient involvement of the orthopsychiatric disciplines with the poor.

A second reason for the disengagement seems to be that the professions, wittingly or not, have joined the rest of society in a generalized rejection of the poor. The poor have a bad reputation in society and are viewed in the mass as having a number of disagreeable characteristics (48, pp. 205–23; 51). They are said to be lazy and shiftless, to have sexual lives akin to those of animals, to be disinterested in attainment or self-improvement, to be unstable and undependable, to live in dirt and be indifferent to it, and so on down the line. Agency professionals often describe the poor as unmotivated, lacking in awareness, holding unreasonable and inappropriate expectations, blaming their problems on outside forces, incapable of insight, and untreatable. They are called multiproblem, hard-core, multigeneration, action-oriented, non-verbal, impulse-ridden, concrete, and disorganized—terms in which the language of diagnosis shades into the language of abuse. While some of these characteristics may be true for some or many of the poor, making them unsuitable candidates for what the agencies have to offer, there has been a reluctance to adapt services to persons in need who would not adapt themselves to the services that were available. One is reminded here of a main theme in the summary report of the Joint Commission—that adequate care was not provided to the mentally ill because they were rejected both by the community and by the professionals (25). A similar circumstance appears to obtain in regard to the poor: to society they are unlovely as people, and to the agencies they are unlovely as patients. While gains have been made by the mental-health professions in the past few years in overcoming this tendency to reject the poor, it must be admitted that there is still a long way to go.

ALIENATION

The disengagement on the part of the professionals is, however, only one side of the coin. The other side is the alienation of the poor, which has hindered them from making use of the services that are available to them.

Particular characteristics accompany the status of being poor in this society at the present time. Being poor in the United States in the 1960's takes one out of the mainstream of the larger community. History is more familiar with a poverty-stricken majority, where the individual at least has the consolation of being in the same boat with most of his fellows. A poor which is in the minority, living in the context of a society of plenty, has given rise to a new situation altogether. This is "the other America (18)" or the "culture of poverty (8; 48, pp. 128–38)," made up of people who simply do not participate in the well-being of the surrounding affluent society and for many of whom aspiration has given way to defeatism and despair. It is a culture with distinguishable value patterns that differ from those of the larger society (50). It has distinctive patterns of family life (36, 44) and parent-child interaction (29; 48, pp. 159–71). It provides processes of socialization and acculturation that—for good or evil—prepare the young for participation within the culture and thus perpetuate it (19, 28).

Riessman and others have argued that there are strengths in the culture of poverty, that the characteristics which the poor show are not simply failures in the management of life but rather are functional for survival in coping with chronic conditions of disadvantage and deprivation (45, 51). One can only agree with this point of view. However, it is a point of view that should not be romanticized or sentimentalized. There are survival and adaptation, but at a cost. Although the families with multiple impairments and no money find ways to continue to live, it is not a kind of living that most people would want to share. Sufficient antidote to any sentimentalization may be found in Pavenstedt's recent portrayal of the appalling conditions under which the children of extreme deprivation live (42), conditions reminiscent of that most famous of disadvantaged families, the Kallikaks (14). Pavenstedt states: "The saddest, and to us the outstanding characteristic of this group with adults and children alike, was the self-devaluation (42, p. 96)." This self-devaluation is an important feature of the estrangement of the impoverished.

The plight of the poor today is aggravated not only by their being a minority in the society, but by certain cultural and intellectual traditions as well. Democracy does not feel comfortable with the concept of a class society and does not quickly come to grips with the issues that are implied. Although social stratification is recognized, it is emphasized that this is an open society and that the boundaries between the classes are almost totally permeable. Presumably, if there is initiative and energy, one should be able to move up the ladder with relative ease. If one does not move up, but remains in deprived straits, the lack is considered to be individual and personal. Historically, Protestantism joined hands with capitalism to link ambition, productivity, and success with ethical goodness, providing as a legacy an image of free and rugged individuals conquering the undeveloped frontier. Social Darwinism, with its doctrine of survival of the fittest, added its scientific voice, decreeing that the poor are poor as a result of their own inferiority. A second and unfortunate scientific tributary appeared in the tendency of psychodynamic psychiatry and psychology to find the causes of an individual's circumstances within himself and his personal emotional history. There is an agreement with Shakespeare that the fault ". . . is not in our stars, but in ourselves, that we are underlings." The poor, then, are seen, by themselves as well as by much of the society, as having their condition caused by some curious admixture of weakness, sinfulness, and psychopathology.

This is not to say that the poor are without their share of psychiatric and emotional problems. As has been pointed out, they have them, and in great quantity. But in organizing a program of services to the poor it is important to conceptualize two domains within which problems have their origin and expression. One is internal, intrapsychic, and within the province of dynamic psychiatry. The other is external, reality-based, and related to the fields of sociology and economics. In Harrington's words:

The drunkenness, the unstable marriages, the violence of the other America are not simply facts about individuals. They are a description of an entire group in the society who react this way because of the conditions under which they live (18, p. 162).

One may think, then, of two kinds of alienation, recognizing that they may work hand in hand and combine in the distress of a given person. One is alienation from the self and the other is alienation from society. Karen Horney has described alienation from the self as one of the basic and most injurious processes characterizing the psychopathological conditions (23, 24). It refers to all those ways in which a person suppresses or eliminates essential parts of himself, lose contact with what he really feels, believes, likes, or wishes, and becomes tyrannized by what he thinks he should be rather than living according to what he actually is or might be. Horney's emphasis is on the neuroses, and her intervention of choice is psychoanalysis or psychotherapy.[1] Alienation from society is another matter; it derives from sociologic and economic origins, and it requires interventions that bring the individual into participation within the larger community. Many of these interventions need to be at the level of community action, vocational rehabilitation, and remedial education.[2]

The emotionally disturbed poor, large in numbers, represent the confluence of the two forms of alienation, which in combination are transmitted with peculiar regularity over the generations. Breaking into the cycle of disability in any meaningful way requires consideration of both aspects of alienation, and the development of coordinated service programs that operate simultaneously at a number of different levels. An example would be the multiservice centers that are being developed in Boston. On a smaller scale, there is the multidimensional approach reported by Massimo and Shore, in which a single practitioner offered intensive psychotherapy, remedial education, and job placement help in a combined treatment program for adolescent delinquent boys (34).

The consequences of alienation are very somber, whether measured in terms of personal distress, social disorder, or financial cost to the community. The estrangement can be seen in the men who seek to numb their loneliness and sense of isolation through the use of alcohol. Others forfeit their responsibilities to their families and abandon them to the welfare rolls. There are the youths who cannot understand any value in continuing their education, even if it is vocationally oriented, and become school dropouts, and others who strike out at the alien society by delinquency and by often senseless acts of destruction. There is, in short, the whole range of people who cannot find a satisfying place in the society and who cannot work out an effective life within it.

---

[1] The conceptions of the neo-Freudians generally, with their emphases on interpersonal relations, cultural factors, and contemporaneous field forces, may be particularly fruitful in psychological theorizing regarding the poor.

[2] Similar ideas are found in Galbraith's distinction between case poverty and insular poverty, and in Cohen's distinction between emotional deprivation and economic deprivation. See refs. 12 and 8.

Out of this comes a dilemma. The people who feel apart from the society often do not trust the agencies and organizations that society has established. To put it another way, the people who need professional services most either cannot or will not—in any event, they do not—voluntarily take advantage of them.

The problem was underscored in an editorial in the *New York Times* late in 1964. The editorial pointed out the difficulties that the Job Corps program of the war on poverty could be expected to face in helping youngsters become suitable candidates for employment. It cited the efforts of the local draft boards to encourage draft rejects to seek job counseling and placement at their state employment offices. Of the nearly quarter of a million young men who received letters to this effect, only a small proportion appeared for interviews, and of these only one out of six was placed, even for a few days. The editorial went on:

> It is plain from these discouraging statistics that the administrators of the anti-poverty program will have to devote much of their energy to combatting the sense of alienation that makes many of those who are most disadvantaged unwilling even to avail themselves of the opportunity for help. They have become so inured to rejection that it amounts almost to a way of life (39).

This is the challenge that faces the orthopsychiatric professions as well. The pattern of setting up services for those who feel the need for and seek out professional assistance is not workable for the disadvantaged. Rather, coming to grips with the psychiatric problems of the poor will require the development of programs that take into consideration their sense of estrangement and alienation.

CONCLUSION

It is tempting to offer here another pious and strident exhortation to the effect that we have failed the poor and that something needs to be done. The current literature, however, is sufficiently decorated with these. Yet it is true that there are many issues concerning the mental-health problems of the poor that we have not begun to master, and others that we are only beginning to face. What can be offered here, then, is a suggestion—namely, that we will be in a more strategic position in developing intervention programs for the poor if we take into consideration some of the background factors discussed above. The problem of magnitude, for example, suggests the need to build on the lesson of medical history and seek control of pathology through prevention rather than through cure; it further suggests the wisdom of extending the reach of professional personnel through the use of volunteers and specially trained subprofessionals, and through the use of such methods as mental-health consultation. Coping with the process of disengagement will require a reexamination of our models of treatment, as well as a purposive orientation to the poor based on determined decisions throughout the administrative hierarchies. The problem of alienation can be approached by developing co-ordinated, multilevel services that can deal with both inner and outer reality, and by bringing these services to the poor in their own neighborhoods. Under-lying all this is the requirement of a spirit of innovation, in which techniques are molded to problems rather than vice versa, and in which there is a readiness to depart from tradition if what it has to offer is unsuited to the job at hand. On foundations such as these we would be in a position to build meaningful and rational mental-health programs for the poor.

REFERENCES

1. American Psychiatric Assoc. *Planning psychiatric services for children in the community mental health program.* Washington, D.C., 1964.
2. American Psychiatric Assoc. *The community mental health center: An analysis of existing models.* Washington, D.C., 1964.
3. Bellak, L. Community psychiatry: The third psychiatric revolution. In L. Bellak (Ed.), *Handbook of community psychiatry and community mental health.* New York: Grune & Stratton, 1964.
4. Brueckner, W. Current thinking on the role of the settlement. In A. D. Spiegel (Ed.), *The mental health role of settlement and community centers.* Boston: Massachusetts Department of Mental Health, 1963.
5. Cambridge Planning Board. *Social characteristics of Cambridge.* Cambridge, Mass., 1962.
6. Chilman C., and Sussman, M. B. Poverty in the United States in the mid-sixties. *J. Marriage and the Family,* 1964, 26:391–94.
7. Conant, J. B. *Slums and suburbs.* New York: Signet Books, 1964.
8. Cohen, J. Social work and the culture of poverty. *Social Work,* 1964, 9:3–11.
9. Deutsch, M. P. The disadvantaged child and the learning process. H. Passow (Ed.), *Education in depressed areas.* New York: Columbia Univ., 1963.
10. Deutsch, M. The role of social class in language development and cogni-tion. *Amer. J. Orthopsychiat.,* 1965, 35:78–88.
11. Dunham, H. W. Social class and schizophrenia. *Amer. J. Orthopsychiat.,* 1964, 34:634–42.
12. Galbraith, J. K. *The affluent society.* Boston: Houghton Mifflin, 1958.
13. Glueck, S. *The problem of delinquency.* Boston: Houghton Mifflin, 1959.
14. Goddard, H. H. *The Kallikak family.* New York: Macmillan, 1912.
15. Gordon, E. W. Help for the disadvantaged? *Amer. J. Orthopsychiat.,* 1965, 35:445–48.
16. Gordon S. Are we seeking the right patients? Child guidance intake: The sacred cow. *Amer. J. Orthopsychiat.,* 1965, 35:131–37.
17. Haggstrom, W. C. The power of the poor. In F. Riessman, J. Cohen, and

A. Pearl (Eds.), *Mental health of the poor: New treatment approaches for low income people.* New York: Free Press, 1964.

18. Harrington, M. *The other America;* New York: Macmillan, 1962.
19. Hess, R. D. Educability and rehabilitation: The future of the welfare class. *J. Marriage and the Family,* 1964, 26:422–29.
20. Heyder, D. W. A contribution to overcoming the problem of waiting lists. *Amer. J. Orthopsychiat.,* 1965, 35:772–78.
21. Hobbs, N. Mental health's third revolution. *Amer. J. Orthopsychiat.,* 1964, 34:822–33.
22. Hollingshead, A. B., and Redlich, F. C. *Social class and mental illness.* New York: Wiley, 1958.
23. Horney, K. *Our inner conflicts: A constructive theory of neurosis.* New York: Norton, 1945.
24. Horney, K. *Neurosis and human growth: The struggle toward self-realization.* New York: Norton, 1950.
25. Joint Commission on Mental Illness and Health. *Action for Mental Health.* New York: Basic Books, 1961.
26. Keller, S. The social world of the urban slum child: Some early findings. *Amer. J. Orthopsychiat.,* 1963, 33: 823–31.
27. Kennedy, J. F. *Message from the President of the United States relative to mental illness and mental retardation,* 88th Congress, 1st. Sess. Doc. No. 58, House of Representatives, Washington, D.C., 1963.
28. Kobrin, S. The impact of cultural factors on selected problems of adolescent development in the middle and lower class. *Amer. J. Orthopsychiat.,* 1962, 32:387–90.
29. Kohn, M. L. Social class and parent-child relationships: An interpretation. *Amer. J. Soc.,* 1963, 68:471–80.
30. Kornhauser, A. Toward an assessment of the mental health of factory workers: A Detroit study," In F. Riessman, J. Cohen, and A. Pearl (Eds.), *Mental health of the poor: New treatment approaches for low income people.* New York: Free Press, 1964.
31. Langner, T. S., and Michael, S. T. Life stress and mental health. *The Midtown Manhattan Study,* Vol. 2. New York: Free Press, 1963.
32. Lapouse, R. Who is sick? *Amer. J. Orthopsychiat.,* 1965, 35:138–44.
33. Lourie, N. V. Impact of social change on the tasks of the mental health professions. *Amer. J. Orthopsychiat.,* 1965, 35:41–47.
34. Massimo, J. L., and Shore, M. F. The effectiveness of a comprehensive, vocationally oriented psychotherapeutic program for adolescent delinquent boys. *Amer. J. Orthophychiat.,* 1963, 33:634–42.
35. McDermott, J. F., Harrison, S. I., Schrager, J., and Wilson, P. Social class and mental illness in children: Observations of blue-collar families. *Amer. J. Orthopsychiat.,* 1965, 35:500–8.
36. McKinley, D. G. *Social class and family life.* New York: Free Press, 1964.
37. Miller, S. M. Poverty and inequality in America: Implications for the social services," *Child Welfare,* 1963, 42:442–45.
38. Muhlich, D. F., Hunter, W. F., Williams, R. I., Swanson, W. G., DeBellis, E. J., and Moede, J. M. Professional deployment in the mental health

disaster: The Range mental health center," *Community Mental Health J.,* 1965, 1:205–7.

39. *The New York Times,* Sunday, November 15, 1964, sect. 4, p. 8 (editorial).

40. Pasamanick, B., and Knobloch, H. Epidemiologic studies on the complications of pregnancy and the birth process. In G. Caplan (Ed.), *Prevention of mental disorders in children.* New York: Basic Books, 1961.

41. Pasamanick, B., Knobloch, H., and Lilienfeld, A. M. Socioeconomic status and some precursors of neuropsychiatric disorder. *Amer. J. Orthopsychiat.,* 1956, 26:594–601.

42. Pavenstedt, E. A comparison of the child-rearing environment of upper-lower and very low-lower class families. *Amer. J. Orthopsychiat.* 1965, 35:89–98.

43. Rabinowitz, C. Human rehabilitation in the sixties. *Amer. J. Orthopsychiat.,* 1963, 33:589–90.

44. Rainwater, L. Marital sexuality in four cultures of poverty. *J. Marriage and the Family,* 1964, 26: 457–66.

45. Riessman, F. Low-income culture: The strengths of the poor. *J. Marriage and the Family,* 1964, 26:417–21.

46. Riessman, F. *New approaches to mental health treatment for labor and low income groups.* New York: National Institute of Labor Education, 1964.

47. Riessman, F., and Miller, S. M. Social change versus the 'psychiatric world view.' *Amer. J. Orthopsychiat.,* 1964, 34:29–38.

48. Riessman, F., Cohen, J. and Pearl, A. (Eds.). *Mental health of the poor: New treatment approaches for low income people;* New York: Free Press, 1964.

49. Ryan, W. *Distress in the city: A summary report of the Boston Mental Health Survey.* Boston, 1964.

50. Schneiderman, L. A study of the value-orientation preferences of chronic relief recipients. *Social Work,* 1964, 9:13–18.

51. Schneiderman, L. Social class, diagnosis and treatment. *Amer. J. Orthopsychiat.,* 1965, 99–105.

52. Srole, L., Langner, T. S., Michael, S. T., Opler, M. K., and Rennie, T. A. C. *Mental health in the metropolis: The Midtown Manhattan Study,* Vol. 1. New York: McGraw-Hill, 1962.

53. Williams, R. Trends in community psychiatry: Indirect services and the problem of balance in mental health programs. In L. Bellak (Ed.), *Handbook of Community Psychiatry and Community Mental Health.* New York: Grune and Stratton, 1967.

54. Witmer, H. L. Children and poverty. *Children,* 1964, 11:207–13.

55. Wortis, H., and Freedman, A. The contribution of social environment to the development of premature children. *Amer. J. Orthopsychiat.,* 1965, 35:57–68.

56. Wortis, H., Heimer, C. B., Brame, M., Redlo, M., and Rue, R. Growing up in Brooklyn: The early history of the premature child. *Amer. J. Orthopsychiat.,* 1963, 33:535–39.

38

Prevention, Treatment, and Social Action: A Strategy of Intervention in a Disadvantaged Urban Area

HARRIS B. PECK, SEYMOUR R. KAPLAN, AND MELVIN ROMAN

COMMUNITY programs in disadvantaged urban areas are customarily characterized as being oriented either toward "mental health" or "social action" despite the fact that such programs often have similar aims. In programs directed at juvenile delinquency or school dropouts and viewed as social action programs, for example, certain types of mental health personnel and procedures may be deliberately excluded, while other programs with exactly similar goals may be led by mental health professionals. In social action programs, which are usually addressed to informal groupings and institutions in the community at large, the effort is to activate the target population to use possibilities for self-improvement available in the community. Such programs attempt to increase the opportunities for community development and encourage client pressure from *outside* the institutions to bring about change, sometimes by means of militant social action. Community mental health programs, on the other hand, tend to emphasize collaboration and consultation with public and private social agencies. By and large, such programs tend to avoid social action approaches, especially those of a militant nature, and endeavor to bring about change by working *within* formal institutional hierarchy.

There are undoubtedly substantial differences in emphasis between the two types of programs. However in practice the distinction often seems arbitrary and based on failure to recognize the potential mental health implications of social action programs or conversely the need to build certain social action components into community mental health programs. In our opinion efforts in any comprehensive community program to bring about change must be exerted both from within existing institutional structures and upon them from without. This paper describes the initial phase of a program of intervention in a disadvantaged urban area in which an attempt is being made to integrate community mental health and social action approaches.

Reprinted from *American Journal of Orthopsychiatry*, 1966, *36*, 57–69, by permission of the publisher and the authors. © 1966, American Orthopsychiatric Association. Dr. Peck is Director, Lincoln Hospital Mental Health Services and Associate Professor of Psychiatry, Albert Einstein College of Medicine, New York City. Dr. Kaplan is Assistant Director, Lincoln Hospital Mental Health Services and Assistant Professor, Albert Einstein College of Medicine, New York City. Dr. Roman is Associate Professor, Department of Psychiatry, Albert Einstein College of Medicine, New York City.

The mental health program to which this presentation refers originated within one of the more traditional bases for such programs, the psychiatric department of a medical school. In 1959, the Department of Psychiatry of the Albert Einstein College of Medicine founded a Division of Social and Community Psychiatry, primarily as a research and demonstration unit. When in 1963 the opportunity presented itself to establish a new department of psychiatry at Lincoln Hospital in a seriously disadvantaged area of the South Bronx, the several years of experimentation and experience already gained had persuaded us that an effective community program must concern itself with issues of social change. The crude statistics of the South Bronx, when we came to study them, confirmed that merely providing direct services would be unlikely to meet even the minimal needs of such an area. Any program, we felt, must embody the possibility of engagement with those aspects of the social system reflected in the demographic data.[1] While the precise form of intervention was dictated by the particular conditions prevailing in this community, deprived urban areas resemble each other in many respects, and thus it may be useful to review some of the specific considerations which have influenced the direction of the program at Lincoln Hospital.

THE NEED FOR INNOVATION

In the South Bronx, the public service agencies, because of their fragmentation, complexity and bureaucratization present a frustrating, powerful, and seemingly insurmountable network of barriers to their effective use. Voluntary family and children's agencies of New York City have only one office to serve the entire Bronx; former neighborhood offices and outposts have been consolidated in the interests of economy. Each office is located, as are many of the public agencies, in middle-class neighborhoods at a considerable distance from populations who need the services most. Their traditional ways of operating (waiting lists, weekly appointments, long-term service, an emphasis on "talking through") are not consonant with the needs, the experience or the life style of low-income people. As for city agencies, the complexity of the urban structure makes it difficult and frustrating for individuals, even those who are

[1] Compared to the Bronx as a whole, most of the Lincoln area falls into the lowest quartile of median family income ($3700–5400) and educational attainment (7.6–8.8 years) and the highest rate of male unemployment. The rate of unemployment in this area is approximately twice that of the Bronx average. Similarly, the amount of overcrowded housing and school facilities are about twice that of the Bronx as a whole.

In addition, compared to the Bronx as a whole:

1. Rates for juvenile delinquency offenses are 25 per cent higher.
2. Rates of venereal disease among youth under 21 are three times greater in some neighborhoods of the Lincoln area and 1¼ times as high as in other areas.
3. The rate of public assistance cases is approximately twice as high.
4. Admission rates to state mental hospitals are 40 per cent higher from this area.
5. Although reliable figures are not available estimates of the percentage of deliveries of the Lincoln Hospital Obstetrical Service in which there is no legal father run as high as 70 per cent. (Comparable figures for the Bronx as a whole are not available).

long-time residents, to ferret out and make proper use of resources as they attempt to deal with problems of employment, housing, education, recreation, income, etc. In particular, because of differences in socialization and life experience, low-income people are even less skilled than their middle-class counterparts in formulating their needs "acceptably," stating their complaints and asserting their rights. Since low-income people require the concrete services of some of these systems for sheer survival as well as for their social and psychological well being, their inability to voice their needs effectively contributes to their sense of powerlessness, anomie and frustration and reinforces their self-defeating behavior.

Nevertheless, as one becomes acquainted with a deprived urban area like the South Bronx, the question is not why there is so much pathology but, rather, why there is not more. How do so many residents maintain their sanity, self-esteem and autonomy? Clearly, the "disorganized" community must have its own unique, informal organizational structure which is at least as effective in maintaining, "treating" and rehabilitating its citizens psychologically and socially as is the limited and deficient formal agency structure. In recognition of this, social action programs usually attempt to potentiate the community's effectiveness by introducing external leadership around whom the indigenous leaders can be rallied. The social impact of this approach appears to have been amply demonstrated by Alinsky (1) and others, but evaluation of the impact in mental health terms has been handicapped by a lack of clarity about the definition of mental health.

CONCEPTUAL ORIENTATION

We are in agreement with Eaton's statement that

. . . mental health is a conceptual abstraction involving relativistic assessment of man's relations to himself, his society, and his values . . . which cannot be understood in isolation from those manifestational phenomena that constitute a person as he functions in society (4, p. 81.).

In *Current Concepts of Positive Mental Health,* Jahoda refers to "autonomy" as a basic criterion of mental health, characterizing this concept as the

. . . relation between individual and environment with regard to decision-making. In this sense autonomy means a conscious discrimination by the individual of environmental factors he wishes to accept or reject (6, p. 45.).

Erikson (5) has recently stated that the individual's psychological defenses are influenced by the nature of the social organization. These writers reflect the growing emphasis upon the importance of seeing the individual as part of his community in order to assess the state of his mental health.

In all our endeavors the basic assumption has been that there is an *intimate relationship between the social organization of the community and the individual psychological organization of its residents.*

A second basic assumption we have made, derived from observations in the social sciences but infrequently stressed by the mental health professional, is the central role played by the small group in community life and particularly in the process of social change. It is our view that *social change is often mediated or effected through small leadership groups.* Because of this assumption we have particularly stressed the use of small groups in the Lincoln Hospital Mental Health program both in the clinical setting and in our efforts to influence leadership functions within the formal and informal structure of the community and its institutions. The community is viewed *as a number of systems of action which in turn consist of interacting subgroups.*

The kinds of groups with which a community mental health program may become engaged include families, gangs and public and private agencies as well as the various cultural, ethnic and informal organizations around which urban society revolves. From a functional viewpoint the challenge is one of centralized planning in order to provide continuity and integration of comprehensive services by the different caretaking segments while at the same time allowing appropriate spontaneous, independent functioning of individual units. To achieve these goals the traditional preventive and treatment functions must be extended to provide means for implementation of change both from within and among subsystems. This requires a radical shift in focus from a primary concern with the individual patient to a program which is in good part directed at the community as a dynamic social system. Such a program must orient itself toward social change which can develop those kinds of relationships among subsystems which will bring about more autonomous levels of functioning both in individuals and in the community as a whole (7).

THE SMALL GROUP APPROACH

Group and family therapy has demonstrated the clinical value of the small group as a diagnostic and therapeutic modality for the more vulnerable individuals in the community. However our interest in the small group extends beyond its value as a treatment method. We see the small group as a means of gaining access to information which pertains to the community at large as well as to the individual. The sociologist and social psychologist have been using the small group towards this end for some time, and we ourselves, in a study of the community of a psychiatric day hospital, have attempted to examine the interplay between followers and leaders for its implications for both individual and social change within a therapeutic community (8). It is difficult enough for clinicians to extend their view to encompass the society of a small hospital. To trace the processes of social and individual change across the arena of the entire South Bronx strains both our imagination and our competence. However, we have tried to use the model of larger social changes as reflected in small group phenomena to intervene in the vastly more complex and less defined community of some 350,000 people comprising the South Bronx.

The implementation of this model by the staff of the Lincoln Hospital Mental Health Services in relation to various individuals and groups which comprise the South Bronx community takes place primarily in three inter-related activities: the work of the Multipurpose Clinical Facility, consultation with selected public and private community agencies, and the Neighborhood Service Centers. The rather cumbersome title, Multipurpose Clinical Facility, was chosen because it is an accurate description and because it serves as a reminder that the functions of the clinic are not primarily those of the usual psychiatric outpatient or mental hygiene clinic even though it does, to be sure, provide some direct services, including information, a walk-in facility, referral and diagnostic studies, and brief treatment contacts generally limited to about six individual or family interviews. All such contacts are viewed as opportunities to gain access to subsystems which may be in crisis. With each individual who appears for assistance, an attempt is made to investigate his association with one or another aspect of the social milieu which may be in difficulty.[2] In practice, this approach leads to an emphasis on involving the total family in the evaluation and treatment effort and directing particular attention to the welfare, housing or other realistic social concerns which almost always accompany the psychological symptoms in the adult population we serve. Whether help to the individual patient requires assistance to a family in crisis or intervention in some critical aspect of the family's relation with a community agency, we believe that our efforts must be addressed both to the individual in distress and to that aspect of the social system which appears to be associated with the difficulty.

Thus the individual patient or his family's problem frequently draws our attention to a community agency or hospital department. Wherever it appears feasible and productive to do so, consultation is arranged. Such consultation is aimed at assisting the staff of the agency or department to serve the case directly or in collaboration with the Lincoln Hospital Mental Health Services. In some instances direct treatment by the Mental Health Services appears indicated either because it is the most appropriate agency to do so or because no other resources are available. In the latter event, when it is evident that an attempt to fill a major gap in the fragmentary network of community services would lead to a swamping of our limited resources (without necessarily meeting the need), an attempt is made to engage the sister agency in planning for the development of additional treatment resources. Where no facilities exist and

[2] The prototype for this approach has been described by Peck (8) in work conducted in a psychiatric day hospital which suggested that changes in the status of an individual necessitating institutional psychiatric care are accompanied by and related to a significant alteration or decompensation in some small group, such as the family, in which the patient is a nuclear interacting member.

it does not seem feasible for them to be developed within the context of the existing agency structure, the Mental Health Services must consider the possibility of initiating a new facility. Such a need was felt, for example, in relation to the aftercare of hospitalized patients. Patients in the South Bronx are hospitalized if they become sufficiently disturbed so that their own lives or the lives of others are endangered. However, their initial hospitalization is likely to be brief, and they are either transferred to a state hospital for a more prolonged stay or returned to the community if the acute phase of the disturbance appears resolved. Whether the stay in the hospital has been brief or extended, the community has few resources to offer the patient with a serious mental illness. Reflected in the high hospital admission and readmission rates is, among other factors, the lack of opportunity for work to help maintain such individuals economically, socially and psychologically. Thus there appeared to be an urgent need for a program which combined some of the elements of partial hospitalization, opportunity for resocialization and assistance to the patient in making the transition to working and living in the community. To meet these needs we have currently under development activity groups engaged in work-for-pay who spend extended periods of the day at the Mental Health facility. Obviously, the needs of such patients cannot be met solely by a mental health agency, and various other resources within the community must be tapped. To this end, collaboration has been established with a private rehabilitation agency, and efforts are being made to integrate the program with the services of such agencies as the Welfare Department, Division of Vocational Rehabilitation, and the State After-Care Services. Although the participation of such agencies provides substantial support, the development of really adequate provisions for this seriously ill group must ultimately involve segments of the community which are not generally considered part of the formal agency structure. For example, the problem of providing appropriate living accommodations may require participation of such organizations as the churches, Puerto Rican hometown groups, settlement houses, and other less formal organizations within the various neighborhoods. Unless the agency structure can be augmented in this way, it is not likely that we will be able to mount a program which realistically contends with such critical mental health issues.

As pertinent as work and housing considerations are for the psychotic individual, they are even more relevant in connection with such widespread problems as delinquency, drug addiction, school dropouts, maternal and child health services, unemployment, etc. Any significant approach to such issues demands access to and participation by the informal organizations within the community and requires some means of integrating and relating their efforts to the work of the agencies and the clinical facilities of the Mental Health Service. It is with this objective in mind that the Neighborhood Service Center and Mental Health Aide programs have been developed.[3]

[3] In addition to this program, we have developed collaborative programs with the Board of Education, the Day Care Centers and many of the group service agencies in the community. The relationship of these projects to our total strategy will be described in detail in a subsequent paper.

THE NEIGHBORHOOD SERVICE CENTER [4]

Integration of mental health and social action approaches requires some means of bridging the gap that exists between the professional staff of a municipal mental health service such as ours and the population who are the actual recipients of the service rendered. Toward this end the establishment of Neighborhood Service Centers is a major innovation. The Centers are housed in only slightly remodeled "store front" locations and are staffed by nonprofessional mental health aides recruited from the neighborhood under the supervision of a professional Center Director. Although nonprofessional aides also work in the Multipurpose Clinical Facility and some of the social action programs originate from the hospital, the locale and staffing of the N.S.C. seem to lend themselves in a unique way to the implementation of social action programs. To amplify, we shall describe something of the N.S.C. program, its organization, and its "bridging" function between hospital and community as reflected in the pattern of services it is developing.[4]

Two Neighborhood Service Centers are now in operation in the South Bronx and another will open in the latter part of 1965.[5] The Centers are located close to transportation hubs and in areas that rank high in the various indices of psychosocial pathology. Locations are chosen on the basis of neighborhood boundaries, potential relationships to existing public and private agencies and facilities and general characteristics and structure of the surrounding community. Since we are developing a network of small decentralized mental health complexes consisting of coordinated schools-settlement house-health department programs, the N.S.C. tends to be located within such constellations in order to facilitate the integration of community-based programs with the hospital-based clinical facility.

Each Neighborhood Service Center is staffed primarily by five to eight Mental Health aides (nonprofessionals) under the supervision of a mental health worker (professional). The Centers maintain a close relationship with the Multipurpose Clinical Facility at Lincoln Hospital. Codirectors of the N.S.C. program are members of the administrative committee of the Lincoln Hospital Mental Health Services. The Centers are encouraged to limit their services to an area and population of "manageable size" within boundaries which permit the Center staff to become intimately acquainted with, known to and used by the people of the surrounding area. The Centers, through the use of indigenous nonprofessional personnel, function as a bridge between the low-income population and the middle-class professionals. Nonprofessionals

---

[4] Much of the material pertaining to the N.S.C. is drawn from an unpublished document, The Neighborhood Service Center: A Proposal to Implement a Community Mental Health Network, Peck, F. Riessman, Hallowitz—Lincoln Hospital Mental Health Services.

[5] Support for the N.S.C. program is primarily derived from a demonstration grant from the Office of Economic Opportunity.

can often be more effective than professionals in those roles which require staff to "reach out." The Centers as part of the larger Lincoln Hospital Mental Health Services complex help to bridge the split which often develops between community and hospital-based services and staff. By virtue of their position in the hospital program structure, the Centers allow for considerable inter-action and facilitate the integration between professional and nonprofessional staff and between clinical and nonclinical services.

THE NEIGHBORHOOD SERVICE CENTER AND SOCIAL ACTION

The Neighborhood Service Center has become the place in the community to which residents turn in time of crisis. In this way the Center is able to keep abreast of the kinds of psychosocial problems with which the residents have to cope, the services needed and their availability. Likewise, the gaps, limitations, and deficiencies in the formal service structure and the informal alternative arrangements currently employed by the community are detected more readily. Thus, the Center serves as an important source of information on the nature of social changes needed as well as a possible focus from which action to implement the changes can arise. The specific manner in which such programs are initiated varies not only according to the nature of the problem encountered but also from one Center to the next in terms of differing priority of needs, relationships to the community and so on. Basically, we expect our Centers and the aides to play a vital role in finding and developing indigenous leadership and in involving those residents in the community who are usually not reached by other social action groups.

The question of the source and initiative for programs directed toward social change is intimately connected with the analysis of the causes underlying the need for change. If we accept the viewpoint postulated by Brager (2) that in disadvantaged urban areas there is a "reciprocal" dysfunctional relationship between client "defects" and institutional "defects," it becomes necessary to attend to the interrelation of the two. We expect the Neighborhood Service Center to contribute to the kind of fundamental changes envisioned by those community mental health and social action programs which hope to influence both institutions and their clients. We do not believe, however, that the N.S.C. is the sole means of achieving such influence. Professional consultation with the Board of Education, the Health Department, the settlement houses, etc., is being combined with efforts to involve parents, the recipients of health services, etc., in active collaboration in the use of the new resources. It is anticipated that change initiated from above (in the institution) and from below (in the Neighborhood Service Center) will feed into, enrich and complement each other. Needless to say, administrative skill in timing and attention to the con-cerns of those involved in order to maintain communication is of the essence in the success of such efforts.

We expect that one of the ways that the N.S.C. will contribute to changes within the community will be by demonstrating the feasibility of some of its own endeavors. Many more than three Centers are required for the mental health services for the 350,000 in our area, and it is hoped that the N.S.C. will become a model which will help to stimulate the development of other centers under the auspices of various other public or private agencies. While centers developed by other agencies would differ in many respects from those sponsored by a mental health service, they may provide direct or ancillary mental health functions that would greatly augment our work, especially if collaborative arrangements can be made. Where an organization in an adjacent area is ready and able to serve as nucleus for the development of a N.S.C. for its own area, we would consider it not only advantageous to assist in its inception but would seek out opportunities to encourage such a development. Hopefully, if a number of centers do evolve, an interdependent network of centers will emerge as part of a community-wide mental health effort.

THE DIRECT SERVICES OF THE NEIGHBORHOOD SERVICE CENTER

The N.S.C. provides a place where a resident may turn for guidance and help with whatever problems small or large are of concern to him or his family. It may be as simple as assistance in writing a letter to a son in the army or making application to a housing project or facilitating application for a day camp. We refer to this as "first aid" for social and psychosocial problems. But a N.S.C. is also called upon for assistance in more complex and emotion-laden situations. In some cases on-the-spot advice and guidance or giving information as to where needed services can be obtained is all that is required. More usually, the seeker of a service must be helped to know how to make application and to deal with the bottlenecks or red-tape, and he may need the encouragement and support of the worker in order to maintain motivation, dignity, self-esteem (and sometimes sanity) in the early stages of seeking and receiving service. In other cases the service required is not readily available because of waiting lists, and the N.S.C. worker is called upon to engage in a psychosocial "holding action," that is, to use his knowledge and skill to keep a crisis situation from deteriorating into relatively irreversible pathology.

Residents appearing at the N.S.C. who need psychiatric evaluation or service have the opportunity of consulting a member of the Lincoln Hospital Mental Health Services team at a designated time during the week when the team (social worker, psychiatrist, nurse, psychologist) is present at the Center. If the problem is more urgent, the resident is referred immediately to Lincoln Hospital, with an appointment being made directly by the N.S.C. worker, thus expediting referral. If necessary, the client is escorted to the hospital.

SOME BASIC DILEMMAS

Before concluding this presentation, it may be pertinent to underline some of the basic dilemmas attendant upon comprehensive community projects. We do not pretend that the Lincoln program can now offer any fundamental solutions to these problems, but only that an awareness of them pervades our program and that we are attempting to address ourselves to them in a planful and systematic fashion.

RESISTANCE TO CHANGE: A BASIC HUMAN DILEMMA

There are basic dilemmas inherent in a comprehensive mental health program which, in essence, are no different from those confronting any organization which sets for itself a goal of bringing about change in existing social structures. These problems are not necessarily linked with issues of power, status, or other realistic issues which consciously concern all of us. We refer here to the human resistances to change. While human resistance to change originates from many sources, most of all we fear the uncertainty of change.

The implementation of a comprehensive community mental health program involves social change, a change for which there is no organized body of theory to dictate program priorities or phasing. We do know that any changes that take place are not likely to occur evenly or harmoniously. While integration and coordination of diverse programs can be planned, the programs will not develop simultaneously, and choices will have to be made. The choice may sometimes require that development in one direction be implemented at the expense of another. We must try to anticipate and prepare for the consequences since it can be no other way in the human situation. There is no human growth without some resistance to it, and rarely does commitment to a choice carry with it certainty as to outcome. If institutions are to change and if the community is to be mobilized, what must occur is not only an expansion of existing facilities, as much as this is needed, but the emergence of new institutions and, if you will, of a new community, one more meaningfully related to and representative of its residents. This does not necessarily mean that the institutions will change their names or their personnel but, rather, that they will alter their functional relationships.

No one can predict the precise nature or extent of these changes for any given institution or segment of the population since these must be truly creative emergents of interaction. But it is important to appreciate the human factor involved because very often conflicts in planning and programming arise from a shared anxiety about change without certainty, an anxiety which the involved staff members displace on to minor differences among them. One of the necessary attitudes for those participating in such programs is a willingness to explore commonalities of issues when differences appear to exist. This is a matter of communication among the involved participants and reflects the style of leadership of the administrative groups, the channels which they establish for communication, their exercise of power, their permissiveness toward the development of autonomy.

THE ADMINISTRATIVE DILEMMA: CENTRALIZED PLANNING AND DECENTRALIZED FUNCTIONS

The small, manageable, semi-autonomous unit is the mainstay of the developing Lincoln program. There has been some discussion as to how large a population a comprehensive mental health center ought to serve: 200,000, the maximum allowed under the new Community Mental Health Center Act? 30,000, the size of the Montefiore program? The five-block radius which seems to be the natural utilization range of Neighborhood Service Centers? The single-block unit which Clifford Shaw said was the optimal size for his kind of community organization?

Clearly, urban organization has a place for institutions of various sizes, dimensions, and functions. Perhaps the real issue is to use the appropriate instrument for the specific task. The size of certain operations must be small enough to give the people who are critically involved as consumers of the service some say in how they would like to be served and what the boundaries of their programs ought to be. If we follow this track, we will deal with a segment of a community very much as we might deal with an individual or a family at intake. The agency would begin with some sense of its own mission and competence but would be prepared to develop an initial contract with the community which allows for the kind of interaction in which both might ultimately modify their initial stance.

THE POLITICAL DILEMMA: SOME BASIC FACTS OF LIFE

It remains a moot question as to whether a publicly supported institution can take leadership in promoting social change which may involve criticism of the supporting sources of that institution. This is most likely to occur around those forms of social action which follow the militant protest model. We perceive our model, in contrast, as one of an active collaboration from both "above" and "below," but it is still an unanswered question whether the Lincoln program can assume the role of a "third force." We are not romanticists unaware of some of the hard facts of life in human endeavors, and we realize that we might be perceived as playing both ends against the middle despite our best intentions. Unfortunately, we are relative newcomers to the intricacies of community politics insofar as understanding the subtleties of how the various segments of the community view institutional operations such as ours. We place some reliance upon the perception by the public of physicians as a humane and non-biased professional group and upon the psychiatrist's potential leadership role in mental health activities within the community. Nevertheless, we are giving serious thought to the establishment of advisory boards constituted in such a way as to provide guidance in the political and technical areas to which our staff's competence does not extend.

THE DILEMMA OF ACTION RESEARCH

The above comments relating to the various dilemmas confronting the Lincoln program represent something more than a statement of the difficult problems which beset us. We lack both the experience and the conceptual clarity required to select out what is truly essential within the Lincoln program. This not only makes for difficulty in setting priorities but also in knowing what to look for once an alternative has been selected.

Although a broad program of evaluation is being designed for the Lincoln program as a whole, we would like particularly to build provision for such study into our more innovative projects. However, our research staff is experiencing considerable difficulty in determining what measures to employ in studying techniques for which there is so little precedent. In the case of the Neighborhood Service Center program, for example, the dilemma looks as if it will be settled by throwing a rather broad net over the entire operation and trying to study simultaneously the impact of the program on the social agency's structure, the direct effects on clients and community, and the selection, training and performance of the personnel with a view to ultimate evaluation.

SUMMARY AND CONCLUSIONS

There are many theoretical and technical problems yet to be resolved in the mounting of comprehensive community mental health programs. The disadvantaged urban area seems to confront us with dilemmas which may be somewhat unique but which we suspect often reflect, in dramatic and acute form, issues shared in common with more favored communities.

If comprehensive programs are truly to serve all of the people in a community and attend to all three levels of prevention, they must address themselves not only to individuals, families, and populations, but to the various formal and informal institutions in the community. Most of the professionals now in the field will find that they must make substantial revisions in their conceptual approach, extensions of their technical armamentarium, and add categories to their personnel rosters in order to meet the new challenges. Training programs must be mounted for the seasoned professional and raw recruit alike. Research and evaluation must be built into the new programs, with adequate provision for effective and timely feedback to program planning and development.

The disadvantaged urban area is perhaps most demanding in confronting the mental health professional with difficult alternatives. These will, however, have to be faced in one form or another by the new programs in every community. What priority will be given to consultation and training over direct services? To what extent will such services employ group and family approaches rather than concentrating on individual psychotherapy? What stance will the agency take in relation to the rising tides of social change? Where will it assume leadership, where participate or facilitate, and where stand aside?

The mental health professionals, the agencies with which they are associated and the disciplines which spawned them, have a great deal to contribute to the new comprehensive community program, in and outside the poverty areas. Many of the concepts, principles, and practices with which we are familiar can be applied, and though they cannot be mechanically transposed, they can be extended and modified to help us in the tasks ahead. In addition, however, we must all be prepared to take on new roles, develop new theoretical tools, and acquire skills we have yet to learn. We must not extend the range of our competence too far or too fast however, lest we lose one identity before we have emerged into the next. Many who have been mostly practitioners may have to devote much of their time to being teachers. We shall all have to learn lessons which will not be brief, easy or painless. They do, however, seem to hold great promise for the people we serve and rich rewards for those of us who can learn to serve them better.

REFERENCES

1. Alinsky, S. *Citizen participation and community organization in planning and urban renewal.* Chicago: Industrial Areas Foundation, 1962.
2. Brager, G. New concepts and patterns of service: The mobilization for youth program. In Riessman, F., Cohen, J., and Pearl, A. (Eds.) *Mental health of the poor.* New York: Free Press, 1964.
3. Duhl, L. H. Some contributions of psychoanalysis to social psychiatry. n.d.
4. Eaton, J. W. The assessment of mental health. *Amer. J. Psychiat.,* 1951, 108:81–90.
5. Erikson, E. H. Identity and the life cycle. *Psychol. Issues,* 1959, 1 (Monogr. 1).
6. Jahoda, M. *Current concepts of positive mental health.* New York: Basic Books, 1958.
7. Peck, H. B. Some relationships between group process and mental health phenomena in theory and practice. *Internat. J. Group Psychotherap.,* 1963, 13:269.
8. Peck, H. B. The psychiatric day hospital in a mental health program. *Amer. J. Orthopsychiat.,* 1963, 33:3.

39

Occupational Mental Health: Review of an Emerging Art

ALAN A. MCLEAN

THE emerging field of occupational mental health is concerned with both the psychiatrically ill employee and with factors in the work environment which stimulate mentally healthy behavior. This report traces historical influences which have contributed to present practices, discusses current activities, surveys selected publications and considers possible implications for future developments.

Historical material has been largely drawn from the pages of the *American Journal of Psychiatry,* its annual reviews and definitive articles which, since 1927, have been addressed periodically to industrial and occupational psychiatry. Other disciplines have increasingly contributed, however, broadening our base of knowledge beyond clinical concepts and applications. From the behavioral sciences, occupational medicine and toxicology have come publications and programs of significant interest to those concerned with mental disorder and mental health in the work setting. Much of this material will also be considered.

HISTORICAL REVIEW

For a century or so prior to 1870, a primary aim of industrial leaders seems to have been the highest possible production at the lowest possible cost. The worker was employed as a source of physical energy, and little consideration was given to his well-being. He knew no material security and "earned too much to die and too little to live (85)."

Around 1850 the average life expectancy of the factory worker was 32 years. In many locations, particularly in England and on the Continent, children started working at age six, putting in the same 12 hours a day as did their fathers.

Reprinted from the *American Journal of Psychiatry,* 1966, 22, 961–976, by permission of the publisher and the author. © 1965, American Psychiatric Association. Dr. McLean is Clinical Associate Professor of Psychiatry, Cornell University Medical College.

In this period the relationship between factory hand and industry was characterized by suffering—materially, bodily and mentally. There probably was a certain kind of adjustment based upon their current interpretations of tenets of Christianity which saw suffering as an essential condition of life, labor as a punishment and happiness as not to be achieved in this life.

The rise of the labor movement was the expression of a challenge to this philosophy that was developing throughout all the ranks of the society. Comfort and ease, even perhaps happiness, were to be attainable. It was in this context that concern with occupational mental health first appeared.

While nothing appears in the literature until the 1940's concerning his activities, C. C. Burlingame in his first annual review of psychiatric progress on "Psychiatry in Industry" (14) notes that his activities in 1915 at the Cheney Silk Company constituted the first full-time function of the psychiatrist in industry. Neither in this article nor in the many later references to Burlingame in this pioneering role is there a detailed outline of his functions.

In the first issue (1917) of the journal *Mental Hygiene,* Herman Adler, previously chief of staff of the Boston Psychopathic Hospital, reported on patients for whom unemployment had been a serious problem (1). Males between the ages of 25 and 55, these individuals were grouped into three classifications: "paranoid personalities," "inadequate personalities" and the "emotionally unstable."

Three years later, Mary Jarrett reported a follow-up of this same group, observing that 75 per cent were successfully adjusted from an occupational point of view (43).

Few articles appearing in the literature prior to Adler's 1917 report could properly be included in the emerging field of industrial or occupational psychiatry. Both his work and Jarrett's appear to have resulted from the stimulus of E. E. Southard, Director of the Boston Psychopathic Hospital and Professor of Neuropathology at Harvard.

In 1919 Southard was asked by the Engineering Foundation of New York to investigate emotional problems among workers. Working with a clinical team that included a social worker and a psychologist, he found that "62 per cent of more than 4,000 cases reached the discharged status through traits of social incompetence rather than occupational incompetence (43)." These statistics are still quoted today as a valid representation of a continuing industrial pattern.

The following year Southard commented as follows:

Industrial medicine exists, industrial psychiatry ought to exist. It is important for the modern psychiatrist not to hide his light under a bushel; he must step forth to new community duties. It seems to me that as psychiatrists we should be able to help this movement wherever it becomes practically possible. The practical possibilities of helping lie in connection with the fact that the majority of our male patients have come out of industry in some capacity. Some investigations of the individual patient with respect to their industrial status and future should be made. I think that we will have a place in the routine of industrial management not as a permanent staff member (except in very large firms and business systems) but as consultants. The function of this occasional consultant would be preventative rather than curative of the general condition of unrest (81).

Thus we set down in Boston some 45 years ago an operating philosophy for the psychiatrist—and, indeed, in later days for the clinical psychologist—in industry.

1920–29

The first "Review of Industrial Psychiatry" in the *American Journal of Psychiatry* in April 1927 (80) summarized the literature to date, defined the field and traced its development. Mandel Sherman, its author, considered the psychiatrist's rightful area of concern to be the "individual's adjustment to the situation as a whole." The psychiatrist also is said to "attempt to forestall maladjustments by aiding in developing interests and incentives."

The stimulus for the development of industrial psychiatry until that time is traced to: (1) the work of the psychologists in the industrial field, whose studies of abilities and intelligence were felt to fall far short of considering the whole man; (2) the adjustment problems of men in the armed forces during World War I; (3) the "propaganda efforts of the mental hygienists" here including Southard; and (4) the introduction of scientific methodology into psychiatry.

By scientific methodology, Sherman meant the study of the individual and his vocation from the standpoint of "development of conflicts in his early life." He attributed this approach to the mental hygienists and termed it a contribution of American psychiatry. He went on to discuss a second "methodological" approach: "Another method stems from the European psycho-analytic method, finding conflicts due to lack of adequate expression of two primary instincts, sexual and self-preservative." Citing W. A. White's paper "Psychoanalysis in Vocational Guidance," he notes that vocational choice often results from drives developed early in life. He further notes that W. Stekel has used three groups to classify vocational choice: (1) those who developed strong positive identification with father, (2) those rejecting a hated father and (3) "the sublimation group."

Sherman cited other methods of explaining intrapsychic conflicts manifest in the work situation. He included the "instinct theory" of O. Tead, whose subsequent books on industrial management became classic, and a theory of "reveries." The latter contribution came from Elton Mayo in 1922, well before the famous "Hawthorne experiments" at Western Electric Company which he led.

The penchant of psychiatrists of the time to classify patterns of emotional reaction did not escape those with industrial interests. In addition to Adler's attempt, which did not meet with general acceptance, Pruette and Fryer spoke of the "repressed" and the "elated" as two categories of disturbed worker.

At the conclusion of this first review of the field, Sherman said that among the various methods of industrial psychiatry, the most successful procedure used to aid the individual in readjusting to industry had been one which attempted to analyze the total situation—the early life history, the social situation, the worker's motives and incentives in addition to the immediate difficulties at work. "Classification of maladjusted individuals into types or groups has been of little help." His final plea was for vocational guidance during the formative years to obviate many later industrial maladjustments.

The year 1922 saw the introduction of the first full-time psychiatrist in an American business organization of which we have a full description; Lydia Giberson was employed by the Metropolitan Life Insurance Company (31). In 1924, a mental health service was introduced at the R. H. Macy department store. V. V. Anderson, in 1929, summarized this program in the first book on industrial psychiatry (3). In a paper at the 80th annual meeting of the American Psychiatric Association, also in 1924, Osnato discussed current concepts of the industrial neuroses, by which he meant post-traumatic reactions (68). His primary concern was in distinguishing between "malingerers and hysterics."

In the 1920's the greatest stimulus to the study of industry as a social organization came from Professor Mayo. Psychiatrists then and now acknowledge his influence on their thinking about the individual and his environment. Professor Mayo became interested in studies on fatigue and monotony at the Harvard Physiology Laboratory. In 1923, he was asked to investigate high labor turnover in a textile mill. He noted that, with the introduction of rest periods for workers in monotonous jobs, morale rose and labor turnover decreased.

In 1927, Mayo and his associates undertook a study of working conditions at the Hawthorne Plant of the Western Electric Company in Chicago. In several years of study at this location, 20,000 employees were interviewed and small experimental groups of workers were intensively observed as changes were made in their work situation. These studies demonstrated the tremendous importance of human interaction as an integral part of the work situation, and that dissatisfactions arising in or out of the plant become entwined, influencing each other and affecting work production.

Mayo's classic volume, *The Human Problems of an Industrial Civilization* (56), describes this work, as does the book *Management and the Worker* by Roethlisberger and Dickson (76).

The Hawthorne studies concluded that an industrial enterprise has two functions: economic and social. Production output was felt to be a form of *social* behavior, and all the activity of a plant may be viewed as an interaction of structure, culture and personality. If any one of these variables is altered, change must occur in the other two. Reactions to stress on the part of individual employees arise when there is resistance to change, when there are faulty control and communications systems and in the adjustments of the individual worker to his structure at work (62).

During the first World War a series of papers from the Industrial Fatigue Research Board in England began to focus attention on the psychological components of industrial accidents (34), on fatigue and on psychiatric illness in the work setting (23). Little mention was made of these studies in American literature until some two decades later. Basic concepts of accident proneness and our first indications of the prevalence of psychiatric disorder in an industrial population came from this work.

The applications of psychiatry to industry in this country during the 1930s are well described in Rennie, Swackhamer and Woodward's 1947 paper, "Toward Industrial Mental Health: An Historical Review (73)."

1930–39

The depression years were characterized by quiescence in the field; even the annual review was dropped from the *American Journal of Psychiatry*. The major clinical activities were those of Giberson (31, 32, 33) and Burling (10, 11), the only psychiatrists operating full-time programs. Some interest continued to be shown by industrial medicine (22). Mayo's work, which continued well into this decade, was the most significant research of the period.

1940–49

World War II had tremendous impact upon clinical applications of the psychiatrist, and to a lesser degree the clinical psychologist, in industry. Concepts of psychoanalytic psychology were introduced and applied. Expectations of industry were high, perhaps unrealistically so, and to a certain extent psychiatry and psychology were "oversold." Yet during the war years greater and more sophisticated applications in the mold of Southard, Sherman and White could be seen (7, 8, 53, 55, 59).

Of the many papers during these years, three will illustrate the pattern of publication during the early 1940's. In a 1944 editorial in the *American Journal of Psychiatry*, C. Macfie Campbell stated that the war had "swept the psychiatrist out of his hospital wards and his administrative routine." It was to be hoped, he said, that the psychiatrist would continue "devoting more attention to that portion of social living which occupies the major portion of an individual's life—his job." He went on to conclude: "Industry turns out two main commodities, material goods and human satisfactions. The wholesome or unwholesome structure and the stability or instability of our modern industrial community may well depend upon the amount of attention given to the latter commodity (20)."

In 1943, Rosenbaum and Romano discussed "Psychiatric Casualties among Defense Workers (77)." They pointed to the need for industrial physicians to concern themselves with the recognition of emotional factors underlying behavior, which so frequently resulted in inferior output, high sickness rates, high labor turnover and absenteeism—"of prime importance under wartime conditions which cannot countenance impaired efficiency."

Among the many articles describing mental health programs in wartime industry, those concerning the Oak Ridge, Tenn. industrial community subsequently received major attention (14, 15, 16, 17). With available psychiatric assistance, primarily through "emotional first-aid stations," a minimum of on-the-job treatment resulted in conspicuous on-the-job improvement. As in publications prior to the war, psychiatrists outlining their wartime experiences noted that the causes of emotional disturbance in industry lie primarily in the individual or in the home or nonwork social surroundings, rather than in the job situation.

Following the war, with the sharp cutback in defense industries which had employed psychiatrists, many industrial mental health programs came to a halt. Interest in the rehabilitation of the psychiatrically handicapped veteran gave impetus to the development of civilian programs such as that at Eastman Kodak Company. Successful application of psychiatric skills in the armed forces during the war stimulated the interest of several psychiatrists to broaden their scope of practice and to include preventive concepts born of their experiences in the service.

The federal government initiated action with the Vocational Rehabilitation Act Amendments of 1943, and the Office of Vocational Rehabilitation issued a pamphlet, "The Doctor and Vocational Rehabilitation for Civilians (84)." Stimulus was given to the training of clinical psychologists in greater number, primarily in programs of the Veterans Administration. Many were subsequently to work in industry.

Roffey Park was established by British industry immediately after the war as an industrial rehabilitation center for "neurosis cases." During the ensuing decade, some 8000 cases were treated. In the introduction to the volume describing this work, Ling states that "Maladjustment to work has been a major factor in the ill health of many of these men and women (60)."

At the Central Institute of Psychiatry in Moscow, Melekhov and his associates also dealt specifically with psychoneurotic World War II patients. An article outlining the rehabilitation of these patients appeared in *Occupational Therapy and Rehabilitation* in 1947 (60).

In the United States, problems of workmen's compensation were receiving increasing attention, since the courts had by then ruled a wide variety of illness compensable. According to Burlingame's annual review in 1949 (17), coronaries occurring on the job following occupational stress, hypertension, cancer and tuberculosis activated by employment, suicide caused by job-related depression and "paralysis by fright" had all been awarded claims. This trend has in the 1960's received closer attention as awards increase for psychiatric disability unrelated to physical accident.

The first fellowship program for training psychiatrists for work in industry was announced in 1948. Under a grant from the Carnegie Corporation, and under the direction of Leighton and Burling, seven psychiatrists were trained at Cornell University's New York State School of Industrial and Labor Relations (13).

The late 1940's also saw the publication of books by Tredgold (82), Ling (54), Brodman (6) and Rennie, Burling and Woodward (72). These and other monographs focused professional interest on the role of the psychiatrist in industry.

Along with continuing concern for the effects of the emotionally disturbed employee on his work environment and the early recognition and treatment of his symptoms came increased attention by psychiatrists for specific problems such as alcoholism, accidents, psychosomatic reactions, the aging worker, the executive and his emotional problems, emphasis on techniques of management education and the structuring of the work environment. These areas were receiving increasing attention from several of the behavioral science disciplines during the same period.

1950–55

In the early 1950's, Dershimer assumed responsibility for the annual reviews in the *American Journal of Psychiatry* (24, 25, 26, 27). From 1943 to 1955 he was chief psychiatrist for the Du Pont Company. His pessimistic notes listing few of the current publications complained about the lack of acceptance of the psychiatrist in business and industry. The reasons, he felt, were that: (1) psychiatrists have no knowledge of the realities of private enterprise; (2) they belittle the practical knowledge of the field of human relations possessed by industrialists; and (3) they resort to "name calling" when industry fails to demand their services.

One trend Dershimer identified was the increasing tendency to treat psychoneurotic employees while they continue at work. Dershimer wrote that, even though the job may be stressful, "end results are better when patients are helped to meet their responsibilities." At Du Pont, he implied, such an approach was then common.

The first few years of the decade saw publication of a series of significant documents. From the Tavistock Clinic in London came the first volume of the Glacier Metal Company studies, led by Jaques (41). Both the methodology and the research results of this pilot application of psychoanalytic concepts to organization behavior had considerable influence on the development of subsequent programs. Jaques' later concepts of equitable wage payment based on the time span of responsibility inherent in any job were mainly published in the late 1950's but had their roots in the earlier work (39, 40, 42). The reactions of the management of the Glacier Metal Company were subsequently reported by the chairman of its board of directors, Mr. Wilfred Brown (9).

Kalinowsky's psychiatric study of war veterans in Germany (44), Pokorny and Moore's "Neuroses and Compensation" (70), Burling, Lentz and Wilson's volume on the hospital (12), Ross' excellent psychiatric text for the industrial physician (78) and the Group for the Advancement of Psychiatry's definitive statement on the role of the psychiatrist in industry (35) are but a few representative samples of U. S. publications.

During these same first few years of the 1950's, Mindus conducted a six-month survey of industrial psychiatry in Great Britain, the United States and Canada for the World Health Organization and later developed his own concept of industrial psychiatry (63). The survey resulted in the most extensive report on programmatic activities in the field (64). The author visited plants, universities, institutions, agencies and union facilities, summarizing his observations and relating them to prior experiences in the Scandinavian countries.

National committees in the United States included those of the American Psychiatric Association, which served as a clearinghouse of information and represented the official professional viewpoint, that of the Group for the Advancement of Psychiatry, which continued to evaluate current developments in the field, and, while less active at this time, those of the American Medical Association and the Industrial Medical Association.

This period, as reflected in the literature, saw concern for management and executive education with more formalized techniques than previously existed. Laughlin's work with government executives (47, 48, 49), lectures and seminars sponsored by individual companies and by community agencies such as local mental health associations and "sensitivity training" as exemplified by programs of the National Training Laboratories received considerable attention from psychiatry. A psychoanalytic view of work and employment (69), significant research on industrial accidents (79), concern with executive mental health, with labor union programs and with the rehabilitation of the previously hospitalized psychiatric patient were all subjects of discussion.

1956–59

Training for psychiatrists, industrial physicians and executives expanded, particularly with the stimulus of the Menninger Foundation and an enlarging number of other sponsoring agencies including the University of Cincinnati, Cornell University, the National Association for Mental Health and the American Psychiatric Association. Interest on the part of the lay and business press in industrial mental health programs became heavier with feature articles in papers such as the *Wall Street Journal,* syndicated stories by a writer for the Associated Press and articles in *Business Week, Fortune* and the *Saturday Evening Post.*

New full-time psychiatric programs were begun at International Business Machines Corporation, America Fore Insurance Group, the Metropolitan Life Insurance Company and elsewhere. At Metropolitan, Giberson, now reporting to an executive vice-president, was no longer associated with the medical department where a psychiatrist was added. With the death of Walter Woodward, the program at American Cyanamid was discontinued in favor of outside psychiatric consultations. The short-lived program at General Electric Company in Cincinnati was discontinued in favor of a part-time consultant. James Conant, a clinical psychologist, was added to the medical staff of the General Electric Company at Hanford, Wash., to concentrate on management education and clinical consultation on a full-time basis. Research activities under Ross at the University of Cincinnati and Levinson at the Menninger Foundation were instituted.

Books included McLean and Taylor's *Mental Health in Industry* (59) and Menninger and Levinson's *Human Understanding in Industry* (61). By this time articles and monographs concerning the psychiatrist and clinical psychologist in industry, publications by them and others about mental health problems in the world of work were issued frequently. The majority of citations in a recent bibliographic definition of the field, which included nearly 2000 items, appeared during the late 1950's and early 1960's (67).

Alcoholism, automation, absenteeism, rehabilitation, research, post-traumatic neurotic reactions, the psychological fulfillment of the individual in the work setting, the ever-present, generally descriptive discussions of psychiatric applications in business and industry—these were frequent concerns in the literature.

1960–65

The first half of this decade had been marked by continuing growth and expansion of interest in the field. On the international level, a world-wide interest in the mental health implications of the industrial setting was evident in the content of papers read at the 14th International Congress on Occupational Health held in Madrid in 1963. More than 40 presentations were concerned with the psychological problems of the industrial environment. The 1964 annual meeting of the World Federation for Mental Health, held in Bern, had its entire program devoted to mental health in industry. The First International Congress on Social Psychiatry in London in 1964 included many formal presentations on this topic.

In this country, surveys indicated more than 200 psychiatrists and 150 clinical psychologists active in industry. New professional organizations were created, including the Occupational Psychiatry Group and the Center for Occupational Mental Health, Inc. The former, in New York City, consists of 75 industrial medical directors and psychiatrists who meet five times a year for formal discussions followed by a social hour and dinner. The latter, a non-profit organization, was incorporated in 1963 to collect and disseminate data in the field and develop research and educational programs and services for the expanding activities of those interested in occupational mental health.

Significant events in the early '60's included the omission of the word

"Physically" from the title of the President's Committee on the Handicapped, with its subsequent emphasis on the "mentally restored" and mentally retarded worker. Legal implications from the Carter vs. General Motors case (86), where a psychosis was held compensable in the absence of specific physical or psychological trauma, stimulated increased psychiatric attention to matters of workmen's compensation.

Concern for the social and psychological implications of automation has been reflected in seminars and symposiums, a major one being held under the sponsorship of the Group for the Advancement of Psychiatry in 1964. Regular sections of the American Psychiatric Association's annual programs included papers on employment and rehabilitation as well as round-table discussions on occupational stress, compensation, automation and research (57, 58).

In the program area, new ones continue to develop and old ones to grow. In the universities these range in focus from the pure behavioral science research activities of the Institute for Social Research of the University of Michigan (30), through the studies on job satisfactions and psychological growth of Herzberg at Western Reserve (36, 37), to the clinical analysis of the organization and application of group dynamics of Argyris at Yale (4, 5).

Typical of the activities in medical and psychiatric centers are those of the Allan Memorial Institute of Psychiatry of McGill University (18) and the Menninger Foundation. The Industrial Relations Center of the former institution conducts a consultative and educational seminar program (19, 72). The Division of Industrial Mental Health of the Menninger Foundation conducts research on the relationship between man and the organization and also operates a fellowship program for psychiatrists in industrial psychiatry and an educational program for industrial physicians and executives (52).

Industry itself currently has a full range of programs, from part-time outside consultants to full-time staff personnel. Their activities may be based in the medical departments or personnel departments or they may report directly to a senior executive. Their work may consist of straightforward clinical evaluation or treatment with varying regard to the circumstance of the work setting, of clinical consultation, education, training, policy consultation, research, or a combination of these; the last arrangement is most common with those spending a major part of their time in the work setting.

The professional literature of recent years demonstrates a continuing concern on the part of medicine, management, unions, the behavioral sciences and psychology for the mental health of people at work. As expressed in publications, interest has most recently been focused on automation, accidents, psychosomatic reactions, alcoholism, job adjustment and work satisfaction, rehabilitation, compensation claims, industrial mental health programs, motivation for work and symptoms of psychiatric illness which disturb effective performance.

Journal articles and books vary in their content from psychodynamic speculations to precise engineering studies of man-machine relationships. Many writers continue the earlier trend of exhorting and directing others to develop better mental health programs or to become interested in psychiatric problems. Carefully executed clinical research is rare and not often seen in the literature. However, many clinical programs of fair sophistication have not seen the light of the printed page, the feeling of some companies being that conduct of clinical programs and the results of behavioral science research within the organization are properly proprietary. Additional reluctance has stemmed from professionals conducting such programs who feel that outlines of their activities are not proper subjects for the scientific literature. And, of course, many journals discourage such purely descriptive articles in favor of those reporting research results. It is fair to say that the literature does not accurately represent the level of activity in the field.

In the periodical literature, in addition to the occasional individual papers, special sections relating to occupational mental health are appearing from time to time. The greater portion of one issue of *Industrial Medicine and Surgery* (June, 1963) was devoted to "The Worker in the New Industrial Environment" while a previous issue dealt extensively with "Emotional Problems of Executives" (May, 1963), and one complete issue was concerned with "The Impact of Psychiatry on American Management" (November, 1962).

This half decade has also produced a number of major publications covering all aspects of occupational mental health. On the clinical side, there is a new textbook by Collins (21). The American Medical Association issued a guide for employability after psychiatric illness (38). Levinson's *Emotional Health in the World of Work* (50) appeared in early 1964 to aid executives' understanding of behavior, and the American Psychiatric Association's Committee on Occupational Psychiatry issued *The Mentally Ill Employee* (2), a management-oriented guide, in early 1965. Research publications include monographs by Levinson and associates (52), by the staff of the Institute for Social Research of the University of Michigan (30) and a volume on the *Mental Health of the Industrial Worker* by Kornhauser (45). A unique publication is a study of industrial mental health by a group of Harvard Business School graduate students, entitled *The Legacy of Neglect* (28).

Publication of a regular newsletter in occupational psychiatry was undertaken by the American Psychiatric Association's Committee on Occupational Psychiatry in 1960. This was recently superseded by *Occupational Mental Health Notes,* a monthly information bulletin put out by the National Clearinghouse for Mental Health Information in connection with its bibliographic and abstracting activities.

LABOR UNION ACTIVITIES

In May, 1964, a conference on Labor and Mental Health was held in New York City, sponsored by the Community Services Division of the AFL-CIO. Organized labor and mental health professionals were about equally represented at this meeting, the first of its kind and the first formal step by the national labor movement to develop a mental health policy.

While this was a major advance in the field, it did not appear de novo but took place against a background of several decades of interest by individuals and groups in the labor movement. As far back as 1944, Clayton W. Fountain of the United Auto Workers addressed the American Psychiatric Association on "Labor's Place in an Industrial Mental Health Program" (29). While confirming the interest of the unions in the workers' mental health, he stated that to be acceptable to labor, any program developed must not be paternalistic, nor should it be used to undermine the grievance procedure or in any other way subvert the union movement. These cautions continue to influence labor's attitude towards industrial mental health programs and have resulted in few programs being developed under joint sponsorship. Where a company has successfully established a program that avoids these pitfalls, the union will often work with it in close collaboration, but formal participation is avoided.

In 1957 labor movement interest in mental health crystallized around the formation of the National Institute of Labor Education, an organization under the joint directorship of union leaders and mental health professionals. The purpose of this group was to stimulate research and program development in the area of labor and mental health. As part of this program, two documents (65, 71) have been published to serve as guides to interested professionals.

Development has accelerated in the program area. Although as far back as 1946 the Labor Health Institute of Teamsters Local 688 in St. Louis had a psychiatric service as part of its comprehensive health program, it was supported by money from a negotiated fund for general medical care rather than through a specific clause of a collective bargaining agreement (83). The latter pattern did not appear until 1959, when Retail Clerks Local 770 in Los Angeles obtained a contract providing funds for psychiatric services. Since that time a number of other programs have appeared. There has generally been something innovative about each of them. An early one was established by the United Mine Workers of America, which contracted with a private mental hospital in Virginia to serve their members and dependents through a program of traveling clinics. As the demand for service grew, these clinics became permanent establishments in several communities, partly supported by a retainer from the United Mine Workers and partly from fees from nonunion patients (65).

More recently, four union locals in Chicago have collaborated to establish a psychiatric clinic at the Union Health Center and have included in its design two training programs in the recognition and handling of emotional problems, one for their general physicians and one for union leaders. A recently initiated program is located at the Sidney Hillman Health Center of the Amalgamated Clothing Workers of America in New York City (87). An outgrowth of a physical rehabilitation project, this project has sent its staff out into the factories where they work with union representatives and into the union halls where they are visible and immediately available to all workers. Cooperation by management has been uniformly high.

The most recent development in this area, and a particularly important one because of its trend-setting features, is the mental health benefit program recently negotiated by the United Auto Workers with the automobile and argicultural implement manufacturers (66). This contract represents a shift from the traditional labor emphasis on prepaid programs in its provision of limited-coverage health insurance of a traditional type. From the point of view of the industrially oriented psychiatrist, it also unfortunately loses the potential benefits of a program tied in with the work setting.

Despite the variation in the programs described here, it is clear that the pattern of union provision of services has been set. The labor movement, in part feeling that management has been neglectful of its responsibilities in this area of health services and also recognizing its own broader responsibility to its members as part of its general concern for their welfare, is continuing to press for mental health services of a kind best suited to its particular needs (75).

OCCUPATIONAL MEDICINE

Physicians in occupational medicine are increasingly concerned with the mental health and illness of employees. They themselves feel their role in industry is one of the most important contributions to the field of occupational mental health. Their effectiveness in dealing with occupational illness is manyfold greater than in times past. No longer is the occupational physician the surgeon restricting his role to repair of the occupational injury. His concern with proper placement in accord with both the physical *and* the emotional makeup of the employee has led to an increasingly effective role. While it is true that his assessment techniques vary with his competence and his resources, he has made successful application of much recent research and experience.

The physician in industry has, over the past few years, seen remarkable advances in insurance coverage for treatment of psychiatric illness among employee groups. Where possible, he has lent his support to this trend. In spite of resistance from some insurance carriers, many responsible employers include psychiatric care, either to the same extent as care for physical illness or at a reduced level, in their employee benefit plans. Pressure from union groups has been an increasingly potent factor in support of this trend.

OCCUPATIONAL MENTAL HEALTH DEFINED

From the foregoing, it would appear that occupational mental health may be defined in several ways. In the narrowest sense, it is concerned solely with the psychiatrically ill worker whose symptoms interfere with his effective functioning on the job. This is the purest clinical concept of the field. In a broader sense, occupational mental health is concerned with thought, feeling and behavior—both healthy and unhealthy—as it occurs in the work organization or as it relates to the performance of a job. In this larger context, the field deals with factors in the work environment which support mentally healthy behavior as well as those which may be involved in triggering the development of symptoms of emotional disturbance.

The literature of occupational mental health has increased in breadth, scope and content. Through it, the clinician has contributed a great deal to our understanding of the individual's motivation for work, his suitability for various occupational roles and the influence of work on his physical and mental health (46).

The volume of sophisticated study from the behavioral sciences is equally great in its contribution to our understanding of work groups, interaction patterns at work, job satisfaction, employee attitudes and morale and of the corporate subculture in which the individual functions. From all this work one might conclude that if there is such a field as occupational mental health at all, it cuts across and through occupational medicine, social, clinical and industrial psychology, cultural anthropology, social psychiatry and psychiatry proper. An indication of this may be obtained from a listing of the subject matter most frequently cited in a partially annotated bibliography published by the National Clearinghouse for Mental Health Information (67): accidents; absenteeism; alcoholism; the executive, his role and psychopathology; industrial health and occupational medicine; organized labor and the unions; leadership and supervision; motivation and incentives; specific occupations. Also, industrial mental health programs; occupational roles and status; the relationship between specific personality variables and the work setting; specific psychiatric illnesses as they relate to the job (traumatic neurosis, psychosomatic reactions and organic brain syndromes are most often discussed); rehabilitation of physically and psychiatrically disabled; psychodynamics of personality functioning in relation to work; the roles of psychiatrist, psychologist, industrial physician and behavioral scientist; the meaning of work; and the structure, function and environment of the work organization.

IMPLICATIONS FOR THE FUTURE

The future development of occupational mental health can perhaps best be seen when envisioned in the context of the change in the world of work during the past century. Today there is a high degree of industrial mechanization and automation, a skilled and educated work force, an acceptance of the results of research from the physical and behavioral sciences, improvements in the health and longevity of the population and legal advances and accelerating change in work style as well as in the social and cultural environments.

Changes in our society have altered the ways in which people satisfy their economic, social and psychological needs. They have required people to find new ways of obtaining job security, new social devices for protection against injury, sickness and death, new modes of developing skills, forms of recreation and sources of emotional support.

The extended family unit can no longer be relied on for support as its members are less likely to be found living in the same area, where they can turn to each other for social activities and mutual aid. Even where the geographic problem does not exist, social class mobility—a comparatively common phenomenon—may often make it impossible to turn to the extended family. Nor can one rely on neighborhood or community roots for psychological sustenance in a nation where 20 per cent of the population changes residence annually.

Instead of a geographical orientation point, many now have developed a corporate orientation point. They identify themselves with an organization—a company, church, university or government department. The work organization frequently provides the thread of continuity for a family moving from one area to another and may become a psychological anchor point for it. Often a man's social friendships arise from his work associations. Old Navy men have long had a ready bond of friendship, and two strangers who work for a nationwide organization are likely to have much in common (51).

While people have increasingly begun to turn to work and the employing organization for many of these lost supports, even in work some sources of gratification and support are being lost. Rapid technical changes have altered the composition of work groups and work tasks. Occupational and status achievements are somewhat tenuous when skills can readily be made obsolete or when their social value can depreciate rapidly, as occurs with technical changes and new industrial developments. When skills become obsolete, they not only lose their meaning as instruments of economic security but also of psychological security, for a man loses an important method of mastering some part of his world.

Many of the services formerly performed by small entrepreneurs are now carried out by larger units of production and marketing; for those who were part of the smaller group, these changes contribute to the loss of a sense of group purpose about work and of group solidarity. Movement from a small business to a larger enterprise usually means some loss of personal freedom. It also results in relatively less recognition of the individual as an individual and relatively more of the individual as part of the organization. It gives added weight to the importance of the relationship between a man and his work organization as a way for the man to gain social power. Within that relationship, however, the individual seeks increasing individual recognition, consideration and responsibility and seeks support from his supervision to obtain them.

Programs of clinical application in industry have begun in the past few years to apply a variety of techniques in support of the mental health of people at work. Many of these applications represent advances over the previous role of evaluator of the employee with mental illness. From psychiatry proper we have major advances in theory and practice. Tremendous strides have been made in occupational medicine as well as the other medical specialties. The behavioral sciences are contributing new research results, concepts and methods of relating to the health of employees and managers—and, indeed, of companies and organizations.

Mindus stated in 1952:

> I do not think that in the present situation the industrial psychiatrist exerts very great influence on management policies. I doubt if he ever will do it. But it is quite obvious that where the management had learned that they could benefit from discussing their problems with a good psychiatrist their points of view always were broadened and they developed a much more careful and understanding attitude (63).

Perhaps we are not clear as to what he meant by "policies," but recent developments indicate a beginning in the application of clinical concepts to the ongoing policies of corporate organizations. Depending on one's definition of "policy," one will attribute varying influence to the clinician and to the behavioral scientist. Does a change in employee benefit plan to include coverage of mental illness as well as physical illness involve a policy alteration? And what does this reflect of a growing union interest in mental health? Does the increased recognition by company management of unconscious process in motivating its employees' behavior represent a policy change? Does the involvement of the clinical consultant in top management staff meetings which determine policy represent such an influence? How is the increasing freedom of the clinician or the behavioral scientist to initiate research activities within the organization to be regarded?

Because of the widespread reluctance to publish work in these areas, referred to earlier, it would appear that these activities have to a large extent developed independently as isolated phenomena in different centers. It is a reasonable assumption that the milieu that fostered their initial appearance will continue to provide a fertile environment for future development along lines already established. Within the limitations of the general area of concern of the mental health professional, and his primary goal of the maintenance and improvement of mental health in the occupational setting, there are at least several new directions in which developments can be expected to take place. The profound changes being introduced into the work setting, mainly as a result of automation, will require a familiarity with the process of change and the stresses consequent to it, together with the knowledge and ability to apply techniques for alleviating them (74).

Management's increasing perception of the industrial organization as an element in the organic unity of the social order and of the work setting as an integral part of man's life will lead to a growing recognition within industry that developments on the industrial scene that may appear to be of only limited consequence to the person at work can, in fact, have considerable impact on his performance. Thus, not only do job loss, obsolescence of skills or early retirement resulting from many of the changes taking place in industry require major reorganization of the individual's life after they occur, but the threat or imminence of these developments can seriously affect his on-the-job functioning. Consequently, the clinician and behavioral scientist will be asked to develop programs for helping ease these transitions and to provide services where difficulties develop.

Union activities in mental health are still too new and too limited to provide more than a suggestion of the likely direction programming will take. Their primary concern has been with the provision of service to their population and will probably continue to be focused mainly in this area. However, limited exploration of the work setting and its potential place in a union mental health program has begun. The returns from this approach, even in these early stages, would suggest that for at least some unions, this will become a major area of development.

The role of the comprehensive community mental health center in occupational mental health is yet to be defined. The relative lack of interest in the area demonstrated by its omission from state planning in all but three states would suggest that development of this role will be primarily on an individual basis, reflecting the concern of the interested staff member. One potential asset of the community mental health center for activity in this field is its third-party position, which may enable it to provide services in areas of labor-management conflict where an impartial evaluation is necessary.

The shift in clinical emphasis from routine diagnostic evaluation in the industrial medical department or in the office of the consulting psychiatrist and psychologist to the broader areas of activity described above has made it necessary for the professional interested in this field to become familiar with an extensive body of knowledge not required of many of his colleagues. The behavioral science contributions to an understanding of group process and mental health education, the legal issues in workmen's compensation, the problems of psychotoxicology and, most of all, the nature of the industrial environment are all subjects about which some understanding is necessary for successful work in industry. It is likely that formal training programs in occupational mental health will have to be developed before widespread acceptance of the clinician can be expected from industrial organizations.

Previous material in this paper suggests the wealth of current research activities relating to the mental health of the American worker. It appears that we may not only expect expansion of research efforts but can anticipate greater application of research results in the ongoing affairs of industrial organizations.

A closer working relationship between university-based research programs and organizational personnel practices has been suggested and appears more frequently in practice. This has led to the training of the behavioral scientist for work as a salaried member of company personnel staffs and develops further the utilization of research data from the campus *and* from within the employing company. From academia we see increasing evidence of concern for the use of the results of research studies. From the viewpoint of the behavioral sciences which participate in organizational mental health programs, the direction of the future appears to be away from pure research on campus and toward the in-company study, with application of research results to the ongoing affairs of the company.

SUMMARY

In the past decade there have been more clinicians quoting behavioral science research, more behavioral scientists quoting clinicians and greater application of the theoretical frames of reference of each of the several disciplines to practical problems within industry. Occupational medicine has largely emerged from its cocoon of emergency surgery and compensation cases with the recognition that, like internal medicine and general practice, half of its case load is made up of patients with emotional problems, either overtly displayed or in the guise of psychosomatic reactions. Borrowing concepts and clues from psychiatry, psychology and the behavioral sciences, industrial medical directors and their staffs have taken steps toward more active involvement with the policies of their organizations—policies recognized as influencing the health of employees.

Becoming involved with the physician in industry, some behavioral scientists have been studying not only the prevalence of psychosomatic disease in industrial populations, but also the influence of the industrial environment on these illnesses. Indeed, health concepts have been applied to the industrial organization itself with the "corporate personality" regarded as "sick" or "well." Factors within its subculture have been studied as one studies the individual personality. It is common to hear a group of social scientists with industrial interests discuss the "health" of a work group, a company or an industry.

The relationship of job satisfactions to mental health has been widely suggested, even assumed, although still unproven. Identification with the work organization—or with one's labors—has received great attention from occupational medicine, clinical psychology, psychiatry and behavioral science. The centrality of interest seems to have focused recently on psychosomatic reactions. The next common area of concern appears to have been the industrial accident with its illusive "human" etiology. More recently the garden varieties of emotional reaction—the psychopathology of everyday life and its relation to the work process, to the exercise of various types of authority, to the cohesive influence of the work group and to productivity—have been discussed.

Finally, we see a common interest in the fulfillment of the individual in the work setting. From each discipline come expressions of concern, research efforts and suggestions and operational programs for allowing greater understanding and fulfillment of the psychological needs of the individual at work. Each discipline has contributed. Each considers itself properly concerned. Indeed, many proprietary feelings continue in each specialty as to who should be looked to by industrial management, who should be responsible, who should direct the efforts of the others, who may "rightly" have the moral, ethical and social responsibility to study and influence these many factors which in turn can be related to the mental health of the industrial employee at whatever level.

Both the clinical disciplines and the behavioral sciences will play an increasing role in fostering healthy employees and healthy companies through increasing influence on the policies and procedures of corporate organizations.

The evidence points to an expanding role for the clinician as well as for the behavioral scientist, but with less concern for the purely clinical function of examining patient-employees. Greater emphasis is suggested at the present time on preventive health programs, research, management education and concern with policies influencing employee mental health. It is by now apparent that the trend toward prevention originally foretold by Southard, Jarrett, Adler, Campbell, and Giberson continues as the main concern of occupational mental health.

REFERENCES

1. Adler, H. M. Unemployment and personality. *Ment. Hyg.,* 1917, 1:16–24.
2. American Psychiatric Association Committee on Occupational Psychiatry. *The mentally ill employee: His treatment and rehabilitation: A guide for management.* New York: Hoeber Medical Div., Harper and Row, 1965.
3. Anderson, V. V. Psychiatry in industry, *Amer. J. Psychiat.,* 1944, 100: 134–38.
4. Argyris, C. *Personality and organization.* New York: Harper, 1957.
5. Argyris, C. *Understanding organizational behavior.* Homewood, Ill.: Dorsey Press, 1960.
6. Brodman, K. *Man at work: The supervisor and his people.* Chicago: Cloud, 1947.
7. Brody, M. Dynamics of mental hygiene in industry. *Indust. Med.,* 1945, 14:760.
8. Brody, M. Neuropsychiatry and placement of industrial workers. *Conn. Med.,* 1945, 9:84–88.
9. Brown, W. *Exploration in management.* New York: John Wiley and Sons, 1960.
10. Burling, T. Personality and the economic situation. *Amer. J. Orthopsychiat.,* 1939, 9:616–22.
11. Burling, T. The role of the professionally trained mental hygienist in business. *Amer. J. Orthopsychiat.,* 1942, 11:48.
12. Burling, T., Lentz, E. M., and Wilson, R. N. *The give and take in hospitals.* New York: G. P. Putnam's Sons, 1956.
13. Burling, T., and Longaker, W. *Training for industrial psychiatry. Amer. J. Psychiat.,* 1955, 111:493.
14. Burlingame, C. C. Psychiatry in industry. *Amer. J. Psychiat.,* 1946, 103: 549–53.
15. Burlingame, C. C. Psychiatry in industry. *Amer. J. Psychiat.,* 1947, 104: 493–96.
16. Burlingame, C. C. Psychiatry in industry. *Amer. J. Psychiat.,* 1948, 105: 538–40.
17. Burlingame, C. C. Psychiatry in industry. *Amer. J. Psychiat.,* 1949, 106; 520–22.
18. Cameron, D. E., and Ross, H. G. *Human behavior and its relations to industry.* Montreal: McGill University, 1944.

19. Cameron, D. E., and Ross, H. G. *Studies in supervision.* Montreal: McGill University, 1945.
20. Campbell, C. M. The psychiatrist and industrial organization. *Amer. J. Psychiat.,* 1943, 100:286–87.
21. Collins, R. T. *A Manual of neurology and psychiatry in occupational medicine.* New York: Grune & Stratton, 1961.
22. Culpin, M. Psychological disorders in industry: Symposium on industrial medicine. *Practitioner,* 1936, 137:324–33.
23. Culpin, M., and Smith, M. *The nervous temperament.* London: H. M. Stationery Office, 1930. (Government Publications—Medical Research Council Industrial Health Research Board, Report No. 61).
24. Dershimer, F. W. Psychiatry in industry. *Amer. J. Psychiat.,* 1952, 108: 536–38.
25. Dershimer, F. W. Psychiatry in industry. *Amer. J. Psychiat.,* 1953, 109: 524–26.
26. Dershimer, F. W. Psychiatry in industry. *Amer. J. Psychiat.,* 1954, 110: 527–28.
27. Dershimer, F. W. Psychiatry in industry. *Amer. J. Psychiat.,* 1955, 111: 534–35.
28. Ferguson, C. A., Fersing, J. E., Allen, A. T., Baugh, N. P., Gilmore, G. A., Humphrey, J. W., McConnell, F. E., Mitchell, J. W., Sauer, J. W., and Scott, T. J. *The legacy of neglect: An appraisal of the implications of emotional disturbances in the business environment.* Fort Worth, Tex.: Industrial Mental Health Associates, 1965.
29. Fountain, C. W. Labor's place in an industrial mental health program. *Ment. Hyg.,* 1945, 29:95.
30. French, J. R. P., Jr., Kahn, R. L., and Mann, F. C. (Eds.). Work, health and satisfaction. *J. Soc. Issues,* 1962, 18:1–129.
31. Giberson, L. G. Psychiatry in industry. *Personnel J.,* 1936, 15:91–95.
32. Giberson, L. G. Emotional first-aid stations. *Personnel J.,* 1939, 16:1–15.
33. Giberson, L. G. Pitfalls in industry for the psychiatrist. *Med. Women's J.,* 1940, 47:144–46.
34. Greenwood, M. A report on the cause of wastage of labour in munition factories. London: H. M. Stationery Office, 1918. (Government Publications—Medical Research Council).
35. Group for the Advancement of Psychiatry, Committee on Psychiatry in Industry. *The application of psychiatry to industry.* 1951 (GAP Report No. 20).
36. Herzberg, F., and Hamlin, R. M. The motivation-hygiene concept and psychotherapy. *Ment. Hyg.,* 1963, 47:384–97.
37. Herzberg, F., Mausner, B., and Snyderman, B. *The motivation to work.* New York: John Wiley and Sons, 1959.
38. Howe, H. F., and Wolman, W. Guide for evaluating employability after psychiatric illness. *J.A.M.A.,* 1962, 181:1086–89.
39. Jaques, E. Some principles of organization of a social therapeutic institution. *J. Soc. Issues,* 1947, 3:4–10.
40. Jaques, E. Standard earning progression curves. *Hum. Relat.,* 1951, 11: 167–90.
41. Jaques, E. *The changing culture of a factory.* New York: Dryden Press, 1952.

42. Jaques, E. *Measurement of responsibility*. Cambridge: Harvard University Press, 1956.
43. Jarrett, M. C. The mental hygiene of industry: Report of progress on work undertaken under the Engineering Foundation of New York City. *Ment. Hyg.,* 1920, 4:867–84.
44. Kalinowsky, L. B. Problems of war neuroses in the light of experience in other countries. *Amer. J. Psychiat.,* 1950, 107:340.
45. Kornhauser, A. *Mental health of the industrial worker*. New York: John Wiley and Sons, 1959.
46. Lapinsky, E. The future of health in industry. *Industr. Med. Surg.,* 1965, 34:71–77.
47. Laughlin, H. P. An approach to executive development: Five years experience with analytically oriented groups of executives. *Dis. Nerv. Syst.,* 1954, 15:12.
48. Laughlin, H. P. Seminars with executives on human relations in the United States Government. *Int. J. Group Psychother.,* 1954, 4:165.
49. Laughlin, H. P., and Hall, M. Psychiatry for executives: An experiment in the use of group analysis to improve relationships in an organization. *Amer. J. Psychiat.,* 1951, 107:493–97.
50. Levinson, H. *Emotional health in the world of work*. New York: Harper and Row, 1964.
51. Levinson, H. The future of health in industry. *Industr. Med. Surg.,* 1965, 34:321–34.
52. Levinson, H., Price, C. R., Munden, K. J., Mandl, H. J., and Solley, C. M. *Men, management and mental health*. Cambridge: Harvard University Press, 1962.
53. Ling, T. M. Roffey Park Rehabilitation Centre. *Lancet,* 1945, 1:283.
54. Ling, T. M. (Ed.). *Mental health and human relations in industry*. New York: Paul B. Hoeber, 1955.
55. Lott, G. M. Emotional first-aid stations in industry. *Indust. Med.,* 1946, 15:419–22.
56. Mayo, E. *The human problems of an industrial civilization*. New York: Macmillan, 1934.
57. McLean, A. A. Occupational psychiatry. *Amer. J. Psychiat.,* 1964, 120:654–57.
58. McLean, A. A. Occupational psychiatry. *Amer. J. Psychiat.,* 1965, 121:659–62.
59. McLean, A. A., and Taylor, G. C. *Mental health in industry*. New York: McGraw-Hill, 1958.
60. Melekhov, D. E. Rehabilitation of psychoneurotic world war II patients in the U.S.S.R., *Occup. Therapy,* 1947, 26:388–93.
61. Menninger, W. C., and Levinson, H. *Human understanding in industry: A guide for supervisors*. Chicago: Science Research Associates, 1957.
62. Miller, D. C., and Form, W. H. *Industrial sociology*. New York: Harper and Brothers, 1951.
63. Mindus, E. *Industrial psychiatry in Great Britain, the United States, and Canada*. Report to the World Health Organization, Geneva, 1952.
64. Mindus, E. Outlines of a concept of industrial psychiatry. *Bull. WHO,* 1955, 13:561–74.

65. Morrow, J. K., King, J. P., Chiles, D. D., and Painter, T. E. The bituminous coal country: A psychiatric frontier. *West Virginia Med. J.*, 1959, 55:164–67.

66. National Association for Mental Health Reporter, Vol. 13, No. 7, October 1964.

67. National Institute of Mental Health. *Selected bibliography on occupational mental health.* Bethesda, Md.: National Clearinghouse for Mental Health Information, 1965 (Public Health Service Publication No. 1338).

68. Osnato, M. Industrial neuroses. *Amer. J. Psychiat.*, 1925, 82:117–31.

69. Pederson-Krag, G. *Personality factors in work and employment.* New York: Funk and Wagnalls, 1955.

70. Pokorny, A. D., and Moore, F. J. Neuroses and compensation. *A.M.A. Arch. Indust. Hyg. Occup. M.*, 1953, 8:547–63.

71. Reiff, R., and Scribner, S. *Issues in the new national mental health program relating to labor and low-income groups: Report No. 1.* New York: National Institute of Labor Education, 1963.

72. Rennie, T. A. C., Burling, T., and Woodward, L. E. *Vocational rehabilitation of psychiatric patients.* New York: Commonwealth Fund, 1950.

73. Rennie, T. A. C., Swackhamer, G., and Woodward, L. E. Toward industrial mental health: An historical review. *Ment. Hyg.*, 1947, 31:66–68.

74. Rennie, T. A. C., and Wodward, L. E. *Mental health in modern society.* New York: Commonwealth Fund, 1948.

75. Riessman, F. *New approaches to mental health treatment for labor and low-income groups: Report No. 2.* New York: National Institute of Labor Education, 1946.

76. Roethlisberger, F. J., and Dickson, W. J. *Management and the worker.* Cambridge: Harvard University Press, 1939.

77. Rosenbaum, M., and Romano, J. Psychiatric casualties among defense workers. *Amer. J. Psychiat.*, 1943, 100:314–19.

78. Ross, W. D. *Practical psychiatry for industrial physicians.* Springfield, Ill.: Charles C. Thomas, 1956.

79. Schulzinger, M. S. *The accident syndrome.* Springfield, Ill.: Charles C Thomas, 1956.

80. Sherman, M.: A review of industrial psychiatry. *Amer. J. Psychiat.*, 1927, 83:701–10.

81. Southard, E. E. The modern specialist in unrest: A place for the psychiatrist in industry. *Ment. Hyg.*, 1920, 4:550.

82. Tredgold, R. F. *Human relations in modern industry.* New York: International Universities Press, 1950.

83. Tureen, L. L. The role of the psychiatrist in a prepaid group medical program. *Amer. J. Pub. Hlth.*, 1959, 49:1373–78.

84. U. S. Federal Security Agency, Office of Vocational Rehabilitation. *The doctor and vocational rehabilitation for civilians.* Washington, D. C., 1947.

85. Van Alphen de Veer, M. R. *Success and failure in industry: A psycho-medical study.* Assen, The Netherlands: Van Gorcum and Co., 1955.

86. Waters, T. C. Mental illness: Is it compensable? *Arch. Environ. Health,* 1962, 5:178.

87. Weiner, H. J., and Brand, M. Involving a labor union in the rehabilitation of the physically and mentally ill. *Amer. J. Orthopsychiat.*, 1964, 34:342–43.

40

Adapting Urban Mental Health Services to Our Aging Population

GEORGE JAMES

YOUTH is the beginning of old age, for the process of senescence starts at least at birth, if not before, and old age is the shadow of youth. Approaching mental health in the very young and the very old is frustrating because each is an important part of the total problem that we cannot quite get hold of. We never really know what sort of world we are preparing the very young to live in. Will they have to stand the stresses of peace or war, or both? What will be the organization and mores of society when they grow up? We can only guess.

The situation is reversed with the aged. They are a product of a world we never made, a world forever beyond our grasp. The man of 75, waiting in our clinic today, developed in a society that existed between 1890 and 1909. Although conditioned by more recent changes, his course was set as he was growing up and receiving his education. It is difficult for us to understand him and for him to accept our point of view. We are strangers, and that is a big part of the problem.

Jung (9) wrote that "a human being would certainly not grow to be seventy or eighty years old if this longevity had no meaning for the species to which he belongs." Many of us may wonder at times, but we must accept this basic premise if we are to succeed with our older citizens.

THE APPROACHING CRISIS IN NUMBERS

Ryan, speaking of what he calls a "tendency to narrowness," comments on psychiatric practice:

> In the course of the Boston Mental Health Survey, it was found that 4 out of 5 patients in private psychiatric treatment are college-educated; the majority are women; and most are between the ages of 20 and 35. Among the patients who are Boston residents, 70 per cent live in a section of the

Reprinted from *American Journal of Orthopsychiatry*, 1964, *34*, 840–851, by permission of the publisher and the author. © 1964, American Orthopsychiatric Association
Dr. James is Dean, Mount Sinai School of Medicine of the City University of New York.

city which has only about 7 per cent of the total population. And 50 per cent of the total number of Boston residents in private psychiatric treatment live in just 4 census tracts.

This is getting down to a very small, specialized constituency to support a profession. If it gets much smaller or much more specialized, a visiting anthropologist would be quite justified in calling the whole business a cult rather than a serious endeavor in community service (20).

These figures weighed against the obvious need do make one think, even though private psychiatry is only part of our armamentarium.

In my own city of New York, we had 814,000 persons aged 65 or older as of 1960 (26). By 1970—only a few years away—we expect to have at least one million (11). It would take twelve days, 24 hours a day for these people to pass a clinic clerk's desk at the rate of one per second. If each had to stay for an hour for some kind of attention, and they were taken in sequence, 114 years would pass before the last patient left the treatment room, assuming we were open day and night.

Figuring out health services for one million older persons is sobering, for these will have to be provided in addition to all else—in addition, for example, to mental health and dental health programs for children. The total need is staggering. Nationally, of course, the numbers are much larger. There were more than 16 million persons 65 and over in the country in 1960 (26) and more than 17½ million by 1963 (10); nearly 25 million are expected by 1980 (10).

Describing our aged citizens as "65 and older" may leave the figure "65" in the mind—perhaps even a picture of vigor at that age. It is, of course, only a starting point; we must deal with substantial numbers of people in their seveneies, eighties and nineties. There are already more than ten thousand Americans over 100 and six million 75 and older (10).

The problem is becoming more an urban one. Already 70 per cent of our people live in urban areas, and older people tend to congregate in the cities (26). In the nation as a whole, as of the 1960 census, the percentage of persons 65 and older was 8.8. For urban areas it was 9.1, for New York City, 10.5.[1] These increases for urban areas represent very large groups of people.

The young and vigorous tend to move out to the suburbs, older people to remain in the city and older people from the suburbs to return to the convenience of the city. Think, for example, of the couple living productively in a suburb. The husband dies. The widow, with a little money, does not feel like living alone in the country, so she comes back to the city, perhaps for a job, perhaps just because it is easier. If she develops a medical problem and expends what funds she has, which is easy to do with chronic illness, she becomes a city problem. The suburb to which she and her husband paid taxes for years has now nothing to do with the matter. I am not criticizing the suburbs but,

---

[1] Percentages calculated from figures published by the U.S. Department of Commerce (25).

when you multiply this lady by thousands, it is clear that such cities as New York and Chicago are doing a lot of the suburbs' work. What it means, of course, is that, in total, we have an enormous undertaking before us.

CHARACTERISTICS OF THE AGED

There are two reasons at least for singling out older people when considering the future: *Society* has singled them out, and they do differ from the average. Characteristics they share with other age groups have different emphases in older people. For example, some chronic diseases only rarely detected in children or young adults are common in the elderly.

In his message of February 21, 1963, the late President Kennedy said: "Our senior citizens are sick more frequently and for more prolonged periods than the rest of the population. Of every 100 persons age 65 or over, 80 suffer some kind of chronic ailment, 28 have arthritis or rheumatism, ten have impaired vision, and 17 have hearing impairments."

He pointed out that the average annual income received by aged couples is half that of younger two-person families. Almost half of those over 65 living alone receive $1000 or less a year and three-fourths receive less than $2000 a year (10). Older people have less education than the average of all adults (11); people didn't go so far in school around the turn of the century (1).

Typically, older people have a combination of medical conditions; five or six concurrent ailments are not at all unusual. These are likely to be conditions for which science does not yet have a biological cure but for which treatment can be effective in maintaining the individual's self-sufficiency. Usually such treatment must be continuous, as in such conditions as diabetes, rheumatoid arthritis, hypertension and the aftereffects of stroke.

To understand precisely the kind of people we are dealing with, consider a typical couple we encountered during a survey. The husband was 90 years old and totally blind. His wife was 82, she was lame, she had a heart condition plus several other serious medical problems. They were living in a public housing project and paying 50 cents every half-month for someone to take their rent to the housing office and a quarter every time they needed someone to get their groceries. It cost $3 a month to have a barber come to shave the husband.

Or consider the couple living in a housing project, the husband aged 77, the wife 75. He has had cancer of the larynx, which has been removed. He has a tracheotomy, he has diabetes, he has chronic bronchitis, he has a cataract of the left eye, he has a left inguinal hernia. His wife also has a tracheotomy, probably due to thyroid surgery, as well as osteoarthritis, diabetes and vocal cord paralysis. These people receive $158 a month—$115.50 from social security and $42.50 from a union benefit. Married 50 years, they are devoted to each other. Despite a catalogue of medical problems, they are still an independent family unit, but only, I might add, because they got help from a very special pilot project clinic.

While the proportion of older people in the country has been increasing, the employment of older people has been decreasing. Although the number of persons 65 and over has almost doubled since 1940, only 13 of every 100 are now in the labor force—half of the 1940 percentage (10). It is hard to over-emphasize how difficult it is for older persons to get and keep work, even when they are fully able to perform it. Many firms refuse to hire anyone over 40. The person who has a job may be able to keep it to age 65 and even beyond, but if he must change jobs, which may happen through no fault of his own, then he is in trouble.

There is no doubt that in our society the portion of the life span during which the average individual is employed and earning his living is diminishing. If a man works from age 20 to 55 and lives to be 75, his productive period is 35 years and his unproductive period 40 years, of which the first 20 are spent in growing up and getting an education, the last 20 in decline and frustration. His total involvement in society as a functioning adult takes up less than half his life span.

The way older people live influences their lives and is sometimes an index of their relationship to society. Many older people live alone, especially in the central city. In some of our studies in low-income housing projects, we have found more than half of our older persons living alone. Srole *et al.* (32) have reported that in midtown New York 24.8 per cent of all households consisted of people living alone, whereas in the less densely populated Borough of Queens the figure was 6.5 per cent. The 1950 census showed that throughout the urban United States 11.1 per cent of the population lived alone. By 1960 this figure had risen to 14.8 per cent, and the figure for New York City to 19.4 per cent (26).

According to studies made a few years ago, two-thirds of all the aged men in New York City have wives, but only one-third of the aged women have husbands (15). This startling bit of statistics simply reflects the marked difference between the life expectancy of men and women, a difference that grows sharper as societies become more advanced. Since husbands are dying off before their wives, the average woman married to a man about her own age can look forward to a fairly long period of widowhood. The chances of remarriage for the older widow, while not zero, are small. There is, incidentally, evidence that the health of widows, and for that matter widowers, is not nearly as good as that of married persons, and that it is notably worse during the first few months after the death of the spouse (12).

In the 70-to-74 year age group, for example, from 1949 through 1951 the death rate for divorced white females was 56 per 1000; for widowed white females, 44; for single white females, (those never married), 42; and for married white females, 39.

After even so brief a look at our older citizens, we can say: (1) They are almost explosively growing in number; (2) they are generally in worse health than other age groups; (3) they have less money than the average of all adults; (4) they are more likely than other age groups to live in the city, and to live alone; and (5) they are, despite attempts at legal correction, ruthlessly discriminated against in employment, and in general they are being pushed out of meaningful involvement in society.

HOW TO CREATE MENTAL ILLNESS

Let me digress to describe how to cause mental illness deliberately. Take a man who is, let us say, vigorous and about 45 years old. Accept the proposition that we want to change this man from one who is mentally sound to one who is mentally ill. How would we accomplish it?

We could injure him or give him drugs of various kinds, or deprive him of sleep for a prolonged period, but there are other measures that involve no particular physical insult to his person. Science is beginning to understand that a human being gets into trouble mentally when the feedback to him from society—that feedback of little messages which establish for him what he is and who he is and where he is—is sharply reduced. Some of this information comes from studies stimulated by an interest in so-called brain-washing and a great deal more from research into what might happen to the human mind during lonely exploration into space. Although such studies have not been actual attempts to drive people insane, they have taught us much about how that might be accomplished (6, 7, 21).

A healthy, normal man placed in a quiet, dark room in a tub of warm water soon loses his sense of contact with his environment and feedback from it. He becomes disoriented and confused and displays signs of mental illness. Even a man kept for a prolonged period in a room with walls of one color, no decorations, a minimum of furniture, nothing to read, nothing to listen to— even this man undergoes sensory deprivation and is likely in time to develop what we would call mental illness.

In the light of this, let us make a plan for our 45 year old. Let us say we remove his wife from the picture. Then we arrange to have him lose his job and unable to get another, leaving him with nothing meaningful to do. Then we remove most of his friends and relatives. He has already lost the human contacts of his job, and now he loses these as well. His income is cut off, his savings start running out and he must change his place of living. He finds a single room somewhere, and he sits.

This vigorous man, I think, would now have a great chance of developing mental illness. Oh, he will struggle, and once in a while we will find someone who, even through years in solitary confinement, has the inner strength to retain full mental health. But our average man, I am convinced, would become disoriented and confused, displaying sooner or later what most of us would diagnose as mental illness.

This fictional attempt to cause mental illness, of course, is very close to what we are actually doing to our older people. We are applying a set of conditions likely to cause mental illness in a vigorous and active young adult to people not nearly so strong, so active or so economically solvent. Certainly older people suffer. Naturally we detect in many of them signs of mental abnormality.

What we have, therefore, is not the development of a condition practically inevitable in the aged, given our present state of knowledge, such as mild osteoarthritis. What we are dealing with is man-made mental illness. Society is running an insanity factory, and running it as skillfully as if it had been planned carefully and with malignant intent.

Of course some older people, like some younger people, will develop mental illness despite anything we can do. There are organic problems. There are also factors we cannot influence beyond a point: We cannot eliminate widowhood, and we cannot prevent the death of the older person's friends, although we might give him a better chance to make new ones.

A list of the factors tending to push the older person toward mental illness and those tending to keep him well-oriented, would clearly show that society today is emphasizing the former. Indeed, one may even ask: Who is less sane, the somewhat disoriented oldster who is unsuccessfully trying to get work, or those who have created employment policies that will play a major part in driving him to the breaking point, in driving him away from the tenuous contact with reality he may be struggling to maintain?

WHY WE DON'T BEHAVE AS HUMAN BEINGS

The inconsistencies of society disturb most of us at one time or another. We can share the feelings of the British dentist Toller (24), who was invited to view some dental health films at a school, and found that the projector had been bought with profits from the school candy shop. "Our society," he was moved to write, "is an inchoate and incoherent mess, no less diseased than our teeth, and needs attention." Well, frequently it does.

Our promotion of mental illness in the aged is not the result of sinister planning; it just grew. We can claim some excuse in that having such vast numbers of older people is new. Furthermore, in times past when the older person retired, voluntarily or otherwise, he or she returned to the family, where three generations generally intermingled. There may have been friction, but there was at least plenty of human contact. In those days there were proportionately fewer old people, and there was far less difference in life expectancy between men and women. Condemnation to the loneliness of the cell of an institution or a rooming house was less frequent.

I shall outline some of the things I think we should do, but I must say, first, that society as a whole must adjust to alleviate this problem. We cannot allow it to turn out the aged mentally ill as products are turned out of a sausage machine, leaving those in the field of orthopsychiatry with a hopeless task.

If there is one key to my own feelings, it derives from a message I have heard in all sincerity and kindliness at dozens of meetings: "We must make older people feel useful and needed." My reaction is: There is only one way to make older people *feel* useful and needed, namely, by making them *in fact* useful and needed. These people are not fools, and they know full well that basket weaving is no substitute for a functional part of life. As Mead puts it:

> Community plans for old-timers are to be commended, but almost invariably too much emphasis is placed on recreation and on outward appearances. Too often, in articles or brochures dealing with activities for the elderly, one finds the ubiquitous illustrations of old timers at a dance or a community sing, old gentlemen playing checkers, and old ladies having their hair styled. Perhaps such emphasis results from the anxiety of the younger people who are working with the old-timers to deny old age in their charges. Recreation is useful and should not be neglected, but it is still a very shallow temporary source of satisfaction . . . (14).

THE MENTAL AND THE PHYSICAL

Certainly no one in this Association needs to be convinced of the close relationship between mental and physical illness. It is a relationship somehow clearer in the aged than in younger people.

Older people are much closer to the brink of collapse than younger ones. You may see an older man and wife seeming to do very well together, yet they are probably struggling to stay within their financial, physical and mental resources. As Pomrinse wrote:

> The one characteristic change caused by aging, as observed by all scientific disciplines, can be described as a *diminution of reserves*. In this connotation, the term "marginal man" would then describe an individual who, because of aging, demonstrates such a significant reduction in physiologic, psychologic, or social reserves as to be in danger of disability from stressful demands in any of these areas. He is, therefore, increasingly close to the margin between functioning adequately by himself and functioning only with outside help (16).

Brain changes in older persons can and do result from cerebral vascular diseases but, as Wahal and Riggs point out,

> Much of the nihilistic attitude toward mental enfeeblement in the aged undoubtedly stems from its traditional association with progressive irreversible disease of the cerebral vessels and infarctive lesions of the brain. . . . The presence of similar brain lesions in younger persons without overt psychological disturbances suggests that functional disability may not depend directly upon neuroanatomic alterations, and may, therefore, be subject to arrest or reversal (27).

And Macmillan says flatly:

The chief manifestations of what is called senile psychosis or senile dementia are not organic; they are an emotional response to unfulfilled basic emotional needs. . . . Over and over again we have found that geriatric psychiatric conditions, which used to be regarded as wholly organic and permanent and necessitating hospital admission, are in fact partly organic and partly reactive, and that the reactive symptoms are the more disabling (13).

The role of society is constantly mentioned. As Chinn notes of the elderly:

Physical or mental illness or both in these patients is more often than not accompanied by social illness. Very obviously, having two major classes of sickness in the same patient at one time magnifies the problem, not arithmetically, but geometrically. It is like having two major systems very sick at the same time, which, indeed, occurs more often than not in old people (2).

We have found in studies in New York City that a great many people suffering the after-effects of stroke are immobilized unnecessarily. In this physical condition, as pointed out by Dovenmuehle and Verwoerdt (3), moderate or severe depressive symptoms are observed in about two-thirds of all patients, at least in those studied while hospitalized. For a personal account of one creative man's fight against the mental as well as physical effects of a stroke, one need only read "Episode," by Eric Hodgins (8).

It happens in many cases we have studied that such patients receive inadequate care following the acute phase of their illness. Emerging from their attacks, balanced between independence and total dependence, they can be pushed either way. Thus we find a patient who did not receive rehabilitation lying in a bed somewhere, utterly immobilized, dependent either on society or his family, and another patient with precisely the same *physical* condition up and about and productive.

In elderly patients the mental and the physical are inextricable. We know the pitfalls of attempting to specialize on the heart or the lung to the exclusion of the patient. An even worse pitfall exists with the elderly in attempting to lift out either the mental or the physical component. The two must be seen together, and treated together, for they are together.

URBAN CARE FOR THE AGED MENTALLY ILL

There are two great misconceptions regarding mental illness in older people, first, that it is irreversible. This very often is just not so. The second is that we can take care of a major part of the illness of older people (physical and mental) through hospitalization or other institutionalization. The fact is, we do not begin to have money or personnel enough to handle the problem this way. Unless we can reduce the number of elderly people needing institutionalization, we are really lost. I believe that those of us in urban mental health can improve our programs in these five ways:

1. *Recognize the small problems that keep patients from getting the care they need, and accept the view that if the care doesn't reach the patient its value is nil.* We have a tendency to set up what we think are magnificent facilities and then not to worry too much if only a few out of all those in need come to them. First-rate surgery or rehabilitation or orthopsychiatry may all just as well never have been invented if they are not made available to the patients who need them. This is the simple language of the primer, I know, but we tend to ignore that part of our medical care system involved in actually delivering such care to the patient.

The small problems that keep people from getting care are really important. Old people tend to be creaky and arthritic. Often they just can't walk to a clinic, which we have established at our convenience. They may be so creaky they can't cross the street in the 45 seconds the traffic light gives them. A combination of weak hearing and eyesight can likewise keep them from getting to the care they need.

We found one old man with a very serious medical condition. He didn't walk to the clinic to have it treated because he had severe callouses on his feet and he was too poor to ride. Medical science does know how to fix callouses, but somehow he had never learned of this. If he had had a mental problem that needed care, I suspect it would not have been found until he was about to become another costly statistic in a hospital.

2. *Integrate mental and physical care.* We have divided human beings into many parts and established a clinic for each part. It is not unusual for an elderly woman to have to go to six clinics because six different organs are involved in medical problems. Since very often she just doesn't go, the problems become worse. If she continues without care long enough, she winds up in a hospital and from there she is shunted to a nursing home. Not only is the meaningfulness of her life destroyed, but it all costs the community a great deal of money.

The picture is bad enough if one leaves out mental illness; add mental illness and it becomes intolerable. Moreover, for elderly people the mental and the physical cannot usefully be separated.

Here is Riccitelli, for example, on such a nonmental subject as the value of exercise in the aged:

> Inactivity has a distintegrative action on the body, muscles undergo disuse, atrophy and become shorter, weaker and stiffer. As a result there is a decrease in functional capacity. A chain reaction sets in whereby there is a loss of appetite due to inactivity, and a slowing down of all the physiological processes due to normal aging. This process, together with the degenerative action of chronic and prolonged illness, combines with aging to disrupt body functions and cripple the patient (17).

The American Orthopsychiatric Association was a pioneer in a team approach to mental illness, especially in children, in bringing together various mental health personnel to concentrate on one problem. There is no question in my mind that in older people we now need a team approach, including both the mental and the physical.

3. *Coordinate the splinters of our medical-care system.* Our medical-care system is splintered and spread. It takes a whole book just to list and describe briefly the social agencies in New York City that impinge on the field of medicine. So complicated is our system that there seems to be no one individual, even in a city like New York, much less in the country, who knows where all the parts are and what they can do. It is common for a patient to be sent from hospital A to hospital B for a kind of treatment hospital B doesn't give, simply because hospital A doesn't know hospital B's rules.

Our favorite depressing story on this is of a patient who became unnecessarily immobilized following a stroke. Sadly enough, she lived right across the street from what is probably the greatest rehabilitation center on the face of the earth. But somehow or other there was no communication. She did not know it was there. She did not benefit from it.

One patient, even with a relatively simple problem, may become involved with agencies representing many different private and governmental interests. Each one has its own rules and restrictions, its own sense of autonomy, its own resistance to concentrating on the patient and his needs. We need to bring together into some sensible pattern the various parts of our medical-care system. We need to break down the go-it-alone, the sovereign-state attitude of some of our units, especially hospitals. We need research on how best to use the resources we have; especially today, it is as important as research on new drugs or treatment methods.

4. *Concentrate on the family and the home.* It is more humane as well as cheaper to hold the elderly family together than to allow it to disintegrate so members must be cared for in hospitals or other institutions. Furthermore, there is growing evidence that the hospital is no place for many mental patients. Dovenmuehle and Verwoerdt point out: "Removal from home surroundings may well be the most consistent traumatic factor associated with hospitalization *per se* (4)." Rossman and a group of hospital-oriented investigators (18) say they were surprised to find out how effective home care of patients could be. They emphasize that home care for many of their patients was actually superior to hospital care and, furthermore, "The opportunity to hold on to things physically has its equivalent psychologically and symbolically. More than one elderly patient who was able to maintain his orientation at home has collapsed into confusion in the hospital setting."

Felix, speaking to this Association in 1963, said: "In Massachusetts, one hospital, by deliberately trying to find suitable alternatives to hospitalization, successfully treated in the community one-half the patients who sought admission to the hospital (5)."

Helping the elderly family usually means getting into, or near the home. These people are simply unable to make repeated visits to distant clinics. It is expensive to give care in the home—to go through a city apartment by apartment, so to speak—but it is less expensive than building institutions block by block.

I have already mentioned an elderly couple married 50 years, with a catalogue of medical problems reading almost like the table of contents of a textbook on medicine, who are still together. They are still together in their own apartment because a demonstration clinic was set up in their housing project. This is the Queensbridge Health Maintenance Project (23). It covers both mental and physical illness, and brings together governmental and volunteer agencies to deal with the elderly people in this particular low-income housing project. It has been most heartwarming to see how, when these agencies concentrate on a problem, their rules and regulations seem to fade away and there is real co-operative effort.

But, for the old people, this project's importance is that it makes care available right in their own housing project. Some patients do have to be sent elsewhere for specialized care, but the minimal care in this small clinic is enough to hold many families together.

5. *Halfway between home and institution.* We need to know more about what a home is, how to support it and how, in some cases, to create it. An elderly couple married 50 years and living together in an apartment they pay for have a home. But what of the widow living alone, with no job and a dwindling number of friends? Does her situation constitute a home? Sometimes yes; sometimes no. Such a person, with good relations with a next-door neighbor, may do well. There have been programs calling for visits between older persons who may not necessarily live close together. Certainly aloneness is to be guarded against. We need a much more imaginative approach to bringing older people together in halfway houses, to spare them both aloneness and the emotional insult of being placed in an old persons' home, or a miserable so-called nursing home.

PREVENTION OF MENTAL ILLNESS IN THE AGED

Back we come, finally, to the most important and yet most obvious point of all, namely, that we, as a society, must stop promoting mental illness in the aged and address ourselves to its prevention.

In many medical areas we need a change in social attitudes. We need society's help in veneral disease, in air pollution, in fighting lung cancer, in the problem of radioactive fallout. But, in mental illness in the elderly, one can say flatly that, unless there is a prompt and profound change in the attitude and actions of society, the situation will be impossible. Our mental health resources in personnel and facilities, used as we use them now, are not nearly enough to make a measurable impact on the problem looming before us. For each patient we reach and substantially help, there will be dozens we do not reach at all, meaningfully, or whom we see too late.

The American Orthopsychiatric Association has for years recognized that mental health is not the personal property or preserve of the mental health worker but involves all who have a function in society. So you number among your members, lawyers, pediatricians, educators, sociologists and others. We need their help.

The idea of prevention is not new. In mental health in the aged, however, any sensible preventive plan leads directly to this need for social change— to an absolute need for changing the employment situation, for example. That older people increase in number and proportion while their proportion in the working force goes down, creates mental illness. You cannot get away from it.

Unless we can help a majority of our older people who are able and willing to make meaningful use of their abilities, they will endure a rising toll of mental illness. We must change our employment policies. We must conquer the two great enemies of sanity in older people: *enforced uselessness* and *enforced aloneness*. With these sinister forces conquered, we might be able to accomplish more overnight than we could through all the care programs we could possibly design and conduct. Right now in New York City we are all carefully watching an intriguing experiment in which old people are working as volunteer homemakers and home visitors for other old people in their own neighborhood. It is fervently hoped that the result will be better physical and mental health for both groups.

A British physician, Thomas N. Rudd, takes the position that the general past improvement in health should not be credited to doctors or politicians but to what he calls "an upsurge in the public conscience, a refusal to allow more inhumanity of man to man or to allow certain conditions of living to be perpetuated." And, he adds, "There is no reason to believe that it can be otherwise in the matter of old-age care (19)."

We who are in the field must continue developing our programs, improving them, refining them. We must conduct research to amass more knowledge. Above all, we must look beyond our immediate spheres to join others in helping to bring about this "upsurge in the public conscience" without which a human solution to the problem of old age cannot be had, without which we cannot bring back to our elderly citizens the mantle of dignity they so greatly require.

REFERENCES

1. Brode, W. R. Approaching ceilings in the supply of scientific manpower. *Science,* Jan. 24, 1964: 313–24.
2. Chinn, A. B. Special medical problems in the care of the elderly patient. *Postgrad. Med.,* 1958, 24(2):90–94.
3. Dovenmuehle, R. H., and Verwoerdt, A. Physical illness and depressive symptomatology. 1. Incidence of depressive symptoms in hospitalized cardiac patients. *J. Amer. Geriat. Soc.,* 1962, 10(11): 932–47.
4. Dovenmuehle, R. H., and Verwoerdt, A. Physical illness and depressive

symptomatology. Factors of length and severity of illness and frequency of hospitalization. *J. Geront.*, 1963, 18(3):260–66.

5. Felix, R. H. Community mental health. *Amer. J. Orthopsychiat.*, 1963, 23(5):788–95.

6. Fiske, D. W., and Maddi, S. *The functions of varied experience.* Homewood, Ill.: Dorsey Press, 1961.

7. Heron, W. The pathology of boredom. *Scientific American,* 1957, 196(1): 52–56.

8. Hodgins, E. *Episode.* New York: Atheneum, 1964.

9. Jung, C. G. *Modern man in search of a soul.* London: Kegan Paul, 1945.

10. Kennedy, J. F. Message from the President of the United States Relative to the Elderly Citizens of Our Nation, Feb. 21, 1963 (Doc. 72, 88th Congress, 1st Sess.).

11. Klarman, H. E. *Background, issues and policies in health services for the aged in New York City.* New York: Health Research Council, City of New York, 1962.

12. Kraus, A. S., and Lilienfeld, A. M. Some epidemiologic aspects of the high mortality rate in the young widowed group. *J. Chronic Dis.,* 1959, 10(3): 207–17.

13. Macmillan, D. Preventive geriatrics: Opportunities of a community mental health service. *Lancet,* Dec. 31, 1960.

14. Mead, B. T. Emotional struggles in adjusting to old age. *Postgrad. Med.,* 1962, 31(2):156–60.

15. New York State Department of Labor. *Characteristics of population and labor force:* Vol. 2, New York City, 1960.

16. Pomrinse, S. D. Marginal man: A concept of the aging process. *Geriatrics,* 1958, 13 (11):765–67.

17. Riccitelli, M. L. The therapeutic value of exercise in the aged and infirm. *J. Amer. Geriat. Soc.,* 1963, 11(4): 299–302.

18. Rossman, I. M., and Rudnick, C. and B. Total rehabilitation in home care setting. *New York J. Med.,* 1962, 62(8):1215–19.

19. Rudd, T. N. Old age: The completion of a life cycle. *J. Amer. Geriat. Soc.,* 1958, 6(1):1–9.

20. Ryan, W. Urban mental health services and responsibilities of mental health professionals. *Ment. Hyg.,* 1963, 47(3):365–71.

21. Solomon, P., and others. *Sensory deprivation.* Cambridge: Harvard University Press, 1961.

22. Srole, L., Langner, T., and Michael, S. T. *Mental health in the metropolis.* New York: McGraw-Hill, 1962.

22. Srole, L., Langner, T., and Michael, S. T. *Mental health in the metropolis.* service for the elderly. *Publ. Hlth. Rep.,* 1962, 77(12):1041–47.

24. Toller, J. R. Teeth: Nutrition and diet (Report of a symposium on nutrition in general practice). *J. Coll. Gen. Pract.* 1963, 6(Suppl. 2):61–71.

25. U.S. Bureau of the Census. Table 21: Metropolitan and nonmetropolitan population, urban and rural, by age, 1960. *In Statistical Abstract of the U.S.* Washington, D.C.: U.S. Dept. of Commerce, 1963.

26. U.S. Bureau of the Census. *U.S. census.* Washington, D.C.: U.S. Dept. of Commerce, 1960.

27. Waham, K. M., and Riggs, H. E. Changes in the brain associated with senility. *Arch. Neurol.,* 1960, 2(2):151–59.

41

Home Treatment of Severely Disturbed
Children and Families

MERRITT H. EGAN AND ORA LOY ROBISON

As the psychobiological continuum of illness is delineated, we need more and improved gradations of treatment techniques between inpatient and outpatient settings for use with the severely disturbed child and family. In an effort to find ways to meet this need, we have extended the scope of the outpatient approach to include home visits and intensive home therapy by medical and paramedical personnel. With some difficult cases, we have found this approach practical, effective and economical. In most geographical areas day treatment and inpatient treatment are unavailable or in short supply. For some children home treatment can act as an alternative to hospitalization or day treatment. For others it is the treatment of choice. It is as serious a mistake to prescribe 24-hour care for a child when he can be treated in better ways as it is not to give such a recommendation when it is indicated.

Our observations are based on our experience with more than 3,000 diagnostic and therapeutic hours in the homes of more than 40 families during the last five years. We have worked intensively with 11 families. The average number of hours to each of these has been 198 over an average of 15 months. If we include all families, the number of hours ranges from 8 to 404 and averages 93.4 hours per home.

HISTORY

References in the literature regarding home visits date back at least to 1796 (3). Reports in the last decade include Querido's Amsterdam Plan (9), the "Worthington Experiment," (2), Moore (7), Alfred Friedman (4), Tobias T. Friedman (5), Pasamanick et al., (8), and Henry (6). In general, these

Reprinted from the *American Journal of Orthopsychiatry*, 1966, *36*, 730–735, by permission of the publisher and the authors. © 1966, American Orthopsychiatric Association. Dr. Egan is Assistant Professor of Pediatrics and Psychiatry and Director, Division of Child and Adolescent Psychiatry, College of Medicine, University of Utah. Mrs. Robison is an instructor, University of Utah.

studies have been with adults and not with children. Some of them were for the purpose of screening hospital admissions and supplying an alternative to 24-hour care. It was found that a large proportion of the psychiatric patients who applied for admission could be satisfactorily treated in other ways at no greater expense or usually at less expense. Others of these reports are concerned with research concerning the psychodynamics of behavior, and still others with treatment of families in the home. We have focused on children in relation to the family and have emphasized treatment.

QUESTIONS

There are many questions that need answering. Is family therapy sometimes better than individual therapy? Is individual, family or other therapy in the home superior to a similar approach in the office? If so, what are the indications and the techniques? Does home therapy have advantages as far as research and training are concerned? How wise is it and under what circumstances should we avoid hospitalization and treat parents or children in the home solely or in combination with office therapy? We cannot answer these questions conclusively at this time, but will make some preliminary observations based on the literature and our experience to date.

METHOD

The family is introduced to the idea of home visits as part of the usual evaluation and treatment plan and to the home therapist as a member of the treatment team. Residence visits are much more successful if they are planned and executed as a part of a master plan to aid a family. After the general plan has been outlined and accepted by the family, the therapist enters the home and participates with the family at whatever level is indicated. A near verbatim account of each home visit is recorded. A key person, a child psychiatrist, correlates all activities and supervises the therapist. In the home one has a host of interpretive opportunities and the level at which one treats depends upon factors such as the knowledge and skill of the therapist, the type and intensity of the pathology, conditions in the home, how other members of the clinical team are involved, etc. If the principal responsibility of therapy is upon another member of the team, then the home therapist's responsibility is to convey information to him and exercise her own judgment in what she says and does to the end that she aids in the achievement of curative goals (1).

Home activities may vary from a primitive to a relatively sophisticated level. They may be with certain families initially little more than a healthy grandmother, sister, neighbor, fellow church member, volunteer, or "community homemaker" could supply. The therapist then may become the organizer and superviser of these auxiliary care givers. Or home therapy may consist of giving the mother support and counsel, helping her learn to tolerate and hopefully to enjoy her own and other children in the yard and home. A home therapist might develop a relationship with a child, help him with a small segment of reality, aid in his domestication, training or retraining, or help him move in with friends in his natural group. This may be in addition to his participation in a structured preschool play therapy group or latency age activity therapy group in the clinic. Or one may be a mother substitute to the child or sometimes a mother substitute to the mother, demonstrating alternative ways of understanding and helping children and later priming or sustaining the mother in these activities. Or one can conduct informal activity group therapy with siblings or with the natural group in the neighborhood. The therapist can "spot live" with the family to gain information and understanding and then do more formal individual, marital or family psychotherapy in the office or home at another time. One often uses a variety of approaches in the same home and sometimes on the same visit. Early in the course of therapy, one approach may be indicated and tolerated and later another.

The time we have spent in the home has varied from four visits of two hours each up to 16 hours per week over a period of more than two years. We have found with many families that home visits lasting two hours three times a week for one or more weeks is sufficient to formulate a problem, and continued expenditure of time at this rate is often sufficient to exert a therapeutic effect of some significance. It is usually necessary to concentrate a great many hours in the early weeks of treatment to overcome some of the resistances and help the family become more comfortable with the therapist in the home.

We enter some homes primarily to further elucidate a problem. In others our purpose is to decide whether home or office treatment will be more effective. Frequently it is soon realized that an all-out effort including home and office treatment is indicated in order to effect change and avoid hospitalization. In still other situations hospitalization is indicated.

Of more than 40 cases with which we have worked there has been no one who has outright refused home visits. There have been several families who have accepted home visits with difficulty and two who have asked us to withdraw. In others, of course, we have elected an early termination.

DISADVANTAGES

We are emphasizing in this paper the advantages of home therapy. It has many disadvantages, and we will at this time only mention some of them. It heightens some resistances, makes some families feel their privacy has been invaded and is a threat to some because of their feelings of dependence and helplessness. It presents special problems to paranoid or near-paranoid families, to families whose status is decreasing, and to families who are upwardly mobile socioeconomically. The geographic area that can be served by central core personnel is limited because of cost and time of travel. It is sometimes difficult to establish one's self as a therapist in the home rather than a visitor or a friend. Under some circumstances, it is healthier for a child to be brought to the office than to be torn between the therapist and severely disturbed parents in the home. This situation usually requires foster parents for the child. Many therapists do not wish to have their lives disrupted by frequent night work which is often necessary if one does home therapy. Others are not sufficiently motivated to withstand the rigors this approach demands. One may create the atmosphere of a state hospital in the home by maintaining a severely ill member of the family in his residence. Some homes are so chaotic that the physical necessities of life and the housekeeping details must be attended to before psychotherapy should be attempted. In general, the higher the socioeconomic class the longer the acclimatization to home treatment requires. The higher class families have difficulty accepting a therapist in their home except as a friendly visitor and on a temporary basis.

ADVANTAGES

The relationship in the home with the child as well as with the rest of the family is of a different nature and quality than that in the office. Alfred Friedman (4) has pointed out that a therapist in a home becomes a "participant-observer," is more actively involved with the family members, and has opportunity for immediate analysis in the "here-and-now laboratory of family therapy." Though the relationship may be closer, it is also more involved. Though it provides more information about the family, one may feel the need of a computer to sort out, understand and use all that is offered. The relationship with the therapist is often the first healthy relationship that a child has had. Other relationships have been either peripheral or abnormal. The therapist often is eventually seen as a being who is an intimate part of their life rather than, as sometimes happens in the office, one whom they see one or two hours a week in that big building, but the rest of life goes on as usual. This is not to subtract from how important a therapist in the office may be to a child and how with some problems, especially when the parents are in therapy, there is excellent transfer value (4). The difficulty a child has attaining a meaningful relationship with a stranger in a foreign environment is sometimes great. Seeing a child on his own ground occasionally is an advantage and may shorten the time of treatment.

One of the principal uses of home therapy is to evaluate a family's problems. In the family's natural setting one often sees more accurately and in greater detail and clarity the conditions and interactions of a family: to what degree family members recognize each other's needs and support or fail one another. Though home evaluation may be used as a routine intake procedure, it is more time consuming and is usually reserved by us for understanding a family that is difficult to formulate. The family secrets, behavior, attitudes and core problems often stand out in greater relief when one observes them on the spot. Even when a home visit is not readily accepted, a great deal can be learned. In some cases of separation anxiety manifest as school phobia, parents who are fairly adequate in their vocation have been able to accept help in the home in getting the child to school, but have been unable to follow through with office therapy for their child or themselves.

Occasionally at intake one gets conflicting reports. This is particularly true in severely disturbed children and parents and also in cases of symbiotic relationships. Home visits often help elucidate the situation.

After the customary intake with parents, one may not be sure that a child needs psychiatric care and rather than have the child come into the office for a psychiatric evaluation, one can scout the home, that is, observe the child, family and environment. Then we have more information upon which to base a decision as to whether the child should be involved. An office psychiatric evaluation of a child affects his self-image and sometimes those in and out of the family label him. The home visit avoids these disadvantages.

It is not too uncommon to see a member of a family in an entirely new light after a home visit as compared to the ordinary intake. There is no better way to experience and understand the people or the atmosphere in a home than to go into it. The verbal and nonverbal communication in the home is rich. It is sometimes more difficult to assess people in the office than it is in the home, and the facade often seen in the office is easier to see through. Indeed, it sometimes is removed too easily, and this may be a disadvantage unless the situation is handled wisely.

In another communication we will detail the use of this technique under various conditions. At this time, we would state that some severely disturbed children cannot be handled with outpatient treatment alone and yet are not ideal candidates for residential or inpatient treatment. Home treatment combined with outpatient psychotherapy under these circumstances can often be the best answer. A home therapist often can decrease the traffic of psychotic parents in and out of hospitals. A home therapist is able not only to get great insight into the underlying forces of a child who is being physically battered but also to recognize the less obvious emotional battering of a child, which is often a prodrome or concomitant of physical battering. Meeting people in their own home sometimes takes pressure off the patient and makes it possible to treat those who are ordinarily considered "unreachables." Home treatment is of help with the borderline psychotic as well as with the lesser degrees of psychosis in children. It furnishes a part-time therapeutic milieu and has as an objective approaching a full-time healthy environment through on-the-spot demonstration to the mother as to how to relate and handle the problems of her child and herself. The phenomenon of schizophrenic teasing of a mother, siblings, or peers is aided by the home therapist in a more effective manner than by any other method with which we are acquainted. Double and multiple binds often can be dissected on the spot even more effectively in the home than in office family therapy. A therapist in the home often aids a new mother in her reaction to a fetus and a new baby. Through this means one often can prevent hospitalization due to emotional illness, maintain the morale of the mother and aid her and the family more effectively than by outpatient treatment alone. Parental distortion stands out in relief when viewed on the spot. The "maladjusted diseases" described by Fritz Redl (10) respond to life space interview techniques that can be applied in the home. Antagonistic symbiotic relationships between parent and child can be understood and severed more effectively with the aid of a therapist in the home. Often this technique must be combined with office treatment by another therapist. We have used this approach with more than 20 cases reported elsewhere (11). From the viewpoint of research or training, there are few techniques with which we are acquainted that are more valuable. In addition to using modifications of classical types of psychotherapy, we find in home treatment that capitalizing on the family ego, using sociotherapeutic techniques, being directive sometimes, and using reality interview methods are particularly helpful.

CONCLUSIONS AND IMPLICATIONS

This article reports an overview of our preliminary experience in treating moderately to severely disturbed children and families using a home therapist on a semi-intensive basis usually in conjunction with outpatient treatment. We have found that it has both disadvantages and advantages. In this communication, we have highlighted the advantages of this regimen and pointed out some apparent indications. We have illustrated how it can be helpful as a "laboratory aid" to formulation, as an alternative to 24-hour care, as a help with the emotionally battered child, and of assistance in reaching "unreachables." It is useful in working with a mother who is having moderate difficulty adjusting to her fetus or baby and in recognizing and treating parental distortion. Preliminary observations suggest that this technique is helpful in treating behavior problems, the less severely psychotic and borderline psychotic child, school phobics and other antagonistic symbiotic problems. It adds a new dimension to our continuum of treatments that can be applied when outpatient care is insufficient or ineffective, yet hospitalization is not indicated or available. This instrument is a step toward matching the degrees of psychopathology with a continuum of therapeutic methods. It is a useful tool when used in an appropriate manner with proper indications. With certain situations it can be used by the less than maximally trained person under supervision. Home, office and residential treatment settings each have indications. Further study is needed to more precisely define when treatment should be undertaken in each of these settings or in combination.

REFERENCES

1. Boatman, M. Nursing and hospital psychiatric therapy for psychotic children. *Amer. J. Orthopsychiat.,* 1962, 32:808–17.
2. Carse, J., Panton, N. E., and Watt, A. A district mental health service: The Worthington experiment. *Lancet,* 1958, 1:39–41.
3. Doyle, J. C. Role of the private physician in coordinated home care. *J. Amer. Med. Assoc.,* 1963, 185(10):782–83.
4. Friedman, A. S. Family therapy as conducted in the home. *Family Process,* 1962, 1(1):132–40.
5. Friedman, T. T., Becker, A., and Weiner, L. The psychiatric home treatment service: preliminary report of five years of clinical experience. *Amer. J. Psychiat.,* 1963, 120(8): 782–88.
6. Henry, J. *Culture against man.* New York: Random House, 1963.
7. Moore, R. F., Albert, R. S., Manning, M. J., and Glasser, B. A. Explorations in alternatives to hospitalization. *Amer. J. Psychiat.,* 1962, 119(12): 560–69.
8. Pasamanick, B., Scarpitti, F. R., Lefton, J., Dinitz, S., Wernert, J. J., and McPheeters, H. Home vs. hospital care for schizophrenics. *J. Amer. Med. Assoc.,* 1964, 187(3):177–81.
9. Querido, A. Early diagnosis and treatment services. *World Mental Health,* 1956, 8:180–89.
10. Redl, F., Newman, R. G., and Keith, M. M. *The school-centered life space interview.* Washington, D.C.: Washington School of Psychiatry, 1964.
11. Robison, O. L., Dalgleish, K. B., and Egan, M. H. Study and treatment of twenty school phobic children and their families. Paper read at 1965 meeting of the American Orthopsychiatric Association, New York, N. Y.

V

TASKS, ROLES, AND
TRAINING OF PROFESSIONAL
AND NONPROFESSIONAL
MENTAL HEALTH WORKERS

WITH THE inclusion of the community into the arena, the mental health professional must seek to understand the transition and the implications it has for changes in his professional role. Treatment remains as a solid base but the scope of prevention and community activities widens greatly. By bringing services closer to the people being served, new techniques and creative applications of old methods have to be attempted. Psychiatrists, psychologists, family physicians, social workers, and nurses need to consider their interrelations within their own ranks and to the community pressing for services. Innovative approaches to the use of urban agents and indigenous nonprofessionals blend together with long-standing, more traditional methods to further shape future programs.

Mental health professionals continue to be trained in traditional roles consistent with a limited model of patient care. This section details some stimulating approaches to the problem of scarce manpower and offers innovative suggestions for adding to the available cadre of workers to function in community mental health programs. While Pasamanick's article deals primarily with psychiatrists, the transfer to other professional roles is obvious and should not be overlooked. The new and imaginative ideas presented in the other articles in this section are only examples of directions that can be considered if our minds are not closed and we concentrate on solving the basic mental health problem through training of new types of workers in the field.

Developments in community psychiatry are creating great controversy within the profession. Daniels examines community psychiatry, assesses its place in the history of medical science and practice, explores possible additions and modifications in residency training, and suggests possible patterns of future practice.

A majority of psychiatrists are currently trained to care for a minority of patients. Pasamanick outlines a radical reconstruction of our conceptualization of mental disorders and the application of new curricula for traditional and new professions in optimally organized and operated community mental health center educational complexes.

Yolles identifies a major role for the psychologist in comprehensive community mental health programs. The psychologist is the bridge between the medical, the behavioral and social sciences. In addition, terms such as "conceptualizer" and "creative generalist" are also being used to describe their role. Psychologists are seen as key professionals in extending the mental health of the community into the schools, the juvenile courts, the home and on street corners.

Although the psychiatric nurse is traditionally patient-oriented, in the community mental health program she must shift her focus to the community and its problems. Lessler and Bridges report on the nurse's developing relations with other mental health professionals and suggest activities suited to the abilities of the nurse in a community mental health program. Included in the tasks are serving as coordinator, integrator, liaison and public relations worker for the clinic.

Bringing concepts and knowledge of the community and community organization to the mental health program, the psychiatric social worker provides a valuable integrating force. Furthermore, Rockmore notes that the social worker also adds a technique of the conference method and the principle of recognition of the right of the individual to self-determination. A sense of responsibility for community welfare augments the contributions of the social worker in the mental health team.

A family physician who seriously wishes to enlarge the scope of his practical operations with respect to the mental health needs of his patients could benefit from a working relation with a psychiatrist of his choice. Caplan feels that this could greatly improve his ability to recognize emotional needs in families, to prepare married couples for emotional aspects of pregnancy, to help families go more normally through periods of separation or bereavement and generally to use his knowledge of the family to contribute to its stability.

A new role for the mental health professions—that of mental health agent —is proposed by Kelly. Based on the knowledge of the functions of the urban agent, nonprofessional helping persons, the mental health agent provides services to population segments or social areas. Characteristics of metropolitan areas most relevant to this new role are identified and discussed as well as alternative planning strategies.

Meeting the needs of the low-income groups and the poor is not only a manpower problem but also an issue of ideology. Reiff states that there is a need for a human link between the mental health professional and the poor and that the new nonprofessional can be that link. Manpower problems are inseparable from the difficulties of achieving institutional change. A new professional is needed who is skilled in changing social systems.

Using parents as therapeutic agents affords new avenues for affecting change in their own children. Relating to the obvious questions of the emotional involvement of the parents and the complexity of the therapeutic role, Andronico and Guerney cite data to indicate the feasibility of the approach.

42

Community Psychiatry—A New Profession, a Developing Subspecialty, or Effective Clinical Psychiatry?

ROBERT S. DANIELS

THE controversy associated with community psychiatry developments is best illustrated by a series of statements which have been frequently heard during the last few years. Advocates have said, "Community psychiatry is the psychiatry of the future. We are in the midst of a third psychiatric revolution which will result in new patterns of psychiatric practice. The community psychiatrist will play an important part in community organization and planning. In this planned society the psychiatrist is a key figure. Social and psychiatric facilities will be coordinated. Any contact with an individual or family will be noted and that record will be available to all planning and treating facilities and individuals." "Psychiatrists must be gotten out of their offices and into the community." "Our training programs need modification. They do not offer enough training in community psychiatry."

Opponents make statements such as, "Community psychiatry is nothing more than good psychiatry. We have been practicing in this way for 15 years." "Our training program has always offered broad training in the use of community facilities. That is all that this so-called 'new psychiatry' amounts to." "The community psychiatry movement is being imposed upon us by the National Institute of Mental Health, the Federal Government, and certain individuals." "There is no basis of knowledge or experience for community psychiatry practice. It is a gigantic boondoggle. We will raise the public hopes for help with their myriad social problems and then we will disappoint them." "Community psychiatry is not psychiatry but a new specialty."

This paper attempts to examine the development of community psychiatry, assess its place in the history of our science and practice, explore the additions and modifications which may be indicated in many of our residency training programs, and indicates some directions in which community psychiatry may influence psychiatric theory and practice. It is based on interrelated but somewhat dissimilar personal experiences and interests during the last several years: (a) A longstanding interest in social psychiatry and the interface between indi-

Reprinted from *Community Mental Health Journal,* 1966, *2,* 47–54, by permission of the publisher and the author. © 1966, Behavioral Publications, Inc. Dr. Daniels is Associate Dean, Social and Community Medicine, University of Chicago, Division of Biological Sciences.

vidual psychodynamics and the current environment; (b) participation in the planning and execution of the first Institute on Training in Community Psychiatry, jointly sponsored by the University of Chicago, Department of Psychiatry, and the Training Branch of the National Institute of Mental Health in October, 1963; (c) continuing discussions within the Group for the Advancement of Psychiatry Committee on Medical Education; and (d) the evaluation of the residency training program at the University of Chicago in the Department of Psychiatry's Residency Curriculum Review Committee.

WHAT IS COMMUNITY PSYCHIATRY?

Community psychiatry is a developing body of knowledge and practice which relates psychiatric and social science principles to large population groups. Its body of theory is known as social psychiatry and is derived from ecology and epidemiology, public health and preventive medicine, social systems theory, and community organization. It is also based on the psychologic insights of individual and small group dynamics and an understanding of family structure and organization. It has as its broad goals the establishment of programs for early diagnosis and treatment, rehabilitation, and, so far as currently possible, prevention. Psychiatrists practicing in this area do so as consultants to community facilities, as planners for the establishment of social and psychiatric resources within population groups, or as providers of traditional psychiatric services through clinic and hospital facilities serving a specified population.

In most community psychiatry programs, certain fundamental principles are followed. These principles are:

1. The population group to be served is defined. It must be small enough that communication among professionals and between professional and client is facilitated.

2. The principle of minimal intervention is the core of the service provided. Maximum use is made of the client's adaptive capacities.

3. The firing-line professional manages most cases.

4. The service is close to the client and especially devised to meet his individual needs.

5. Emphasis is on increased awareness, early detection, and immediate intervention, particularly at times of crisis.

6. Simple and immediate services are available first.

7. Complex, special or lengthy services are obtained by referral to centrally located facilities.

8. The ability to pay is not a primary requisite for service.

9. The community psychiatry specialist spends more time in consultation with firing line professionals than in direct contact with patients.

10. Individual cases are viewed as examples of groups of cases. Case finding in similar populations and in families is important.

11. At the time of referral, there is a free flow of client and information from one professional to another. On completion of the service, referral back to the original source is not only possible but encouraged.

12. Institutions have an optimum size. Large institutions are psychologically, socially, and economically unsound. In some instances, they may lead to sustaining mental illness rather than to treating it.

A typical community psychiatry program might take as its focus a population unit varying from tens of thousands to several hundred thousand people. This unit could be defined politically as a city or a county, geographically as a neighborhood or section, or functionally as an industry or school system. Centrally located within this unit would be a community mental health center which would consist of a large consultation and outpatient facility and a small hospital of several hundred beds. The inpatient facility would be composed of several units which provide flexible services for particular ages or special problems. Special services might consist of units for children, adolescents, aged, alcoholics, and the mentally retarded. Halfway house, day care, night care, and full-time units would be included. Emphasis within this setting would be on diagnosis and brief reconstitutive treatment. Long-term treatment and custodial treatment would occur in a separate and different setting.

This center would emphasize its outpatient and consultative functions. Therapy in the outpatient section would be brief, and the focus would be crisis and reality oriented. Whenever possible the staff avoids direct patient contact; evaluation is accomplished, rather, by utilizing the information the referring person or agency already has available. When referring a patient or client, the consulting agency or individual participates in the consultation and continues its primary responsibility. Relinquishing responsibility is ordinarily temporary and occurs when the consultant has a service available which is indicated for the patient and which the referrer cannot provide. Examples of such services might be comprehensive psychiatric diagnosis, the evaluation of certain medical-legal problems, or specialized psychiatric treatment. If the center accepts the client or patient in transfer, it is for a brief period and the accomplishment of explicit goals, after which transfer back to the referring individual or agency is indicated. If possible, the original referrer continues to be active while the specialty facility performs its particular function.

Consultation services are provided for individuals and institutions in the community. Attempts are made to appraise collaboratively the programs of emotional support available through schools, churches, social agencies, legal institutions, and others, and to relate them to one another in order to provide a variety of services available in continuity. Consultation may be offered on classes of problems such as delinquency, school failure, school dropouts, illegitimacy, alcoholism, mental retardation, broken families, child care, etc. It is hoped that such consultations are educational as well as problem oriented and will increase the capacity of the individual or the agency to manage similar problems in the future.

Under ordinary circumstances, the firing line professional is an individual who does not define his role as a primary mental health one. Included in this group are physicians, public health and visiting nurses, teachers, clergymen, lawyers, policemen, and others. Their advice or counsel is frequently sought early by individuals with emotional problems. They are usually readily available in the community. Also the troubled person often has a preexistent relationship which facilitates contact. These firing line professionals already manage most instances of emotional disorder. These principles are demonstrated in Table 1.

TABLE 1. AN EXAMPLE OF A COMMUNITY PSYCHIATRY PROGRAM

Level I Major Firing Line Professionals	Level II Agencies for Social and Medical Diagnosis and Brief Treatment	Level III Community Psychiatry Centers	Level IV Large Hospital Facilities
Nonpsychiatric Physician	Community psychiatric clinics Psychiatric services in general hospital	Consultation services to fellow professionals (a) To all levels (b) To all individuals	
Visiting or Public Health Nurse Teacher Minister Lawyer	Guidance-counseling systems in schools Social agencies Vocational and psychologic rehabilitation services	Consultation services to patients (outpatient) Inpatient services (200-300 beds) (a) Diagnosis and short-term treatment (b) Special services	Long-term treatment and custodial facilities
Policeman Other	Diagnostic services in courts Other		

EXAMPLES OF COMMUNITY PSYCHIATRY PRACTITIONERS

Many psychiatrists spend some time in activities which could be called community psychiatry. These activities often involve a half-day or a day each week. They are a break in their usual private practice, academic or institutional routine. In such activities, the psychiatrist usually visits a community facility such as a clinic, hospital, social agency, court, or school. His purposes are to offer consultation and educational opportunities to the staff of the agency or institution. Although he may see patients, usually he does not. His consulting activities may be patient centered, either directly or indirectly, staff centered or program centered (1).

An example will clarify these various kinds of activities. A psychiatrist consults a half-day each week at a halfway house and rehabilitation agency. The agency is staffed by social workers, nurses, occupational therapists, vocational rehabilitation workers, and volunteers. The client population is a group of approximately 200 chronic ambulatory schizophrenics. At times the psychiatric consultant sees clients directly. More often he is presented data by a staff member about a client. In this type of consultation, he emphasizes the training aspects of the interaction, helping to increase the staff's capacity for understanding and dealing with the problems presented by their clients. At other times, the psychiatrist may consult with staff about intrastaff problems or about planning new programs. On still other occasions he plays a more clearly educational role with staff and volunteers. The consultant might be asked to perform any or all of these functions during a particular day.

For a few practitioners who conceive of themselves as community psychiatry specialists, the mental health consultation has become the major vehicle of their practice. Kiesler (4) is responsible for the psychiatric and social services in a three-county area in rural northern Minnesota. His staff consists of himself, a psychologist, and a social worker. They insist that the referring individual or agency retain primary responsibility for the patient or family in distress. Whenever possible, the clinic staff sees the referring professional, rather than the patient, using his information to understand the case and plan with the professional his course of action. Approximately 80 per cent of their staff time is spent in indirect and program consultation with such widely diverse professionals as physicians, visiting nurses, teachers, welfare workers, and ministers. Only 20 per cent of their time is occupied with direct patient service.

Another model of community psychiatry practice results from a request to a psychiatrist by an organization, institution, or population unit to plan and organize social and psychiatric services. Examples may be found in colleges, industry, and the military services. This model also exists in population and political units such as cities, counties, or states. The activities of this psychiatrist include planning for primary, secondary, and tertiary prevention. The head of a department of mental health for a political unit, such as a large city or state, is an illustration. He recommends and implements the establishment of programs of maternal care and adoption which will provide adequate and consistent care for children with absent or disturbed maternal relationships (primary prevention). He establishes clinics which are available for the early detection and treatment of a patient's disability (secondary prevention). He organizes state hospitals and a continuity of post-hospital services to provide social and vocational rehabilitation (tertiary prevention).

The mental health consultation model and the planner and implementer model are currently the two primary modes of functioning for the community psychiatrist. In urban or well developed areas most general psychiatrists, who spend a limited time in community psychiatry activities, will follow a consultation model. In areas poorly supplied with social and psychiatric services, the psychiatrist may be asked to assist in planning, facilitating, and arranging services for his community.

THE HISTORICAL AND THEORETICAL BASE
OF COMMUNITY PSYCHIATRY

Some psychiatrists have felt that the community psychiatry movement has been imposed from outside the profession and is not based on developments occurring naturally and spontaneously from within. Some have complained that the Federal Government, the National Institute of Mental Health, or their representatives are imposing the community psychiatry program onto an unwilling and uncertain profession.

However, a careful evaluation of psychiatry since 1940 demonstrates certain trends which are the bases for the community psychiatry development. During World War II, many psychiatrists left their private offices or institutions and entered military service. There, they provided direct services to personnel and often advised command about questions concerning the organization of psychiatric and social services, education for officers and enlisted personnel, policy formation, and problems of morale. The beginnings of many of the principles currently utilized in community psychiatry are to be found in these military experiences; e.g., early recognition, treatment close to the source of disability, crisis-oriented treatment promoting adaptation and return to duty, and consultation to command about issues of general concern.

In the late forties and early fifties, a series of developments occurred which significantly changed the large mental hospital. They included the therapeutic community development, milieu therapy, the open hospital, and the new tranquilizing and anti-depressive drugs. Experimentation in new techniques for approaching and understanding patients also contributed their share. Family diagnosis and therapy, short-term treatment, and crisis-oriented therapy are examples. For the first time hospital populations began to decrease and it became apparent that most patients could be maintained in the community. Changes were also occurring in education. Increasing time in the medical undergraduate curriculum and mushrooming residency training programs, led to increasing human resources both in number and quality of personnel. Literature, the popular press, and various art forms became preoccupied with psychiatry and psychoanalysis. The public was enthusiastic about what psychiatry seemed to know and the possibility that this discipline might have information which would promote improved mental health and a vague entity called happiness.

As a result of these changes and an increasing recognition of the nature and extent of the problems faced, the Joint Commission on Mental Illness and

Health (3) was empowered by Congress to make a five-year study. Thirty-six national agencies concerned with mental health and welfare participated in this multidisciplinary study. Included were many respected and experienced psychiatrists. As a result of this report President Kennedy proposed legislation which would promote services for mental health and retardation. His proposals led Congress to enact legislation which, when it is implemented, will promote community psychiatry programs.

This brief examination of recent history suggests that community psychiatry is based on sound developments within general psychiatry. Application of this knowledge could lead to better treatment and rehabilitation, and possibly even prevention for broader population segments. However, the theoretic and experimental bases for community psychiatry continue to be uncertain. Since psychiatry is at the beginning of this endeavor and our results are likely to be uncertain and erratic, ongoing methods of appraisal must be included with programs. Without research with careful design, clinical impressions will emerge, but these may not be translatable into principles. Psychiatry must move as rapidly as possible to confirm or deny these impressions so that new programs may be based on solid data and old mistakes will not be repeated. Out of such research may come a scientific basis for what is currently a beginning discipline.

EDUCATION IN COMMUNITY PSYCHIATRY
FOR PSYCHIATRIC RESIDENTS

Varying opinions are common when questions arise, such as how, when, and to what extent community psychiatry should be included in our residency curriculum. Many psychiatric educators believe that the curriculum is already crowded and could not possibly be extended to include new or different training. Others express the opinion that community psychiatry is nothing new. It only represents a formal expression of what they have been doing all along. A few discuss community psychiatry training as unimportant and unnecessary. Some educators conceive of these community psychiatry experiences as the basic ones within their residency program. For others, the solution has been to conceive of training in community psychiatry as occurring in the post-residency period and as comparable to subspecialty training, such as child psychiatry. Many residency programs are including some training in the community psychiatry arena. A few have decided, either because of lack of facilities or interest, that this training will not be included in their program. At the University of Chicago, Department of Psychiatry, a committee has examined these issues. The following paragraphs summarize a program which seems possible and productive within a particular setting.

In order to understand accurately a new training development, a brief examination of the environment in which it occurs is essential. It is only with such information that it becomes possible to evaluate critically the reasons for certain decisions, planning, and action. This Department is staffed by a complete, full-time staff which is permittted no outside compensation. The University of Chicago Hospitals and Clinics include a 750-bed general hospital complex that serves a private socioeconomic population, ranging from upper lower class to lower upper class. Almost no indigent patients are treated. The Department and training are psychoanalytically and socially oriented. Biological psychiatry is not strongly represented. Organization within the Department is according to clinical function and includes the following sections: Inpatient, Consultation and Liaison, Outpatient, Child Psychiatry, and Student Mental Health. In addition, the Department is affiliated with a 60-bed unit at the Illinois State Psychiatric Institute, a research and educational state hospital approximately 20 minutes away by car.

There are 15 residents in adult psychiatry equally divided between three years. The residency program has consisted of three- or six-month rotations on each of these services, ongoing outpatient contacts, intensive supervision of both of these, a didactic curriculum, and a six-month elective period in the third year. In addition, each resident spends a half-day a week for several months in community facilities including a home for the aged, the municipal court, a social agency, a community receiving hospital, and a state hospital. In the past, residents completing this program have predominately entered analytically-oriented private practice (almost 80 per cent) or academic settings (about 20 per cent). Significantly, 24 of the last 25 residents to complete the program are spending at least one-half day a week in work which follows the community psychiatry model.

Recent changes in psychiatry, particularly the community psychiatry development, and in increasing interest in research training led the Department to reevaluate its curriculum. The question repeatedly asked during this evaluation was whether a core program can be defined for the education of residents. What is essential? What is superfluous? Where does the resident learn? Where are there service demands which exclude optimum learning? What is resident training for? Is part of this training general and for all? Is a part of the training specialized and for a few?

In the course of this evaluation a core curriculum was devised. The core includes a two-year sequence of clinical rotations, ongoing outpatient treatment, supervision of both of these, and a series of didactic seminars. The third year will be elective; opportunities for a fourth year will also be available. The resident may choose one of the following four paths at the third year level: (a) individual psychotherapy, (b) child psychiatry, (c) community psychiatry, or (d) research. Each path has a coordinator who facilitates the arrangement of an individually different curriculum for each resident during the third and elective fourth year. The core of the first two years is in basic clinical psychiatry plus diagnostic and therapeutic work with individual patients, families, and small groups. In addition, the first two years will encompass an introductory experience in each of the other potential paths. These introductions involve a

3-month rotation in child psychiatry, an 18-month seminar in research methods, a half-day a week clinical experience in community psychiatry, and a 24-month seminar in community psychiatry.

For the purposes of this presentation, attention will be focused on the community psychiatry segment of the curriculum. Daniels and Margolis (2) have commented previously on the integration of community psychiatry attitudes and knowledge into traditional service rotations. Emphasized in that presentation were the understanding of small group or family diagnosis and therapy, community organization, leadership, decision-making, communication with experienced and inexperienced collaborators, leading a team, becoming a team member, teaching, consultation in the medical setting, the use of community resources, and case finding. Simultaneously with these experiences on the clinical services, residents will spend a half-day a week in a community facility where, in the first year, he will be a member of a working team. This rotation will include three months at each of four facilities: a home for the aged, a family court, a social agency, and a community-oriented state hospital. During the second year, the resident will have a prolonged experience with one agency or facility and brief observational experiences in several others. He will actually participate in consultative and educational roles under the supervision of the full-time staff. In addition to those mentioned above, further possibilities for such community experiences in depth include a school, a halfway house, an agency for the physically handicapped, a visiting nurses association, work with ministers, and work with the police. Members of the faculty have already established consulting relationships with these facilities and professionals.

The seminar will provide the opportunity to share and examine the different experiences that residents have had. In addition, it will be a place to probe the structure of the Chicago community and interact with its political and social leaders. Among the participants in the seminar will be individuals such as the Chief of Police, aldermen, representatives of the Board of Health, directors of community organizations and agencies, and others. Also considered, will be a basic introduction to ecology and epidemiology, public health psychiatry, social psychiatry, and community structure and organization. Understanding and applying research methodology to the evaluation of programs of practice will be emphasized.

The third- and fourth-year programs will include additional intensive field experiences with one or more placements. The training will be tailored to the individual needs and goals, but research will play a significant part. Opportunities are available through other segments of the University for intensive work in basic science areas or for consultation with experts in specialized areas of research interest.

The purpose of this program is to provide all trainees with experience and supervision which will lead to competence for part-time functioning in community psychiatry. For a few trainees it will provide a specialized opportunity comparable to subspecialty training.

THE FUTURE OF COMMUNITY PSYCHIATRY

Predictions are difficult and uncertain. However, psychiatric educators attempt to orient their educational endeavors to the practitioners of the future. Thus, the future of community psychiatry must be appraised whether, eventually, the appraisal proves right or wrong. Some psychiatrists will certainly choose to remain uninvolved in this type of practice. However, as interest within psychiatry increases, as social and political support is intensified, and as educational programs are improved, most psychiatrists will probably devote more time to this type of activity. For most, this effort will continue to be limited and partial. But for an increasing number of psychiatrists, community psychiatry will become a predominant area of practice. These psychiatrists will be receiving increasing training opportunities and ultimately there may well be a subspecialty comparable to child psychiatry.

Experiences and research in community psychiatry will certainly influence general psychiatric practice. Now community psychiatry programs are largely based on insights derived from the rest of psychiatry and other disciplines. As experiences multiply and program and basic research is accomplished, certainly valuable clinical insights will be translated back into the theory and practice of general psychiatry.

However, there are certain danger signals in current public support and pressure. Constructive developments will require more than money and community approval. Too often the general public has believed that the psychiatrist has solutions to its many problems: e.g., delinquency, criminal behavior, drug addiction, alcoholism, illegitimate pregnancy, school dropouts, unemployment, automation, mental retardation, school integration, and aging. Although psychiatry has a contribution to make toward understanding these syndromes and problems, and although it may participate in planning programs of treatment and rehabilitation, it does not have ready or easy answers. The public should not be led to expect more than psychiatry can deliver and there must be constant interaction about psychiatry's strengths and its limitations. To promise a great deal and to accomplish little courts disaster where continuing public and political support are essential.

The broad trends seem clearer although the details remain obscure. Community psychiatry will attract an increasing number of psychiatrists. For most it will be integrated into their usual practice activities. For others it will be a part-time endeavor which will offer a welcome break in ordinary office and hospital routines. For an increasing number it will become a subspecialty. It seems unlikely that community psychiatry will develop into a new profession. Psychiatric training programs are undergoing changes which will probably result in more effective training in community psychiatry. Training will include experiences in the community, opportunities for supervised consultation, and didactic teaching. Most residency programs will include part or all of these. A few programs will continue to offer specialized training.

The arbitrary and unreconcilable arguments which introduced this paper have been examined. An appraisal of the current state of affairs reveals that community psychiatry is neither without basis nor certain of success. However, community psychiatry clearly has developing potential which requires attention and exploration.

REFERENCES

1. Caplan, G. *Principles of preventive psychiatry*. New York: Basic Books, 1964.
2. Daniels, R., and Margolis, P. The integration of community psychiatry training in a traditional psychiatric residency. *Ment. Hyg.*, 1965, 49:17–26.
3. Joint Commission on Mental Illness and Health. *Action for mental health*. New York: Basic Books, 1961.
4. Kiesler, F. Is this psychiatry? In S. Goldston (Ed.), *Concepts of community Psychiatry*. Bethesda: Public Health Service, 1965.

43

The Development of Physicians
for Public Mental Health

BENJAMIN PASAMANICK

RECENT developments in mental health care have prodded us sharply
on the decades-old dilemma of insufficient and inadequate psychiatric manpower. Essential to any discussion of the problem is some review of how we
arrived at our present state in the context of possible solutions.

But first I would like to state some assumptions. Of course these assumptions are not universally acceptable; but because their bases are historically
essential to the comprehension of why I make certain proposals, I find it necessary, contrary to common procedure, to discuss the assumptions before building upon them. I must stipulate that my examples and arguments are not universally applicable, particularly when stated in dogmatic form.

The first assumption is that the mental disorders are, in the common sense
of the terms, disease entities or syndromes. Years ago this would have appeared to be a truism, but it no longer is. The point must be discussed, because
if the assumption is false, the physician should not be concerned with the problem of mental disorders since his function as a physician is to diagnose and
treat disease. Questioning of the validity of this assumption is largely due to
three factors. One is the universal application of so-called dynamic theories
of the origin of mental disorders in which unconscious intrapsychic stresses
are posited to be etiologic. The second is the belief that mental disorders fall
along a continuum of psychologic difficulties which are present in most individuals. These two factors are themselves assumptions and as such have formed
the bases of much of the psychiatric thinking in this country. In the context of
these assumptions, the claim that mental illness is a myth is indeed a valid one.
All the arguments that have been offered against this statement are themselves
invalid if these assumptions are not disclaimed.

It is only when mental disorders are seen in the model of all disease entities
(i.e. as physico-bio-psycho-social phenomena, with varying emphases on the
contributions from each of the levels of integration) that physicians are warranted in being concerned with their management. Only when disorders are

Reprinted from *American Journal of Orthopsychiatry*, 1967, *36*, 469–486, by permission of the publisher and the author. © 1967, American Orthopsychiatric Association. Dr. Pasamanick is Associate Commissioner for Research, New York State Department of Mental Hygiene.

recognized socially as *qualitatively different* states from that of health, rather than quantitative additions on a continuum, does it follow that as members of the social institution medicine, physicians have been assigned them as their social concern (3). It is because this distinction has not been recognized that every anxiety and confusion stemming from the problems of living in a rapidly changing, complex society has been adopted as the concern of the psychiatrist.

The third factor leading to the claim that mental illness is a myth has been the entrance of large numbers of nonmedical professionals into disciplines concerned with the treatment of these psychologically defined conditions, using, and in identical fashion, psychologic methods promulgated by physicians.

What I am driving at is this: Psychiatrists have accepted undiscriminatingly the doctrines of a number of schools of psychiatric thought whose contents are traditionally and logically not primarily the concern of medicine, and do not rationally require medical training for comprehension and practice. They then have applied them to every unhappiness and emptiness present in middle- and upper-class individuals willing and able to pay for their concern. During the course of this social process, largely a phenomenon of the last two decades, psychiatrists have grossly neglected those disorders which in large measure are unchallenged as their province—the mental subnormalities, the functional psychoses, and the organic psychoses of the aged. In terms of suffering, disability, and social cost, these are unquestionably the major problems of psychiatry and medicine. They have been neglected despite the quadrupling of the number of psychiatric practitioners during these 20 years.

This leads us directly to our second assumption, that we do want to be concerned with the control of these mental disorders. Stating this assumption would appear to be gratuitously insulting were it not for the realities so painfully documented in the distribution of psychiatric care in this country. In no other medical discipline can there be found such marked disparity between the care available for those able to pay and those unable to pay. It has been said that only the poor and the well-to-do secure good medical care in this country. Like many generalizations of this type, it is not true. However, it is not so grossly untrue that it would have manifest invalidity. Certainly, the nature of other medical care is not as different as it frequently is in psychiatric care. How are we to interpret a situation where despite the quadrupling of psychiatrists in the past 20 years, there may be even less psychiatric time available for the hospitalized indigent than there was 30 years ago? This is true despite the greater needs of the indigent, both in terms of the absolute numbers ill and their depth of illness and despite the enormous effort and governmental funds that went into the training of psychiatrists. I would prefer to interpret this result as a concomitant of the type of training which emphasizes the one-to-one relationship of middle-class therapist to middle-class responsive patient in intensive, long-term care as the most desirable and status-invoking activity rather than a result of its well paying nature. I believe these inconsistencies have weighed heavily upon the conscience of psychiatry. I would wager that if shown what to do, it would be willing to act.

The third assumption states that the best method of care, and not merely the best substitute, for those major illnesses with which we should be most concerned is that which has received so much discussion and is described as comprehensive, continuous, community-mental-health-center care.

There has been a good deal of critical and cynical discussion of what might be termed the crusade for community mental health care and its program. Some of it is based on the fact that extraordinarily little experimental investigation of the feasibility and efficacy of the program as a whole or any of its aspects has occurred. In addition, some of the proposals, particularly for prevention and social change, have been painfully amateurish, particularly to academic sociologists and political scientists who are aware of social process. However, what most of the critics apparently have ignored is the fact that community mental health care as it is seen by NIMH and Congress is a phenomenon in the history of social institutions.

The total type of institution also was an historical phenomenon. It was established in western society in the first half of the nineteenth century, consequent to industrialization and urbanization, as an efficient and humanitarian move to care for the mentally ill, the aged, the poor, the crippled, orphaned children, prisoners, and other helpless and handicapped persons as liabilities in a rapidly changing, complex social organization. In time, this institution was found to be either inefficient, harmful, or unnecessary and has in many areas of our culture either wholly or partially disappeared.

Our concern is the proper preparation of physicians for their efficient functioning in this community mental health care, and not whether we consider this phenomenon good or bad, since it is inevitable. What does remain open for discussion are the nature of the care and the function of psychiatrists within the program. Discussion and decision are needed since these inevitably will shape the training required. Unfortunately, we neither have the time nor the predictive potential to discuss them adequately at this time. In broad terms, however, they almost certainly will follow, at least for the next decade or two, the guidelines offered by NIMH, which require no further detailing here.

One of the first and obviously justified concerns, in view of the present distribution of our profession, has been manpower. For the most minimal programs foreseen, using psychiatrists in the traditional fashion, we cannot begin to approach fulfillment of need.

In our Baltimore studies, for instance, we found that, at any moment in time, one-eighth of the population had a definite mental disorder, and we were criticized for being overly conservative in our estimates. Further, 2.5 per cent of the population were close to total social disability (5). On a national scale this latter datum would mean 5 million individuals, or more than 300 for each of the psychiatrists in the country.

Let me now give a more specific example. Two years ago we completed an experimental study demonstrating the feasibility and efficacy of preventing the hospitalization of schizophrenics, using drugs prescribed by a psychiatrist after a single diagnostic interview and administered in the homes of patients by regularly visiting public health nurses over a period of years (6). Little more than what I have just stated was done for these patients, and, in a cohort of quite ill schizophrenics, hospitalization was prevented for three-quarters. We might add that, as far as estimates of functioning are concerned at this time, we do not appear to have done them any harm; on the contrary, the data indicate that the mean social functioning of the patients in the experimental group was better than that of the group which was sent to hospital and that their families and the community suffered no harm. With this seemingly absolutely minimal program, we estimate that, were we to institute such a program throughout the United States just for schizophrenics, we would require one-third of all the psychiatrists in the United States. This would not cover the need for all the other psychiatric conditions, including mental subnormality or even for those schizophrenics whose hospitalization could not be prevented. I should add parenthetically that were we to institute programs for the schizophrenics more closely approximating an optimal level, the need obviously would be multiplied.

Because of the anarchic form the provision of medical care has assumed and the similarly irresponsible manner in which we have trained psychiatrists to participate, we are confronted by the disconcerting fact that in large measure we have trained the majority of our discipline to care for a minority of our problems, and these are the least serious. We cannot in good conscience continue in this fashion. It is true that in the end the type of mental health care program will determine the nature of psychiatric education. It behooves us to be careful about what we create and plan. But all this takes time, and the marketplace is a slow responder. I think we cannot avoid facing the fact that, as responsible social scientists, we ought to be able to predict and plan for the future.

Let us first take a look at the nature of psychiatric resident training today. In large measure it is a form of apprenticeship or on-the-job technical training during which, for a large portion of his so-called training period, the resident provides the definitive care for patients. He presumably is repaid by a moderate salary, a minimal amount of formal instruction, and some supervision of his activities and practice. This is, of course, not graduate education in the academic sense of the term but the old preceptor training. The resident's clinical instruction depends upon patient intake, and it must be admitted that the resident does over and over again things which are relatively rapidly learned and need very little practice, but which are repeated because of patient care needs. The serious question has been raised as to whether the primary intent of resident training is indeed the training of residents, or, rather, the provision of a cheap form of physician care in the institutions and clinics of our approved centers. I think it would be safe to state that in many of our centers, if not a majority of them, medical care by physicians would collapse if the residents were removed.

A number of unfortunate concomitants follow upon this type of training and medical care. In the first place, a good deal of the time of the resident which could be used for education is wasted. Secondly, since the psychiatric center is so dependent upon the relatively short supply of these residents, he is frequently overworked so that he does not have even proper clinical instruction, let alone basic scientific education. Third, in the form of psychiatric care presently available, we face terrible shortages. Psychiatric centers, particularly for the indigent, are competing desperately for the services of residents. We have arrived at the point where we must import large numbers of physicians from foreign countries (frequently with extremely poor command of English, in an area where communication is crucial) and even from underprivileged countries, whose need for physicians is infinitely greater than ours. In psychiatry we do not even have the excuse that we are training psychiatrists for these countries, since the last thing that most of these countries need in terms of medical care is psychiatry of the American pattern.

It also leads, paradoxically and unfortunately, since the resident is in a seller's market, to the determination by the resident of what he will be taught and what he will do. Responsible training administrators, aghast at our inability to provide the psychiatric manpower needed for the type of care planned, complain that the residents no longer listen to them and are interested only in psychodynamics, psychotherapy and their analyses. I can only describe this as health-care anarchy and social irresponsibility. It can only lead to poor psychiatric care, poor education, and loss of respect internationally. What I would suggest is a radical change of psychiatric training to true graduate education on the doctoral level with a considered distribution of available time for the necessary content.

What then should be the content of this training? When I think of all the things a good psychiatrist should know, and what he will have to know to lead competently in the new programs, I feel that unless we are prepared to throw an enormous amount of effort into training the necessary people and change our methods and outlook ruthlessly, it might almost be better to turn mental health care over to a body which would lead responsibly. In view of this enormous content coming from all levels of integration with an exponentially increasing load of new knowledge—good, bad, and indifferent—we must turn to a qualitatively different type of professional training. This now has become apparent to intelligent medical educators. In the good medical schools, slowly and with great trial and pain, new patterns of education are emerging. It just is not possible to teach medical students all that we know about medicine and the basic sciences underlying it. We cannot continue to pour fact, dogma, and method into the individual in sufficient quantity to mirror reality. We have become aware of the danger of drowning the student or forcing him to make undiscriminating selections from the mass so that he becomes obsolete soon after he graduates. The alternative is to teach him principles and to show him how to operate as a member of a team, since the individual practitioner is, in large measure, also an obsolete social phenomenon.

Before continuing with curriculum content, I would prefer to consider the context of this education and offer for consideration a program for a state psychiatric institute. This institution is the type from which most of the mental health personnel should come in future years. I intend to discuss the organization and integration of the institute under three main heads: service, training, and research. It must be apparent that it will be necessary to turn from research to service to training as each is discussed, for they are really inseparable.

Another obvious principle is that all possible modalities of treatment which we can accept and summon up should be available for both teaching and experimental evaluation. Fortunately, as far as service, teaching, and research purposes are concerned, they all call for components of the highest quality. Since teaching and research are primary goals, there must be unquestioning acceptance of random assignment, differential treatment and other selection necessary either for teaching or research. (Obviously, at times, special and higher considerations would alter such thinking but never to the extent that they seriously could affect or bias either teaching or research.)

A number of service-connected variables come flooding for comment but would make this paper impossibly long. However, an important one concerning how organization and facilities probably would have to be altered is that of residential care, the number of beds, and distribution of efforts at the institute. Having accepted the assumption that we are to have a true CMH center as the core of the institute, it becomes apparent that residential care can be only *one* of the treatment methods, prescribed only where considered or demonstrated to be most efficacious and not merely for convenience. It follows, therefore, that for the same number of permanent employees and persons to be trained, we will require a drastic reduction in the number of beds. This arrangement also has the virtue of making space available for intake and similar office and other needs for CMH care.

It also might be wise to consider unit team care, rather than the ward, as the organizational base. This would mean that a therapist and the team with whom he operates would serve a patient wherever he or she is to be admitted or cared for rather than being assigned to a specific ward, since the intake pattern to be described under training would require that an individual and/or his team would serve a patient continuously throughout all treatment areas and modalities whether in the home, hospital or elsewhere in order to make the treatment truly continuous.

The matter of integration of services for children and adults, including those mentally retarded, requires very careful consideration. It would seem to me that there is everything to be gained and little or nothing to be lost by integration of all services, except for the residential. Since, in large measure, the family will be the unit of care and planning, treatment, community services, provision of welfare, etc., also should be mostly on a family basis; the fragmentation into various services would seem quite unwise. Besides, the latter contains within it the very realistic and, at present, frequent neglect of various types of patients, such as the mentally retarded or certain age groups. Present patterns also tend to omit or give only partial coverage to important areas of training. A final and telling reason, in my estimation, is the constant consideration of the need for continuous care. If our trainees are to start with chronically ill patients and carry them through for long periods, they must start with a patient at the begining of their training and carry the same patient through until they leave the center. If we accept this, then we cannot have blocks of time devoted to child psychiatry, mental retardation, geriatrics, neurology, etc. Residents must be involved with these types of patients right from the beginning and carry through with them. This is both the best type of care for the patient and the best type of clinical instruction, since it gives the longitudinal view that we always have deemed the most valuable. Again, this would seem to call for family type care and the necessity for integration of services. The transfer of personnel in training from one center or substation to another for different types of patients would be extremely wasteful of time and most confusing to the trainee; he would have to deal with innumerable people and agencies, both in terms of the patients' families and professional and nonprofessional personnel. (The question of training for psychiatric specialization will be discussed later.)

Intake services would call for a single intake area (or subarea if we are to consider setting up substations in the catchment area for even closer operational activities). Under these circumstances, one could foresee a physical plant design in which the three areas for residential care in mental retardation, adult and child psychiatry would be in the closest physical proximity, possibly surrounding an administration and intake facility.

The subject of training can be discussed under a number of different topics such as types and selection of differing disciplines and personnel to be trained, methods, curricula, integration of service and training, and so on. Again, only a few of the highlights can be touched upon as examples, with some concentration on specific and crucial areas. I think that we ought first to recognize the truism that, although we may be professionals in one or more areas, we are not necessarily good or effective instructors in any of them. There does exist a profession of education, and we ought to use its best possible resources as we intend to do in others. I would suggest, therefore, that we set up within the institute an educational section with the best possible full-time or part-time people in terms of professional educators. Its mission would be to help plan, monitor and test our educational efforts for the wide variety of traditional professionals and nonprofessionals, new professions and nonprofessional disciplines which the institutes should be responsible for producing. In this way duplication and waste of time can be avoided, efforts constantly improved, and whatever is valuable disseminated.

I strongly recommend most extensive and intensive use of the newest audiovisual and self-teaching aids, such as closed circuit television, videotape recorders and eventually programmed instruction devices. These days, with the use of television tape-recording, it is possible to record and rapidly edit the material of the best teachers. This procedure avoids endless repetition by the instructor of the same material, permits him to improve it, makes him available for discussion rather than didactic instruction, as well as for supervision of practical work. The student can use the material at his own speed and repeat it if necessary. It has been amply demonstrated that the method is at least as good as the classical types of instruction. We ought not to fall behind in teaching methods as we have in many other areas of professional activity.

Since it should have the most complete program, the best trained teaching personnel, the best teaching facilities, and should be accessible to other educational institutions and state facilities, the institute should be considered the chief short-term and long-term teaching center for both professional and nonprofessional employees of the state department of mental health. It should be unnecessary to send state employees to any other center, except for the most highly specialized traditional instruction and for some newly developed techniques. The different types of programs that should be considered for development are almost endless, limited only by the imagination of the developers of new programs.

An intimate and continuous part of the teaching program should be not only the testing of teaching methods, but also the continual testing of personnel with differing backgrounds for the same functions. As automated equipment takes over more and more skilled and unskilled jobs in industry, there will be a continuous flow of young and older people available for service occupations. We should be ready to take advantage of this opportunity and be prepared with training programs. Undoubtedly there will be increasing support for these programs from federal sources.

Training would cover a broad range of occupations. Partially new roles would be developed for the traditional occupations of psychiatry, psychology, and social work. In addition, we could contemplate such programs as refresher courses for psychiatrists about to take the specialty boards and for pediatricians in both mental retardation and child psychiatry. Instruction for teachers of disturbed children, vocational rehabilitation workers, school counsellors and for volunteer leaders should be included. We might develop short courses for general practitioners who could be used in state service for many purposes, including definitive rural mental health care (using consultation by closed circuit television from central experts, or even videotaped interviews on standardized instruments televised to those experts). Instruction could extend all the way to residential care aides; to home visitors who can serve in the traditional role partially filled by the public health nurse; to nurses, both for public health and for residential care; to occupational and recreational therapists; to new types of personnel equivalent to the Scandinavian ombudsman (the so-called indigenous worker); and to such personnel as family caretakers, cottage mothers, homemakers, and, as has even been suggested, women on Aid-to-Dependent Children who could serve nutritious meals and provide stimulation to elderly residents of public housing.

With such widely varying, extensive and intensive training programs, it would be highly economical and efficient to develop a teaching division staffed, as discussed previously, by nonpsychiatric professional educators. They could take most of the organizational responsibility and a good deal of the non-instructional burden from the shoulders of the psychiatric service and teaching personnel. The latter currently look upon instruction, particularly when it must be repeated many times during the year, as a burdensome chore, especially since it is frequently added to duties which already fill most of the working day. Teaching can become a pleasure when the size of the program makes it possible to use all the new methods and to program instruction on a stimulating discussion basis.

Some mention of the curricula and duties contemplated for the classical mental health triad might be profitable. I am thinking not only in terms of the specific content for such instruction, but also hope to cast some light on the nature of the service programs themselves.

Let us first take the exceedingly distressing situation in which clinical psychology finds itself at this time. The role of the psychologist as skilled administrator of diagnostic instruments has proved itself most disappointing. Most of the instruments deemed to require skilled interpretation have shown themselves to be of low reliability and little validity. Such instruments as tests of intelligence or batteries for neuropsychologic impairment can be administered by technicians and largely interpreted by the computer. The recent Washington Conference on Nosology, in large measure, demonstrated that the skilled classical psychiatric approach is still more predictive, when done reliably, than any of the objective measures except in the neurologic impairment category. In this latter area, in infancy certainly, highly trained judgments of child neurologists can be shown to be equally highly predictive. As for the psychologist's role in psychotherapy (and for that matter, other psychotherapists as well), where psychotherapy has been tested, it has not proven to be too satisfactory. In any event, it would seem to be unwarrantedly expensive in terms of training and time of highly educated individuals. (Here we might contemplate the training of less educated personnel for a specialized job.)

What then remains for the psychologist? This is a problem that has exercised the profession for some time without consensual solution. A number of necessary roles might be considered (aside from the usually offered ones of research and evaluation) such as in highly skilled individual psychotherapy, family therapy, and so on. We already have discussed varying programs in education. Here, the psychologists might very well play a major role, since it is an area in which they have already made major contributions. A number of them, if capable of teaching in varying areas, also could supervise and administer portions of the service program. We also can think of the development of new psychological treatment methods coming from social learning theory, classical and operant conditioning techniques and their continued testing and administration. Other possible roles and the curricula involved require long and intensive thought by the professions.

The changing role of the social worker in a CMH program is also one which cannot be discussed fully in this paper or, indeed, decided upon without consultation and discussion with members of the profession. However, a few comments are in order on one problem of concern for all the mental health professionals and nonprofessionals alike, that is, the least possible overlapping in function. Roles should be as clearly defined as possible, with functions as definitive as feasible. It is obvious that some overlapping always will be necessary in order to give complete coverage to patients. But vague, ill-defined, and duplicating roles are unfortunate for the patients, highly destructive of morale in personnel, and dysfunctional in organizations. Studies have shown that under the latter conditions job satisfaction is low, status rivalry high, decision-making poor and, probably, patient benefit impaired (2). It would seem rational that when professions of differing status and with different amounts of preparation and reward have precisely the same functions and roles in the treatment of patients (i.e., usually individual or group psychotherapy), then the differential status and rewards received become problematic. It is in this context that the role and training of the social worker must be developed. We will need very badly in CMH programs individuals who can function as liaison between patient and community, serving as the integrating mechanisms for the patient in his various contacts with social institutions. This function should be primary in the role of the social worker. If the profession does not assume this role, then we will have to develop a new profession for this purpose.

I would like to devote a bit more space to discussion of the training of the psychiatrist and implicitly bring in his role in the CMHC. In the discussion I assume that the program has been in effect for some years, thus not taking into account the relatively long period of transition during which trainees and the program would have to adjust.

I see the new resident preferably entering training in July, when service demands are at a fairly low ebb (with a minimum of vacations permitted to supervisory personnel and possibly none to other residents) and undergoing a period of orientation for a month. At that time the principles of CMH care could be intensively presented and discussed in the context of a dynamic presentation of the historical process in which public mental health care evolved as a social institution—in sociological, political, and economic terms. The resident would be given reading material prepared specifically for this purpose.

At the same time the resident would be offered a rapid review of clinical psychiatry with concentration on diagnosis and methods of treatment. The administrative and operational structure of the institute with its components would be available on paper and for discussion in the framework of its community functions and interrelationships with community agencies. The roles and functions of other personnel would be described and discussed, and his own educational program, with all the possibilities of specialization and variation, would be offered.

This orientation program would have to be very carefully planned and presented, since it would be hoped that these initial experiences would set the background for the resident's future activities and, even more, establish the pattern for his work at the institute and after graduation. It should be as well organized, as stimulating, and least confusing as possible—structured, but with adequate time for informal discussion and interchange. It should be on the highest intellectual plane and be carried out by the best instructors available, with all the educational techniques and facilities previously discussed. It should also be made clear that intensive effort is expected from the student. And, if it is done adroitly and in the context of graduate school education rather than as apprenticeship training, hopefully that pattern could be continued throughout. The 40-hour week should not be the model for the residents. Intensive reading and discussion amongst themselves as well as with staff might very well be planned for evening and weekend periods in order to reinforce this expectation. A good deal of this and what follows, of course, presupposes top-level candidates for residences. If and when we can establish the qualitatively newer and better CMH institute I am discussing, I think it will be possible to recruit candidates without too much difficulty. Bright, willing, idealistic, hardworking residents are a tremendous incentive to teaching and clinical staff as well as to research and service. The efforts inevitably spiral.

In the following month the new resident would be placed squarely in the mainstream of service activities. He would be placed in the office and under the jurisdiction of a third- or fourth-year resident with whom he would work for, let us say, two months. He would examine patients intensively, plan and prescribe treatment, and participate fully in all the varied components of CMH care, all under the direct instruction of the senior resident with, of course, the added supervision of the permanent staff who, by this time, would need to devote lesser time to the senior resident and more to the newcomer. He also would have time during this period for observing and participating in the activities of the other professional personnel in clinic, home, court, police station, school, ward and so on. The thinking behind this period has a number of goals. First, it should be direct orientation and should increase the resident's knowledge of the components of CMH care. It should introduce him to methods he will be using, but without the worry and confusion of direct responsibility. It also introduces him to the patients for whom he will be responsible in his share of the catchment areas, since a constant concern in continuity of care in a teaching institution is the turnover of personnel in training and the fact that none of the personnel are on 24-hour call. He would first take on responsibility for the care of the senior resident's patients on an emergency basis, having become acquainted with them by both direct contact and reading the records. He thus will be able to take over when the senior graduates. (On the other hand, the senior should receive training in supervision and instruction since the entire program is seen as a graduated program of increased and differential knowledge and experience and responsibility. This training would prepare him for his future role in CMH care and possibly in an academic setting.

By October, then, the resident should be ready to move into the service program. This program should subserve the function of providing the laboratory and practicum for what will be taught through seminars, reading, individual supervision and discussions, field experience, and preparation of reports and papers. The service and practical experience would be most heavily weighted towards those functions which are seen as primarily those of a psychiatrist, that is, traditionally those of the physician—history and anamnesis taking, diagnosis and prescription, with constant evaluation of the results of continuous care. There are additional aspects of practical experience which will have to be given him since he eventually will have to play a heavy supervisory role, particularly in various aspects of therapy. He will need experience, but obviously with minor weighting, in the roles of other professional and non-professional personnel. As I have indicated previously, the various roles and the functions attached must be delineated and clarified, but the minor roles can be described as educational, psychotherapeutic, relationships with the community and its social institutions, and so on.

The areas of didactic instruction, hopefully with a minimum of lecture as any true graduate school instruction should be, can be named but hardly outlined in this paper. Their order of presentation remains to be determined. It would seem obvious that some are needed earlier than others. But, with good initial orientation, some can be delayed to second and third years of residency. Such areas as personnel management obviously could be left to the last year; others, such as clinical psychiatry, must be begun early.

Let me then discuss briefly some of the content areas I think should be included in the training of the psychiatrist. Hopefully, with sufficient permanent staff and not too heavy a service load, we can give more didactic instruction in the first year and more practical experience in succeeding years. These content areas would include public health method and administration, epidemiology, and medical care organization as introductions to public mental health care. In the sciences basic to his profession, we would want to develop an introductory course, including neurophysiology, neurochemistry, neuroanatomy, specifically aimed at him and taught in an integrated fashion. A similar program in the behavioral sciences of psychology, sociology and anthropology could be offered, with heaviest concentration on the behavior of groups, community organization and relationships, etc. As indicated, the clinical areas necessarily would receive heaviest concentration. These would include child development (as the basis for the neuropsychological and behavioral development of the individual), neurology, neuropathology, child psychiatry, and their relationships to the totality of health care for patients of all ages.

The resident also should receive early in his training an intensive and thorough introduction to the scientific method. This is aimed largely at creating the critical attitude towards his activities and reading and to make him amenable to change. Most of this is unfortunately lacking in medical instruction, and must, therefore, be supplemented in a true graduate school atmosphere. Thus he would receive an introduction to biometrics, research method, and their applications in clinical and nonclinical sciences, all with mental health examples. He also should be given some grounding in the tools available (such as computer techniques, information storage and retrieval systems, and so on). The intention would be to give him awareness of the potentialities of these facilities and sufficient knowledge of their language and content to communicate intelligently with the consultants with whom he must be involved.

The practical experience which he is receiving is, without further description, in the CMH model. This means that he takes the psychiatrist's role from the initial entrance of the index case into care, and this is for all types of cases, without exception as to age or diagnosis, all the way from infancy to senility, organic or functional. It is here that the permanent staff and senior and specializing residents are of the utmost importance. They must serve at the same time in both the instructional and clinical consultative roles for these novices who gradually can assume increasing responsibility. It is, for instance, quite obvious that, at the outset, the first-year resident will be unable to perform an infant developmental examination. However, with the use of screening devices, which can be taught rapidly, he not only gains an introduction to this clinical area, but is able to determine when he needs specific consultation. Of course, initially, his judgment would be carefully scrutinized. As he goes on, he would learn the direct clinical examination methods and the management problems which follow. This is given as an example of how clinical experience also will be graded up to full responsibility.

Instruments, both paper and hardware, unquestionably will be playing an increasing role in medicine and in psychiatry. The use of these, their development, and their testing should and must play an important part in the instruction of psychiatric residents. At the same time, the role and importance of psychiatric theory and schools of thought must not be neglected. These can best be taught in a historical and critical framework. Their scope and limitations, backgrounds, and validity must be taught in the framework of the milieu in which they developed and the direction in which they are traveling. Specific therapeutic modalities should be taught and related back to the basic science and clinical disciplines previously named. In this fashion, psychopharmacology, psychotherapy (individual, group and family), shock therapies, and others of both historical and present interest, would be taught and practical experience offered.

By the third year those residents wishing it could begin to receive specialized instruction and experience. They already would have had considerable experience in mental retardation, problems of the aged, child psychiatry, administration, alcoholism, and so on. Some, however, might wish to devote more time to one area than another, and opportunities should be offered for such specialization, but without complete concentration on any of these areas (except possibly for child psychiatry, which has its own subspecialty boards). It is hoped that special status and facilities would be offered to fourth-year men to continue or begin specialization.

This latter brings up the subject of the partial or even complete transformation of the instruction to a formal graduate school level. We should contemplate and, if decided upon, plan for the granting of masters' and even doctoral degrees to residents suited for such activities. However, the degrees should not be granted as formalities (as is frequently done at some centers); true graduate-school devotion should be expected and demanded. A degree gained at the institute should mean something and be recognized as such elsewhere.

This is associated with the problem of research for residents. The facilities and opportunities for research should be opened widely and the residents encouraged, and degree candidates required to enter upon studies, either independently or as members of a working team already in operation. Preparation of reports and papers should be encouraged and aided by personnel experienced in such activities, including the educational section. The participation of the residents in the presentation of papers at societies, locally and nationally, also should be encouraged and aided by travel funds.

As indicated previously, all types of educational methods and devices, where useful and feasible, should be available. Visiting lecturers, field visits and surveys, with reports on findings and recommendations by residents, and many others can and should be used. Since the institute should serve an important consultative and service function for the state and elsewhere, the residents should participate in such activities, not only thereby gaining experience for later functioning in these roles, but helping to bind them in a mutually collaborative fashion after they leave and, hopefully, assume state positions.

The instruction of medical students should play an important role within the institute because, if planned and carried out as suggested, the institute would be a model CMH center and would prove ideal for instruction and then possibly recruitment into mental health care. (What is said for medical students also should hold for students in psychology and social work as well as others.) The model of instruction for medical students would, in miniature, follow that of the residents. Hopefully, they would have received the basic behavioral and biological sciences in their schools and come to us as early as possible for graded activity in the CMH center. They would participate in all the integrated care modalities that family care would require. In this way the conceptual framework developed for them would be filled in, i.e., of the group-practice, community oriented medical care model (unfortunately not too well presented in some schools).

The supplementation of professional salaries by universities should be sought since staff would be heavily involved, beyond their departmental responsibilities, in instructional activities, and this should be paid for. Such an arrangement should help in recruiting better personnel and avoid the necessity of supplementation by private practice.

A few additional comments on the roles of permanent staff might well be in order at this point. In addition to their primary instructional and research goals, the permanent staff also should be filling service functions not necessarily connected with these goals. They should provide service for part of the catchment area, not only to serve as models for the residents and students and as sources of research data, but for constant personal stimulation and, in turn, sources of new programs suggested by this stimulation.

It would seem unnecessary to indicate the need for research in the area of CMH care. Nevertheless, I would like to introduce this subject by a quotation from the Surgeon General's address to the Conference of State and Territorial Mental Health Authorities on January 5, 1966:

> I hope that you are obtaining scientific documentation for community psychiatry as your program gains momentum. We need to know who is being treated, for how long, with what results. In short, we should be compiling solid evidence as to whether or not community mental health works as well in practice as it looks in theory. Only thus can it be intelligently defended and improved (7).

The questions that require investigation are endless, and the research arduous and expensive. Nevertheless, we will have to enter upon them if we are to fulfill our goals; otherwise, we will continue to work in the dark as we have in the past. At this time in the history of the social institutions of science and mental health, this is impermissible and should create serious criticism if neglected. We not only have a tremendous backlog in untested treatment methods and obvious needs for testing new methods but we no longer have the excuse that the methods for testing arc unavailable and too difficult to enter upon. (It has been adequately demonstrated that there are dependent variables of patient outcome, using a number of rational and important indices, which indicate efficacy, clearly and unequivocally, when our treatment methods are good. It is only when they are questionably efficacious that we come out with negative results, and it would seem that the excuse of insensitivity of the measures is only a rationalization.) The methods of multivariate analysis in assigning specific weights to the responsible variables can now, with the new computers, be done easily and quickly. Indeed, for a long time to come, the research methods already developed can give us answers to the questions we now pose.

The question of organization of research in an institute is an important and moot one. The principles involved might be, first, that research personnel should be available for teaching functions in their disciplines and, when interest and need arise, for service functions as well, but only to the extent that this is mutually agreed upon. We must not use highly trained and expensive, specially prepared people for service functions which might be fulfilled by others. The second principle is that of integration of efforts. It would seem apparent that, in the highly complex, multivariate area of mental illness and mental health problems, approach and attack are best done by surrounding the subject and not permitting variables to escape through loopholes by lack of forethought. Our methods of analysis these days permit this kind of approach and, indeed, demand it. The problem of integration of efforts is a difficult but necessary one. At the same time it must be recognized that certain activities must be pursued individually because the information secured from these investigations is intrinsically important and valuable. Also, the individuals involved are necessary for instruction and for a well rounded program of research. It would seem, therefore, that a judicious mixture of individual and team effort should be sought with the same type of judicious mixing of so-called basic and applied efforts and finally with the same individuals hopefully pursuing all four ends simultaneously.

The question of financing such efforts is one that is also of concern. Here one should seriously contemplate state support of principal investigators to secure the permanence and tenure necessary for such research efforts these days. Those problems devoted largely to state-posed questions involving care programs should secure as much of the state funds as is necessary, with supplementation from federal and other funds to the utmost of the ability to secure them.

Other principles which should be considered are the closest possible integration of personnel in service, training and research activities, with no sharp demarcation between any of them, and the greatest possible use of facilities for cross-over from one area to another. Nevertheless, it is apparent that some of the individuals will confine their efforts to one of these fields, and no undue pressure should be exerted to have any person operate in more than one unless he so desires and can be used.

At the 1965 annual meeting of the American Psychiatric Association, I was invited to present my thinking on resident training, and I chose as a title, "Education for the future instead of the past." A good deal of what I offer here comes from that paper. I must say that the diagnosis and the psychopathology were in large measure accepted gracefully even if ruefully. Psychiatrists are an unusually tolerant lot. However, some of the treatment I offered did not go down at all well.

I indicated that if there is anything that seems to be almost universally accepted about community mental health care it is as Dr. Barton has stated:

> The number of persons requiring help are such as to make prolonged psychotherapy impractical in the majority of cases. . . . The psychiatric disorders of the blue-collar worker and of the medically indigent are the hard-core problem. The community mental health program was designed to assume much of the responsibility for treatment, particularly of acute illnesses heretofore delegated to the public mental hospital. To effect such a drastic change requires an eclectic approach with great emphasis on group and milieu therapy as well as chemotherapy (1).

One might add that other forms of short-term psychotherapy, such as family therapy, behavior therapy, and so on, might also be looked into. It was partially with this in mind that I tacked on the phrase "instead of the past" to emphasize the need for therapies dwelling on reality, and present and future goals, instead of the questionably useful and endless dwelling in and on the past.

In view of these considerations and the relatively enormous disproportion of psychiatric psychotherapists to psychiatrists with the training I have proposed, I said that we could very well afford a *moratorium* for a decade or two on the production of psychiatrist-psychotherapists, with a proportionate saving of time now devoted to heavy concentration on theoretical psychodynamics and psychotherapy, which still, after a half-century, remain in large measure undemonstrated in their validity and efficacy. In this 10- to 20-year interim, the necessary research to test and validate hypotheses and methods could be accomplished by the individuals already trained to enter upon these efforts, and we could proceed to the training of whatever type of psychotherapist we would require. These would not necessarily be physicians and so would not need the tremendously heavy investment in time and money required for the type of psychiatrist I described. (It was at this point that I looked up from my paper and detected the shocked look I anticipated. I did not, however, anticipate the rather large number who came up afterwards to say that they agreed with me but wouldn't dare say so publicly.)

Under these circumstances I do not think we would require the additional 10,000 psychiatrists that have been described as necessary. We would need a large number for the administrative, clinical and educational requirements of the country. The remainder of our needs could be supplied in a number of ways. First, as mentioned, a good many of the functions could be assumed by nonphysicians who would then have specific functions to serve other than as miniature psychiatrists, with the low status that miniaturization offers them. They would work in teams where these functions would be uniquely comprehended by well trained psychiatrists.

Second, it might be necessary to provide lesser trained, more specialized, psychiatrically oriented physicians or, alternatively, offer sufficient specialized psychiatric training to general practitioners to assume certain medical functions as highly trained technicians. It already has been proposed that in the general area of medical care we train two types of physicians: one, the academically trained investigator and teacher; second, the lesser trained general practitioner or specialist-technician. This is in contrast to the American practice of making no formal differentiation between the two (thus wasting enormous amounts of time, money and personnel for unnecessary functions) and failing to provide the best, highly educated leaders and investigators. The former pattern has existed abroad in more formal terms for decades. It is about time that we recognized the need and institutionalized the practice.

I am deliberately omitting from discussion the problem of primary prevention of mental disorder upon which our hopes of control rest. At this time there is little or nothing the psychiatrist can do directly toward primary prevention except as a consultant and responsible citizen. We must leave this to the public health and welfare programs, which even now, if adequately supported, could reduce the load enormously (4).

The complex but not unrelated problem of retraining psychiatrists for functioning in the new mental health centers cannot really be discussed here either. It is not an insuperable problem and could be dealt with in the context of what has been offered. I have been told by more than one prominent educator that he has been approached by acutely unhappy and depressed private practitioners who feel that they are wasting their lives and efforts in their present solo activities. It might not be amiss for educators to take these experiences to heart and to their residents. The increasing spate of criticisms in the lay press on present psychiatric practice undoubtedly will have its effects as well.

It is obvious that the reforms that I have advocated cannot and will not be put into practice tomorrow; however, I think it is apparent that the need for discussion and review is urgent. The qualitatively new social institution of community mental health care proposed will neither be new nor effective without a concomitant change in the form and content of psychiatric education, which was grossly inadequate even for the old form of psychiatric care.

In summary, assuming that it is really our responsibility to care for mental illness, that we want to do it adequately and equitably, and that the pattern for the immediate future is the comprehensive community mental health center, I suggest that we drop our present form of apprenticeship training for the primary cadres of psychiatric leaders. We should institute true graduate, doctoral level instruction at state psychiatric institutes, in association with universities, in all the necessary scientific methodic tools and basic and applied bio-psychosocial sciences needed, along with clinical instruction and practice in optimal mental health centers, to enable them to deserve leadership of teams of basic and applied scientists including lesser trained but more specialized physicians. In view of the obvious present need, it would appear inappropriate, and indeed irresponsible, to continue to train physicians for lengthy dyadic relationship psychotherapy, or possibly for any psychotherapeutic function which may well be assigned to nonmedical team members after demonstration of efficacy. Above all, the reforms proposed will require a planned form of mental health care which should include the provision of education for specific, well paid, and respected participation in this activity, and for no other.

REFERENCES

1. Barton, W. E. Introduction to *The community mental health center: An analysis of existing models.* In R. Glasscote, D. Sanders, H. M. Forstenzer, and A. R. Foley. Washington, D.C.: American Psychiatric Association, 1964, p. xvi.
2. Lefton, M., Rettig, S., Dinitz, S., and Pasamanick, B. Status perceptions of psychiatric social workers and their implications for work satisfaction. *Amer. J. Orthopsychiat.*, 1961, 31:102–10.
3. Pasamanick, B. The scope and limitations of psychiatry. In J. Wortis (Ed.), *Basic problems of psychiatry.* New York: Grune & Stratton, 1953.
4. Pasamanick, B. The prevention and control of chronic disease, II. Mental disorders. *Amer. J. Publ. Hlth.*, 1959, 49:1129–35.
5. Pasamanick, B. A survey of mental disease in an urban population, IV. An approach to total prevalence rates. *Arch. Gen. Psychiat.*, 1961, 4:151–55.
6. Pasamanick, B., Scarpitti, F. R., and Dinitz, S. *Schizophrenics in the community: An experimental study in the prevention of hospitalization.* New York: Appleton-Century-Crofts, 1967.
7. Stewart, W. Opening address to the conference of state and territorial mental health authorities, January 5, 1966, Washington, D.C.

44

The Role of the Psychologist in
Comprehensive Community Mental Health Centers:
The National Institute of Mental Health View

STANLEY F. YOLLES

I AM very pleased to have the opportunity to join this Conference of State Chief Psychologists and Psychologists of the United States Public Health Service. Meetings such as this between state professionals and those in the federal establishment typify our close alliance on behalf of public health, and I speak as a colleague devoted to a cause we share in common.

In your strategic posts as administrators and leaders of your profession throughout the states, you have been in key positions to affect the role of the psychologist in that most significant pursuit of interest to us all—the strengthening of the mental health of our society.

Today, the swift movement of events in both the fields of mental health and of social action presents all mental health professionals with fresh opportunity and equally fresh challenge. Just a few weeks ago President Johnson signed into law new mental health legislation which brings even closer to realization the community mental health services we have tried for many years to make available to all our citizens.

Under this new amendment to the Community Mental Health Centers Act of 1963, federal aid will help pay the cost of staff as the centers get underway. This support, coupled with the Federal assistance for construction, means that the mental health professions can and must devise within the community mental health center model ways for the most effective practice of their respective disciplines.

It was the Roman General Fabius who said of his famous adversary, Hannibal, "You know, Hannibal, how to gain a victory, but not how to use it." If the mental health of this nation has gained a victory in the current move toward community care and prevention of the mental illnesses, we are now called upon to use the skills and knowledge of all the mental health professions for the benefit of the people themselves who are in need.

At the outset, I should like to clarify the position of the National Institute of Mental Health on the role of the psychologist in the community mental health center. I do not intend to suggest, as the assigned title infers, a special

Reprinted from *American Psychologist*, 1966, *21*, 37–41, by permission of the publisher and the author. © 1966, American Psychological Association. Dr. Yolles is Director, National Institute of Mental Health.

"National Institute of Mental Health View." Indeed, NIMH superimposes no special view concerning the work of the mental health professions in the network of community mental health services to be established across the land. Rather, the role of each profession is being established in and by each profession itself, as witness this and many other conferences which are being held among leaders of training, and leaders of public health practice.

Each profession must undergo its own self-review, its own innovations in preparation and training, its own explorations as to how it can best serve as a member of the community mental health team.

In its effort to insure the effectiveness of the nationwide program, NIMH has and does lend its support to these endeavors. In psychiatry, the Institute is supporting various types of pilot training programs in community and social psychiatry. In psychology, the Institute is supporting various programs in community mental health training. In social work, training is being extended to expose students to elemental problems in mental health. In nursing, several pilot projects in community mental health nursing are being conducted under the auspices of universities or colleges.

In addition, as you all know, the Institute has supported many of the major conferences on training in the four mental health disciplines. In psychology, this includes a number of major conferences beginning with the Boulder meeting in 1948 and continuing on to the Conference on the Professional Preparation of Clinical Psychologists which just ended here in Chicago. These conferences have, of necessity, paid major attention to the changing direction and needs in professional training and in professional services.

It is through such conferences, and other processes of self-examination and self-improvement, that guidelines to manpower utilization are developed—as well, of course, as from down-to-earth experience and demonstrations and studies of what works best.

The shortages of personnel in mental health, as well as in welfare and health services in general, have long since made evident the need for innovations in the roles of professional and nonprofessional manpower.

The Report of the Joint Commission of Mental Illness and Health reflected an awareness of this trend. Its statement on the use of mental health personnel may serve as a useful preamble for our discussion this morning. It is, in part, as follows, and I quote:

> psychiatry and the allied mental health professions should adopt and practice a broad, liberal philosophy of what constitutes and who can do treatment within the framework of their hospitals, clinics, or other professional service agencies (3, p. 248).

The Commission outlined the fundamental ABC's of the clinical functions of our respective callings. They are:

> A: That certain kinds of medical, psychiatric, and neurological examinations and treatments must be carried out by or under the immediate direction

of psychiatrists, neurologists, or other physicians specially trained for these procedures.

B: That psychoanalysis and allied forms of deeply searching and probing "depth psychotherapy" must be practiced only by those with special training, experience, and competence in handling these techniques without harm to the patient—namely, by physicians trained in psychoanalysis or intensive psychotherapy, plus those psychologists or other professional persons who lack a medical education but have an aptitude for, training in, and demonstrable competence in such techniques of psychotherapy.

C: That nonmedical mental health workers with aptitude, sound training, practical experience, and demonstrable competence should be permitted to do general, short-term psychotherapy—namely, treating persons by objective, permissive, nondirective techniques of listening to their troubles and helping them resolve these troubles in an individually insightful and socially useful way (3, p. 249).

"The principle that must guide us in questions of authority, professional prerogatives, and qualifications involved in treatment of the mentally ill," the Commission held, "is one of individual competence. . . .

"The matter of competence applies equally to the psychiatrist, the psychologist . . . the social worker and occupational therapist . . . the nurse . . . and the ward attendant . . . (3, p. 248)" the Commission concluded.

Since mental and emotional problems vary so widely as to kind and degree, the Commission's view of individual competence as a guideline for appropriate types of treatment has been widely accepted by the mental health disciplines.

I am most aware that my audience here this morning is a highly sophisticated one in the employment and practice of psychology in public health. I shall, therefore, attempt to place my remarks within the framework of the role of the psychologist in the community mental health center.

To this end, we may clarify first just what a community mental health center program is, what it is intended to do, and what further potential it may have, if any, as it matures beyond the starting point.

I will begin with the statement that the community mental health center program is an entirely new approach to the care, treatment, and prevention of the mental illnesses. I say this knowing full well that there is a body of psychological opinion that the centers approach is not revolutionary enough. The program is an integrated network of treatment services based in the community, where people live and work, where they can get proper care when they become ill, where they can be maintained, and where they can be helped to lead productive lives.

That is the treatment aspect of the center—giving to the mentally ill alternatives to lengthy hospitalization, alternatives to no care at all. With the use of psychoactive drugs, with the use of short-term intensive treatment in the psychiatric wards of general hospitals, with the opportunity to serve patients as the course and degree of their illness or difficulty requires—we hope at last to be able to put to use more broadly whatever skills and knowledge we now possess.

We know, for example, various psychiatric tenets which we have not been able to employ widely enough. Among them, we know that illness detected and treated early is more reversible than illness long ingrown. We know, too, that the often slow process of rehabilitation is a crucial factor in healing, and may need special attention, such as home nursing visits, or a special setting, such as the halfway house.

The treatment of illness, however, is but one phase of the mission of the community mental health center. It is also conceived as an instrument for the *prevention* of mental illness and the promotion of the community's mental health.

The center program is in fact not simply a medical step into the community —although that in itself would be new enough—it is a starting point for new departures in looking at problems of mental health.

An outstanding result of multidisciplinary mental health research has been our present knowledge concerning environment as a factor in producing illness or health. The behavioral and social sciences, as well as psychiatric research, have all pointed to factors of environment which help shape the individual's ability to withstand stress. Thus, the environment of the individual has become our laboratory. In psychiatry, we have been studying the immediate environment of the family, both as to the role of the family in the illness of one of its members, and in normal growth and development. In psychology, too, the family structure is under close study, as well as the wider environment of the community in which people learn and grow. A major contribution of psychology has been the theory of social competence—in what ways can we intervene to help people become competent within their society to withstand its stress and to realize their fullest potential?

An essential element of the community mental health centers program, therefore, is the provision of preventive services. In addition to the four treatment services—inpatient and outpatient care, partial hospital and emergency care—a vital preventive service is a requirement for Federal aid. That service is consultation to community agencies and professionals, and educational programs for the community at large.

Obviously this network of services is not entirely comprehensive. Full comprehensive services also include diagnostic and rehabilitative services, pre-care and aftercare, training, research and evaluation—categories in which psychologists as well as other behavioral sciences can make a major contribution.

The centers program is a workable and flexible nucleus. It is a core around which other important services may be offered as the centers become part of community life. We believe that the program as it now stands—and as it may be expanded—embodies both treatment and prevention of illness, and it can become an effective instrument for the promotion of mental health.

It is quite true that varying views have arisen within some segments of the mental health professions concerning which of the comprehensive services should be considered most essential. In a long-neglected field of endeavor—the supply of services and the use of knowledge on behalf of community mental health—it is, perhaps, understandable to desire full comprehensive services all at once.

In some professional quarters, very healthy discussions have been taking place as to just how a pioneering program should look, where it should go, what it should accomplish. I say this is healthy because above all, the program is designed for maximum flexibility, to suit the community and the population it is to serve.

On one hand we have heard, from those who are oriented to the state mental hospital system, that the center program cannot work, that it is too "far out," too great a departure from the system of care as it is organized today.

On the other hand, we have heard from other serious practitioners of mental health—at times from the psychologist—that the center model is too medical, that it is not "far out" enough, that it is too restricted to the treatment of disease, that it cannot work as a positive agent for community mental health.

Personally, I am inclined to feel that a community mental health system that is subject to constructive questioning and exploration from both the treatment and the preventive points of view must be a fairly rounded system that has a strong potential for both. While the program is not referred to as a "center" because it fulfills both functions, it appears, after all, that it may be a "center," too, in terms of its potential for serving both as a medical model and as a model in which the psychologist can practice his preventive as well as clinical skills.

A major point, therefore, that I should like to make about the role of the psychologist in the community mental health center is that the program need not limit, but in fact, can stimulate the creative practice of psychology as a tool for the prevention of mental illness and the promotion of mental health.

The clinical psychologist will, of course, participate in the treatment or therapy aspects of the program, as the ABC's of the Joint Commission make clear. But beyond that, he or his coprofessionals can contribute uniquely to the success of the overall program in whatever community it has been designed to serve. He can work in liaison with and in consultation with community agencies and with the new social action programs which have a direct bearing on people's lives. He can work with his colleagues in industry, in the schools, in employment centers. He can become one of the center's connecting links with the community, trained as he is in the preventive view of the competence of individuals as they go about their daily life.

While we in psychiatry will be trained to treat the mentally ill as part of the mental health team, the psychologist will seek to make of the centers program a true community agent of illness prevention and promotion of health. It is he who is the bridge between the medical and the behavioral and social sciences. It is he who has been trained to ask: What are the community social problems and the solutions? What are the problems of living and how does the individual deal with them? It is the psychologist who is trained not only to be a participant in the treatment process, but to be, to use a term that is becoming popular, a "conceptualizer," as well. To the psychologist, the mental health of the community is in the school room, in the juvenile court, in the home, and on street corners, as well. It is he, then, who will hold a key role in making of the community mental health center something more than a headquarters, however unique, for treating mental illness.

Leaders in the training of psychologists have already begun to develop and to explore curricula and programs out of which the community-oriented psychologist may emerge. For example, the clinical psychologist may, like the psychiatrist, need to add to his clinical training a social consciousness, an awareness of the workings of community structures, a willingness to apply his skills outside of the one-to-one individual treatment setting. In many instances, he may need to cross the many varieties of specialties within his profession to acquire the variety of skills needed to be most effective in community mental health work.

In exploratory conferences on training psychologists in community mental health—such as the one held recently in Boston—the psychologist is being discussed as the "creative generalist" of the community mental health center, and as such, some aspects of social psychology, behavioral psychology, and other specialties may become part of the community psychologist's skills.

The second point about the psychologist in the community mental health center is that he will function—as will each mental health discipline—as part of a mental health team. This may require that each profession modify and broaden its perspective. After all, a real team does not work together with separate points of view. In the new training programs, each of the professions —psychiatry, psychology, nursing, and social work—is examining its training process, exploring its possibilities as effective helping agents in a community program setting, as part of the center's mental health team. We can and will arrive at a fruitful synthesis of all mental health professions in the community care system, and the psychologist is a major member of the team.

Finally, I should like to clarify the question of leadership of the community mental health centers program. Professional prerogatives are, we realize, no less dear to the heart of the psychiatrist and the psychologist than to other professions which invest years in highly specialized training. The question of leadership, however, is not predicated simply upon prerogatives. Even more, it has been of keen interest to the professions because of the prevailing belief that the discipline of the program head will determine what direction the program will take.

Whether justified or not—and that is another question—the fact that the subject of leadership has appeared again and again in professional councils as a rather indestructible query which does not seem to yield easily to simple and direct response.

The simple and direct response is, of course, that leadership is based upon individual competence, and not upon membership in a particular discipline.

In the federal regulations for construction aid to community mental health centers, for example, it is provided that a qualified *psychiatrist* will be responsible for the *clinical* program, with the medical responsibility for every patient vested in a physician. Nowhere in the regulations is it suggested that administrative leadership be limited to psychiatrists.

Furthermore, the new legislation similarly places no restriction on the leadership of the center program. Indeed, the Senate report on hearings for the staffing aid includes a very clear statement as to this point.

"There is no intent in any way in this bill to discriminate against any mental health professional group from carrying out its full potential within the realm of its recognized competence," Senator Lister Hill reported from the Committee on Labor and Public Welfare in June.

"Even further," the report states, "it is hoped that new and innovative tasks and roles will evolve from the broadly based concept of the community mental health services. Specifically, overall leadership of a community mental health center program may be carried out by any one of the major mental health professions (2, p. 4)."

For its open view as to leadership, the new legislation was commented upon by Arthur Brayfield (1965), Executive Officer of the American Psychological Association. In the course of the hearings, he said, "we are pleased to see that this amendment places no restriction as to the administration of these centers, and it is not assumed that an MD must be placed in charge (1, p. 429)."

This open view illustrates an essential quality of the centers program: that is, flexibility. It is a flexible system not only as to program and leadership, but as to its entire staffing structure. The technical and professional personnel will, of course, represent the traditional mental health disciplines. But new departures within the disciplines and in the use of auxiliary personnel—such as volunteers and indigenous workers—will contribute to the success of our new community approach. The open view, then, is more than nonrestrictive; it is a positive recognition of developments in all the mental health professions that are sharpening their skills needed in community mental health work.

The new departures and the creative approaches of which I speak are already past the planning stage. They are at work in pioneering programs in various parts of the country. In Minnesota, for example, new community mental health centers will operate under program directors who are psychologists, with psychiatrists as heads of their clinical services.

Another state providing leadership positions for psychologists is Kansas.

At the South Shore Mental Health Center in Massachusetts, Leonard Hassol, a psychologist, actively working with a group of psychologists, has developed a program which is receiving wide attention from those interested in the needs of the profession to "tool up" for community mental health. The program has evolved out of a philosophy of planned social change in which community mental health plays an integral role.

The South Shore program includes mental health consultation in schools, and with police and court authorities. It includes aftercare services through a halfway house, an evening clinic, nursing service, social and recreational programs, drug and supportive therapy. It offers therapeutic tutoring for disturbed youngsters, and emergency services for children whose parents become hospitalized. It participates in the domestic peace corps, in Operation Headstart, in a well-baby clinic, in an anti-poverty program, and in the teaching of behavioral science in elementary schools.

The significant point is that the potential of a mental health program in its relationship to the community is bounded only by the skill, the competence, and the imagination of its director and its staff.

As I have suggested earlier, the mandate to the mental health professions has been made clear. Financial support for the centers can and will be worked out through Federal sources, through mental health and social and welfare programs, through local and state tax revenues, and through private funds. Finances are a problem, but not an insoluble one. An adequate supply of professional help can be forthcoming, too, through Federal support of mental health training and in-service training as well. Staffing may be a problem, but not an insoluble one.

I believe that the success of the new community mental health centers program will rest ultimately not on any one of these factors, but upon the skill and the competence and the creativity of each mental health profession as it takes its place in service to the community's mental health. From a public health viewpoint, of course, that service is to attack illness by devising means to help prevent it. In this, the psychologist as well as all health professions find their highest role.

REFERENCES

1. Brayfield, A. H. Community mental health centers "staffing" legislation. *Amer. Psychol.,* 1965, 20:420–30.
2. Hill, Lister, *Mental Retardation Facilities and Community Mental Health Centers Construction Act Amendment of 1965.* S. Rep. No. 366, 89th Cong., 1st Sess., 1965.
3. Joint Commission on Mental Illness and Health. *Action for mental health.* New York: Basic Books, 1961.

45

The Psychiatric Nurse in a Mental Health Clinic

KEN LESSLER AND JEANNE BRIDGES

WHAT contribution can a psychiatric nurse make to a community mental health clinic? To explore this, a 14-month demonstration project was established with a North Carolina State budget. The project was at a new clinic in Sanford (Lee County). This county is in a predominantly rural area, containing some 27,000 people, of whom 20,000 are white. The county seat (Sanford) has 10,000 residents. The project began in April 1963 when a psychiatric nurse with hospital training was added to the existing staff of a full time social worker—director and a secretary, as well as part time personnel including a psychiatrist and a clinical psychologist.

During this project, the nurse was involved in numerous activities as a member of the clinic staff and as a consultant with the Health Department, the Department of Public Welfare, the schools and education centers and other community agencies.

THE MENTAL HEALTH CLINIC

The Sanford Clinic was new, small and composed primarily of a part time professional staff held together by a full time social worker—director. The services provided by the Clinic included patient care (individual diagnosis and treatment, family treatment, long and short term therapy with children and adults) and community services. Among the community services were consultation with teachers, talks with civic groups, liaison with the public health and welfare departments and other attempts to integrate the clinic into the community.

In keeping with the exploratory approach, the nurse participated in a *potpourri* of consultative, treatment and diagnostic services. These included:

Reprinted from *Mental Hygiene,* 1965, *49,* 324–330, by permission of the publisher and the authors. © 1965, National Association for Mental Health. Dr. Lessler is a psychologist in private practice in Chapel Hill, North Carolina. Mrs. Bridges was formerly Head Nurse, In-patient Psychiatry Unit, North Carolina Memorial Hospital, Chapel Hill, No. Carolina.

consultation with individual mental health clinic staff members, individual counseling, psychotherapy, family counseling, psychological testing, supervision of patient medication, intake interviews, home visits, liaison between clinic and referring agencies and, alas, some clerical duties. This variety of activities has much in common with those reported by Glittenberg (2) for nurses working in outpatient clinics.

The social worker-director provided weekly supervision on clinic procedures and policies as well as supervising case work and intake interviewing. The clinical psychologist and the psychiatrist supervised the nurse in psychotherapy and diagnostic techniques. The psychotherapeutic experiences included goal-limited therapy with six children, an adolescent and three adults. The length of therapy varied from a few contacts to a year of continuous treatment. Patients were seen from once a week to once a month. One of the patients was seen in play therapy by both the nurse and the psychologist, as a propaedeutic device.

The psychodiagnostic work began with the Vineland Social Maturity Scale. Then the Peabody Picture Vocabulary Test and the vocabulary scale of the Stanford-Binet were added to the nurse's diagnostic equipment. These scales provided a natural supplement to the social maturity testing and also allowed the nurse to provide a valuable quick service in the field: that is, to make a brief estimate of a child's academic and social functioning. Finally, during the one-year period the nurse was introduced to projective testing *via* the Children's Apperception Test. This allowed the nurse to integrate the interpretive skill that she was learning in therapy with her interviewing skills. The types of tests learned were thus dictated by practical service needs as well as the manner in which the instruments could contribute to the general program. Had the project been longer, the testing skills would have been extended toward further thematic testing, individual intelligence testing and then testing for brain damage.

In a setting in which all types of service were scarce, the orientation was always toward determining how the nurse could provide an extension of the services of the part time professional staff as well as how the nurse could provide what was uniquely hers. The nurse was able to play her traditional role through providing drug checks for patients carried on medication. She was also able to communicate medical information to the nonmedical staff who were not able to communicate directly [1] with the psychiatrist. Her medical orientation made her an important link between the physicians in the community and the clinic.

A function which melds the nurse's work with the public health nurse's was the domiciliary service (3). Home visits were made to provide intake and diagnostic information. Thus the nurse was able to provide a service which integrated nursing skills with a diagnostic and therapeutic effort oriented toward the family in its natural setting.

[1] Their clinic hours did not overlap.

PUBLIC HEALTH DEPARTMENT

Traditionally the public health department has provided health services, such as home visits to the chronically ill, sanitation and immunization services and maternity and cancer clinics. Only recently has there been an interest in treating the psychiatric patient (1). This interest has developed largely out of the emphasis on aftercare treatment of mental patients. The public health nurses have a tradition of home visiting which allows them to be on hand in crisis situations, to be in the position to recognize early emotional disturbances and to implement primary preventive procedures when they note an unhealthy situation.

During the early part of the psychiatric nurse project, the public health nurses were chosen as an ideal target for liaison and reciprocal exchange of ideas. It was believed that the psychiatric nurse could contribute her psychological orientation and psychiatric knowledge while receiving an education in domiciliary methods. With this in mind, the psychiatric nurse spent one day a week making home visits with the Public Health Nurse and holding conferences on case histories to share knowledge, attitudes and techniques. Largely because of the pressure and demands on the P.H. Nurse's time, these contacts became less frequent and finally were left on an "on call" consultative basis.

DEPARTMENT OF PUBLIC WELFARE

The Lee County Department of Public Welfare carries the responsibility for administering funds to the indigent and providing services to families and children. Such services include child placement and counseling in home management. These contacts place welfare workers in close contact with the traditionally "hard to reach" psychiatric patients. They are also strategically able to disperse funds and services in a way that may increase or decrease the already overwhelming number of stressors that their clients experience. In many senses the public welfare workers may intervene with primary, secondary and tertiary mental health measures without interrupting the general dialogue with other helping agencies.

The psychiatric nurse made herself available to the welfare workers on an informal basis during the inception stage of this contact. Quickly she was asked about the "problem" cases and began to attend conferences. As a result, referrals were made to the mental health clinic and other agencies. The help and collaboration extended to joint visits, co-counseling of frightened, teenage expectant mothers and speaking with relatives of patients with severe psychiatric disturbances. To cement the relationship between the clinic and welfare department, the nurse administered screening tests for some children to be placed in children's homes.

EDUCATIONAL FACILITIES

The local public school system had a start toward a mental health program. Some counselors were available and in some high schools mental hygiene courses were provided. No screening or individual testing services (except group intelligence testing) were available except on a state level. There were two new classes for the mildly retarded and plans were in progress for a program for the moderately retarded. No facilities were available for the emotionally disturbed child, though there were several helpful and understanding teachers who did the work of helping children in trouble and even provided their own screening, counseling and remedial services.

The paradigm for the entry of the nurse into the schools was much the same as that used with the welfare workers, i.e., available waiting. She was quickly used as a contact between school and clinic. This eventuated in on-the-spot consultations with teachers, principals and counselors. Finally the students themselves initated contacts on an informal basis, requesting that the nurse speak to classes. She responded by speaking on mental health topics on several occasions to high school and junior high school classes.

Within the Lee County area there is a center for training high school graduates for skilled and semi-skilled jobs. One of the courses in the Industrial Education Center trains practical nurses. The psychiatric nurse was contacted to plan and coordinate a series of talks on the practical nurse's contribution to the recognition, prevention and treatment of emotional disturbance. This program soon became a regular part of the curriculum and provided a broad-range contact between the mental health clinic and an important help giving group.

OTHER COMMUNITY AGENCIES

Liaison was initiated with the hospital and the courts during the project. The contacts followed a similar pattern: individual communication and statement of availability, or contact around a case: then wait. The hospital did not accept the invitation for help, partly because of engrossment with its own internal problems at that time. Contact with the courts centered around the trial and rehabilitation of two patients. Neither the contact with the hospital nor the courts meshed well at the time. It was felt that a strategic withdrawal was in order and that a relationship with these agencies could wait for another day. It seems clear, however, in view of the experiences of other clinics, that the nurse may well find a place in these settings. The hospital would seem to be a particularly appropriate center for the activities of the psychiatric nurse.

DISCUSSION

Although this project was entitled a "demonstration" project, it may more appropriately be called an adventure in community mental health. As in so many adventures, there were new things discovered as well as many things which were missed. New roads were opened, some of which we would like to travel again and others which could best be avoided. This adventure was an exploration of new territory to assay whether it was appropriate, fertile and receptive, and to learn whether its natives wanted new associates. The first part of this discussion of the "trip" will center on the heartland, the mental health center and then the environs, i.e. the community and community agencies. Finally, some recommendations will be drawn for future travelers.

The nurse quickly finds that within the new setting of a mental health clinic there are new bosses, new roles and hence some new role expectations and conflicts. The psychiatric nurse is traditionally patient-oriented. Her job has typically been to help develop an appropriate milieu or adjunctive therapeutic relationship with individual patients. In contrast, the work of the psychiatric social worker is community minded. He focuses on agencies and agency relationships, on the community and epidemiology and on groups, and he serves a therapeutic and data-gathering role with individuals. The reorientation from an individual to a community model of helping, as mediated *via* the social worker, was a transition for which a nurse is little prepared. It is this emotional and intellectual reorientation, however, which provides the basic ingredients for the change from "psychiatric nurse" to "community psychiatric nurse."

The clinical psychologist's role is possibly more congruent with the nurse's past experience. That is, it has tended in the past to be more individual-diagnostic-treatment oriented. The learning of psychological testing seemed in many ways an extension of the laboratory, adding to it one's knowledge of interviewing and personality dynamics. In this case, as with the social worker, the relationship has the possibility of reciprocal benefit which is helpful to the nurse's self-esteem, as well as enabling her to perform an important service. When there is a staff of part time personnel, the nurse may serve as a mediator of medical information, as an interpreter and generally as an extension of the psychiatrist's part time services. A knowledge of behavior-influencing drugs and their effect, a medical diagnostic attitude and an understanding of the physician's wishes and needs was a major contribution of the nurse as a full time member of the small staff.

The relationship to the psychiatrist was probably the most natural for the nurse because of her long and traditional association with medical personnel. Such a ready-made relationship in foreign territory, of course, always provides the temptation of isolation and regression. However, if it is seen as yet another opportunity to develop, this relationship can be one of the most productive. The nurse can provide a needed extension of the psychiatrist's services through, for example, drug check of aftercare patients or patients carried on drugs by the nonmedical specialists. She can also serve as a natural link with the community's general practitioners for the psychiatrist and the clinic. She may provide an important service through hospital visits and primary preventive work with patients in medical crisis or in childbirth, or in handling the impending death of a relative.

Many of the roles and tasks were new, different and sometimes provoked a feeling of insecurity. Initially the nurse is faced with the problem of being a jack-of-all-trades and master of one (traditional nursing) which must be remolded to fit new situations. This requires a unique adaptation in which the nurse must absorb the best and the most appropriate of all of the specific disciplines with which she comes in contact and learn to utilize techniques from all of them. At the same time, she must add to the brew whatever is hers alone and whatever she brings from her background in psychiatric nursing. The problem is one of integration and differentiation, one of incorporating while learning to separate, one of being useful to all members of the team while still being an individual and contributing uniquely.

Learning new roles and new skills necessitates a good deal of didactic work and supervision. In the present project, the division of labor for supervising the nurse was along traditional lines. That is, the social worker supervised the intake, administrative and community activities, the psychologist supervised the individual and group psychotherapy and diagnostic experiences and the psychiatrist supervised the medical endeavors, as well as giving additional supervision in psychotherapy. Since the psychiatrist and psychologist were on a one-day-a-week status, there was a good deal of competition for their time. The nurse always felt she needed more of it, and yet there were always the conflicting service needs. Although these conflicts are probably inevitable, the nurse cannot perform her full role without initial intensive supervision and didactic sessions. It would seem to be false economy for the professional personnel to substitute service for supervision, since the nurse (or the minister, or the public health worker or the physician) extends and multiplies the direct service potential of scarce mental health professional people.

At least one-third of the psychiatric nurse's time was spent working with the Health Department, the Department of Public Welfare, the schools and other agencies. In these settings, the psychiatric nurse who lives in the community and is part of the community has a definite advantage and usefulness which is difficult for part time personnel to develop. She is not an expert with a briefcase but a traditionally understood and known entity who lives within the community. As such, her lines of communication are more open, with less static than exists, at least in the initial stages, between other of the mental health professional people. Since she is a member of the community, her role of agency contact and liaison with local physicians was valuable, and a role which may be uniquely a nurse's.

The facilitators mentioned are not intended to indicate that the contacts are easy and that the psychiatric nurse's mission is completely understood. On the contrary, the somatic orientation of the public health nurses made it difficult for them to accept a psychiatric approach. The service demands made it hard for them to see their way clear to spending the necessary time for consultation and case discussion. In addition, there was the tendency of some local physicians to see the nurse (and hence the clinic) as a service available on call.

To illustrate some of the ideas concerning inter-agency cooperation and the benefits which may accrue as a result of having a psychiatric nurse on the staff of a community mental health clinic, a sketch of a case will be presented. In this case the psychiatric nurse served as a facilitator of the referral and treatment of a boy living within the community who had both physical and emotional problems.

The psychiatric nurse was called upon by a public health nurse to consult on the case of a 17-year-old boy who was bedridden with poliomyelitis. Bob had been followed by the Public Health Nurse for two years. During this period many other agencies were involved. The boy was becoming progressively withdrawn, depressed and showed signs of emotional instability. The P.H. nurse noted these symptoms. Her perceptiveness, as well as a previous relationship with the mental health clinic's psychiatric nurse, eventuated in a case consultation.

The psychiatric nurse met with staff members from the Health Department, the Department of Public Welfare and the mental health clinic to collect information and to try to understand the present situation before intervening actively. The psychologist of the mental health clinic was asked to visit the boy's home. He did, and concluded that there was a severe emotional disturbance with continuing decompensation. The second step was a complete reevaluation of the patient's physical condition by a specialist in the field of rehabilitation at a university hospital. His report indicated physical deterioration beyond what could be expected from the poliomyelitis. As a result of these evaluations it was advised that this patient receive intensive inpatient therapeutic and rehabilitative treatment.

An inpatient facility was called by the psychiatric nurse, now serving as a representative of the community. She presented the case to the psychiatrist there. Here was another relationship which already existed because of the nurse's unique interdisciplinary role. Hospitalization on the psychiatric service was considered appropriate and in keeping with the total approach (medical, surgical, physical, social and psychiatric). The continuity of care was furthered by the hospital, during the patient's stay, through conferences between hospital personnel and representatives of a wide range of community agencies. When the patient was returned home, the services provided by the hospital were understood and the services within the community became a continuation of the hospital treatment.

RECOMMENDATION AND CONCLUSION

1. The nurse must consciously strive to develop the ways in which she can be uniquely useful as a person and as a nurse within the community mental health setting. Without this nucleus of personal and professional identity, the nurse may become both personally uncomfortable and professionally dissatisfied.[2] Other recommendations are proffered in the light of this primary recommendation.

2. The psychiatric nurse may usefully and beneficially serve as an extension of the services of other professional staff, e.g. psychologists, psychiatrists and social workers. For example, she might do drug checks, hospital visits (maternity, pediatric wards, surgery and emergency wards) psychological testing, limited goal psychotherapy, intake interviewing and domiciliary visits.

3. The psychiatric nurse may also profitably provide a natural extension of mental health services into the community, e.g., consultation with schools and agencies or the development of group discussion programs oriented to the primary prevention of mental illness. Finally, the psychiatric nurse may serve as coordinator, integrator, liaison and public relations worker for the clinic in relation to medical and non-medical groups, community agencies, clubs, informal organizations and individual medical practitioners.

The satisfactions gained by the psychiatric nurse in this project were many. They included the professional fellowship with other workers in the community, contacts with individuals and groups that have mutual interests, a sense of contributing to the health and welfare of those who need it and a deep feeling of having met a challenge.

REFERENCES

1. Dorsey, J., *et al.*, *Arch. Gen. Psychiat.* 1963, 11:214.
2. Glittenberg, J. *Amer. J. Orthopsychiat.*, 1963, 33:713.
3. May, A. R. and Moore, S. *Lancet,* 1963, 1:213.

[2] May and Moore (3) handle this identity problem by keeping the nurse's services more closely within the framework of a hospital and a medico-nursing administrative structure.

46

A Psychiatric Social Worker
in Community Mental Health

MYRON JOHN ROCKMORE

COMMUNITY mental health as currently considered assumes a variegated hue, depending upon the professional discipline which views it. Indeed the length and breadth of "community mental health" have so far not been agreed upon, nor has the substance been found to fill these nebulous outlines. Nor is it possible to consider mental health from the additional dimensions of depth or height, *i.e.,* depth of program or height of ambition for the program.

As far as weight is concerned, we would do well to avoid mention of the heaviness of the tax bill· which our communities carry under this variously budgeted item. Frankly, in most instances when there is reference to mental health at the state level, we are really referring to activities largely confined to the care and treatment of the mentally ill, outpatient as well as inpatient.

As effort· of psychiatry have joined with other professional disciplines (and the list of these added professional disciplines grows daily), the focus of efforts have broadened from the narrow confines of the mental hospital or the clinical psychiatrist's private office to the magnitude of being recognized as our country's No. 1 public health problem. Organizational efforts, hitherto sporadic or isolated, have grown in size and interest, recognizing that regardless of the primary identification they are in some way related tributaries of this mainstream of concern. The recognition of and publicity attendant on the size of the mental illness problem was crystallized as a matter of national concern twelve years ago with the passage of the National Mental Health Act. This piece of legislation would, in and of itself, make an interesting study if one could assess the impact of this act on the growth and development of mental health services to the communities of our country. The subtlety is not lost when we recall that the National Mental Health Act was an amendment to the Public Health Service Act. The provisions whereby grants were made have markedly affected the state and local administrative picture and have served to place the spotlight on this problem where it belongs—in the community!

Reprinted from *Social Work*, 1958, *3*, 86–92, by permission of the publisher and the author. © 1958, National Association of Social Workers. Mr. Rockmore is Director, Psychiatric Social Service, Connecticut Department of Mental Health.

ADVANTAGES OF SOCIAL WORK TRAINING

The word "community" assumes interesting proportions, depending upon who uses it and in what context it is employed at a given moment. In social work the concept is probably most easily transmitted from social worker to social worker without misunderstanding. This is probably because in our training we have been geared to thinking of encompassable boundaries for our fields of practice. Social work programs are conceived and administered through individual and interrelated agency structures which seek to meet identifiable needs of individuals and groups within geographical boundaries. Community organization as such is an integral part of the social work curriculum. This obvious fact is stressed since it adds an unusual quality and qualification for the social worker who carries an assignment in mental health programs at whatever level he may function. It is a unique and undervalued part of our professional armamentarium which takes on considerable worth in interprofessional relationships. This is to emphasize that social workers bring to the concept of "community" an operational knowledge and sensitivity to factors which add up to the development of health and welfare services which is not matched by any related professional preparation. Even those professions which recognize the importance of forces in the community that influence the level of community health and welfare services do not have the preparation or method for dealing with the issues on a dynamic basis.

There are other aspects of our training which need not be spelled out here but should be mentioned as particular strengths we rely on as we apply social work education and experience to fields where we join with related professional disciplines whose social welfare objectives are similar to our own. Some of the more easily identifiable are the ability to both differentiate and integrate functional responsibility, our taken-for-granted concept of supervision, our technique of the conference method, our basic professional attitude which recognizes both the right of the individual to self-determination, and the sense of responsibility for community welfare. These are the muscle and blood which make our professional body—augmented by the conviction which adds the heart, and our creativity which gives us head.

If we add nothing beyond these few ingredients of social work training and experience, we have a basis of appreciation of our complementary contribution to the professional preparation of psychiatrists, psychologists, epidemiologists, public health nurses, educators, lawyers, sociologists, anthropologists, statisticians, journalists, the clergy, and other professions involved in some aspect considered in the community mental health field. We should also make very special mention of an ever growing group who, while not identified by training as professional, have a key role in any program, that is, the informed layman! The social worker operating in various relationships with such a formidable array of colleagues must have assurance that he is prepared to contribute a variable of considerable proportions.

As social workers, we are taught that people have needs which they feel and express in various ways. These are expressed sometimes intrapsychically, sometimes environmentally, and more often in a combination of the two. As they are expressed in concert they become group needs and as the groups multiply in an identification around specific issues, ways to satisfy and resolve them are sought. Plans are made by these individuals, groups, and multiples thereof, and sometimes are implemented through organizations with a variety of structures and purposes. This academic formulation is seen in practice as voluntary agencies, chests and councils, or legislation carrying appropriations for public agencies with service or grant programs. We have only to call the names of national annual fund drives or identify the various governmental services and institutions to labor the validity of this transposition. As these groups develop a history and are insulated with emotionally-charged motivation, they have become potent interests and influences in our communities. Anyone in a planning position recognizes them as forces with which to reckon.

OPERATION AT STATE LEVEL

The state level is an operational base which offers an unusual vantage point in the matrix just suggested. It is a midway point between federal and local participation. It is close enough to have an appreciation of the variations among the states which require broadly couched federal legislation to be locally applied and sufficiently geared to the service needs of localities so that practical measures of administration can be adopted. The problems are multiple and fascinating. One has only to scan the proceedings of the ten annual conferences of chief social workers from state mental health programs to have some appreciation of the ground covered. The recurrent themes of evaluating or designing community programs, training programs for community mental health, analysis of the role of the consultant, relations of public and voluntary agencies, the varied definitions of community clinic function and responsibilities are just samples to give the flavor and range of considerations of this group.

Implicit in state level responsibility is the cold fact that the social worker, whatever his job title may be, is a state official, usually in some executive branch of the government. Although the program operational responsibilities may be similar, one need only meet semiannually with the Northeast State Governments' Conference on Mental Health to have an appreciation of the administrative variation in community mental health programs. They may usually be found in an administrative subdivision of state departments of health, welfare, or mental health. One can frequently find "bits and pieces" of the program in state education or other departments, not to mention that readily created legislative creature known as a "commission." A social worker moving in these channels needs rapidly to develop an awareness of interrelationships and means of communication if he is to identify and make use of the resources of the "agency" he represents. By and large, these administrative structural

growths have interesting historical backgrounds which it serves well to understand. This is equally true of the individual patterns of state-local relations
where the variation may also be important. For example, in some states the
primary subdivision of government to which the state organization relates may
be the county; in others the town may be the local operating unit of primary
importance.

Another variable is found in the area of finance. The dynamic importance
of money as a factor in the casework process is one from which the practitioner,
until recently, has shied away. It is only within the last two decades that the
literature has begun to be spotted with communications concerning fees. It is
only within the last five years that a social casework agency was created to
demonstrate that the individual public would buy and support such a service.
This is an area in which our training is weak and our attitudes usually naïve.
In the voluntary agency there has been too little appreciation developed of the
chain of events which goes into making it possible for a caseworker and a client
to get together in an office to consider, almost in sanctuary, a client's problem.
Fortunately this is changing. Interestingly enough, as the practitioner has begun
to appreciate more the dynamics of dependency in theoretical terms and our
assurance of our professional identity has bloomed, we have been less reluctant
to reserve money matters to the market place. Our psychological understanding is just picking up the pace of our social work understanding of almost three
decades ago when we knew that indiscriminate relief-giving was "pauperizing"
and not motivating an individual. Now where fees are not charged we can talk
of indulging a person's passive dependency needs. This augurs well for our
professional maturity.

The social worker at the state level must immediately become familiar
with the tune of the cash register. The commissioner of Finance and Control
(and don't ever underestimate the "control"), the Department of the Budget,
the Comptroller's Office are the pivotal points around which the activities of
community planning for mental health or any publicly supported program
will revolve. The introduction of the program budget as a replacement for the
line-item budget is a development to watch as an aid in planning program, and
equally important in the interpretation of program to the fiscal and legislative
authorities. The social worker at the state level who cannot communicate with
his fiscal officer is all but fatally handicapped. The decisiveness of this relationship is further underscored when one realizes that estimates agree that more
than 90 per cent of the support for all mental health programs are derived
from public tax funds.

The legislator is the spokesman for community need and the potential
instrumentality to crystallize and implement this need. He is the individual
who creates and nurtures a bill through the legislative process so that it becomes a mandate on the statute books which gives the latitude and the limits
to a public official to move a program forward, or to be hamstrung. He is the
individual who will decide whether the appropriations or finance committee
will include, exclude, or restore items in the gubernatorial budget. The importance of communication in this area needs no emphasis; the delicacy of the

relationship needs to be experienced to be fully appreciated. However, it should be noted that the legislative statute itself has far more durability than the changing fortunes of the political leadership under which it was sponsored. This observation is added as a principle to the unwary social worker who may be tempted to leave the confines of his professional competence or lose the focus of his identification in the relationship.

Up to this point there has been an attempt to sketch briefly some of the complicated interrelated areas in which the social worker in mental health moves. Little note has been given the protective or correctional forces, the judicial components, or the state personnel picture. Nor has more than passing mention been made of the public health, public welfare, and education responsibilities. And yet each of these fields must be recognized as having a primary stake in the field of mental health, regardless of definition of the term. Each has grown out of a symptomatically expressed community need which has been translated into program by lay and professional collaboration. The relationships of these agencies, social institutions, and forces are difficult enough to define specifically, their relatedness to mental health, or even mental illness is more difficult—how they become co-ordinated is a daily Herculean task. Lest this appear to be overwhelming we have the comforting examples of the development of antisepsis before the discovery of bacteria, and control of typhoid by applying the lessons of empiricism. So today, without knowing the causes of most mental illness, we have an appreciation of some preventive efforts, some symptomatic treatment, some rehabilitative procedures, and are beginning to develop some realistic leads to extend and apply our knowledge.

IMPORTANCE OF LEADERSHIP

Thus the social worker at the state level must have a point of view, or at least develop a viewpoint. It is all too easy to become absorbed to the point of preoccupation in the individual technical problems of the individual case. We can easily view with alarm the projected estimates of professional manpower shortages (1) in the face of a rising population and an increased clinical demand (4). We can take refuge and comfort in proclaiming the need for recruitment, in increasing training facilities, and in supporting research. These positions are easily sustained in the face of the facts. However, before righteously pursuing this rainbow we must be certain that the people we have trained in the available knowledge are using both the training and the knowledge to the maximum in solving the problems placed before them. This means a clearer organization and utilization of our training and research talents so that their primary functions are safeguarded. The implication is that service agencies must primarily address themselves to the solution of community problems by employing their maximum skills only where indicated, and be aware of and use all community resources to the fullest extent. In this statement we have the seeds of conservation of scarce professional resources and the assumption of responsibility to make readily available our knowledge and skill, not only to individual clients but to related professions, not only to identifiable social agencies but to the host of organized efforts we have suggested earlier in this presentation.

Lest this exhortation seem out of context we need only remind ourselves of the difference in the rate of military psychiatric casualties in combat units which were attributable to a qualitative difference in leadership (10). That is to say that it is fair to assume a similarity in potential for breakdown in a selected cross-section of population which will occur under a given set of similar experiences. The x factor was observed to be the leadership exercised in developing group identification. As we begin to analyze populations and have more appreciation of subclinical problems, we may be able to design and implement programs of much broader effectiveness than our individualized clinical efforts which too frequently are misplaced (2). This should stimulate our overtures to leadership groups, *e.g.,* teachers, public health nurses, PTA's, industrialists, and civic leaders. It also illustrates the areas in which leads to developing mental health principles can be pursued.

COMMUNITY-BASED SERVICES

It is less than four years since the Biometrics Branch, NIMH, inaugurated a system of clinic reporting for psychiatric outpatient community services. Some data is beginning to trickle through and will in time become a torrent of information on which to plan. For example, a tiny bit of data—of 1,234 clinics (95 per cent reporting), 91 per cent of the professional manhours are given in metropolitan areas comprising 57 per cent of the population. Of interest is that 38 per cent of the total professional clinical time is supplied by social workers. Incidentally, 64 per cent of the clinics are federally or state-aided or operated (3). In the social work field the work of Community Research Associates in extending their initial findings of 1948 in St. Paul is being currently reported (5). Here we have the data illustrating the need, and offering a method for a co-ordinated effort to relate to definable problems. The public health field has in recent years begun to beam its techniques (7) on the field of community mental health (8). We have also heard some preliminary content of the work of the Joint Commission on Mental Illness and Health, and expect that this group will add to our factual knowledge. The prodigious efforts of the Council of State Governments in gathering data in the mental health field has been extremely valuable. These are signs of the times that the related mental health fields can no longer operate on considered professional opinion alone, without the data to support such opinion. Nor can we expect or do we deserve support for our programs if we cannot interpret them successfully. We have examples of clinical services—well organized, staffed, and financed—which folded after a few years, principally because they were unable to recognize community forces or unwilling to be flexible, or just unaware of their unrelatedness to the community or its demands for service. There may be some correlation between this observation and the statement that less than 6 per cent of clinic time is used for other than treatment time (9).

Perhaps the implementation of the community mental health center idea will fill the void left by services addressing themselves to highly specialized needs. A comprehensive agency needs to be available to provide the gamut of services necessary to insure the continued responsibility to see problems to a conclusion. The necessary differential diagnostic services for sound case planning and follow-through would be at hand. We would be less concerned with the policies of short-term or long-term treatment and more attuned to case needs based on realistic objectives. Our services would become community based and not "case-bound."

The implications for social workers are becoming clearer. As they move into administrative and policy making positions, especially after years of clinical experience, they are in a strategic position. In their roles as planners of community services in chests and councils they are equally influential in asking for an evaluation of agency services and can establish the measure whereby they serve the community. In these councils the procedures of communication and integration are developed. It is at the decision-making level that the functions of agencies are determined. The translation into services to people becomes a technical problem of adaptation. This was demonstrated by the World War II military mental hygiene units and consultation services. Those "agencies" could not close intake or build waiting lists. They worked out solutions to problems within the limits of their resources and within the reality limitations of their "community." They dealt with acute, chronic, and recurring problems and demonstrated that they were helpful to individuals and effective to the "community" which sponsored them. This was accomplished by developing an understanding of the individual clinical problem and looking beyond it to the dynamic influences in the military environment which could be brought to bear on the amelioration of the difficulty. This involved open channels of communication, an intimate knowledge of resources, and the ability to affix the continuing responsibility for the problem (6).

OPPORTUNITY FOR SOCIAL WORKERS

The psychiatric social worker in a community clinic has a similar opportunity. In the clinical process he is the integrating member of the clinical team, who at the case level brings cohesion to the service. He has an opportunity at any point in his clinic performance—at intake, at case conference, during treatment or at the closing of a case—to relate the understanding of the patient's pathology to dynamic community factors, which may help or exacerbate the problem. At the supervisory level his influence may be broadened. He can be the interpreter of the community and its needs to the clinic staff. At the administrative level he must participate in policy-making and introduce the reality factors which in the final analysis govern the practices of the service. In his interagency contacts, he can strive for a down-to-earth appreciation of what clinical services have to offer and where continued social agency help is indicated. He is in the enviable position of preventing a retreat to the ivory tower on the one hand and, to mix a metaphor, he can puncture the balloon of clinical omnipotence on the other.

At the consultant level, the field is wide open. Here the social worker moves from a position of authority, even if sometimes it is only an aura of expertness. From this overview it is possible to develop an appreciation of the community resources, or lack of them; of the agency interrelationships, or lack of them. It is vital to identify the community leadership and involve these moving interests in participation for the planning of services. Usually unhampered by local operational responsibility, the consultant has considerable mobility in addressing himself to the problem for which his services are sought. As he is able to help those engaged to define their problems and assess their resources, he has an opportunity to assist in creating a solution. If he is able to avoid becoming involved in factions and sticks to issues, his chances of success are increased.

We have studiously avoided attempts at definition. We have just as carefully refrained from an enumeration of principles. There has been an attempt to identify some of the prerequisites of professional knowledge and assurances, to apply to a number of variables we are just beginning to appreciate as having a bearing upon the state of a community's mental health. There is the suggestion that our individual case efforts have a potential for a wider application if we apply our knowledge so gained in the creation of integrated services. There is the recognition of a growing body of fact upon which to plan and a broader horizon of participation. There is also the inference that we need to set some of our sacred cows out to pasture. Running through the content is the need to transpose our understanding of dynamics into terms that are practical and able to be communicated.

To participate in community mental health programs, one must avoid blueprints. There is no formula that can be didactically transmitted—no less nor more than casework can be taught or learned through memorizing a set of rules. There must be an awareness of oneself, one's attitudes, knowledge, and convictions. Add to these a willingness to be of help and the ability to evaluate and profit from experience. With these qualifications, a strong heart, and a thick skin we welcome you to our ranks.

REFERENCES

1. Albee, G. W., and Dickey, M. Manpower trends in three mental health professions. *Amer. Psychol.*, 1957, 12 (2):57–70.
2. Anderson, F. N., and Dean, H. C. *Some aspects of child guidance clinic*

intake policy and practice. Washington, D. C.: U. S. Department of Health, Education, and Welfare, 1956. (Public Health Monogr. No. 42.)

3. Bahn, A. K., and Norman, V. B. *Characteristics and professional staff of outpatient psychiatric clinics.* Washington, D. C.: U. S. Department of Health, Education, and Welfare, 1957. (Public Health Monogr. No. 49.)

4. Blain, D., and Robinson, R. Personnel shortages in psychiatric services. *New York State J. of Med.,* 1957, 57 (2).

5. Buell, B., Beisser, P. T., and Wedemeyer, J. M. Reorganizing to prevent and control disordered behavior. *Ment. Hyg.,* 1958, 42 (2):155–94. *See also* Glabe, D. B., Feider, L. J., and Page, H. O. Reorientation for treatment and control. Supplement to *Public Welfare.* 1958, 16 (2):i–xxiii.

6. Greving, F. T., and Rockmore, M. J. Psychiatric case-work as a military service. *Ment. Hyg.,* 1945, 29 (3):435–506.

7. Epidemiology of Mental Disorders (eleven briefs). *Pub. Hlth. Reports,* 1957, 72 (7):572–97.

8. *Evaluation in mental health: A review of the problem of evaluating mental health activities,* Washington, D. C.: U. S. Department of Health, Education, and Welfare, 1955. (Public Health Service Pub. No. 413.)

9. Southard, C. G. Eighth Annual Conference of Chief Social Workers from State Mental Health Programs, St. Louis, Mo., May 17–19, 1956.

10. Spiegel, H. X. Preventive psychiatry with combat troops. *Amer. J. of Psychiat.,* 1944, 101 (3):310–15.

47

Practical Steps for the Family Physician in the Prevention of Emotional Disorder

GERALD CAPLAN

THE etiology of emotional disorder in any individual case is very complicated. Many interacting factors are involved, including those based on constitution, childhood experiences, later life problems and their solution, and details of the unfolding of the processes of growth and development in interaction with the forces of the emotional and material environment.

If one looks at this problem from an epidemiologic point of view it is still complicated, but it is simpler: by this I mean a study of the factors in one community which are responsible for its having a higher incidence of cases of emotional disorder than another community. Such studies isolate certain common factors which operate to influence all members of a community. These factors do not determine the fate in any individual case, but they lead to communitywide differences in the frequency of certain psychological illnesses.

Viewed from this standpoint it is possible to discover certain general factors which can be combated on a communitywide level. Programs to alter these factors may not affect the fate of any particular person but are likely to reduce the number of cases which occur during a subsequent period in that community.

In connection with these factors the following consideration seems important: The mental health of an individual is dependent on the continuous satisfaction of special requisites in the pattterns of his psychological interaction with certain other people. We can speak loosely about a person having psychological needs which have to be satisfied in his interactions with others. The most obvious need is the basic psychological stimulation of having people to talk to. For years we have realized that isolation has a potent harmful effect on mental health. For centuries men have tortured their fellows by marooning them on desert islands, by solitary confinement in prisons, or by ostracism in the social setting. The list of needs also includes the opportunity to give and receive love and affection, to be dependent and to be depended on, to satisfy cravings to be controlled and to control, and to be a member of a social group

Reprinted from *Journal of the American Medical Association*, 1959, *170*, 1497–1506, by permission of the publisher and the author. © 1959, American Medical Association. Dr. Caplan is Clinical Professor of Psychiatry, Harvard Medical School.

in which one's identity and personality are respected and accepted, so that one's achievements are rewarded by praise and one's difficulties are lightened by sympathy and understanding.

In all cultures there exist within the structure of the society small groups of people who are bound together by significant emotional ties, and within these groups the psychological needs of the individual members are satisfied. Biological ties are usually the basis of these fundamental groupings, and some form of family structure is universal. In different cultures the pattern of families varies, but, whether one studies the small family of modern Western urban culture, the large extended family of earlier Western rural culture or certain present-day Oriental cultures, or the matriarchal families of other cultures, we find that certain roles or tasks of psychological significance are allotted by tradition to each of the family members, that the sum of these tasks usually satisfies the needs of all the members, and that this sum is distributed among the members of the group so that no necessary role is left out.

In recent years we have discovered that the interactive possibilities afforded by the intact structure of the family are as necessary to mental health as the provision of adequate nutritional supplies are to physical health. When the traditional pattern of any family is altered by situational factors, the mental health of its members is endangered. This danger is greatest for the younger children, in the same way that nutritional deficiencies are most dangerous during early developmental phases, but the danger is also present for the mature adults.

Another similarity to physical nutrition is that if all goes well we do not usually realize the importance of these factors. The satisfaction of needs in an intact family takes place silently and automatically. It is only when the family structure is deficient that difficulties become obvious; since families are ubiquitous it has taken us a long time to realize the obvious fact of their importance for mental health and the close connection between defects in their structure and subsequent emotional disorders among certain of their members.

IMPORTANCE OF THE FAMILY PHYSICIAN IN PROMOTING MENTAL HEALTH

From all this it follows that professional workers who deal with people as members of a family have a special place in programs of mental health promotion. The family physician is a worker with a uniquely important role in this regard. He is usually called in to a family to handle symptoms of physical disorder in one or more of its members. In dealing with this traditional task he may well add another dimension to his practice and focus his interest on those elements of the situation which involve dangers to the social structure of the family group, therefore involving dangers to the future mental health of its members. The concept of the family as a unit, and the physician as a worker with responsibilities to the whole unit, implies not only that he may accept as a patient any individual family member but also that when he is called in to deal with the symptoms of one member he will widen the focus of his interest to include all the others, whether from the point of view of their involvement in the etiology of his patient's condition or from the point of view of the effects of his patient on them as a group. This responsibility has been clear for years in cases of contagious disease, but we now realize that it applies equally, if not more so, to the social and psychological side-effects and sequelae of any illness. This latest insight is, as is often the case in medicine, a reformulation of old traditional knowledge; the family physicians in our parents' generation understood this quite well, although they may not have been able to spell it out as explicitly as we can nowadays. Increasing complexity in the medical sciences, increasing specialization, and increasing concentration on the exciting new discoveries in somatic medicine have to some extent pushed these old insights into the back of our minds. In the hurly-burly of busy practices, and in the absence of strong protagonists, they have fallen into disuse.

Moreover, the older training of physicians by the apprentice system allowed young men to acquire many of the skills of psychosocial management of the family by modeling themselves on the practice of experienced preceptors. The knowledge they acquired was not to be found in books but in the life situations of their apprenticeship. Nowadays the old type of apprenticeship is usually missing, and the books still say very little about all this—at least very little that is useful at a practical level—because the writers of these books have usually not carried out their studies within the framework of the actual situations of general medical practice but in the very specialized and unique conditions of psychiatric clinics and psychological laboratories.

Exhortations by psychiatrists that the family physician should play his part in promoting mental health are no great help. The family physician asks, "Exactly how should I do this?" and the psychiatrist usually has no concrete answer. In this paper I will attempt to begin to give a concrete answer—or at least to indicate specific avenues for practical exploration.

Before ending this introduction, I would like to mention one other point which supports the importance of the family physician in community programs of preventive psychiatry. He is one of the key community workers who has contact with people when they are in a state of crisis. Physical illness may be a turning point which determines a change in the whole course of a person's existence; it is important to realize that during the relatively short period of the few weeks or months of the illness all kinds of decisions may be made and all kinds of psychological reorientations, as well as alterations in the structure and functioning of families, may be worked out which will affect the type of interpersonal relationships and character of intrapersonal functioning for a long time to come.

Psychiatrists have recently joined the ranks of those who are very interested in the way people solve the emotional and social problems of periods of life crisis. Previously, it was mainly novelists and dramatists who were interested in this topic, but nowadays we psychiatrists realize that the future mental health of people may be determined at crisis times by the quality of their problem-solving methods. One type of solution of a set of problems may lead to greater mental health, which explains why many people become more mature as a result of satisfactorily overcoming life's difficulties. Another type of solution may lead to mental ill health, either immediately or in the future, and either directly for that individual or indirectly for his dependents due to damage of his emotional relationships with them.

People become emotionally disturbed during these crisis periods, but the anxiety, depression, tension, and hostility are not to be confused with symptoms of psychiatric illness, which they superficially resemble. They are the signs in the emotional sphere which show that an active struggle is in process inside that individual in his attempts to wrestle with his problems. At the end of the few weeks of crisis these symptoms will disappear, once some kind of solution has been achieved. This solution may be a healthy one. On the other hand it may be an unhealthy one, and in that case either at once or in the future the individual will manifest neurotic or psychotic symptoms which represent a pathological way of dealing with his life problems through some form of irrational and psychologically distorted pseudo-solution.

The most important point for preventive psychiatry is that the type of problem-solving during a crisis can be powerfully influenced by the helpful or hindering intervention of other people, both in the family circle and from the outside, in the form of the physician and other community agents. When the balance of forces is upset in a crisis a minimal intervention may produce major and stable results by determining to which side the balance will come down.

This means that the operations of the family physician during any of his visits for whatever reason to a family in crisis may have a major effect on the pattern of resolution of that crisis and on the members' future mental health.

I wish now to concentrate on examples of certain practical implications for the operations of the family physician that arise out of these theoretical considerations.

SAFEGUARDING THE INTEGRITY OF FAMILY STRUCTURE

The general practitioner has many opportunities in his practice to help keep families from breaking up temporarily or permanently; or, if this can not be avoided, to help them find substitutes for roles which the family break-up has left vacant.

Most important is the prevention of separation of the mother from the family circle or from one of her children. Bowlby (1) and other workers have shown fairly conclusively that the separation, for any appreciable time, of the stable mother figure from a child during the first few years of its life exerts a damaging effect on the development of the child's personality, leading in severe cases to extreme forms of psychological and psychosomatic illness. If the physician is aware of this, he will be alert to explore practical alternatives to any plan for removing a mother or a child from the home because of illness. Often the removal from home is quite inevitable because the nature of the illness demands hospitalization, but frequently the physician may be able to plan for this absence to be short and for the remainder of the treatment to be carried out at home. The fact that the mother is physically incapacitated certainly will influence her ability to fulfill many of the demands of the mother role, but her mere presence in the home will allow her, through repeated contacts with other family members, to maintain the emotional bonds of comfort and sympathy and mother love which are the emotional nutrients the others need.

Of course such a plan implies the need for nursing and homemaker services to care for the patient at home and to take over her housewifely duties. The physician should be active in helping the family secure such services either from the ranks of the extended family of grandparents, aunts, sisters, and cousins; from neighbors and friends; or, if these are not available, from professional workers. When the latter are not available I believe that local physicians should actively campaign among appropriate community agencies for their provision. Family physicians should be as interested in the adequacy of community agency provision in this area of homemaker services as they are in the standards of their local hospitals, since both affect the quality of the professional care they can give their patients.

The feeling in regard to hospitalization of young children should be that of avoiding or postponing or shortening it whenever possible. With modern methods of diagnosis and treatment and effective home nursing, many types of cases which in the past necessitated admission to children's hospitals can be treated at home.

When separation is inevitable the physician should encourage frequent and regular visiting to maintain channels of communication and continuation of the emotional links.

In 1952 in England, as a result of Bowlby's researches, the Ministry of Health issued a directive to permit and encourage daily visiting in children's wards. In the United States this is also becoming common pediatric practice, and some new children's hospitals have facilities for parents to sleep in the ward near their child and help with certain nursing procedures. This has led to inevitable complications in ward management and new problems for the nursing staff, but none of these have proved insoluble and they are a small price to pay for the results in terms of the safeguarding of the personality development of the children.

The physician interested in the whole family should also be on the alert for the neglect of the other children when one child is hospitalized. He should try to mobilize the efforts of other family members to cover the hiatus left when a mother is concentrating her efforts on the ill child, and his activity in this regard should not stop when the ill child comes home. We are familiar with many cases of neurotic disturbance in children which started during periods of parental neglect due to the illness of a sibling.

If the mother has to go into the hospital, the physician should try to promote communication from her to the other family members, particularly the children, through frequent verbal and written personal messages; he should also use his best efforts to help the rest of the family stay together in their home. If the family stays together they may close their ranks and take over, as a group, some of the absent member's functions, whereas if they are split up this group strength is dissipated.

In order to keep the family together the physician may have to mobilize other family members to come in and do the housekeeping, or he may have to call in a homemaker. Placing the children as individuals in other homes may seem the easier way, but it is actually more expensive in both the short run and the long run.

Another area where the family doctor can give invaluable mental health help is that of helping the father take over some of the maternal role left vacant by the absence of his wife. Husbands may need support and explicit encouragement and advice in mothering their children during this period and in assuming unaccustomed leadership in housekeeping. Some men may be rather inhibited in doing what is needed because of false feelings of shame about such activities being effeminate. The physician can watch out for this and throw the power of his prestige behind the medical prescriptions to the hesitant father.

When the separation of the mother is permanent due to death or desertion the physician should interest himself actively in helping the family plan for her replacement by a substitute. Assistance in this direction, as in the other issues which have been mentioned, may be obtained from a family social agency; but the family physician, who is the professional person with continuing contact and responsibility for the whole family, should help in mobilizing this assistance and should coordinate these activities with his own and with those of other helping agents such as clergymen and teachers.

The physician should be equally active if it is the father and not the mother who is separated from the family by illness, death, or social factors, such as employment demands or wartime needs. A wife needs her husband's support, and children need the controlling influence of a father figure. This issue has been relatively neglected until recently. Interest in it has now been aroused by the realization that many common disorders of personality devlopment in children, which lead to delinquency, have been influenced by the absence of a stable controlling father during the child's upbringing, so that the external discipline which is the precursor of the internal discipline of the socialized person has been missing or defective.

If there is no man in the house, the role of discipliner of the children devolves largely on the mother, and she may need the support of the physician, himself a potent father figure, in order to add this to her other roles. It may also be possible for him to help her out directly in certain crisis situations and to invoke the help of teachers and recreational group leaders.

Perhaps by now it seems that I am advocating turning the general practitioner into a social worker. Nothing is further from my intention. His primary role must remain that of the practitioner of the healing arts; but if our talk of treating the whole person rather than the diseased organ is to be more than a mere slogan, we must expect the physician to add an interest in some of the above psychosocial points to his traditional preoccupation with physical functioning. The family physician may well realize that his role in the family provides him with both the responsibility and the opportunity to affect its functioning in ways which will have direct effects on the health of its members. So long as mental health and mental illness were conceived of as being quite separate from physical health and physical illness, the physician could afford to neglect some of these issues; but nowadays such a dichotomy is hard for most of us to accept and very hard indeed for the general practitioner who deals not with bits of people or special aspects of their functioning, as isolated in special clinics, but with the whole fabric of life within the family circle in the home.

SAFEGUARDING HEALTHY RELATIONSHIPS

The satisfaction of individual psychological needs in the family is dependent not only on the preservation of the integrity of its structure but also on the quality of the enduring interpersonal relationships among its members. The mother may not be geographically separated from her child, for example, but her prevailing feelings toward him may be so anxious, ambivalent, or rejecting that she cannot perceive his needs, or, if she does, she may have no interest in satisfying them.

Once disordered relationships between family members have fully developed, treatment by a psychiatric specialist is usually needed to improve them; unless such intervention is forthcoming, a significant proportion of the people will eventually need psychotherapy for manifest psychiatric illness. In the past few years, however, we have discovered that the disordered relationships which are harmful take quite a time to develop to their full pathogenic intensity and that during this period the family physician may interrupt this harmful development. His helpful intervention can best be focused at certain crucial periods when disorders in relationships are most apt to occur in response to characteristic temporary situational factors.

PREGNANCY

One such crucial period, both for the development of the mother-child relationship and for the other interpersonal relationships in the family, is the period of pregnancy. The mother's relationship with her new baby does not begin at his birth but is being built up during her pregnancy; the complicated metabolic development of this period has a characteristic effect on her emotional functioning, which in turn has reverberations on the emotional life of the family as a whole. These reverberations may lead to changes in the way the family members relate to the expectant mother and to each other, and these changes may become stable and may have far-reaching consequences for mental health by altering the pattern of need satisfaction within the family circle.

Recent studies (3) on the emotional manifestations of normal pregnancy have yielded information about characteristic series of emotional changes which occur in many expectant mothers and which are apt to frighten them and to interfere with family life. The physician who knows the details of this predictable development may make powerful use of this knowledge.

His main technique will be anticipatory guidance, whereby he warns the patient and her husband ahead of time what to expect and thus gives them the chance of preparing themselves psychologically for the difficulties. For instance, quite early in pregnancy the physician should have a joint interview with husband and wife and let them both know that many women become more irritable and more sensitive than usual during pregnancy because of complicated and little-understood somatopsychic factors; therefore, if in this case the expectant mother suddenly gets angry with minor provocation, laughs or weeps for no adequate reason, or has sudden attacks of depression, neither she nor her husband need get alarmed. These changes, however dramatic, are not preliminary signs of psychiatric illness and they will disappear after delivery.

At this early conference the physician will also be well advised to mention the likelihood of changes in the pregnant woman's sexual desire and performance. Changes in appetite are frequent in pregnancy, and this relates not only to foods but to sex. In regard to this topic the physician not only gives needed anticipatory guidance but often is able to act as a channel of communication between husband and wife in relation to topics which in our culture may not be easily discussed between them. In the absence of necessary knowledge and in the presence of communication blocks so that difficulties cannot be worked out by discussion, tensions may easily arise between husband and wife based on distorted interpretations of each other's attitudes. A wife, not infrequently, gets very upset if she loses her sexual desire or capacity for orgasm; she imagines she has become permanently frigid or that she is losing her love for her husband and that he will reciprocate in kind. A husband sometimes fears that his wife is rejecting him because he made her pregnant, and sometimes he seeks alternative sources of sexual satisfaction as a reaction to this imagined rejection. Such unfortunate fantasies can be easily alleviated by the physician's prior discussion of the realities of the situation. He can also help both parties become aware of the strain under which each will be laboring during pregnancy and help them pay special attention to the need to support and sympathize with the partner's difficulties and to make allowances for signs of tension.

Such joint interviews with husband and wife, which should if possible be repeated at least once or twice more during the pregnancy, have a more essential function than just the smoothing out of expected difficulties in the marital relationship, important as this is. My studies have shown that toward the middle of pregnancy most women become more passive and demanding of affection than usual. Instead of being the giving person in the home, actively attending to the needs of others, they now turn in on themselves and feel the need to sit around and be waited on. My studies have also shown that the adequate satisfaction of these needs for increased attention and affection is not only important for increasing the expectant mother's comfort but also plays an important part in preparing her for adequate motherhood in the first few months after delivery. If she receives enough affection during pregnancy, she can give out enough affection to the baby. Those women who are deprived during pregnancy later have a tendency to deprive their babies.

Recognition of this by the physician allows him to play an important role in ensuring adequate emotional supplies at the crucial early period of the newborn infant's life. He cannot give the expectant mother affection himself, but he can try to make sure she gets it from the natural sources. There are many cultural and psychological factors which may block a husband's demonstrations of affection during pregnancy. He may be so irritated by his wife's petulant behavior and by her inability to afford him his usual sexual satisfaction that he turns away from her. He may be frightened by her increased demands, and he may feel she is changing her personality and becoming lazy and spoiled. He may resent what he feels is her exploitation of the privileges of pregnancy. His feelings of security in his manly role, which are in our culture often weakened by the lack of respect we pay to expectant fathers, may be further endangered by his wife's demands that he take over some of her maternal functions in the work in the house or caring for the other children.

The physician has the opportunity during his joint conferences with husband and wife, or if necessary during an individual interview with the husband, to prevent the difficulties which may emerge from these factors. He can reassure the husband as to the normality of his wife's reactions and as to their temporary nature, and he can enlist the husband's active help in preparing for the baby by, as it were, "charging up his wife's battery of affection," so that she can eventually pass the emotional supplies on to the baby. Most important, the physician can by his own attitudes during these meetings help increase the husband's feeling of respect for the importance of his own role as an expectant father. This may help to prevent a not infrequent cause of family difficulty after the baby arrives, when some fathers are hampered in their paternal role by feelings of jealousy in regard to the baby.

I do not wish to leave this very brief reference to the physician's preventive role in emotional disorders originating during pregnancy without mentioning the results of some recent research which has specific practical implications. My studies have shown that certain traumatic events occurring during the period of pregnancy exert a powerful harmful effect on the future mother-child relationship. Such events include the severe illness or death of a near relative of the expectant mother, particularly of a parent, her husband, or one of her children. It is very easy for the woman to displace some of her painful feelings about such an event onto her relationship with her unborn child, and her attitudes toward him get distorted by irrational ideas, such as identifying him as a reborn representative of the dead person or blaming him and sacrificing him because of unresolved feelings of personal guilt in connection with the bereavement. The physician should be especially on guard to ensure an adequate process of mourning along lines I will describe below, and he should help the mother to see and to feel that her new baby is an individual in his own right and has to be recognized and treated as a person with quite a separate fate from everyone else, including the dead person.

ABORTION

Another traumatic event during pregnancy which is likely to have a major harmful effect on the future mother-child relationship is an attempt by the mother to abort herself, if this act is against the rules of her culture and traditions, and especially if she keeps it as a guilty secret. It is this guilt which blossoms in secret fantasies and which invades and distorts the relationship with the child. If nothing is done about it, the chances are high that a particularly pernicious disorder of the child's personality will eventually be produced. The important point is that this pathological sequence of events can usually be easily interrupted by the family physician, if he identifies either during pregnancy or soon afterward what has happened. The technique to be used is one which is not usually a part of the general practitioner's therapeutic armamentarium but one which can be fairly easily learned, namely, specific reduction of conscious guilt. I have discussed this at some length in a recent paper (2) and here I will only mention it briefly. It consists essentially of the physician helping the woman to talk about what she has done in two to three short interviews, in which he adopts an understanding and nonjudgmental attitude toward her behavior, without in any way pretending that what she did was a good thing and yet with the clear demonstration that despite what she has done he continues to accept her as a worthwhile person.

DIRECT HELP TO PEOPLE IN CRISIS

The traditional role of the physician brings him into contact with many people during the critical period when they are wrestling with acute life problems, and at such times he can exert a particularly powerful effect on their mental health by steering them toward adequate solutions and away from maladaptive solutions. The clearest example of this is in connection with problems of bereavement.

BEREAVEMENT

Eric Lindemann (4), my colleague at Harvard, has carried out some interesting studies on the nature of the process of mourning which carry clear and specific implications for medical practice. He has found that a bereaved person goes through a well-defined process in adapting to the death of the relative, that this process usually takes four to six weeks to complete, and that it is characterized by a succession of specific psychological steps with accompanying emotional side-effects. It seems that when a key figure is removed by death or desertion from a person's life, that person has to work quite hard, psychologically, in order to adapt to the loss and in order to fill in the resulting emotional hiatus.

Lindemann also found that whereas the majority of people manifest these characteristic mourning reactions, which show they are satisfactorily doing their "grief work," and recover their psychological and psychosomatic equilibrium by the end of the four to six weeks, a small but significant group of bereaved people do not show these changes, or show them in distorted form; many of these people either immediately or later show definite and sometimes extreme signs of psychiatric or psychosomatic illness, particularly depression and disorders of the gastrointestinal tract, such as peptic ulcer or ulcerative colitis.

Lindemann postulates a direct causative link between the absence of a normal mourning process and the later development of these illnesses. He has also shown that sometimes these illnesses can be interrupted by helping the patients revive the problems of their bereavement and belatedly do their undone grief work.

Among the characteristic manifestations of a healthy mourning reaction are withdrawal of interest from the affairs of daily life and business, feelings of mental pain and loneliness, weeping, disorders of respiratory rhythm with frequently repeated deep sighs, insomnia, loss of appetite, and—most characteristic—preoccupation with the image of the deceased person, usually in connection with the revival of numerous memories of joint activities with him. Lindemann feels that this last phenomenon is the key to understanding the essence of the mourning process. The bereaved person withdraws his energy from most of the aspects of everyday life and concentrates it on reviewing, detail by detail, those aspects of his past life which were enriched by his association with the deceased. In each of these life segments he has to realize afresh the pain of his loss and rather concretely to experience its permanence. In each of these segments he has to make a special act of resignation to the inevitable. This can only be achieved through suffering, but not until it is completed can the person achieve mastery and independence in that segment of his life, so that he can return to normal activity and emotional stability.

Each bereaved person must do this grief work for himself, and mourning is a lonely process; but the traditions of most cultures illustrate to us that neighbors and friends and representatives of the larger community can help the mourner both by the general emotional support of condolence and by practices which permit him or encourage him to go through the steps of his grief work. In our modern culture the weakening of religious and other cultural systems of values and traditions has thrown many people largely on their own emotional resources, and the family physician is one of the people whose work may call him to step into the breach. In doing so in this area he may well try to enlist the support of the priest or clergyman or rabbi, each of whom has his own traditional approach to these problems.

In order to understand specifically what the family physician might do to help the bereaved person mourn successfully, it is helpful to list some of Lindemann's findings among the unsuccessful mourners, who later developed various illnesses. No single simple picture was characteristic of this group, but combinations of the following reactions were common. Instead of withdrawing interest from daily life many of them showed more business activity than usual and by diverting their interest to the problems of outside life appeared to escape the inner turmoil of mourning. They did not weep. They felt little or no pain, either saying they felt numb and empty or showing a strange cheerfulness. Many of them showed marked hostility, often directed toward the physicians and nurses who had cared for the deceased. In all cases there was an absence of preoccupation with the deceased, and on direct questioning many said they were quite incapable of recalling in memory the image of the deceased person. The over-all picture which was most commonly found was an attempt to deny the emotional importance of the whole business and to get on with problems of living without the burden of mourning. In the short run the external emotional manifestations of this group seemed easier and happier than the group of active mourners, but in the long run many of them paid very dearly for their temporary ease.

The guideline for the physician who wishes to profit from these studies is to try and help his patients grieve along the lines of the first group and to be particularly active in giving his help whenever he recognizes in one of his patients, during the mourning period, signs which resemble those of the maladaptive group. Experience has shown that to help such people grieve successfully it is not necessary to know the inner psychological reasons for their being hampered in this regard. The uncovering of these deeper complications is not necessary; all that seems important is to get them by whatever means to dwell on the image of the deceased and to go over and over in their minds the many activities which they shared with him in the past, in order little by little to realize that from now on he will be missing from their lives. What is also necessary is for the physician to give the patient the full measure of his emotional support and sympathy in bearing the pain of this process and for him to mobilize other sources of support within the family and outside it. In this regard the physician should realize that emotional support depends, among other factors, on the quantity of personal interaction, so he should realize the special importance of even short extra visits to his patient during the mourning period, or, if these are not possible under the pressures of a busy practice, at least of phone communication. Since the pathological sequelae of inadequate mourning are usually so severe, these extra visits are well worthwhile.

When the physician is not able on his own to stimulate a proper mourning reaction, when his efforts to enlist the aid of ministers of religion and members of the extended family also lead nowhere, and when mourning is absent or continues without apparent resolution long after the expected period of four to six weeks, the physician would be well advised to take active steps to refer the patient to a psychiatrist at that stage and not wait for the psychiatric illness to develop. This is a situation where a specialized "stitch in time" may well "save nine."

OTHER CRISES

Space does not permit me to go into detail about other examples of direct help by the physician to people in crisis, and I hope that some general principles may have emerged from my discussion of help with bereavement. I wish, however, to make brief supplementary mention of two other crises commonly met in medical practice, the crisis faced by parents who have to adapt to the realization that their baby has a congenital abnormality or is mentally defective and the crisis of a patient or his relatives having to adapt to a chronic or an incurable illness, a major disability, or to death itself. These situations all call for special activity on the part of the physician, in addition to the customary "frank" or "not so frank" talk.

The physician must face the fact that the impact of the news of the diagnosis is likely to be followed by a period of psychological reorientation similar to the grief work of the mourning period and interestingly enough also lasting for about four to six weeks. Patients and their relatives should not be expected to handle these psychological burdens on their own. They may need a good deal of support from the physician in facing the painful implications of the situation and help in avoiding facile escape into denial or obliteration of the problem by wish-fulfilling fantasies. The physician should try to help them keep the problem in consciousness during this period and deal with its implications piece by piece. It is remarkable the power that ordinary people have to adapt to reality, however unpleasant. It is not realities but dreams which "make cowards of us all," and insofar as the problem is allowed to sink into dreams and into fantasies it gets removed from the strength which derives naturally from our universal adaptive mechanisms.

On the other hand, the physician should realize that in its initial impact a problem may be quite overpowering and some partial or initial denial is a fundamental defense mechanism. He should not interfere with this, nor with the occasional rest periods during the adaptation process when the patient tries for a while to forget his problems by diverting his interest to other matters. In fact the physician who knows his patient may be able to recognize when he is becoming too fatigued by facing the unfaceable, and he may then prescribe a temporary respite by diversion or drugs. He should be on the alert, however, to call a return to the fray once the rest period has resulted in the replenishment of resources.

I would like to sound here a word of warning against the indiscriminate and continuous use of tranquilizing drugs for people in crisis. Studies are at present under way to determine not only their pharmacophysical ill-effects but also their possible psychological complications; among the latter I predict we will probably find that, by damping down too drastically the impact of crisis situations, tranquilizers may be preventing the active processes of healthy adaptation to important life difficulties and thus laying the stage for subsequent psychiatric illness.

NEED FOR PSYCHIATRIC CONSULTATION

The family physician who seriously wishes to enlarge the scope of his practical operations in order to cater to the mental health needs of his patients and their families would be well advised to build up a collaborative working relationship with a psychiatrist of his choice. If a psychiatrist is not available, such help can also be obtained from a well-trained clinical psychologist or a psychiatric social worker. The important thing is wherever possible to use the same person each time, so that the two can learn each others' language and ways of working.

In talking about consultation I do not have in mind the occasional necessity to refer a patient with some psychiatric illness to a specialist for investigation and treatment. This will certainly be necessary, and the more sophisticated the family physician becomes in dealing with emotional problems in his patients the earlier he will be able to identify such conditions and the more easily and surely he will be able to effect the referral procedure.

MORE EFFECTIVE UNDERSTANDING AND MANAGEMENT

The kind of consultation I am particularly referring to here is different: it is consultation by the general physician with the psychiatric specialist in order to enlist the latter's help in rendering the family physician's own understanding of the case and his own management of it more effective. However well trained the general physician may be, he will inevitably come across situations involving the emotional life of his patients which are outside the area of his previous learning and experience. The psychiatrist may, by discussing the case with him, be able to enlarge his understanding and to deepen his insight by pointing to the relevance of certain items of information about the field of forces which the physician had previously ignored. The psychiatrist's specialized knowledge of patterns of intrapsychic functioning and unconscious motivation may allow him to explain previously puzzling aspects of the patient's personality and that of his relatives which throw new light on their behavior and afford new opportunities for helpful action by the physician. It is very important for the doctor to tailor his intervention in the family to the special individual personality characteristics of its members. Most family physicians will build up a store of relevant knowledge of the weaknesses and strengths of their patients from their years of experience with them, but every now and again there will be some reactions which are quite unexpected and the physician may find his best efforts frustrated. On such occasions the psychiatrist's knowledge of the deeper unconscious aspects of personality functioning may clarify the situation so that the physician may find a new way to help his patient.

IMPROVING USE OF THE SELF

Another type of help which the physician may expect from the mental health consultation is that of sharpening and improving his own use of the self in his professional medical functioning. A physician constantly makes use of different aspects of his personal influence on his patients as part and parcel of his daily work. This use of the effect of one human being who is being helpful on another who is in need becomes especially important in dealing with those needs which are predominantly emotional rather than physical.

Unfortunately, although physicians make use of personal influence all the time in their medical practice, this usually remains an amateur, somewhat haphazard set of operations with most physicians rather than a consciously directed professional therapeutic instrument. Some physicians have a more consistently therepeutic personal effect on patients than others, and we ascribe this to innate personality gifts or to a generalized "bedside manner" of uncertain origin. Even these physicians often fail in their efforts to support or stimulate or reassure certain patients, and when they fail they can no more understand why this has happened and deal with the consequences than they can understand their successful cases. The average physician is no better off when it comes to understanding his own special emotional reactions to certain patients —his feelings of liking and warm protectiveness, his irritability and anger, his frustration, his anxiety, or sometimes his guilty withdrawal. He does his best to control these feelings and not allow them to interfere with his objective medical approach, and his training usually helps him to succeed—but often at the expense of becoming rather distant and cold. It is the rare general physician who is able to capitalize consciously, both for diagnostic and for therapeutic purposes, on his awareness of his own feelings as they are stimulated by the behavior of his patient.

The psychiatrist, on the other hand, has by a long and arduous training not only learned to know and accept his own human reactions in his reciprocal interaction with his patients but he has learned to make explicit and differentiated use of them in the professional setting. Through the consultation process the physician may gain from him some understanding and skill in this matter. This will only come gradually, which is another reason for working with the same consultant over a lengthy period. This is not a matter of the giving or the receiving of intellectual prescriptions but the emotional education which comes from numerous discussions about the details of practical life situations and one's feeling about them.

CONSULTATION, A TWO-WAY PROCESS

So far I have talked as though the psychiatrist were the teacher and the family physician the pupil in the consultations, and to some extent this is so; but the physician who imagines that all he will have to do is to ask questions and get the answers from the psychiatrist will be sadly disappointed. He will quickly discover that with all his specialized knowledge the psychiatrist does not have many answers to the circumscribed questions about the practical issues of management of ordinary patients in the situations of general practice.

I said before that mental health consultation is a joint collaborative endeavor, and what I meant to imply is that it has to be a two-way process, in which not only the psychiatrist but also the physician must be an active partner. It is essential for the physician to realize that he must take active steps to educate the pyschiatrist during these consultations so that he will understand the special nature of the management problems involved, which will be quite different from what he is used to in the very unusual circumstances of his psychiatric clinic or office practice. Working with the same psychiatrist over a period of time the physician may be able to teach him enough about the daily problems of general practice and the life situations of ordinary people who do not consider themselves psychiatric patients that he can eventually get answers which come reasonably close to being useful, but he will usually have to work quite actively to take what the psychiatrist has to offer and to translate it for his own use.

A psychiatrist who has himself had experience in general practice before undergoing psychiatric training sometimes finds this type of consultation easier, but it is surprising how specialized psychiatric training and experience, which dwell constantly on the abnormal and the unusual and on unconscious motivation and irrational fantasy formation, impair the memories of this previous experience with the world of normality. A psychiatrist usually realizes the extent to which this is so and realizes and respects the degree of expertness of the family doctor's specialized knowledge in his own field only after he has been educated by his consultee.

I can vouch personally for the importance of this process because in the course of my own experience in community psychiatry I have been successively educated by social workers, public health nurses, pediatricians, obstetricians, and nutritionists, most of whom were initially a little surprised to find how much they were teaching me during their consultations.

RESPONSIBILITY FOR PLAN AND IMPLEMENTATION

This leads me to my last point. The management plan which emerges from the consultation may have been arrived at as a result of a fruitful joint collaborative endeavor, but the type of plan and the responsibility for its implementation must remain with the family physician and must fit into the general framework of his traditional methods of functioning. Both parties should beware of working out a psychiatrist's plan instead of a family physician's plan and of turning the physician into a "proxy psychiatrist." The style of work of the family physician is fundamentally different from that of the psychiatrist.

For instance, take the time relations of their professional work. It may seem that a busy general practitioner would never have the time to make use of the kind of knowledge I have been discussing in this paper; he could never spend the time which the psychiatrist can apparently allot to his small select group of patients. This is a red herring. It presupposes that, to cover the same problem, members of the two professional disciplines will use the same approach. This is neither necessary nor desirable, since the different professional roles have been differentiated over a long time in order to cope with problems in a very special way which has been found empirically to be effective and which is recognized by being embodied in the traditional culture of that profession. In this case, for instance, the practices of the psychiatrist in relation to time are based on the fact that his patients are strangers to him; since he has to penetrate below their surface defenses and deal with unrecognized and unacceptable material, his relationship with his patient, however intimate the content of their discussions, remains a highly structured stranger relationship, in which each takes care to keep outside the boundaries of each other's customary social life. The regular appointment and the 50-minute hour are derivatives of this situation, the interview between patient and psychiatrist being specially separated from the rest of the patient's life so as to give him the security to lay down temporarily some of his defenses. The length of the usual psychotherapeutic treatment is also dictated by the fact that the psychiatrist has to deal systematically with much complicated material in working down from the surface of consciousness to those hidden areas in which he searches for the unconscious sources of the illness.

The family physician by contrast knows many of his patients as friends. He has known them and their relatives for years, and even in the case of a new patient he can assume that this will be a prolonged contact. He does not need to collect important information about the personality of his patients in a few long highly structured interviews; it comes in dribs and drabs, either directly or indirectly from many and various collateral sources. He penetrates the patient's social life and home as a friend, and very often his patients come into his own home as a friend. Certainly he learns many secret and intimate things about his patients, but the level of such knowledge and the confidence in professional secrecy are such that this rarely leads to a patient feeling the need to hide from the physician in social situations.

Finally, one must realize that, in helping his patient handle emotional problems of the crisis type I have referred to, the family physician does not need to make long speeches. The most powerful interpersonal messages in which one person influences another are often very short. When the time is ripe at the height of the crisis, the right word or the right few words in the right place give better results than a lecture. Often it is a brief aside or an implication of some statement which ostensibly deals with some detail of management of a physical symptom which does the trick. Very often the most powerful messages are conveyed without words—by one's understanding manner, by one's patience, by one's warmth of greeting, or by a sympathetic nod or gesture. These do not take time, and these are the stock in trade of the physician. The results will be determined by their appropriateness in relation to the specific condition of the patient in his current predicament; but if success is only partial the family physician can always rely on being able to wait for additional opportunities in the future, since his relation with his patient will probably be continuing for many years to come. Through his consultations with the psychiatrist, he will gradually become more and more skillful in these areas. I believe that this skill is a main prerequisite for success in preventing emotional illness in our communities.

REFERENCES

1. Bowlby, J. *Maternal care and mental health.* Geneva: World Health Organization, 1951 (Monogr. Series No. 2).
2. Caplan, G. Disturbance of mother-child relationship by unsuccessful attempts at abortion. *Ment. Hyg.,* 1954, 38:670–80.
3. Caplan, G. Psychological aspects of maternity care. *Am. J. Publ. Hlth.,* 1957, 47:25–31. *Concepts of mental health and consultation: Their application in public health social work.* U. S. Department of Health, Education, and Welfare, Social Security Administration, 1959 (Children's Bureau Pub. 373).
4. Lindemann, E. Symptomatology and management of acute grief. *Amer. J. Psychiat.,* 1944, 101:141–48.

48

The Mental Health Agent
in the Urban Community

JAMES G. KELLY

THE interest of state and local governmental units in developing plans for the comprehensive mental health services provides a challenging opportunity to evaluate present aims and future directions of mental health work in urban areas. I would like to discuss some ideas about the characteristics of metropolitan areas that seem most relevant for planning mental health services, give some examples of how the mental health professions may utilize research activities for the planning of such services, and discuss alternative strategies for implementing various types of mental health services. My remarks will be presented as personal views about the ways in which the mental health professions can relate their work to the increasing changes in the urban environment.[1] In discussing this latter topic, I am also proposing a new role for the mental health professions which I view as adjunctive to psychotherapeutic and consultative activities.

These ideas are based upon the assumption that metropolitan areas are composed of identifiable social areas (1, 13, 51, 52, 60, 61, 83, 112, 113, 118, 119). These areas are also assumed to differ with respect to economic status, location and the division of labor, social class, ethnic position, religion, styles of life, etc. On the basis of these two assumptions, the resident population of such areas will have differential access to formal and informal facilities for maintaining health (25, 26, 38, 69, 103). It is affirmed that effective allocation of mental health services is dependent upon the knowledge of existing formal and informal resources as well as the relationships between these resources and the structure of social areas in metropolitan areas.

Reprinted from *Urban America and the Planning of Mental Health Services.* 1964, 474–494, by permission of the publisher and the author. © 1964, Group for the Advancement of Psychiatry. Dr. Kelly is Associate Professor of Clinical Psychology, University of Michigan.

[1] While the author accepts the responsibility for the presentation of the ideas expressed in this paper, he acknowledges the sustained contributions of the staff of the Community Projects Section, Mental Health Study Center, particularly to Howard J. Ehrlich, Sheila Feld, Harold F. Goldsmith and J. R. Newbrough, who are actively contributing to the research program that is basic for the development of these ideas. This paper has also been helped by the comments, criticisms and editorial assistance of Robert Shellow, Raymond Seltser, Bertram Brown, Mrs. Janet Moran and Mrs. Gertrude Peller.

The *formal* health and welfare resources include such agencies and individuals as physicians, police, public welfare personnel, public health nurses, etc. To use Elaine Cumming's phrase, these resources can be viewed for the local areas as the "net agents" (27, 82). The *informal* health and welfare resources are individuals who occupy positions where their primary function is not health and welfare maintenance but who nevertheless facilitate health maintenance. Such informal resources include persons like the apartment house manager, the barber, the corner grocery store owner who, while dispensing goods and services for the community, may potentially give advice or personal services or help solve health problems for their customers. These informal resources are defined as *urban agents* and are distinguished from the specialized *mental health agent.* By the *mental health agent,* I refer to those members of the mental health professions who provide services that are based upon the systematic and continuous knowledge of and contact with the informal and formal health and welfare resources. The model for such a role is the agricultural extension agent (22, 32, 122). The concept *urban agent* has been selected in order to indicate the significance of informal resources as they provide accessibility to the formal health resources for particularly the working and lower classes of metropolitan areas.

My comments can perhaps best be understood if it is clear that they emerge directly from my attempts to develop a research program which will begin to specify the relationship of the social structure of local urban and suburban areas to the expression of health and illness and the utilization of mental health services (88).

POPULATION CHANGES IN THE METROPOLITAN AREA

Before discussing the implications of research services for the functioning of both the urban agent and the mental health agent, I would like to comment on some of the important population changes of the metro area.

Technological advances have increased and will continue to increase the demand for highly trained white-collar and blue-collar persons—particularly professional, technical, and kindred workers. Employers of such skills tend to be located in metropolitan areas. Accordingly, more persons with technological and scientific skills are already visible to us in the metropolitan area (93, 94). Are not home builders and suburban developers already marketing for such groups? Are we not beginning to become aware of changes in the urban landscape? New suburban towns and high-rise apartments in city centers seem to be becoming the new settings in which migrating scientists, engineers, managerial personnel, and skilled technicians will live (18, 99).

Associated with this type of population change are equally important changes in the status of the semiskilled, blue-collar and personal service workers and their families. Whether located in the urban hub, or the rural hinterland, these persons often lack the economic resources to adjust to the rapidly changing urban and metropolitan world. However, a shifting about of these populations does occur, often within the restricted confines of less desirable and less adequately planned urban and metropolitan sites. As a group they tend to have relatively high rates of geographical mobility (15, 105, 106, 123). The pressure of increasing population density and displacement by urban renewal and freeway construction seem to be important factors affecting such mobility. With the continued shifting and sorting of persons in this urban setting, will this population become more physically segregated? Will this population be socially and psychologically isolated from the dominant community?

In this redistribution of population, each of these groups will develop its own new set of problems with which its individual members must cope (86). Relocation and displacement pose new problems for the economic underdog; his deep sense of futility, pessimism, and self-awareness of isolation may be intensified when he must establish a new residence (39, 40, 42, 43, 57, 58, 97, 101, 108, 110). What happens when the members of this group are not able to successfully adapt to a new physical environment? Many times their failure to adapt will be expressed in a quite public fashion. Such displays are often responded to by those informal and formal resources concerned with maintaining personal and group identities and the management of tensions. Thus, expressions of unsuccessful problem-solving in these subgroups can be reflected in behavior that is defined by the dominant community as a "social" problem rather than as a "psychological problem" (12, 41, 64, 116). As an example, it is expected that family disputes that occur in the home of the economic underdog will receive police rather than psychiatric intervention.

The scientist-technician may generally develop different responses to relocation and displacement. It is probable that his attempts to cope with his new job will be visibly smoother. Not only is he likely to be a better problem solver, but he probably has more access to persons who can help him make the transition. Even when he does experience difficulties during periods of transition they are more apt to be expressed in private reflections or worries and thereby identified by the educated elite as well as their urban agents as "psychological problems" (19, 55). The scientific organizations which employ large numbers of scientists have recently been adding to their staff mental health specialists in order to provide easily accessible psychiatric consultation for the organization (50, 80, 84). These services, located on the premises, emphasize the significance of the work environment for the scientist. It is rare that the work setting for the blue-collar worker will contain such services (37).

The fact that persons from different social-economic statuses react to external stress differently has been adequately demonstrated by a vast research literature (4, 16, 20, 21, 30, 63, 65, 66, 67, 68, 74, 77, 78, 79, 85, 90, 91, 92, 102, 107, 109, 117). There are also differences in the forms of medical treatment that are given persons of different social positions. The changing population structure of metropolitan areas will probably exaggerate these differences and raise even more serious questions about the appropriateness of current mental health treatment practices for different population subgroups. It then will be even more important that we understand the positive response of the educated toward mental treatment and the reluctance of the semiskilled to seek treatments from a professional. The differential receptiveness to various forms of treatment cannot be attributed solely to differences in values or attitudes (28, 62, 100, 124, 125). The analysis of the problem seems to require a more intensive study of the experiences of both population groups in their specific residential areas, in order to understand the types of problem experiences and the way in which they try to cope with them. I conclude from these observations on population changes in metropolitan communities that the mental health professions need knowledge about the specific functions of the informal and formal social structures that promote and deter social adjustment within each social area. With such knowledge, treatment procedures can be assigned to reduce maladaptive, or inappropriate behavior within these local areas.

URBAN AGENTS AND THEIR MENTAL HEALTH FUNCTIONS

I would like to turn now to a closer look at the urban agent and his mental health function. Eric Lindemann and his staff have used the term "caretaker" or "caregiver" to define primarily professional persons who assume an active role in providing helping functions to local citizens (71, 72, 73). I have been using the term *urban agent* to refer to those caretakers in the metropolitan area who are *non*professional helping persons. They are seen as the indigenous individuals or groups whose diversity is potentially unlimited. They are assumed to be important mediators between the larger population and the formal health and welfare resources. The taxicab driver, the bartender, the poolroom proprietor, the barber, the street-corner manager, the corner grocery store operator, are examples of some of the potential key links for promoting the continuation of business and leisure activities of the metro area. Such urban agents are also considered to be important persons who impede or facilitate access to public health and welfare services for residents living with close proximity to them.

The interaction between the local residents, the various types of urban agents, and the formal community health and welfare resources, as well as their perceptions of each other, are the factors which seem important in determining the kind of behavior which is defined to be acceptable or unacceptable for local social control (33). Studies of these interactions have a high priority for specifying the precise characteristics of the urban agent as a mediating link between local residents and more formal health resources. My personal point of view is that health and welfare services are utilized differently by urban populations depending upon their social status and their accessibility to various urban agents.

The examples of urban agents just cited were selected with special reference to the economic underskilled, because it is this population group that seems to provide the greater challenge for the mental health professions. The urban agents for the educated class are assumed to exist in smaller numbers but are expected not to have the same crucial mediating function as with the blue-collar population. The urban agents for the educated elite also are believed to be characterized by fewer persons with multiple roles who are scattered over diverse portions of the metro area.

Such agents carry out mental health functions via their daily activities when they give emotional support and provide methods for the local population to achieve both short- and long-range goals. To the degree that urban agents are successful, individuals are prevented from becoming designated a "problem" needing formal help. When these urban agents are not able to give such adequate support, they can still act as referral agents to the more formal helping resources. Here, too, they perform a key role in the allocation of mental health services in urban communities by establishing ties between the urban population and the formal community resources.

RESEARCH SERVICES FOR THE METROPOLITAN AREA

If this analysis of the urban agent's role as a health maintenance officer and gatekeeper is accurate, then I believe that the mental health professions need access to continuous and systematic research activities of the relationships between the structure of the urban environment and the functions of the urban agents in order to best carry out their work (17, 47, 59, 70). Without such research support, it is likely that the distribution and allocation of mental health services will take on a more uncoordinated and duplicated function (8, 36, 87). Such research activities would deal with the relationship of the structure of metro communities, the function of urban agents, and the expression of psychological and social problems. The primary charatceristic of such a research program is that it requires an integrated set of studies that are oriented to examine various sectors of the organization and functioning of community life (88). Secondly, such a program requires an interdisciplinary staff. The strength of the interdisciplinary approach is that it minimizes the accumulation of disconnected empirical data. While the analyses of relationships between generalizations, hypotheses, and observations within the perspective of a single discipline may lead to relatively complete knowledge for each profession, it may not lead to complete knowledge of the relationships between social structure and the utilization of health and welfare services. Some of the examples of research activities I will mention, have benefited from the contributions of the psychiatrist, urban sociologist, social psychologist, social anthropologist, and epidemiologist.

In order to assess the functions of local urban agents, it is necessary to carry out studies of the informal leadership in metropolitan areas. It is believed that local influentials play an important role in linking the informal and the formal networks of health facilities (9, 10, 56). In the social areas which are largely of working class or lower class, these leaders may be located by participant observations of informal gatherings during recreational activities. Local sites for recreation may be the places where help-support is provided and where standards for problem-solving are developed. In the social areas which are populated by the well-educated, an investigation of recruitment and participation in voluntary associations may be more appropriate. Such a study is in process at the Mental Health Study Center (31). To date it has been interesting to note that certain civic organizations, whose primary goals are not health and welfare matters, contribute considerable time and money to supplement the health services provided by public and private resources.

Studying the informal resources is not enough. If the informal resources have a linking function, we must know how they operate. For example, we need to be able to identify interagency relationships in order to learn the conditions under which interagency collaboration or conflict produces specialized or duplicated services. Health and welfare services for the working class are characteristically fragmented. Due to heavy case loads they can only carry out surveillance functions rather than extensive or comprehensive services. Services in the metropolitan regions which cater to a more educated clientele tend to become specialized, providing a more intricate health maintenance function. In both instances, coordination of services is often inefficient.

The exact enumeration of the extent of duplication in services can be specified by a second type of research program, namely, the operation of case registers. There are several psychiatric case registers now in existence in the United States which are designed to specify the characteristics of local residents who receive mental health services (5, 6, 7, 44, 45, 46, 49, 54, 76, 98, 104, 121). These case registers provide information on characteristics of persons receiving treatment from public and private hospitals and clinics. The development of these registers has led to elaborate precautions to protect confidentiality of personal data. These precautions include elaborate coding procedures to ensure confidentiality during the initial tabulation of data and the development of electronic programming techniques which make identification of personal data almost impossible. These registers not only provide routine information on persons receiving treatment from different resources but also can indicate those segments of the population which are receiving multiple treatments from same or different services. The reports of the Maryland Psychiatric Case Register indicate that the psychiatric wing of the general hospital is the primary entry point for mental health services by residents of one Maryland county. There is an active flow of patients from this facility to the local outpatient clinic and state hospital. At the present time we are attempting to understand this array of multiple treatments from the three institutions. The finding of an extensive number of residents who receive multiple treatments from all three agencies may be a reflection of the psychiatric ward's policy to serve as a first aid receiving station. On the other hand, it can indicate that there are specific types of problems which receive similar treatment from different facilities. Preliminary inquiry, however, has suggested that each of the three agencies is providing similar treatment services to the same persons within short periods of time (11).

It is becoming obvious that if a register is to become an affective monitoring and planning tool, it must also be related to an inventory of the health and welfare services provided within the metropolitan area (89, 96). The operation of a psychiatric case register in conjunction with a metropolitan register of recipients of health and welfare services would make it possible to specify more accurately the functions of mental health services in a particular community as well as to specify prior health and welfare histories of persons with subsequent hospitalization. A combined psychiatric and health register can give an additional analysis of the social structure, particularly when continuous analyses of population movement and migration for both the general and psychiatric population are being conducted as we are developing at the Study Center (48).

Intensive studies of selected population groups provide still another variant of research work that is strategic in fulfilling the gap between the analysis of social organization and the analysis of utilization of services. These are studies of groups of persons who may have a high probability of receiving mental health services or of being designated as a social problem, such as the test-anxious child, low-achieving child, or the retarded reader (34, 35, 95). The low-achieving child or the retarded reader may be a likely recipient of mental health services if his parents are from the highly educated strata. The teenage drinker or the runaway child may be a candidate for police contact if the parents are from the working class (111). In each example, there is an array of urban agents who may influence the need for referral for such action. Studies which concentrate on an intensive analysis of such behavior, when related to an analysis of the urban agent, can provide more information on the relationship between community factors and their effect on the status of maladaptive behavior.

THE MENTAL HEALTH AGENT
IN THE METROPOLITAN COMMUNITY

The mental health agent is proposed as a specific role for the mental health professional when he provides mental health services to population segments or social areas based on the knowledge of the functions of urban agents and the structure of these social areas. I have mentioned the type of research which is considered important for the analysis of the role of the urban agent in mediating between discrete populations and the formal health and welfare resources. The mental health agent can then utilize such data in planning alternative services which can be rendered to selective portions of the metropolitan region. This new role is proposed as an extension of the current activities of the mental health professions. In creating this new role of mental health agent, it is important to emphasize that it will require the continued contribution of psychotherapeutic techniques. It is particularly important that the analysis of the urban agent be integrated with the activities of the mental health agent to make the provision of services more efficient. It is stressed that data gained from examining the components of differential responses to clinical treatment also extend our knowledge of the social structure.

The emergence of a state plan which incorporates this point of view about the mental health agent will depend upon the specification of a series of skills which at present have not been completely formulated. Mental health services for the scientist-professional as opposed to those for the working class are quite distinct allocation problems. In both instances, however, it is important to search for those areas of living which require of each group the most intense emotional investment and which function as major and continuous definers of one's personal and social identity. The immediate work environment of the scientist is considered to be the most important setting where pathology could be easily observed and more fully interpreted. If we can trace the implication of this statement, we are led to instituting consultation services to the organization which employs the scientist (14, 23, 24, 114, 120). Although this may be an unfamiliar role for the mental health professional, it is a conceivable one. On the other hand, if we evoke a parallel logic in planning services for the blue-collar worker, we are confronted with the task of providing consultation for vast numbers of informal urban agents. Making decisions regarding which specific treatment to create or select emphasizes that the mental health agent can benefit from knowledge about such persons as managers of the local bowling parlor, the local tavern, dance halls, and lodges. Implementation of consulting strategies to the scientist's organization or the urban agent requires additional training and knowledge about organization theory, values of the scientist and his work, as well as techniques for relating to large industrial and research organizations (2, 3, 81, 115). Such information would enhance the mental health agent's provision of both treatment services to the scientist and to his organizations. Similarly, an intimate knowledge of the styles of living of the economically deprived, along with data regarding the interests and values of business men who cater to the leisure of the working class, become indispensable for understanding the psychosocial dilemma of any individual in this group.

The mental health agent cannot develop all of the specialized skills which are required to manage pathological reactions in an urban locale. He should not be expected to become a specialist in urban or community affairs. Still the mental health professions need to become familiar with the scope of the urban agent's activities. When the mental health agent begins this acquaintanceship, he will need to be alert to the ways in which the urban agent provides emotional support and improves problem-solving techniques to persons within his immediate environment. If the mental health professional is successful in entering the discrete social system of the metropolitan area, he has an opportunity to help the urban agent do a more effective job, whether it be police work or managing a large apartment house.

If the mental health agent is successful with his consultation or education work, the urban agent may aspire to the values, preferences and techniques of the professional ideology of the mental health agent. Some urban agents may even try to become a "junior psychiatrist," with a consequential decrease in their effectiveness as policemen or apartment house managers (29). It is important that such changes in values be made clear. When such clarity is given, the mental health agent has provided the type of emotional support that is predicted to be highly significant for the endurance of the urban agent.

The activities of the mental health agent are considered as a primary example of additional services which can be provided within the metropolitan area. The specific manner in which each mental health profession takes part in the development of such activities requires increasing examination by all of the mental health professions. It is likely that the psychiatrist, social workers, public health nurse and psychologist may have complementary skills and interests. I have attempted to provide a point of view and set of goals for all the professions. I now would like to see the mental health professions take part in more intensive discussions regarding the appropriate skills that can be developed and extended in building such a role, so that the manpower resources and services can be distributed efficiently.

CONCLUSION

It is only recently that mental health services have been added to the agenda of the metropolitan planning body along with topics of land use, transportation, and sanitation. Development of such traditional community services is difficult enough. Bringing the insights from clinical experience and social research to the city planning office makes a hard job even more complex. The point of view expressed here and the research services which it has generated are presented as one example of how community research can facilitate the continuous and long-range planning of mental health services.

REFERENCES

1. Anderson, T. R., and Egeland, J. A. Spatial aspects of social area analysis. *Amer. Soc. Rvw.*, 1961, 26:392–98.
2. Argyris, C. *Understanding organizational behavior.* Homewood, Ill.: Dorsey Press, 1961.
3. Argyris, C. The integration of the individual and the organization. Paper

read at Univ. of Wisconsin School of Commerce, Madison, Wis., May, 1961.

4. Avnet, H. H. *Psychiatric insurance.* New York: Group Health Insurance, Inc., 1962.

5. Bahn, A. K. The development of an effective statistical system in mental illness. *Amer. J. Psychiat.,* 1960, 116:798–800.

6. Bahn, A. K., Chandler, C. A., and Eisenberg, L. Diagnostic and demographic characteristics of patients seen in outpatient psychiatric clinics for an entire state (Maryland): Implications for the psychiatrist and the mental health program planner. *Amer. J. Psychiat.,* 1961, 117:769–78.

7. Bahn, A. K., Chandler, C. A., and Lemkau, P. V. Diagnostic characteristics of adult outpatients of psychiatric clinics as related to type and outcome of services. *Milbank Mem. Fd. Quart.,* 1962, 15:407–42.

8. Baldwin, J. A. A critique of the use of patient-movement studies in the planning of mental health services. *Scot. Med. J.,* 1963, 8:227–33.

9. Barker, R. G. Ecology and motivation. In M. R. Jones (Ed.), *Nebraska symposium on motivation.* Lincoln: University of Nebraska Press, 1960. Pp. 1–49.

10. Barker, R. G., and Wright, H. F. *Midwest and its children.* Evanston, Ill.: Row, Peterson, 1954.

11. Barnett, L. A., and Kelly, J. G. A study of socioeconomic and family characteristics of Prince George's County residents admitted to psychiatric services, July 1, 1960, to June 30, 1961. Unpublished manuscript. Community Projects Section, Mental Health Study Center, National Institute of Mental Health, January, 1964.

12. Beilin, H. Effect of social (occupational) role and age upon the criteria of mental health. *J. Soc. Psychol.,* 1958, 48:247–56.

13. Bell, W. The social areas of the San Francisco Bay region. *Amer. Soc. Rvw.,* 1953, 18:39–47.

14. Bindman, A. J. Mental health consultation: Theory and practice. *J. Cons. Psychol.,* 1959, 23:473–82.

15. Blau, P. M. Social mobility and interpersonal relations. *Amer. Soc. Rvw.,* 1956, 21:290–95.

16. Bloom, R., Whiteman, M., and Deutsch, M. Race and social class as separate and independent environmental determiners. Paper read at American Psychological Association, Philadelphia, September, 1963.

17. Bobbitt, J. M., Libo, L. M., Hurder, W. P., and Simmons, A. J. Community mental health research. Symposium. *Publ. Hlth. Rep.,* 1963, 78:57–64.

18. Bogue, D. J. *The population of the United States.* New York: Free Press, 1959.

19. Bradburn, N. (Ed.) In pursuit of happiness. Chicago, Ill.: National Opinion Research Center, 1963 (Report No. 92).

20. Brill, N. Q., and Storrow, H. A. Prognostic factors in psychotherapy. *J. Amer. Med. Assn.,* 1963, 183:913–16.

21. Brill, N. Q., and Storrow, H. A. Social class and psychiatric treatment. *Arch. Gen. Psychiat.,* 1960, 3:340–44.

22. Brown, E. J., and Deekens, A. Role of the extension subject-matter specialists. *Rural Soc.,* 1958, 23:263–76.

23. Caplan, G. Mental health consultation in schools. In Milbank Memorial

Fund (Ed.), *The elements of a community mental health program.* New York: Milbank Memorial Fund, 1956. Pp. 75–85.

24. Caplan, G. *An approach to community mental health.* New York: Grune & Stratton, 1961.

25. Chapman, L. F., Hinkle, L. E., Jr., and Wolff, H. G. Human ecology, disease, and schizophrenia. *Amer. J. Psychiat.,* 1960, 117:193–204.

26. Clausen, J. A., and Kohn, M. L. The ecological approach in social psychiatry. *Amer. J. Soc.,* 1954, 60:140–51.

27. Cumming, E. Phase movement in the support and control of the psychiatric patient. *J. Hlth. Hum. Behav.,* 1962, 3:235–41.

28. Dohrenwend, B. P. Some aspects of the appraisal of abnormal behavior by leaders in an urban area. *Amer. Psychol.,* 1962, 17:190–98.

29. Duhl, L. J. The changing face of mental health. In L. J. Duhl (Ed.), *The urban condition.* New York: Basic Books, 1963. Pp. 59–75.

30. Dunham, H. W. Social structures and mental disorders: competing hypotheses of explanation. In Milbank Memorial Fund (Ed.), *Causes of mental disorders: A review of epidemiological knowledge.* New York: Milbank Memorial Fund, 1960. Pp. 227–265.

31. Ehrlich, H. J. Voluntary associations and community leadership. Unpublished manuscript. Community Projects Section, Mental Health Study Center, National Institute of Mental Health. December, 1963.

32. *Evaluation in extension.* Washington, D. C.: Division of Extension Research and Training, Federal Extension Service, U.S.D.A., 1956.

33. Fantl, B. Casework in lower class districts. *Ment. Hyg.,* 1961, 45:425–38.

34. Feld, S. Need achievement and test anxiety in children, and maternal attitudes and behavior toward independent accomplishment: A longitudinal study. Paper read at American Psychological Association, Cincinnati, September, 1959.

35. Feld, S. Response set, test structure, and demographic correlates of test anxiety and defensiveness in an elementary school population. Unpublished manuscript. Community Projects Section, Mental Health Study Center, National Institute of Mental Health, December, 1963.

36. Flagle, C. D. Operations research in the health services. *Operations Res.,* 1962, 10:591–603.

37. French, J. R. P., Jr. The social environment and mental health. Presidential Address, Div. 9, American Psychological Association, Philadelphia, September, 1963.

38. French, J. R. P., Jr., Kahn, R. L., and Mann, F. C. (Eds.). Work, health and satisfaction. *J. Soc. Issues,* 1962, 18(3):1–129.

39. Fried, M. Grieving for a lost home. In L. J. Duhl (Ed.), *The urban condition.* New York: Basic Books, 1963. Pp. 151–71.

40. Fried, M., and Gleicher, P. Some sources of residential satisfaction in an urban slum. *J. Amer. Inst. of Planners,* 1961, 27:305–15.

41. Fried, M., and Lindemann, E. Sociocultural factors in mental health and illness. *Amer. J. Orthopsychiat.,* 1961, 31:87–101.

42. Gans, H. J. The human implications of current redevelopment and relocation planning. *J. Amer. Inst. of Planners,* 1959, 25:15–25.

43. Gans, H. J. *The urban villagers.* New York: Free Press, 1963.
44. Gardner, E. A., Bahn, A. K., and Mack, M. Suicide and psychiatric care in the aging. *Arch. Gen. Psychiat.,* 1964, 10:547–53.
45. Gardner, E. A. Miles, H. C., and Bahn, A. K. All psychiatric experience in a community—a cumulative survey: Report of the first year's experience. *Arch. Gen. Psychiat.,* 1963, 9:369–78.
46. Gardner, E. A., Miles, H. C., Iker, H. P., and Romano, J. A cumulative register of psychiatric services in a community. *Amer. J. Publ. Hlth.,* 1963, 53:1269–77
47. Gelfand, S., and Kelly, J. G. The psychologist in community mental health: scientist and professional. *Amer. Psychol.,* 1960, 15:223–26.
48. Goldsmith, H. F. Impact of residence upon social and personality organization. Unpublished manuscript. Community Projects Section, Mental Health Study Center, National Institute of Mental Health, October, 1963.
49. Gorwitz, K., Bahn, A. K., Chandler, C. A., and Martin, W. A. Planned uses of a statewide psychiatric register for aiding mental health in the community. *Amer. J. Orthopsychiat.,* 1963, 33:494–500.
50. Grace, E. J. Keep your employees out of the hospital. *Harvard Bus. Rvw.,* 1959, 37 (5):119–26.
51. Greer, S. Urbanism reconsidered: A comparative study of local areas in a metropolis. *Amer. Soc. Rvw.,* 1956, 21:19–25.
52. Greer, S. *Emerging city.* New York: Free Press, 1962.
53. Greer, S., and Kube, Ella. *Urban worlds: A comparative study of four Los Angeles areas.* Los Angeles: Laboratory of Urban Culture, Occidental College, 1955.
54. Group for the Advancement of Psychiatry, Committee on Preventive Psychiatry. *Problems of estimating changes in frequency of mental disorders.* New York, 1961 (Report No. 50).
55. Gurin, G., Veroff, J., and Feld, S., *Americans view their mental health.* New York: Basic Books, 1960.
56. Harding, J., Devereux, E. C., Jr., and Bronfenbrenner, U. (Eds.). Leadership and participation in a changing rural community. *J. Soc. Issues,* 1960, 16 (4):1–86.
57. Harrington, M. *The other America.* New York: Macmillan, 1963.
58. Hartman, C. W. Social values and housing orientations. *J. Soc. Issues,* 1963, 19 (2):113–31.
59. Harvard Medical School and Psychiatric Service, Massachusetts General Hospital. *Community mental health and social psychiatry: A reference guide.* Cambridge, Mass.: Harvard University Press, 1962.
60. Hatt, P. The concept of natural area. *Amer. Soc. Rvw.,* 1946, 11:423–27.
61. Hawley, A. H., and Duncan, O. D. Social area analysis: A critical appraisal. *Land Economics,* 1957, 33:337–45.
62. Hollingshead, A. B., and Freedman, L. Z. Social class and the treatment of neurotics. In National Conference of Social Work (Ed.), *The Social Welfare Forum,* 1955. New York: Columbia University Press, 1955. Pp. 194–205.
63. Hollingshead, A. B., and Redlich, F. C. *Social class and mental illness.* New York: Wiley & Sons, 1958.

64. Hrubec, Z. The association of health and social welfare problems in individuals and their families. *Milbank Mem. Fd. Quart.*, 1959, 37:251–76.
65. Hunt, R. G. Socio-cultural factors in mental disorder. *Behav. Sci.*, 1959, 4:96–106.
66. Hunt, R. G. Social class and mental illness: Some implications for clinical theory and practice. *Amer. J. Psychiat.*, 1960, 116:1065–69.
67. Imber, S. D., Nash, E. H., Jr., and Stone, A. R. Social class and duration of psychotherapy. *J. Clin. Psychol.*, 1955, 11:281–84.
68. Jackson, E. F. Status consistency and symptoms of stress. *Amer. Soc. Rvw.*, 1962, 27:469–80.
69. Kelly, J. G. A preface for an eco-system analysis of community mental health services. Paper read at American Psychological Association, Philadelphia, August, 1963.
70. Kelly, J. G., and Newbrough, J. R. Community mental health research: Some dimensions and policies. Paper read at American Psychological Association, New York City, August, 1961.
71. Klein, D. C. The minister and mental health: An evaluation. *J. Pastoral Care,* 1959, 13:230–36.
72. Klein, D. C. The prevention of mental illness. *Ment. Hyg.*, 1961, 45:101–9.
73. Klein, D. C., and Lindemann, E. Preventive intervention in individual and family crisis situations. In G. Caplan (Ed.), *Prevention of mental disorders in children: Initial explorations.* New York: Basic Books, 1961. Pp. 283–306.
74. Kleiner, R. J., and Parker, S. Goal-striving, social status, and mental disorder: A research review. *Amer. Soc. Rvw.*, 1963, 28:189–203.
75. Kohn, M. L. Social class and parental values. *Amer. J. Soc.*, 1959, 64:337–51.
76. Kramer, M., Pollack, E. S., Locke, B. Z., and Bahn, A. K. National approach to the evaluation of community mental health programs. *Amer. J. Publ. Hlth.*, 1961, 51:969–79.
77. Langner, T. S. Environmental stress, degree of psychiatric impairment and type of mental disturbance. *Psychoanal. Rvw.*, 1960, 47:3–16.
78. Langner, T. S., and Michael, S. T. *Life stress and mental health.* New York: Free Press, 1963.
79. Leighton, D. C., Harding, J. S., Mackin, D. B., Macmillan, A. M., and Leighton, A. H. *The character of danger.* New York: Basic Books, 1963.
80. Levinson, H. The psychologist in industry. *Harvard Bus. Rvw.*, 1959, 37 (5):93–99.
81. March, J. G., and Simon H. A. *Organizations.* New York: John Wiley, 1958.
82. McCaffrey, I., Cumming, E., and Rudolph, C. Mental disorders in socially defined populations. *Amer. J. Public Health*, 1963, 53:1025–30.
83. McKenzie, R. D. The ecological approach to the study of the human community. In R. E. Park, E. W. Burgess, and R. D. McKenzie (Eds.), *The city.* Chicago: University of Chicago Press, 1925.
84. McMurry, R. N. Mental illness in industry. *Harvard Bus. Rvw.*, 1959, 37 (2):79–86.
85. McPartland, T. S., and Cumming, J. Self-conception, social class, and mental health. *Hum. Organization*, 1958, 17 (3):24–29.

86. Meier, R. L. Measuring social and cultural change in urban regions. *J. Amer. Inst. Planners,* 1959, 25:180–90.

87. Meier, R. L. *A communications theory of urban growth.* Boston, Massachusetts Institute of Technology Press, 1962.

88. Mental Health Study Center. Annual report, 1962. Unpublished manuscript. Mental Health Study Center, National Institute of Mental Health, Adelphi, Maryland. 1962.

89. Metropolitan Data Center. First interim report. Unpublished manuscript. Metropolitan Data Center Project, Tulsa, Okla., October, 1963.

90. Miller, S. M., and Mishler, E. G. Social class, mental illness and American psychiatry. *Milbank Mem. Fd. Quart.,* 1959, 37:174–99.

91. Mishler, E. G., and Waxler, N. E. Decision processes in psychiatric hospitalization: Patients referred, accepted, and admitted to a psychiatric hospital. *Amer. Soc. Rvw.,* 1963, 28:576–87.

92. Munson, B. E. Personality differentials among urban, suburban, town and rural children. *Rural Soc.,* 1959, 24:257–64.

93. National Science Foundation. Metropolitan area distribution of scientists in the national register of scientific and technical personnel, 1960. November, 1962 (Scientific Manpower Bulletin, No. 18).

94. National Science Foundation. *Profiles of manpower in science and technology.* Washington, D. C.: National Science Foundation, 1963.

95. Newbrough, J. R., and Kelly, J. G. A study of reading levels in a population of school children. In J. Money (Ed.), *Reading disability: Progress and research needs in dyslexia.* Baltimore: Johns Hopkins Press, 1962. Pp. 61–72.

96. Perloff, H. S. Social planning in the metropolis. In L. J. Duhl (Ed.), *The urban condition.* New York: Basic Books, 1963. Pp. 331–47.

97. Pittman, D. J. Social pathology, urban renewal, and the homeless man. Paper read at American Psychological Association, St. Louis, August, 1962.

98. Pollack, E. S., Redick, R. W., Norman, V. B., Wurster, C. R., and Gorwitz, K. A study of socioeconomic and family characteristics of patients admitted to psychiatric services: background and preliminary analysis. Paper read at American Public Health Association, Miami Beach, October, 1962.

99. Redick, R. W. Population growth and distribution in central cities, 1940–1950. *Amer. Soc. Rvw.,* 1956, 21:38–43.

100. Redlich, F. C., Hollingshead, A. B., and Bellis, E. Social class differences in attitudes toward psychiatry. *Amer. J. Orthopsychiat.,* 1955, 25:60–70.

101. Riesman, D. Styles of response to social change. *J. Soc. Issues,* 1961, 17 (1):78–92.

102. Robins, L. N., Gyman, H., and O'Neal, P. The interaction of social class and deviant behavior. *Amer. Soc. Rvw.,* 1963, 27:480–92.

103. Rogers, E. S. *Human ecology and health: An introduction for administrators.* New York: Macmillan, 1960.

104. Rosen, B. M., Bahn, A. K., and Kramer, M. Demographic and psychiatric characteristics of psychiatric clinic outpatients in the United States, 1961. Paper read at American Orthopsychiatric Association, Washington, D. C., March, 1963.

105. Rossi, P. H. *Why families move.* New York: Free Press, 1955.
106. Rossi, P. H., and Dentler, R. A. *The politics of urban renewal: The Chicago findings.* New York: Free Press, 1961.
107. Ruesch, J. Social factors in therapy. In Association for Research in Nervous and Mental Disease (Ed.), *Psychiatric treatment.* Baltimore: Williams & Wilkins, 1953 (Research Publication No. 31). Pp. 59–93.
108. Ryan, E. J. Personal identity in an urban slum. In L. J. Duhl (Ed.), *The urban condition.* New York: Basic Books, 1963. Pp. 135–50.
109. Schaffer, L., and Myers, J. Psychotherapy and social stratification. *Psychiatry,* 1954, 17:83–93.
110. Scott, J. C. Portrait of the underdog: Adjustment to chronic poverty. Unpublished manuscript. Department of Sociology, University of Michigan, February, 1961.
111. Shellow, R. The missing child: An illustration of the use of social science research in the formation of public policy. Unpublished manuscript. Adolescent Process Section, Mental Health Study Center, National Institute of Mental Health, December, 1963.
112. Shevky, E., and Bell, W. *Social area analysis.* Stanford, Calif.: Stanford University Press, 1955.
113. Shevky, E., and Williams, Marilyn. *The social areas of Los Angeles.* Berkeley and Los Angeles: University of California Press, 1948.
114. Simmons, A. J. Consultation through a community mental health agency. Unpublished manuscript. Human Relations Service, Inc., Wellesley, Mass., 1960.
115. Simon, H. A. *Administrative behavior: A study of decision-making processes in administrative organization.* New York: Macmillan, 1957.
116. Smith, M. B. "Mental health" reconsidered: A special case of the problems of values in psychology. *Amer. Psychol.,* 1961, 16:299–306.
117. Srole, L., Langner, T. S., Michael, S. T., Opler, M. K., and Rennie, T. A. C. *Mental health in the metropolis.* New York: McGraw-Hill, 1962.
118. Tryon, R. C. Identification of social areas from cluster analysis. *Univ. Calif. Publ. Psychol.,* 1958, 8:1–100.
119. Tryon, R. C. The social dimensions of metropolitan man. Paper read at American Psychological Association, Cincinnati, September, 1959.
120. U. S. Children's Bureau. *Concepts of mental health and consultation: Their application in public health social work.* By Gerald Caplan. Washington, D. C.: U. S. Children's Bureau, 1959 (Publication No. 373).
121. University of Rochester School of Medicine and Dentistry, Department of Psychiatry. Cumulative register study. Psychiatric service during 1960 and 1961, Monroe County, New York. Unpublished manuscript. University of Rochester School of Medicine and Dentistry, Department of Psychiatry, Rochester, New York, May, 1963.
122. Wilkening, E. A. The county agent in Wisconsin. Madison: University of Wisconsin, Agr. Exp. Sta., September, 1957 (Research Bull. 203).
123. Wilson, J. Q. Planning and politics: Citizen participation in urban renewal. *J. Amer. Inst. Planners,* 1963, 29:242–49.
124. Zigler, E., and Phillips, L. Social competence and outcome in psychiatric disorder. *J. Abn. Soc. Psychol.,* 1961, 63:264–71.
125. Zigler, E., and Phillips, L. Social competence and the process-reactive distinction in psychopathology. *J. Abn. Soc. Psychol.,* 1962, 65:215–22.

49
Mental Health Manpower
and Institutional Change

ROBERT REIFF

MENTAL health manpower problems may be approached from many different points of view. The most fruitful approach is to begin with the greatest social need and to examine what the manpower resources are and their potential for meeting it.

In recent years there has been a growing and vital concern of the professional in human services and the more enlightened public-service-minded government agencies for reaching the lower socioeconomic groups, and particularly the poor. The increasing recognition that there is a vast multitude of people with unmet needs has resulted in two national programs—the community mental health program and the antipoverty program. Both of these programs have as their aim attention to the problems of those in society whose needs are greatest. Both are concerned with developing programs in the community.

It is to the credit of professional and political leaders that both these programs have come into existence as a result of their sense of social responsibility, their vision, and their initiative, but without the stimulus of a vocal and organized demand from the suffering people themselves. The absence of such a demand from below poses a question of crucial importance. What strategies can be developed to *convert the very great existing need into effective demand for services?*

A great deal of productive thinking is going into this problem. Many new strategies relating to program, technology, and other aspects are being devised and demonstrated. The extent to which these will succeed depends ultimately on three factors: whether the services offered are appropriate, whether they are utilized, and whether there is sufficient manpower (13). These factors are closely interrelated, but before the manpower question can be tackled it is necessary to understand what accounts for the lack of utilization of present services by the poor, and if change is necessary, what must be changed to make them appropriate.

Reprinted from *American Psychologist,* 1966, *21,* 540–548, by permission of the publisher and the author. © 1966, American Psychological Association. Dr. Reiff is Associate Professor and Director, Division of Psychology, Albert Einstein College of Medicine, New York City.

The development of mental health services has been one of increasing acceptance on the part of the middle and upper classes in this country. There has also been an ever-increasing expansion of its influence on child rearing practices, education, marriage, etc. In fact, there is hardly an area of social living over which the umbrella of the mental health professional has not been extended. On the other hand, there has been a long history of persistent alienation from mental health professionals of the lower socioeconomic groups in this country (1). This alienation represents a critical failure. It is not merely the failure of each individual mental health professional, although there is the element of the individual's social responsibility involved here. Neither is it primarily a matter of tools and skills, although, again, this element is also involved. Basically, the problem is an ideological one. The roots of this alienation from the low-income populations lie primarily in the middle-class ideology of contemporary mental health services and secondarily in its technology. Ideology is probably most often used to refer to attitudes and values of people. This is not the sense in which it is used here.

By ideology is meant the body of knowledge, the set of integrated assertions, theories, and aims, primarily psychoanalytical, which constitutes the individualistically oriented program for restoring to society the mentally sick and socially deviant.

There is a basic dichotomy between the popular point of view about mental illness and mental health, and the mental health professionals' point of view. Studies by Star (19), Reiff (12), and others have shown that the popular point of view starts with normal behavior as its reference point. It seeks to explain normal behavior as the distinctive and essentially human qualities of rationality, and the ability to exercise self-control. Given this premise, normal behavior is viewed as a rational response to the immediate circumstances in which the individual finds himself, which is at the same time fully within the conscious control of the person. Mental illness is defined as the extreme opposite of normality. It is behavior in which rationality is so impaired that the individual has lost control and can no longer be responsible for his acts. It is, therefore, quite logically, only the extreme form of psychosis which is considered mental illness by most workers. It follows from this that mental illness is a very threatening thing. It represents a loss of the distinctly human qualities, the ultimate catastrophe that can befall a human. Thus, in their view, mental health and mental illness are not related to each other as on a continuum but they are discontinuous phenomena.

The professional point of view starts with abnormal behavior as its reference point and extrapolates to the normal. It views mental health and mental illness as on a continuum, and it holds that personality characteristics and behavior are *universal,* differing only in degree. It contends that there is really no such thing as a completely normal person, and that the same phenomena seen in mental illness are present in all people. In fact, mental health professionals can hardly use the word "normal" without prefacing it with the words "so-called" normal. Further, the professionals' point of view holds that characteristic emotional patterns are not entirely within the rational control of an individual. The modifications of behavior patterns do not depend entirely on rationality, self-help, willpower, reasoning, or even purely environmental manipulations. It assumes that a large part of our motivations are unconscious or unknown to us and that until they become conscious they are unmodifiable. Finally, the professionals' point of view makes the implicit conclusion that mental illness is not necessarily an overwhelming threat nor must it inevitably arouse fear or alarm. But, while it may be reassuring to a middle-class patient to hear that the emotional mechanisms of sick people are not so different from anyone else's, it is anything but acceptable to a healthy worker that his emotional mechanisms are not so different from the mentally ill, especially if he holds the point of view that mental illness is about as far from normal as you can get. It is not being suggested that the validity of a scientific concept depends upon its popular acceptance, but merely that a practical concept of normality is necessary to find a basis of understanding with low-income groups essential to successful treatment as well as primary and secondary prevention (7). The key to developing such a practical concept of normality is the recognition that, though personality characteristics and behavior may be universal, their meaning and significance for illness and health must be assessed within their social-cultural context. The failure to control violent acts of aggression has different implications for normality and illness in a civil rights demonstration, a quarrel in a working-class bar, a middle-class family quarrel, or a meeting of clinical psychologists.

Furthermore, while the worker acknowledges there is such a thing as mental illness which he equates with severely psychotic behavior, from his point of view he has difficulty accepting the concept of a neurotic emotional disturbance as an illness. The term itself is confusing to him. If he sees a raving psychotic screaming or a psychotic depressive crying and wailing, he can see how that can be called emotionally upset. In that sense it is simply a synonym for excessive emotional behavior out of control. However, if he is told that a man with a lame back or a particularly passive person who lets everybody walk all over him is emotionally disturbed, this idea of sickness is incomprehensible to him. To him there is physical illness and mental illness. In mental illness one sometimes sees severe emotional upsets. Sometimes people get upset over physical illness, death, stressful situations; but to him this is not mental illness. It is either a normal reaction to a stressful problem of living or a sign of physical or moral weakness. It follows then that the professional point of view, that failure to meet the problems of living is an emotional disturbance, a milder form of mental illness, to be treated by the same kind of doctor that treats the more seriously mentally ill, only alienates him. To the worker, emotional disability or impairment is either related to a physical illness and should be treated as such by the doctor, or it is the result of undue stress or strains in the environment; or it is related to a moral weakness and should be treated by a minister or priest or conquered by oneself or accepted and lived with. If one attempts to treat what is considered to be a moral weakness, the worker, with his present view, considers it a tremendous invasion of his privacy. Also, the general practitioner reinforces his tendency to identify emotional disturbance with physical illness, by making it so easy for him to find a physician to treat it as physical illness. Can present professional ideology make an impact on the "moral weakness" problem? It can, of course, work through ministers and priests. That may help the small minority who seek help from them; but for the most part, there is little hope of getting workers or low-income groups to accept failure to meet the problems of living as an illness, and as long as problems of living continue to be diagnosed as diseases and treated within an institutional framework for the treatment of disease, the alienation will persist (20).

The present ideology and technology of mental health professionals will continue to fail with low-income patients unless the focus is shifted. Riessman (16) points out that low-income people are task oriented, concrete, concerned primarily with the here and now and focused on solving immediate problems. If they have troubles they are interested in finding a way to cope with them. If they are to be helped the response must be to their need, as they see it, for more successful coping techniques. It is necessary to shift the focus from how they are *reacting* to how they are *acting,* from *defensive reactions* to *coping styles,* from changing their reactions to teaching them more successful *actions.*

This change of focus also has implications for the aims and goals of treatment. The fundamental justification and aim of most psychotherapy today is self-actualization. Everyone should realize his full potential, and if he is not able to do so, then he should be in therapy so that he may fully actualize himself. This, of course, meets a responsive chord in the feelings of most middle- and upper-class persons about themselves and their lives. They see themselves in many possible roles and their hope is to select those roles which enable them to actualize themselves. The view that one can realize his full potential presupposes a view of society in which there are many possibilities and opportunities and that one need only remove the internal difficulties to make a rich, full life possible. For the most part, disturbed middle-class patients see themselves as *victims of their own selves.* Low-income people, on the other hand, are not future oriented. They live in a world of limited or no opportunities. There is little or no role flexibility. They see themselves as *victims of circumstances.* Self-actualization under these conditions is meaningless to them. Before they can become interested in self-actualization, they have to believe that they can play a role in determining what happens to them. Thus, *self-determination* rather than self-actualization is a more realistic and more meaningful goal for them.

Another ideological problem is the domination of the treatment relationship by the values and mores of a "fee for service" ethic. Even where the service is rendered by an agency this is true. Goffman eloquently describes this relationship which he says involves a set of interdependent assumptions that fit together to form a model.

. . . When services are performed whose worth to the client at the time is very great, the server (that is, the professional mental health worker) is ideally supposed to restrict himself to a fee determined by tradition—presumably what the server needs to keep himself in decent circumstances while he devotes his life to his calling. . . . When he performs major services for very poor clients, the server may feel that charging no fee is more dignified (or perhaps safer) than a reduced fee. The server thus avoids dancing to the client's tune, or even bargaining, and is able to show that he is motivated by a disinterested involvement in his work.

The server's attachment to his conception of himself as a disinterested expert, and his readiness to relate to persons on the basis of it, is a kind of secular vow of chastity and is at the root of the wonderful use that clients make of him. In him they find someone who does not have the usual personal, ideological, or contractual reasons for helping them; yet he is someone who will take an intense temporary interest in them. . . . It therefore pays the client to trust in those from whom he does not have the usual guarantee of trust.

This trustworthiness available on request would of itself provide a unique basis of relationship in our society . . . (5, pp. 327–28).

These implicit characteristics of the therapeutic relationship are understandable and acceptable to most middle-class people who themselves are often engaged in trading their expertness to other individuals. But the worker finds it difficult to trust the person who expects a fee for helping him with what he believes to be a moral problem. Children, too, have difficulty understanding; and they are confused when they discover that the therapist is paid for "being his friend." Thus, the treatment relationship itself is confusing and untrustworthy in the eyes of low-income people. The fact is that for any person in a low-income group, having a mental illness means being a medical indigent with all the unhealthy effects this situation has on a person's self-esteem.

In addition to these there are the ideological differences in the more usual sense, values, goals, and styles of life between the low-income patient and the professional himself which effect communication and the nature of the relationship between the two (14).

It is clear that what will be required first are bold and even drastic changes in the mental health service, within the professional structure, and in the professional himself. The innovator of such institutional change will need to break out of the mold of institutional thinking and to be constantly alert, to all the forces within the professional ideology, within the technology, and within himself that are constantly straining to oppose or weaken innovation.

Already the weakening of innovation can be seen in the comprehensive community mental health program enacted into legislation which promised to change the whole nature and direction of treatment for mental illness in this country. The idea that the mentally ill can be treated in the community is relatively new and has become possible because of advances in drug therapy during the last 10 or 15 years. The new drugs, although they do not cure mental illness, often change the behavior of the patient sufficiently so as to make it possible for him to live in the community with certain kinds of support from its resources. This has led to a shift in emphasis, a change in goals, in the treatment and care of the mentally ill. Once, custodial care was the only alternative to the failure to qualify for treatment. Now, with an emphasis on a return to functioning rather than cure, rehabilitation and habilitation have become the organizing goals of the treatment process, and the alternative of institutionalization is less necessary.

It has been proclaimed that the community mental health development signals a revolution in mental health care. Such a view is a gross exaggeration. The concept of community mental health has the potential for introducing revolutionary innovations, but a sober look will reveal that institutionalized community mental health under the federal programs tends to become an extension of current professional ideology with modified goals, tactics, and techniques, over that part of society from which it has been hitherto alienated. It is in fact a process of consolidation rather than revolution, a consolidation motivated by the realization of the failure to adequately perform the social function of restoration of those whose needs are greatest. Such a consolidation may be a step forward. But it must be kept in mind that it solves none of the ideological problems but rather perpetuates them. It does more: It legitimates a two-class system of mental health treatment in this country—self-actualization for the rich, rehabilitation for the poor. To hail this as a revolution will only result in increasing cynicism and discouragement both among the poor and the professional as well.

Sometimes changes in tactics or techniques are necessary and sufficient to solve a problem. Miller and Rein (10) point out, however, that frequently when professionals face the issue of ideology they escape into technology. But when the problem has ideological roots, changes in techniques without the necessary ideological innovations often result in nothing more than old wine in new bottles. Witness what is already happening in many instances to the walk-in clinic. The idea of the walk-in clinic was a bold attempt to deal with the problems of delay in providing service. It was to be the means of doing away with the problem of waiting lists, delayed referrals, etc., and its primary purpose was immediacy of service. It was to be the means by which the mentally ill could enter and be routed without delay to whatever kind of service was needed. It was to be the open door to a full array of comprehensive services.

But for the most part the new walk-in clinics have become brief psychotherapy clinics. The idea of an open door to comprehensive mental health services has already in many instances been converted into the old revolving door. They have become brief psychotherapy clinics because that is what the professionals who man them know how to do. They have spent many years acquiring psychotherapy skills and they want to practice what they know. Here, out of this little illustration, emerges a major mental health manpower problem. A really innovative community mental health program requires greater clinical skill, knowledge about social process and social organization, and an ability to be versatile in shifting one's focus from individual, to group, to social systems.

Community mental health programs are becoming institutionalized before the manpower with the appropriate skills necessary for its new operations can be trained. Out of necessity they will be manned by traditionally trained professionals who will practice what they know.

Comprehensiveness, an important aspect of the new programs, is slipping away. In some instances, the situation has developed where the kind of treatment patients get depends on which door they walk into. If they come to the walk-in clinics they get brief psychotherapy, if they come to the outpatient clinic they get long-term psychotherapy, and if they come to the emergency room they get drugs, or are hospitalized.

Rehabilitation, the major goal of the community mental health programs, hardly exists. First, because traditionally trained mental health personnel know little or nothing about rehabilitation, and second, because of the ineffectiveness of present rehabilitation programs.

These are some of the ways that the manpower problem threatens the community mental health programs. The manpower problem, however, is fundamentally inseparable from the problem of institutional change. Changing institutions of training is a slow and painful process and meets with great resistance from faculty and students alike, both of whom are much more interested in traditional psychotherapy training. There is still a great demand for this kind of mental health service. When it comes to providing psychotherapy to middle-class patients there is indeed a manpower shortage.

By its very nature a manpower shortage sets in motion a compelling drive to deal with the problem from an empirical short-range point of view. The need is urgent and immediate and there is a tendency to feel that if only we had more "bodies" our problems would be solved. Those who take this viewpoint look to the industrial model for solving manpower shortages.

The industrial model is to break up complex highly skilled operations into a series of more simple tasks. The simplification of the production process reduces the amount of training necessary and thus makes increases in the manpower pool feasible. Human services cannot be simplified in the same way without dehumanizing them. The last 20 years of medical practice have amply demonstrated that.

In the past, industry's manpower shortages were created by a sudden and urgent need for increased production when machines alone could not do that job. Today, industry's manpower crisis is of a different kind. Not manpower shortage but manpower excess plagues it and it has no solution.

But today, in mental health, we still look to the old industrial model and talk about breaking down the professional role into subprofessional classifications or subroles, each of which may be filled by people with less than complete professional training and whose training is specific to the roles. This model is proposed by Jesse Gordon (6). It is the model out of which grow programs such as Margaret Rioch's (17) training of mental health counselors.

Paradoxically, her counselors probably receive better psychotherapy training than the majority of social workers, psychologists, and residents get. They fill a real need in providing manpower to traditional existing services. But her counselors do nothing new. They simply render some aspect of service that mental health professionals give and as such are a useful stop gap attack on the manpower problem. But from the point of view of greatest social need this solution contributes little because it is based on the assumption that manpower shortage is the crucial factor in the failure to tend to the problems of those in society whose needs are greatest.

Nothing could be further from the truth. The mental health professionals' posture is not that of a group of people with a successful product harassed by a clamoring demand, it is more like a group of desperate men struggling to hold back a flood and who cannot find the hole in the dike. This kind of manpower crisis is totally different from the usual shortage, for while it is true more bodies are needed to stem the tide, unless the hole is found and repaired or the water redirected, it will be a losing battle.

There are some who suggest that any attempt to halt the tide of mental illness by treatment alone is doomed to failure and that it would be better to concentrate efforts on primary prevention. The idea has great promise. Duhl (3, 4) has pointed out the compelling need to direct our energies toward changing social systems for the benefit of whole communities and societies. But here too there is a manpower problem. The fact is that there is hardly anyone in the mental health profession or the behavioral sciences who is trained in a body of knowledge, a set of concepts, or an adequate theory on which to base such training. But this is the greatest need and the most promising approach. What is needed is a new profession of experts in changing social systems for the prevention of mental illness and for the improvement of the psychological effectiveness of all individuals in society to deal with the problems of living. It is an exciting prospect but it also contains the same problems of manpower and institutional change.[1]

Caplan (2) has pointed out that primary prevention should be an integral part of community mental health programs. He sees no basic contradiction in the requirements of the clinicians' role which is primarily consultation and treatment, and the requirements of changing social systems. He acknowledges that there may be difficulties but feels they are basically compatible. Actually, at present the prospect of any really effective primary preventive programs in community mental health—at least in the ones that are being planned now —is minimal; first, because with a few outstanding exceptions, institutionalized community mental health is not taking this direction and, second, because few clinicians, even those in community mental health, have the know-how.

---

[1] In my early thinking about the problem, I thought that this new professional would be a social systems clinician, with a combination of clinical training and social science. But as I help develop social action programs and try to stimulate other clinicians to think about them, I am rapidly becoming convinced that clinical training with its emphasis on changing the individual and its focus on the psychodynamic or interpersonal is an impediment to thinking about changing social systems.

And finally, even more importantly, the social criticism, reorganization, and institutional change needed require the concepts and technology of social scientists; and the functions of social scientists and clinicians are, at this stage of our knowledge, not easily integrated. Reciprocity between the two is all that can be achieved given the present state of knowledge. The social function of a clinician and of a social scientist are different.

It is necessary to recognize how society is affecting and frequently limiting the development of the mental health professions. Miller (9) calls attention to the fact that professionals often act as though all they have to do is to decide what professional skills are necessary and that will solve the social problems. They act as though there are no social forces other than those they set in motion operating on the profession.

At the present time there is no adequate theory or set of concepts which integrates the social process and the individual. Until such a time the clinician, who is the repairman, and the social scientist, who is the engineer, perform different social functions. These two functions have different concepts, values, motivations, interests, and aims as well as different roles. Every social function for which there is a need tends to become institutionalized, and the process of institutionalization tends to rigidify and restrict the role necessary to accomplish the function. The result of this institutionalization process is to rigidly define the professional role and to proscribe sanctions for those who may be tempted to contaminate their function through role flexibility. In the absence of an integrative *theory* the social forces at work on professional roles will prevent the integration of the social scientist and the clinician. The best that can be hoped for is a reciprocal team-type relationship between the two until such time as a new professional emerges.

But it is not necessary to wait for a theory. What is needed is to start now to develop a body of knowledge and to encourage social and behavioral scientists, and mental health professionals, to become *participant-conceptualizers* in community action programs and public service functions where they will have the opportunity to influence decisions on social changes.

This opportunity now exists in a social program which is outside of the community mental health program—but which has the potential for playing a more decisive primary prevention role than the community mental health program. The Community Action Program of the Office of Economic Opportunity is in much better position to succeed where the mental health professionals have failed because it is not bogged down by the difficulties inherent in the ideology of mental illness.

The Community Action Program addresses itself to the normal. The poor are not considered sick. The goal of the poverty program, particularly the Community Action Program, is self-determination not self-actualization. Its focus is on coping techniques, not on psychodynamics. In brief, it is free from many of the characteristics of the mental health professionals' ideology which make for alienation. Thus, it has a better chance of reaching and maintaining contact with the poor. It is an excellent opportunity for mental health professionals to become involved in social action, a prerequisite for anyone who wishes to become engaged in primary prevention. It is a significant reaffirmation of all that is being said here, that, for the most part, the new community mental health programs are being developed independent of and isolated from the most significant development in urban communities in the United States in the last 20 years, i.e., the Community Action Programs.

There are one or two places, however, which have become exciting experimental labs for community mental health social action programs. The Neighborhood Service Center of the Lincoln Hospital Mental Health Program is one of these (11). It has been and continues to be a great learning experience. In it was revealed all of the tensions, conflicts, attitudinal, and ideological differences that have been mentioned here. Yet, the mental health professionals have remained excited, cohesive, and their spirit and working relationships could not be better. Out of such laboratories as these we may learn how to develop a social systems mental health specialist.

One of the most exciting aspects of community action programs is the use they make of nonprofessionals recruited directly from the ranks of the poor in the neighborhoods they serve.

There is no question that the use of these new nonprofessionals opens up a great reservoir of manpower for mental health activities as well. But, unless this manpower is used effectively they can become nothing more than wardens and nursemaids tending the mentally ill who are waiting for the professional to serve them. They can also become a garbage heap where the professional dumps the patients he feels he can do nothing for. And, finally, the nonprofessional can become the menial who perfoms all the "dirty work" that the professional resents and wishes he could get rid of so that he could have more time to do the same old things. Used this way, the nonprofessional will reinforce all the tendencies in institutionalized mental health practice that mitigate against change.

Reiff and Reissman (14) have pointed out that the ability of the nonprofessionals to do the things that the professionals cannot do, such as, establish a peer relationship, take an active part in the patient's life situation, empathize with his style of life, etc., is bound to affect the nature of the mental health services, the role of the professional, and may even have an impact on the ideology of the mental health professional. The training of the nonprofessional then, becomes itself a strategy for affecting desirable change in the field of mental health. The demand characteristics of the effective use of the new *nonprofessional* in this way will of necessity create a new *professional*.

Through the nonprofessional the professional has a greater repertoire of preventive, remedial, treatment, and care modalities. But the nonprofessional cannot decide what kind of service the patient needs. Rapid and appropriate assessment of each individual case will be required. Thus, the new professional will have to become skilled in making early assessments and referrals to the appropriate modalities. This is in contradistinction to quick and rapid assessments that are made in today's emergency rooms by first-year residents.

Appropriate use of the nonprofessional will require the judgment of the most highly skilled clinicians who are thoroughly familiar with all the modalities of care, and who have developed criteria for making such decisions. Furthermore, the role of the professional will change. He will need to be more of a consultant, supervisor, and administrator. And if he should venture into primary prevention or become involved in community action programs, he will probably also be required to play the role of organizer, politician, and educator. All of which will compel him to face new conceptual problems, such as when does community action become political action, how shall he differentiate his citizen role from his professional one, etc. One thing he will need to learn for certain is the harsh reality of power struggles.

One cannot enter the field of institutional change without forthrightly facing power issues. The problem of creating institutional changes in mental health cannot be solved by the strategy of manpower alone. Bureaucratic and professional rigidities are not matters of protecting practices alone but, in the final analysis, are power issues. There is a tendency among professionals to ignore power issues and to act as though intelligence and rationality will conquer all. But the power issues are there, and more often than not, determine the outcome of efforts at change and innovation. Within the field of mental health there are both intraprofessional and interprofessional power issues which limit the efforts of those who are struggling for institutional change. It often happens that intraprofessional power issues get contaminated with interprofessional ones. For example, the recent attempt of neuropsychiatrists to take legal action against a therapy training institute of psychologists. Interprofessional power issues, however, seldom became intraprofessional ones because the risk of losing an intraprofessional power struggle is greater than in an interprofessional one. The most significant power issue in changing the field of mental health will inevitably be around the question of the medical model. At the present time, it appears that this is primarily an interprofessional struggle. Let us analyze the situation and see what are the likely effects of this power struggle on the development of new and innovative mental health programs and the utilization of new kinds of manpower.

Cinical psychiatry, responding to social pressures, developed its branch of social and community psychiatry so that now that legislation makes possible the development of community mental health facilities, psychiatry has a conceptual and a professional organization structure which can take responsibility for the community mental health centers. It is significant that no comparable organizational structure has grown within the professions of clinical psychology and social work. For this reason the institutional community mental health programs have been and will continue to be primarily influenced by the forces operating within the institution of psychiatry. They will reflect not only the innovative thinking of community and social psychiatry, but the powerful forces of medicine as well.

The clinical psychologist, on the other hand, is not recognized particularly by the other mental health professionals for his therapeutic skills and technology. He has never achieved recognized independent status in this area, but he is respected and recognized where clinical psychology has made a theoretical or technological impact on mental health from work which is indigenous to psychology. Modern psychoanalytic thinking, for example, has incorporated a great deal of academic developmental psychology. This is one of the heritages of psychology. Psychoanalysis draws heavily on developmental psychology. In this area, the clinical psychologist's views are respected. In psychological testing, again an area indigenous to psychology, modern psychiatry finds the contributions of clinical psychology useful and acceptable as an independent function. But as far as treatment is concerned, the clinical psychologist is regarded as ancillary. As long as psychologists continue to operate within the ideological framework of psychiatry this state of affairs will continue. When and if psychologists can overcome their own intraprofessional power issues and move into the field of community action and primary prevention on the basis of their own body of knowledge about normality, development, cognitive processes, and social psychology, only then will a truly interdisciplinary relationship with psychiatry be possible. This point is forcefully made by Rosenbaum and Zwerling who write

> The social scientist in his (the social psychiatrist's) milieu is not the familiar psychiatric social worker or clinical psychologist but rather the sociologist, the anthropologist, and the social psychologist. Whereas the traditional social worker and psychologist operate from within the framework of psychoanalytic theory, the social scientist operates from social system theory and the psychoanalyst in a unit in social psychiatry is forced to work on a more truly interdisciplinary team basis (18, p. 34).

Clinical psychologists are not seen as extradisciplinary and, therefore, requiring interdisciplinary team relationships, but because clinical psychologists operate within the framework of psychoanalytic theory, they are seen as an intradisciplinary substrate of psychiatry, and, therefore, the relationship assumes a hierarchical rather than team form. Klein asks

> Will [the training of clinical psychologists] be geared to the nature and requirements of institutional social and community psychiatry just as clinical psychology developed with the needs of clinical psychiatry as a critical determinant (8, p. 2).

It is necessary to add to this the question: *Will they be able to develop a body of systematic knowledge, a set of integrated assertions, theories, and aims based on psychological tradition, which constitute a socially oriented program for improving the psychological effectiveness of all individuals in our society to deal with the problems of living?* Unless this is done the psychologists will continue to put themselves in the position of having to argue over rights to employ the technological skills which are rooted in psychiatric ideology. The issue will always be posed as one of skill; and as long as psychologists continue to justify their existence on the basis of technological skills, they condemn themselves to an interminable power struggle in the form of a jurisdictional dispute with the other sections of the mental health skilled trades. Power struggles on the basis of technology result in power struggles and nothing else. A power struggle on the basis of ideology can be an important catalyst for institutional change.

The introduction of the nonprofessional into mental health services will add a new dimension to the power struggle—that between nonprofessionals and professionals. Tensions will inevitably exist. If the nonprofessional is to serve the functions of doing what the professional cannot do he must be integrated into the mental health service establishment without being absorbed. He must be permitted to develop a power structure of his own.

In order to win a power struggle, one needs political clout. The political clout of community psychiatry lies in the federal community mental health program. But this is fraught with dangers and too much subject to other political forces. The political clout of psychology and social work resides in their respective professional organizations and in their middle-class constituency, primarily in agencies.

One of the most effective forms of political clout is the development of a constituency. Rein (15) has called attention to the power of the recipients of services. One of the major reasons why psychologists and social workers can do therapy is because they have an unorganized, informal constitutency. These are the people who are asking for their help and for whom they fulfill a social need. But now that the social need is being redefined, clinical psychology and social work will need to build a new constituency. Meanwhile the pull of the old constituency will make it difficult to attract psychologists.

While it is true that there will continue to be a social need for psychotherapists working with middle-class patients, the direction of mental health *service* is shifting to low-income groups and meeting their social need. This paper tries to indicate some of the issues that will have to be faced if existing need is to be converted into *effective* demand. In terms of the power issues, that is another way of saying a constituency must be developed, a group of people within the population who are demanding the new mental health services being offered. The nonprofessional being closer to the people to be served can be of inestimable value in helping to develop this constituency. But here again the medical model, as has been pointed out earlier, limits the possibilities for changing the relationship between the professional and the poor, as well as between the professional and nonprofessional.

To summarize: The greatest social need for mental health services today comes from the low-income groups and the poor. Meeting this need is not primarily a problem of manpower but a problem of ideology. The task is to develop concepts, methods, programs, and services that are appropriate, effective, and related to the life styles of low-income people and to their needs, in a way which will create an effective demand for them. This will require significant institutional changes. Whatever manpower problems do exist are inseperable from the problem of institutional change. The solutions to manpower problems can reinforce existing institutionalized mental health [care] or they can constitute a strategy for promoting institutional change. Two things are certain. There is need for a *human link* between the professional and the poor; the new nonprofessional can be that link. And there is need for a new mental health professional; a man who is skilled in changing social systems to improve the psychological effectiveness of all people in society to deal with the problems of living. The road to achieving these is also the road to changing significantly the mental health services and professions of this country.

REFERENCES

1. Bockoven, J. S. *Moral treatment in American psychiatry.* New York: Springer, 1963.
2. Caplan, G. *Principles of preventive psychiatry.* New York: Basic Books, 1964.
3. Duhl, L. J. *The urban condition.* New York: Basic Books, 1963.
4. Duhl, L. J. Social planning, Paper read at Athens Center of Ekistics, Athens, July, 1964.
5. Goffman, E. *Asylums.* New York: Anchor Books, 1961.
6. Gordon, J. Project cause: The federal anti-poverty program and some implications of subprofessional training. *Amer. Psychol.,* 1965, 20:334–43.
7. Jahoda, M. *Current concepts of positive mental health, Joint Commission on Mental Illness and Health.* (No. 1). New York: Basic Books, 1958.
8. Klein, D. C. Community needs: A challenge for psychology. Paper read at American Psychological Association, Philadelphia, September, 1963.
9. Miller, S. M. *Stupidity and power, two competing modes of explanation.* Syracuse University, Youth Development Center, 1963.
10. Miller, S. M., and Rein, M. *Change, ferment and ideology in the social services.* Toronto: Council of Social Work Education, 1964.
11. Peck, H. B., Riessman, F., and Hallowitz, E. *Neighborhood service center program.* New York: Lincoln Hospital Mental Health Services, 1965.
12. Reiff, R. *The mental health education needs of labor.* Washington, D.C.: National Institute of Labor Education, 1960 (Working Paper No. 2).
13. Reiff, R., and Scribner, S. *Issues in the new national mental health program relating to labor and now income groups.* Washington, B.C.: National Institute of Labor Education, 1963 (Report No. 1).
14. Reiff, R., and Riessman, F. The indigenous nonprofessional. *Comm. Ment. Hlth. J.,* 1965 (Monog. No. 1).
15. Rein, M. Strategies of planned change. Paper read at American Orthopsychiatric Association, New York, March, 1965.
16. Riessman, F. *New approaches to mental health treatment for labor and low income groups.* Washington, D.C.: National Institute of Labor Education, 1964 (Report No. 2).
17. Rioch, M. J., Elkes, C., and Flint, A. A. *Pilot project in training mental health counselors.* Washington, D.C.: United States Public Health Service, 1965 (Publ. No. 1254).

18. Rosenbaum, M., and Zwerling, I. Impact of social psychiatry on a psycho-analytically oriented department of psychiatry. *Arch. Gen. Psychiat.,* 1964, 3:31–39.

19. Star, Shirley. The place of psychiatry in popular thinking. Paper read at American Association for Public Opinion Research, Washington, D.C., May 1957.

20. Szasz, T. *The myth of mental illness.* New York: Hoeber, 1961.

50

The Potential Application of
Filial Therapy to the School Situation

MICHAEL P. ANDRONICO AND BERNARD G. GUERNEY

FILIAL therapy is a method of treating emotionally disturbed children under ten years of age (1, 2, 3, 4).[1] As presently conducted, filial therapy is not intended for children who are mentally retarded, perceptually or neurologically impaired, or psychotic. Also excluded are parents who appear to be pre-psychotic or suicidal. By virtue of circumstances rather than design, a truly lower class population has not yet been represented to a significant degree.

The children are not directly given therapy by a professional. Rather, parents are relied upon to effect changes in their children as well as themselves. The technique involves training the parents to play with their own children at home for prescribed periods of time, and under observation at the Clinic.

Training is conducted with groups of six to eight parents. The role that the parents are taught to take in the special play sessions is modeled after that of the client-centered play therapist. The importance of attempting to achieve genuine emphatic understanding and acceptance of the child's needs and feelings during the play sessions is stressed. The goals of the sessions are as follows: (a) to help the child change his perceptions or misperceptions of the parent's feelings, attitudes, and behavior; (b) to allow the child—mainly through the medium of play—to communicate thoughts, needs, and feelings to to his parents that he had previously kept from awareness, thereby helping to resolve anxiety-producing internalized conflicts; and, finally, (c) to bring the child a greater feeling of self-respect, self-worth, and confidence.

Following the explanation of the rationale underlying the treatment, the parents observe the therapist demonstrating the technique in individual sessions with their children. Interspersed with these demonstrations over the course of training, the parents themselves conduct play sessions at the Clinic under the supervision of the therapist and under observation by the other group members.

Reprinted from the *Journal of School Psychology*, 1967, *6*, 2–7, by permission of the publisher and the authors. © 1967, Journal of School Psychology. Dr. Andronico is Chief Psychologist, Hunterdon Medical Center, Flemington, New Jersey. Dr. Guerney is Professor of Psychology and Director of the Psychological Clinic, Rutgers—The State University.

[1] The preparation of this article was facilitated by Public Health Services grants MH 11975 and MH 02506, National Institute of Mental Health.

The parents thus have an opportunity to observe the therapist, be observed by other members of the group, and to observe the rest of the group and their children, all under similar play conditions.

After the training period, which lasts for about eight weeks, the parents begin play sessions at home. The specified time (initially 30 minutes, later 45 minutes) is set aside, and the parents engage the children in these play periods at home on a weekly basis. The parents continue their own group sessions throughout the course of the therapy, discussing the previous week's play periods with the therapist and the other group members. Also, from time to time throughout the therapy, sessions are again conducted at the Clinic under the group's observation.

In the beginning, the orientation of the parents' weekly group meetings, which continue for a year or more, is toward learning the method, and is so oriented partly in order to maximize motivation and minimize resistance. No pressure is put on the parent to apply the therapeutic principles outside of the sessions; he is allowed to make such generalizations when ready to do so. While technique remains a pertinent area for discussion for the duration of the parents' sessions, the emphasis may later move more in the direction of exploring the parents' own emotions, attitudes, and problems in relation to their children (especially as these are illuminated by their reactions and observations of the children's actions in the play sessions) and toward other significant persons in their lives.

Although filial therapy has so far been conducted only in the Psychological Clinic of Rutgers University and in the Hunterdon Medical Center, there is no reason apparent to the writers that it should not be tried out by qualified school psychologists in the public schools. Certainly the magnitude of the mental health problem as it makes itself apparent in the schools presents a challenge that invites, even demands, innovation. School psychologists are a group who, because of their present small numbers, can hope to become a truly effective force in bringing about change on a broad scale only if they drastically change (a) their number, (b) their role, by concentrating very heavily on research, and/or (c) their impact, by training and using others as extensions of themselves. The last of these alternatives is being focused upon here.

The small number of school psychologists, the heavy diagnostic load they typically must bear, and even the shortage of physical space, pose severe obstacles to the school psychologist who contemplates undertaking therapeutic action. Because of these obstacles, one-to-one therapeutic sessions on a broad scale obviously are impossible. Group methods offer some economy of time, space, and facility. Filial therapy offers the potential of still greater economy in these respects. It can be termed a "high leverage" treatment method—high leverage in this sense: by imparting to others who are significant figures in the life of the child those skills that are most relevant to a given type of problem, and supervising the application of those skills, the psychologist increases his power—he multiplies the force of his action. Through the use of such intermediaries, a given expenditure of the profession's time is multiplied in its application to a given individual, and/or affects more individuals. In filial therapy, in addition to having more time in therapeutically oriented play sessions with his parent than a school psychologist could give him, the child has the benefit of any generalizations the parent can make from what he has learned about therapeutic approaches to problems arising between them in everyday living. Considering the needs versus the resources in the mental health field in general, and the schools in particular, any technique offering such leverage should not go untried. Trial is especially indicated in additional settings when initial experience elsewhere suggests that a method is effective. This is the case with filial therapy, since experience to date with 12 groups in clinic settings has been quite encouraging.

An additional advantage that might be expected in adopting a filial therapy program in school would be the increased motivation of many parents to undertake and stay with a therapeutic program for their children. Frequently, parents' reactions to a recommendation for therapeutic action is negative. They tend to blame the school for the problems that the children are having. One of the reasons that this is so is that they have feelings of helplessness about their ability to help the child to adjust better in school. The schools themselves encounter frustration along these lines, since often they have problems in offering concrete suggestions to parents other than to say, "Go to the local child guidance clinic."

It has been our experience that parents who become involved in filial therapy generally maintain high motivation and a positive attitude toward treatment. Possibly one reason for this is the implicit and explicit attitude toward parents that is involved in the filial therapy approach that differs from attitudes implicit in traditional methods. Conventional approaches take the child away from the parent to treat him, with the underlying implication that the parent cannot deal with the child effectively, and that the child must thus be taken away from the parent for a certain period of time each week in order to be helped. Another implication is that not only must the child be taken away from the parent in order to be helped, but that the parents themselves have been directly responsible for the child's problems, and therefore also need to be treated. The filial therapy approach, on the other hand, explicitly states that the therapy is proceeding with the indispensable help of the parents; that the parents are necessary and directly involved in the treatment of their children. This factor may similarly enhance the motivation of parents to communicate more closely with schools, rather than to avoid schools and the anxieties involved with their children's having difficulties in school.

The hypotheses that are being put forth here are as follows: Filial therapy, with its clearly structured approach to helping the parents, will enable the school and the parents to help the children modify their behaviors, and the parents will thus see themselves as being a vital part of the child's treatment. This will presumably increase the parents' motivation to continue contact with the school, and will put the parents in a position to accept more readily discussions with school personnel, since, being collaborators with school personnel, they will be less likely to feel threatened by school authorities.

The preventive aspect of this approach is also noteworthy. Some "problem families" in the making may well be prevented from becoming problem families through this method. That is, a parent with a problem child, say, in the second or third grade is also encouraged to work with the younger children in filial therapy. This may eliminate or reduce some potential school problems that might develop in the younger children had the problems in the family gone unchecked, or had the family concentrated on the problems of only one child. It has been our experience that in some families the child who is initially referred for treatment is later thought by the parents to be less of a problem than another child in the family. The inclusion of all children within the age range appropriate for play techniques, therefore, can be conceived of as a corrective or preventative method in family mental health. Also, the group meetings always get around to discussing child rearing and attitudes toward children. These discussions modify parental viewpoints and help create better child-parent relationships for all children in the family.

In addition to the direct adoption of the filial therapy technique with groups of parents within a school setting, filial therapy principles have a possible application to teachers. The use of parents as therapeutic agents is based upon the belief in the efficacy of significant figures in the child's life in bringing about attitudinal and behavioral change. This means that, *given the skill to do so,* people who are already, by the nature of their everyday roles, important in a child's life are in a better position to bring about change than an outsider who is seen only an hour a week, even if that person is a trained therapist. Thus, *given the skill,* parents, who are the most important figures in a child's life, have more opportunity to make significant improvements in their child's mental health than anyone else. Similarly, teachers who are with children for a large part of the children's week—again, given the skill to do so—are also in a position to make very important contributions to a child's mental health.

Starting with the most direct application of filial therapy, it might be helpful to have some teachers learn the nondirective play techniques of filial therapy and give play sessions to one or two problem children in a class on some regular basis. Time and scheduling considerations would, of course, be a problem here, and would have to be worked out. The appropriately trained school psychologist would be able to teach and supervise groups of interested teachers in the same fashion as filial therapists do with parents. We would anticipate little difficulty in obtaining parental consent for extra time spent with teachers, as compared with the difficulty encountered in convincing parents to undertake and maintain clinic contacts. This would involve not only the increased ability of the special services team to reach many more children than they themselves could see directly, but would also enable the teachers to see continuing numbers of children in subsequent years. That is, one group of eight teachers might be seeing 16 children during one year. In subsequent years, they would be able to see similar numbers of children, and therefore increase the total number of children who are seen. Once these teachers had sufficiently mastered the attitudes and technique, supervision might be done on less than a weekly basis. After the first year, for example, supervision might be altered to an every other week schedule, and eventually to a monthly one, allowing the school psychologist to see many more groups of teachers.

Added to the direct help that the problem child would receive from the teacher is the importance of the therapeutic, empathic skills that would be conveyed to these teachers. The teachers will have been taught specific techniques for enhancing the child's self-concepts and for increasing their own ability to understand situations from a given child's viewpoint. The technique of clarifying children's feelings while at the same time firmly enforcing certain limits on behavior will have been another important technique practiced and learned. We would add here that other psychological principles and techniques appropriate for the classroom per se might be taught in addition to those having to do with the play sessions; for example, reinforcement principles, and techniques for applying them in the classroom setting.

It has been the authors' experience that in filial therapy, parents tend to generalize certain appropriate attitudes and methods from the limited situation of the play period to situations and events outside these sessions. If and when teachers do this, they will also tend to apply those principles that are relevant and appropriate to all their students, thus increasing the mental health milieu of the school. Although most teachers have encountered these principles in one form or another during their formal education, the presentation proposed here would be on a far deeper and more intensive level, with supervised practice; and thus, hopefully, would be more meaningful and realistic to them than their prior tutorial experiences.

As with parents, teachers' true willingness to communicate and cooperate with the school psychologist often leaves something to be desired. Again, as with parents, the training and use of teachers as direct therapeutic agents might increase their desire and ability to cooperate and communicate more fully with the psychologist. That is, teachers may become more favorably disposed to discuss freely some of the problems they have with children, and feel more directly involved with problem children they encounter, and have fewer feelings of frustration and helplessness. This might arise not only by virtue of the acquired skills themselves and the greater mutual understanding because of shared vocabulary and concepts, but also, most importantly, because of the implied trust and collaborative nature of the filial training process.

Another, less intensive application of filial training than that in which teachers work to help individual children would be to have teachers engaged in special, limited, individual sessions with children *only* for training purposes. The goal here would be limited to helping them to see how certain similar techniques could be employed in their day-to-day classroom interaction with children. Controlled empirical research in filial therapy has demonstrated that parents can learn the required role with their own children quite satisfactorily in the time allotted to training, and suggests that therapists who themselves have more experience in conducting client-centered play therapy with young children, and conducting filial groups, will be more effective in training parents (5).[2]

Qualitative observation of teachers now receiving similar training suggests that they are at least as adept in mastering the required role as are parents, despite the initial handicap of an almost "reflexive" teaching response to children.

Empirical research is currently under way exploring parent and child personality variables, process variables, and outcome variables in filial therapy.

In summary, attempts have been made to spell out some of the ways in which approaches based on the assumptions and principles employed in filial therapy might be applied in a school setting. These attempts include a direct transfer of conventional filial therapy from the clinic to the school under the auspices of the school psychologist, using parents as therapeutic agents, the utilization of teachers as direct therapeutic agents, and the training of teachers to help them apply therapeutic principles in the classroom. The possible advantages of these applications in terms of increased parental and teacher motivation for helping children and collaborating with the psychologist were also discussed.

REFERENCES

1. Andronico, M. P., Fidler, J., Guerney, B., Jr., and Guerney, L. F. The combination of didactic and dynamic elements in filial therapy. *Internatl. J. Group Psychother.*, 1967, 17:10–17.
2. Fidler, J. W., Guerney, B., Jr., Andronico, M. P., and Guerney, L. F. Filial therapy as a logical extension of current trends in psychotherapy. Paper presented at Sixth International Congress of Psychotherapy. London, August, 1964.
3. Guerney, B., Jr. Filial therapy: Description and rationale. *J. Consult. Psychol.*, 1964, 28:304–10.
4. Guerney, B. G., Jr., Guerney, L. F., and Andronico, M. P. Filial therapy. *Yale Scientific Magazine,* March, 1966.
5. Stover, L. Efficacy of training procedures for mothers in filial therapy. Doctoral dissertation, Rutgers, The State University, 1966.

[2] Naturally, any psychologist undertaking the role of filial therapist should himself first have studied, practiced, and received supervision in client-centered play therapy. Knowledge of group therapy principles would also be valuable.

VI
RESEARCH AND
EVALUATION

ALTHOUGH some of the practical aspects of research have been touched upon in other articles, this section deals with the more basic building blocks of research. In an area where we still do not know the true value of treatment, the contributions here point out the essential ingredients to be considered in planning to measure the results of community mental health efforts. The article on the rise of the computer is included as a specific example of breaking away from hidebound tradition and opening up the use of automation to mental health professionals.

The section opens with a report of a symposium which relates research to new developments in community mental health. Bobbitt defines community mental health and ties in evaluation, innovation, and scientific concepts and formulations. Libo discusses the role of researchers with a service agency. Selling research to the community is the theme of Hurder's contribution, and Simmons develops a philosophy for research scientists.

Although the title of Glidewell's article is specific for psychology, the actual content is generic to all mental health researchers. The author illustrates research aimed at learning about the nature of community processes and directed toward evaluation of ongoing programs. Limits set by the values of the social system and how these limits are changing are also cited. Specific attention is directed to the importance of really using what is already known about research design.

Evaluative research concerns itself with the key question: Have the individuals been helped? However, this question then breaks down into many others and relates to three types of evaluative research: ultimate evaluation, preevaluative research, and short-term evaluation. Herzog lists research "don'ts" and "do's" and calls attention to the realities of claims and expectations.

Schwartz suggests three methods of evaluating mental health programs. One technique measures the reduction of rates of symptoms of mental illness such as homicide, drunk driving, mortality, and juvenile delinquency. Another method suggests measurement of rates of preventable mental illness such as the incidence of cretinism, phenylpyruvic oligophrenia, and lead encephalopathy. The last suggestion in the article aims to evaluate mental illness is terms of illness in general.

Colby, Watt, and Gilbert have written a computer program which can conduct psychotherapeutic dialogue. Their article contains examples of the program illustrating how a patient utilizes the computer. A central question is whether or not communication with a computer can benefit a person suffering from mental disorder, and a second question is whether this method can enhance program efficiency.

51

Community Mental Health Research

JOSEPH M. BOBBITT, LESTER M. LIBO,
WILLIAM P. HURDER, AND ALVIN J. SIMMONS

COMMUNITY mental health activities encompass more than what the mental health professions do within and for a community in the name of individual adjustment. Such activities require the redefinition and redirection of mental health services to include the application of theories, methods, and knowledge from sociology, political science, and public health. The binding spirit for the creation and evaluation of such activities is a concern about the patterns of living within the organization of communities.

The point of congruence between these activities and research was thoughtfully examined at a symposium, "Community Mental Health Research: Facts From Fancies," held at the 69th annual convention of the American Psychological Association in New York City, August 31, 1961. This symposium, organized by Dr. James G. Kelly and Dr. J. R. Newbrough of the National Institute of Mental Health, Public Health Service, provided an opportunity for diverse examples of research activities to be discussed. Four of the papers presented at the symposium are briefed in the following pages.

JOSEPH M. BOBBITT:

DEFINING COMMUNITY MENTAL HEALTH

Twenty years ago, the term "community mental health" was not in the vocabulary of psychology. A decade ago, it was used, but ill-defined. It is still ill-defined, and one cannot avoid some effort to deal with its meaning. What operations in the community today aim at the improvement of mental

Reprinted from *Public Health Reports*, 1963, *38*, 57–64, by permission of Public Health Reports and the authors. Dr. Bobbit is Executive Director, Joint Commission on Mental Health of Children. Dr. Libo is Associate Professor and Director, Behavioral Science Program, Department of Psychiatry, University of New Mexico, School of Medicine. Dr. Hurder is Superintendent and Director, Adler Zone Center, Institute for Research on Exceptional Children, Urbana, Illinois. Dr. Simmons is Associate Director, John F. Kennedy Family Service Center, Charlestown, Massachusetts, Assistant Professor, Boston College, and Assistant Psychologist, Massachusetts General Hospital.

health? A listing of such activities may help to determine whether we are dealing with facts, fancies, or possibly, frauds.

First on such a list are treatment efforts. Mental hygiene or mental health clinics and private practitioners have a long history. Both have increased in the last 10 or 15 years, and perhaps there has been some increase in the range of conditions treated, particularly in clinics. In addition, new approaches to treatment are developing: day hospitals, night hospitals, sheltered workshops, and aftercare and rehabilitation programs for patients released from mental hospitals. The growth of psychiatric services in general medical and surgical hospitals has been outstanding. Today more patients are seen for the first time in these facilities than in mental hospitals.

Other new developments are not directly oriented toward treatment. There is a concern about the effects of the whole matrix of community operations upon the mental health of all persons, upon the factors associated with life history and outcome from childhood to maturity. Attention is now given to the mental health effects of school on all children, not merely preoccupation with the classic "problem child." The impact of the work situation and the effects of suburbanization, urban renewal, and the changing pattern of work, recreation, and human relations are being examined. Mental health is being studied in the context of social class variables.

In short, we are becoming self-conscious about the way the community does business, since these modes of community conduct do affect mental health, and we are trying to use the indigenous structures of the community as resources to improve mental health.

A major technique appears to be consultation between mental health professionals and those responsible for a wide range of community services. The states are attempting to develop related programs. The state chief psychologists, co-sponsors of this symposium with the American Psychological Association, face these challenges daily. These new approaches are included as important referents for the term community mental health.

There is also today a renewed interest in what educational and communication techniques can do to support mental health and facilitate the management of the symptomatic or treated person by the community.

How is research related to these new developments?

First, of course, is the need to evaluate. Do clinics help people? What are the measurable effects of schools on personality development? How does the work situation affect the worker and his family? What do suburban living and urban renewal do to a family's style of life and psychological characteristics? Does consultation by mental health specialists actually change the way in which administrators and other professionals behave? Present and changing programs of service and the sociological transitions of our day must be assessed or evaluated. This is one task for research.

Second, research should generate new ideas and innovations. Trends can be influenced by research as well as measured in concurrent or after-the-fact ways. Research can be provocative to those who plan programs.

Finally, what are the scientific concepts and formulations to which these new community activities can be ordered? What are the measures that are to be used? My impression is that a large range of scientific conceptual systems must be utilized, and we can no longer content ourselves with the sick-well continuum. Effectiveness of group function, for instance, cannot be ignored; there is more to be studied than a multiplicity of individuals.

Anthropological, sociological, economic, and political science concepts must be invoked, as well as psychological, psychiatric, and psychoanalytic points of view. The research worker must choose his concepts as carefully as the workman his tools. To understand the increasing complexities of community mental health programs, carefully differentiated and systematic programs of research must be developed. If we enlist our behavioral and social science colleagues to assist us in this task, perhaps we can discriminate fancies and do-goodism from realistic and pragmatic activities that contribute to operationally defined mental health variables.

LESTER M. LIBO:

MENTAL HEALTH CONSULTANTS

"Mental Health Consultation in Underdeveloped Areas" is the title of New Mexico's current state project in community mental health services. Begun in 1959, it stations a lone mental health consultant as a full-time, locally based professional resource person in a two- to four-county district. The program covers three districts. These districts encompass peripheral communities, distant from centers of professional practice and having no other mental health facilities or practitioners.

Serving one district is a nurse mental health consultant; in the second, the community consultant is a psychiatric social worker; and in the third he is a clinical psychologist. They provide case consultation to local health, welfare, education, and law enforcement agencies, and to lawyers, physicians, and clergymen. They serve as sources of information and education to the community at large, conduct inservice training for related professions, and assist in expanding or improving services relevant to mental health programs. A psychiatrist visits each district once a month for consultations. Airplane travel, tape recordings, the telephone, and weekly reports are used for communication between the widely separated service areas and the State office.

Manpower shortages, vast distances between population centers, and lack of specialized agencies and practitioners in mental health dictated this "lone consultant" approach, similar to the county agricultural extension agent.

The goal of the project is to study the development and impact of a novel mental health service program in communities lacking psychiatric facilities. There is careful documentation of all program activities as they are introduced and continued in the three markedly contrasting districts.

The three field consultants participate in research by keeping detailed daily logs of all contacts so that relative emphases on consultation, education, and community organization activities can be compared, and experiences with various agencies and practitioners can be evaluated. Each consultation contact is coded by date, place, agency, and person contacted; whether the consultant was alone or had a collaborator; who initiated the contact; its purpose, what transpired, what materials, if any, were used; how the consultant judged the emotional tone of the contact (positive, negative, neutral, or uncertain); how successful it seemed (to him) to be; and disposition or next steps indicated. Consultants also write reports of local developments, describing community events which have a potential bearing on the mental health program.

A full-time anthropologist is employed to interview community leaders and agency personnel and to study the development of the program. The nature and demands of the role of the community mental health consultant are getting special emphasis.

During the first few months of the project, all communities scheduled to receive the consultation service were visited. Civil leaders, agency staffs, and practitioners were interviewed, prevailing attitudes and practices were ascertained, and mental health facilities and related services available in each town were inventoried. A special effort was made to find out how the idea of a mental health consultation service was being accepted and how potential consumers defined it. Each community was studied prior to the entry of the consultant and soon after his arrival. In each community, response ranged from extremely favorable to extremely unfavorable; some people were gratified to see the beginning of mental health services in the community, and others were frightened about possible interference with their prerogatives or impatient that little or no clinic services were being provided.

New Mexico is a natural laboratory for the study of societies in transition and of cross-cultural relations, with missile centers and Spanish colonial villages, atomic research laboratories and Indian pueblos, uranium boom towns and isolated ranches. Two distinct social philosophies prevail. In the northern, Spanish-influenced counties, the number of welfare recipients is large, the patrón system in business and politics is strong, and family kinship is cherished. In the southern and eastern counties, the rugged individualism of the Wild West and distrust of government prevail. Outside interference is loudly resisted and counter-dependency needs are strong.

To function in these varied settings, the state division of mental health has an unusual staffing pattern. It includes a cultural anthropologist who conducts community interviews and observations and analyzes field reports. The developing mental health program is itself an object of his study. A sociologist specializes in epidemiologic studies. A recent study analyzed first admissions to the state mental hospital to determine characteristics of patients from different areas and social groups. In the services roles, all the primary mental health professions are represented, both in the state office and in the field programs, and an information specialist is also employed.

Several observations can be made about the research aspects during the early stages of this project. A state mental health program is engaged in a wide variety of activities. For the researcher, there are many inviting prospects, but there is also the danger of diffuseness. The research staff can be caught up in the general level of excitability.

The personality of the researcher is crucial. Budgets often do not provide for sufficient staff, so there are attempts to cover large areas with few resources in brief periods of time. Much depends on the ability of the research worker to establish immediate rapport. He must make his contacts in a variety of settings, many of which are social and recreational, while at the same time preserving the integrity of his research role.

Frequently, social scientists, especially anthropologists, accustomed to intensive work in one community, are uncomfortable trying to cover many communities over short periods. Furthermore, the researcher appears as a stranger to the community, and time must be given for greater familiarity before the most meaningful data are obtained.

Confronting respondents with elaborate questionnaires, schedules, and social distance scales may be better postponed until the town's leaders are interviewed informally and the researcher is better known.

The researcher's position within his employing agency is sometimes difficult. In a service agency, he may become a mediator or confidant for various factions because he is new, presumably uncommitted, and, as a research worker, presumably objective. How well he guards confidential material he is given is carefully observed. There is danger that he will try to raise his unclear status in the service agency by showing that he knows more of what is really going on than the service personnel themselves. If he can maintain his position as an objective observer, he has many valuable opportunities to evaluate the place of the mental health program within the agency.

Employing the research staff within a service division means that researchers must analyze the program that employs them. Because of the pitfalls of this situation and because state agency practices in budgeting, purchasing, and travel are often too restrictive for research goals, there is a trend toward establishing private, nonprofit research corporations to handle project funds and personnel.

WILLIAM P. HURDER:

SELLING RESEARCH TO THE COMMUNITY

The charter of the program of training and research in mental health of the Southern Regional Education Board states these objectives: (*a*) to enter upon stronger and more significant state and regional research programs and (*b*) to obtain larger and more effective state and regional training programs.

The staff of the board act as middlemen between the scientific and educational concerns and the legislative and executive branches of state government. This function arises partly because of the unusual character of the board, which is composed of governors, university presidents, legislators, and key administrators of state programs in education and related fields. In effect, the board is a forum which permits continuous conversation about matters of mutual concern to academic and administrative decision makers.

In such a framework the staff has unique opportunities to see the various issues that arise when the goal is selling research and gaining acceptance and realistic support to conduct it. I have selected two issues for consideration: how much to promise when selling a community on research and how to deal with the issue of invading the privacy of individuals in the collection of research data.

Before discussing the issues, however, I must state that in my opinion research on community mental health is at a very primitive stage; much of what is called research is better referred to as preliminary study; most often such "research" would more properly be described as an early stage of counting and sorting followed by preliminary analysis and comparison.

The issue of how much to promise in return for an investment in research is especially critical in mental health research. The combination of a primitive body of substantive and methodological knowledge and the extremes of interest of agencies and individuals poses a serious dilemma to the entrepreneur of community mental health research. Interest ranges from apathy through violent aversion to grossly unrealistic expectations. How does one motivate a community to support an activity which holds so little promise for the immediate solution of problems? How does one clarify the motivations of the researcher or the community for the solution of problems?

One pitch, which I have seen frequently, is give us funds and freedom to apply an "established body of psychological theory" to such community problems as incipient schizophrenia, mental retardation, and juvenile delinquency, and we will demonstrate how mental illness can be prevented, the retarded individual made self-sustaining, and the level of delinquency significantly reduced. In formal supporting documents, aspirations and expectations for the proposed program are usually qualified, and some attention is given to an estimate of the probabilities of success. Rarely, however, are the theoretical bases from which the experimental operations were derived put to critical scrutiny.

The study committees, representatives of the scientific community, almost invariably reject such proposals. The nonscientific community in our experience poses such questions as: Can you really apply things that will work with rats, pigeons, and monkeys directly to human beings? Can you get people in trouble to take part in such experiments? Is it possible or feasible to teach techniques of the type proposed to school teachers, preachers, and such people? If, as we are told by the professionals, normal people have transient periods of mental abnormality, how can a 10-minute test single out one whose abnormality is lasting? Isn't the personality of the director an important factor in the success of this proposal?

The implications of these questions to the issue of how much to promise when selling the community on research are obvious. Don't underestimate the critical faculties of the leaders of the nonscientific community. They know or can find out the limits of effectiveness of present-day knowledge in mental health. The only effective course is absolute honesty in appraising the probabilities that a given piece of research will provide the answers of immediate concern to a community.

What recourse does this leave the research entrepreneur? He must speak largely from faith for any particular method of attack on problems of concern. This faith draws substance largely from analogy to what research has done in other areas of human concern. He can make clear that research findings in the physical and biological sciences came only after prolonged and systematic inquiry. Community leaders need to share this faith in problem solving and they need to know the primitive state of affairs of knowledge if they are to give the kind of support which is meaningful to the goals of both the scientific and nonscientific community. With such an understanding one can speak frankly and realistically of the need for measurements as a standard part of the existing mental health programs of communities.

The second issue, how to deal with the invasion of privacy of individuals as an implied threat of restriction of individual freedom, may flare up when research on human behavior is proposed. Professionals in mental health work are sometimes painfully aware of the misunderstandings and fears generated in studies of attitudes of children toward their parents and their family circumstances, of attitudes of college students toward society, and of attempts at early detection of mental illness among healthy populations.

Professional reactions to this issue vary from ignoring it, to working with community leadership so that a direct and objective examination can be made, to dismissing it with the charge that those who press the issue are either "sick" or "ignorant." If the mental health professionals meet criticism of their community efforts with the charge that those who criticize are expressing symptoms of mental illness, they tend to confirm the charge that "this mental health business" is a form of thought control available for the pursuit of the user's own purpose.

The most helpful single approach to these concerns, in our experience, is to examine the trends for voluntary selection of mental health services. The trend appears to be toward the provision of greater freedom for the individual in need of these services. Examples are the increase in voluntary admissions to State hospitals, the increase in the number of community general hospitals which follow the same admission and discharge procedure for mental patients as for medical surgical patients, and the increases in the numbers of mental health centers, clinics, and practitioners. The trend, in short, has been to increase the freedom of choice by the affected individual and to increase contacts of the citizen with those who have had a mental disorder. Not only are there alternate courses of action within the community but also increasing resources short of hospitalization. A review of these facts is helpful to a lay leader who must take a position with respect to the issue of individual freedom.

As in the first issue, the only reasonable course seems to be for the researcher to rely only on honest statements. Mental health research does constitute some degree of invasion of privacy. This fact can be admitted, and assurance given that the researcher will seek the understanding and acquiescence of the individual respondent. The contribution that any individual can make to the better understanding of man and to our increased ability to help people can be emphasized.

Professionals in mental health have a responsibility to recognize the fundamental dilemma inherent in this issue. As our knowledge of the determinants of behavior increases and the resources for controlling behavior become greater, this problem will force much soul-searching by all segments of the community.

A. J. SIMMONS:

A PHILOSOPHY FOR RESEARCH SCIENTISTS

In the behavioral and social sciences, certain contingencies preclude the kind of explanation, exactness of prediction, degree of generality, and preciseness of control attained in the physical sciences. Because man is both subject and object in the human sciences, the task of the research scientist is even more challenging. Methods, tools, sophistication in instrumentation, and degree of quantification fall far short of the ideal.

Moreover, the behavioral and social sciences rest on assumptions less amenable than the physical sciences to logic, experimentation, or demonstration. The researcher must assume that man's behavior is predictable and purposive. He must use logic and reason to explain illogical or irrational behavior. He is confronted with the truths that most of human behavior is essentially unrepeatable just to the extent that it is merely historical, is more variable and less uniform, and it is much more difficult to isolate one factor at a time. These facts lead the research scientist to question the legitimacy of abstraction, the degree of generalization, and the accuracy of prediction possible in the sciences of man.

Furthermore, in these sciences we do not, as yet, have the elaborate safeguards against false observation that exist in the natural sciences. Because social phenomena are more familiar, we are more likely to be misled as to the amount of accurate knowledge we have about them.

Since man's behavior is interlocked with his environment, isolating and separating him from it is a hazardous if not a false distinction or abstraction. Social situations are networks in which one cannot change one factor without affecting others. Moreover, the behavior of the same individual will not, in general, be the same from one context to another. In the sciences of human behavior, a scientific generalization is a very modest type of assertion. At most, it can only maintain some things about some people in a certain time and place under certain very restricted and precise conditions.

How do these generalizations apply in a specific community mental health agency, the Human Relations Service of Wellesley? The philosophy, orientation, and practices of this agency in which and through which research scientists operate are reflections of both professional and lay society. The agency, for example, practices a dynamically oriented psychiatry, is oriented toward prevention, and adopts an epidemiologic approach toward disease.

The research scientist in community mental health may question the rationale of eradication of disease, and ask what relationships, if any, exist between eradication, prevention, and treatment. Also, within this framework, events and things to be prevented must in some sense be considered undesirable. The researcher's task is to identify such topics, to assess their relationships to mental health and illness, and to investigate the basis for such value judgments by the professional and lay community.

The application of epidemiologic methods to mental health work is an attempt to use a different (but complementary) method from the clinical study of individual patients or the laboratory experiment. Epidemiology concerns itself with the distribution (description) and determinants (analysis) of the occurrence of disease in a population. Use of information gained through such study results in the acquisition of new knowledge about the origins and nature of a disease and explanations of the local characteristics and variations in disease frequency. If such work is linked with prevalence studies in modern communities, some knowledge for the planning of mental health resources, preventive techniques, and educational and therapeutic programs can be obtained. The creativity and resourcefulness of a research scientist may further refine epidemiologic methods and develop a theoretical epidemiology which arranges established facts into orderly chains of inference extending beyond the bounds of direct observation.

Ignorance and impatience on the part of the community as well as his more clinically oriented colleagues often hamper the research scientist in community mental health. Through education, communication, and perseverance he has to destroy images and prejudices while enhancing confidence and cooperation. In short, there needs to be a resolution of the divergent motives and aspirations of the research scientist (intellectual curiosity) and the practitioner (utilitarian ends and the improvement of the human condition). These motives affect the type and scope of research work. However, the research scientist often does not know enough about the actual community to be able to formulate a problem that is immediately relevant to practical needs.

Successful completion of research depends on cooperation between the researcher and his staff and between the community mental health agency and the community. The mixed team approach is not only fraught with the difficulties arising from the fierce loyalty of each member to his own discipline with its own assumptions and methods, but also it is not acceptable to most scientists because they are too individualistic to take cooperative research seriously. However, the research scientist in community mental health should at least contemplate the possibility that only a mixed team can observe adequately and comprehensively the multidimensionality of community events.

In seeking to promote a cooperative effort between a mental health agency and the community, the scientist's obligation and duty is to interpret his activities and objectives. He must make it clear that to be objective is also to have objectives, that he is goal creating while he is being goal directed. In this capacity, the research scientist in community mental health seems obliged to defend basic research and advertise that knowledge per se as well as a detached intellectual curiousity are legitimate and proper whether or not useful results follow. He can thereby avoid reinforcing the gap between the scientific community and the lay community and, in fact, can help bridge this gap by emphasizing the disinterested aspects of knowledge instead of claiming that all scientific discoveries eventually prove useful. There is no evidence to support the claim of usefulness. Such a claim ignores the fact that today, as in the past, men crave for understanding almost as much as for nourishment. When the research scientist compromises the intellectual honesty of the scientific community, he is helping to foster a fundamental skepticism about and even contempt for science itself.

The findings of his research also create certain obligations for the scientist in community mental health. He must report back to the participants in the research, the citizenry of the community, some of whom may have sanctioned, governed, sponsored, and directed the investigation itself. The questions of what to feed back, how, when, and to whom are significant, for the findings will effect some measure of change in the community. The nature and degree of change may now become the subject of scientific inquiry. The process of reporting back to the community should serve to strengthen the image of a mental health agency *of* a community thereby insuring against an image of a mental health agency *in* a community.

The research scientist also is concerned with the dissemination and application of knowledge accumulated through his investigation to his research colleagues or to the operations of the sponsoring facility or to both. In so doing, he sheds the doctrine of the ethical neutrality of science, since he is assuming a responsibility for the way in which his findings are used. That is, the research scientist in community mental health not only says what he knows but also asserts how, when, and where his new knowledge may most appropriately and productively be practiced to maintain health and prevent illness in the specific community. It is not incompatible with a scientific attitude to have a purpose and direction nor does it seem grandiose to feel that, as a research scientist, he has a meaningful role in shaping the functioning of a community.

52

Research Problems in Community Psychology

JOHN C. GLIDEWELL

SOME research in community psychology is aimed at learning about the fundamental nature of community processes; some research is aimed at learning about the fundamental nature of ongoing service programs. Consider first that research which is aimed at cumulative knowledge of community processes —physical, biological and social, as well as specifically psychological. There is a special need to know more and more about how all sorts of interpersonal phenomena make their appearance and run their course in a community. Attitudes, morale, fears, rumors, panics, marriages, divorces, suicides, mass murders, and especially those problems of living most typically called mental illnesses—all of these are community phenomena with psychological aspects about whose appearance and course a great deal more needs to be known. Just knowing more about such processes does not prevent anything or promote anything. Such knowledge may, however, bring to light new points of feasible intervention, like the best age for counseling in school, or the best time for mental health education for young parents—or for aging grandparents.

It is also important to note that detailed and dependable knowledge about how a phenomenon makes its appearance and runs its course in a community is also extremely useful in evaluating the extent to which a program of intervention does, in fact, alter the subsequent stages of the processes. When well-known processes are predictable through time, the need for control groups may be eliminated. (For example, you don't need a control group to tell you what happens when ringworm of the scalp isn't treated.)

Other research in community psychology is aimed at testing the effectiveness of programs of intervention already in progress (like mental health consultation). Evaluation research must try to answer the question: Does the intervention actually do what it is supposed to do? The main thing it is supposed to do is prevent some phenomenon or improve some condition. There are, however, other things which must be studied. Does it reach the population it is supposed to reach? Does it intervene in the community processes at the most propitious time and place? (Emergency detention of drug addicts clearly

From an unpublished paper, 1966, by permission of the author. Dr. Glidewell is Professor of Psychology, University of Chicago.

does not.) Does it produce side effects of significance? (Mental hospitalization clearly does.) Does it produce a supportive and sustaining community response to the intervention? (Uncoordinated release of hallucinating schizophrenics clearly does not.)

Research in community psychology is plagued with problems of measurement, but these problems are not discussed in this paper. They are problems big enough for several other papers.

Research in community psychology is influenced not only by the intellectual objectives of the psychologists but also by the values developed consensually by the members of the social systems which make up the community. Such values make some research easy and other research hard.

In this paper, I shall try to illustrate some research aimed at learning about the nature of community processes; some research aimed at evaluation of ongoing programs. I shall also try to point out some of the limits set by the values of the social systems within which the research is done, and how the limits may be changing. I shall say nothing new. I shall try to illustrate the importance of really using what is already known about research design.

SURVEILLANCE OF COMMUNITY PROCESSES

Some research in community psychology is aimed at cumulative knowledge of community processes. This kind of research requires repeated assessments of the correlates of the appearance and course of a phenomenon in a community. It requires multiple correlational designs in many replications, on cohorts and on changing populations. It seeks both actuarial patterns and isolated relationships.

THE SEARCH FOR PATTERNS

There is much to be learned from correlated patterns as they occur in nature. Such patterns set specifications which allow prediction and forewarning; and sometimes, prevention.

For example, in some of our correlational studies of maternal attitudes (11, 24), the data showed (Table 1) that every mother who felt potent to influence the outcome of a behavior problem in her child also felt responsible to try to influence the outcome (the 364 mothers in column 1, Table 1). There were other mothers who felt responsible, but not potent (the 80 mothers in column 2, row 1). Still others felt neither responsible nor potent (the 91 mothers in column 2, row 2). The other hypothethetically possible category did not occur in nature. There were, in our sample, simply no mothers at all who felt potent to influence the outcome of a behavior problem and, at the same time, *not* responsible for exerting such an influence.

TABLE 1. PATTERNS OF MATERNAL ATTITUDES

	1 *Felt* *Potent*	*2* *Felt Impotent*	*3* *Total*
1. Felt *responsible* for the outcome of her child's behavior problem	364	80	444
2. Felt *not responsible* for the outcome of her child's behavior problem	—	91	91
3. Total	364	171	535

Under these conditions, we may study the actuarial relationship of two simultaneous variables—responsibility and potency—to the adjustment of the child. We cannot isolate the relationship between adjustment and either one of the two attitude variables. Nevertheless, the pattern is interesting. In part, the pattern is interesting in itself, interesting as knowledge about maternal conceptions of their role. The varying prevalence of the pattern in different parts of the community was interesting, also; the variations in the prevalence reflected variations in the social and economic conditions under which the families lived. In addition to the intrinsic interest, the pattern improved our ability to predict adjustment. Although we could not isolate its association with either one of the two attitude variables, the improvement in predictability was very important and supportive for a mental health consultant on a home visit with a public health nurse. Data about feelings of potency are considerably more enabling for a public health nurse than data about social class.

Such patterns have long been studied, and in their most complex form. We have studied patterns of living arrangements and disability in search of intervention points in the social processes of aging (12). Sears and his colleagues (35) used the term and the approach in their study of patterns of child rearing practices. Guttman's circumplex model is a design for dealing with patterns in two basic dimensions (20), and Schaefer has applied it in community mental health (33, 34). Kramer and his staff have used the approach in national surveillance of community mental health services (25). Patterns of attitudes toward the mentally ill have been widely studied. The report of the Joint Commission is a good example (19). Freilich and Hirsch (9) have examined such patterns in rural Missouri. The work of Freeman (8) in England and Frets (10) in South Holland are excellent examples of non-quantitative pattern analyses. The search for "cookbooks" in clinical psychology is a search for predictive actuarial diagnostic patterns (30). I conclude that the search for patterns is a feasible and productive enterprise, worth much investment for a psychologist.

THE ISOLATION OF RELATIONSHIPS

While actuarial prediction is readily available from patterns of correlated data, one often has reason to isolate the relationships between two variables, independent of their correlates. Partial correlation designs, and part-correlation designs, based upon multiple regression, have been highly developed for such work (7). The designs sometimes seem complicated, and they take the investigator many computational steps away from his raw data, but they can be exceedingly useful in trying to understand multivariate community phenomena.

Partial correlation designs are not limited to multiple regression analysis, however, and it seems to me useful to illustrate a simple design with categorical data. In a study of behavior symptoms in children in St. Louis County by Mensh and his colleagues (13, 32), it was possible to show the relationships between symptoms of withdrawal and teachers' ratings of adjustment, while by analysis of contingency tables, sex and social class were, in effect, "partialed out."

The data in Table 2 show how, in a sample of school children, the rela-

TABLE 2. THE RELATIONSHIP BETWEEN SYMPTOMS OF WITHDRAWAL AND TEACHERS' RATINGS OF ADJUSTMENT, SEX AND SOCIAL CLASS BEING CONSTANT

Boys	Lower Class			Middle Class			Upper Class		
	+	−	Σ	+	−	Σ	+	−	Σ
Well adjusted	00	104	104	11	133	144	01	13	14
Maladjusted	06	79	85	07	49	56	03	12	15
Total	06	183	189	18	182	200	04	25	29
Chi-square (1 df)	$\chi^2 = 5.46$[a]			$\chi^2 = 0.65$			$\chi^2 = 0.22$[a]		
Girls									
Well adjusted	06	166	172	08	139	147	00	12	12
Maladjusted	12	25	37	03	30	33	00	08	08
Total	18	191	209	11	169	180	00	20	20
Chi-square (1 df)	$\chi^2 = 28.84$			$\chi^2 = 0.15$[a]			$\chi^2 = 0.00$		
ΣChi-square (2 df)	$\Sigma\chi^2 = 34.30$			$\chi^2 = 0.80$			$\Sigma\chi^2 = 0.22$		
ΣΣChi-square (6 df)	$\Sigma\Sigma\chi^2 = 35.32$						p < .001		

[a] Computed on small theoretical frequencies for illustrative purposes.

tionship between withdrawal symptoms and teachers' ratings can be examined while two contaminating correlates—sex and social class—are held constant. The data show that children rated as maladjusted show a higher prevalence of withdrawal symptoms in all but one of the six subclasses defined by the two sexes and the three social classes. The summed chi-square is significant at a high level of confidence. The findings confirm that the tested relationship exists —and independent of the two correlates, sex and social class.

The contingency tables, however, yield more information than parametric partial correlation methods. Partial correlation, in accord with its assumptions, produces an average correlation over all values of the "constant" variable. Table 2 shows that the relationship is very largely confined to the lower-class children and even more narrowly to lower-class girls. Accordingly, this design makes it possible not only to "partial out" sex and social class, but also to determine the variations in the relationship over the several values of the variables being held constant. Similar attempts to isolate specific relationships were characteristic of the work of Graham (18) on brain injury in children, Hollingshead and Redlich (21), and Srole and his colleagues (38).

IMPLICATIONS OF CAUSATION

A crucial aspect of surveillance research is that assessments are repeated, time after time. Under some conditions, subject to specification, the time dimension makes it possible to infer causation from correlational data. Lazarsfeld (26) has made much of the time component in his panel studies. Campbell and Stanley (6) have elaborated Lazarsfeld's "sixteenfold" matrix design and its implications for causation. I shall not attempt an elaboration of Campbell, but I would strongly recommend a careful review of his work on "Quasi-experimental designs" (5) to anyone involved in community mental health research—especially surveillance research. Starting from the work of Simon (36), Blalock (2, 3) has clarified a number of conditions under which causation can be inferred from correlational data.

I have tried to propose that much can be learned from the surveillance of community processes—patterns of development whether in children, families, neighborhoods, or diseases; isolated relationships between two variables, continuous or categorical; and even implications of causation. All such data can be highly relevant—without mounting a single experiment—to the question of when, where, how, and with whom to intervene into community processes, whether one intends to prevent something or promote something.

SCIENTIFIC EVALUATION OF ONGOING PROGRAMS

Some research in community psychology is aimed at the evaluation of the effectiveness of ongoing programs. Both MacMahon (28) and Bloom (4) have published comprehensive reviews of approaches and designs for evaluation of community programs. The central question in evaluation research has to do with whether or not the intervention actually induced the outcome intended. The most aggravating thing about evaluation is that it often requires withholding services on a random basis—to create a comparable control group. If the service is an old and well-established one, withholding it for research is often seen as unfair deprivation. It *can* be seen as an immoral breach of ethics. Practitioners are often under oath to provide services, as well as they know how, to anyone in need of the service who comes to their attention.

STUDY OF COMMUNITY RESPONSE

Entry into evaluation research is often more nearly feasible if one begins by studying subsidiary questions. Does the service program reach the population most at risk? Does it come at a propitious time? Does it receive overt acceptance? What are its side effects?

One organization had kept systematic records of a number of variables related to its mental health education program. The records, however, were never systematically reviewed or studied. As in many community mental health agencies, the records were just collected.

Armstrong (1) subjected the available data to treatment which: (1) provided an annual summary, (2) could be accomplished in a few days, and (3) gave some insight into the nature of the community's reaction to, and acceptance of, the program. The outcome was a small correlational study, using dichotomized data and tetrachoric correlation coefficients, which could be quickly computed using Thurstone's computing diagrams (39). The findings for one year are reproduced in Table 3.

TABLE 3. INTERRELATIONS BETWEEN VARIABLES RECORDED FOR 193 GROUP DISCUSSION PROGRAMS IN MENTAL HEALTH EDUCATION *

	D. L. Eval.	*Phys. Sit.*	*Ldr. Effect*	*Prev. Req.*	*Supsq. Req.*	*No. Attng.*	*Social Class*
	2	3	4	5	6	7	8
1. Program chairman's evaluation	.54	.39	.48	−.05	.05	.16	−.02
2. Discussion leader's evaluation		.50	.20	−.10	.16	−.08	−.00
3. Adequacy of physical situation			.16	−.03	.29	−.14	−.23
4. Ratings of leader effectiveness				.10	.25	−.07	−.10
5. Programs previously requested					.62	−.40	.10
6. Programs subsequently requested						−.50	.33
7. Number of persons attending							−.34
8. Social class of neighborhood							

* Tetrachoric correlation coefficients

The coefficients have been grouped in Table 3 to show two remarkably independent clusters: (1) concerning satisfaction and dissatisfaction, and (2) concerning the social organization of the participating groups, their size, social class, and the extent of their requests for programs (12).

The reported satisfaction of the discussion leader and the client group's program chairman are associated with the physical setting and the effectiveness of the leader, in the first cluster. This cluster is, however, generally—and surprisingly—unrelated to the second. This second cluster indicates that small middle-class groups repeatedly ask for mental health education programs, but that the large, working-class groups are not "repeaters." While the small middle-class groups repeatedly request the programs, their expressions of their evaluative judgments are negative as often as positive. It is clear that requesting programs did not "cause" their social class, although both may have been caused by the same factor—like the values placed on education. It would be interesting to report and evaluate all the various dynamics which have been proposed to explain these findings about groups who repeatedly ask for programs they often do not like, but my subject is research design.

Such studies as the one cited can take special advantage of all the developments of correlational design. They can be repeated regularly to provide the required replication, because they use routinely recorded data. They make few demands for time; no demands for controls. They never answer the ultimate evaluation question, but they provide findings from which much functional understanding and service improvement can come.

EXPERIMENTAL PREVENTIVE INTERVENTION

The easiest true experiment to mount is that which is designed to test the effects of a new and untried service. Such a new service has not yet been professionally approved or codified. To establish a control group, it is not necessary to withhold service; just to postpone it.

One very careful evaluation project has been designed and conducted in St. Louis County—on new services (Fig. 1). It was possible to mount an incomplete blocks design with some new variations. The variations were both interesting and useful. Note in Figure 1 that the first and last rows extend the standard I-B design. The details of the extensions have been discussed previously (15).

It was possible randomly to assign pairs of classrooms in fifteen elementary schools to three treatment levels: (1) a dual program of in-school services and education, (2) mental health education only, and (3) controls. It took a full year to mount the experiment—a year of community discussion—and community modification of the plans. About 5 per cent of the sample refused to participate. A schematic representation of the design is shown in Figure 1. After the experiment was completed, a detailed analysis of how well it worked was published (13). The retrospective analysis showed that (1) a series of small homogeneous experimental units can produce satisfactory data—if the data are not to be often subdivided in analysis; (2) pretesting and selection can be controlled by homogenization only if restricted generalization is acceptable; (3) standardized variation in experimental program availability is difficult to maintain over even a one-year period: (4) determining a time interval short enough for program constancy and long enough to demonstrate program effects

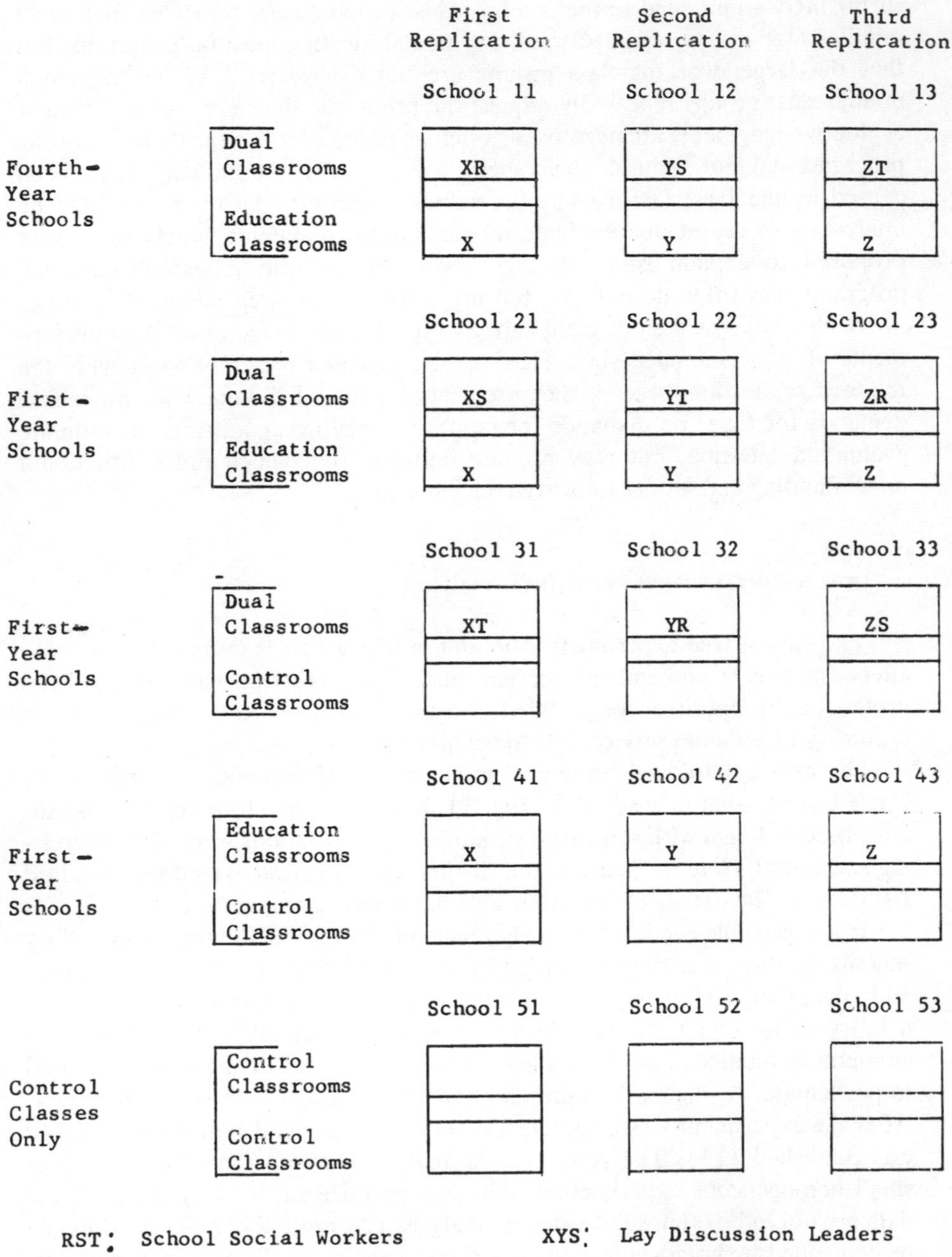

		First Replication	Second Replication	Third Replication

		School 11	School 12	School 13
Fourth-Year Schools	Dual Classrooms	XR	YS	ZT
	Education Classrooms	X	Y	Z

		School 21	School 22	School 23
First-Year Schools	Dual Classrooms	XS	YT	ZR
	Education Classrooms	X	Y	Z

		School 31	School 32	School 33
First-Year Schools	Dual Classrooms	XT	YR	ZS
	Control Classrooms			

		School 41	School 42	School 43
First-Year Schools	Education Classrooms	X	Y	Z
	Control Classrooms			

		School 51	School 52	School 53
Control Classes Only	Control Classrooms			
	Control Classrooms			

RST: School Social Workers   XYS: Lay Discussion Leaders

Fig. 1.—Schematic Representation of an Incomplete Blocks Design Applied to the Evaluation of Community Mental Health Programs (Ref. 15)

was the most difficult design problem; (5) control by randomization, in fact as well as in theory, can reduce the probability of contamination of extraneous variables but it cannot eliminate the possibility of the contamination; (6) control of the interaction effects of the independent experimental variable and the subject characteristics is accomplished more effectively by restricting variation than by randomization. Variables requiring special attention were the act of pretesting, selection, prior experience, sex, social class, family structure, initial level of adjustment, variations in assessment methods, sample reduction, and the experimental side effect of creating a sense of relative deprivation in randomly designated control groups.

One particular defect in the St. Louis design was its vulnerability to mortality. The design was effective for only those families whose children remained in the same school for three years. Only half of them did, and the study ended with a sample half as large as that with which it began. The findings are generalizable only to families whose children stay in the same school for three years.

Hutchison has suggested that the critical research problem is *not* to identify a representative sample of a population to which one wishes to generalize, but rather, starting with an available sample, to decide just what population it is a sample of. Perhaps his pessimism is justified.

Kantor has been able to take advantage of the local movements of the subjects in that experiment to study the effects of short-range mobility on adjustment in school (23). While such studies of mobility are much needed, also much needed are designs which are not so vulnerable to mortality. If one studies a community as it changes, from birth, death, in-migration, out-migration, etc., one must take account of the varying composition of the community. Kantor's work makes clear that the migrants are from a significantly different population. If one studies a nonmobile cohort, one must study an atypical group. It is an area for much more work to develop designs for community psychology.

VALUES RELEVANT TO RESEARCH

ART AND SCIENCE

I would like to propose that the social systems making up communities of the United States are experiencing a change in values. For a number of decades a greater and greater value has been placed on scientific underpinnings for professional practice. At the same time, intuition is still an essential component of professional practice. Internships, residencies, field training and clinical training are strongly valued and are specifically aimed at the development of intuition and sensitivity in the intern. Especially in public health, acts of intuitive competence have been recorded and rewarded—at least since

1854, when Snow, in famous and brilliant intuitive extrapolation from a very limited pre-germ theory of disease, stopped a cholera epidemic in London by removing the handle from the Broad Street Pump (37).

EVALUATION AND SCIENCE

I would also propose another change is in progress. There are more and more insistent demands for scientific evaluation of existing community services in health, education, and welfare. I maintain the position (supported previously by Glidewell and Domke (16), that the fact that there are so few scientific underpinnings for community services places a great obligation on the scientist-practitioner to demonstrate that one is, in fact, moving toward his objectives. On the other hand, public health engineers tell me that no case of communicable disease has ever been traced—with scientific rigor—to a dirty dish in a restaurant. Restaurant inspection, nevertheless, continues relentlessly. The community has come to depend upon professional inspection of restaurants for their protection. To stop the inspections would be a very real and important threat.

I propose that the same situation applies to mental hospitals. Some communities—although not yet a majority of them—have come to depend upon the hospitalization of the mentally ill. The dependency may develop from perceptions like these: as crazy as psychologists may be, it takes more than responsible citizenship to cope with the kinds of crippling or bizarre behavior disturbances I have sometimes seen in my neighbors. Although research may some day demonstrate that psychotherapy is no more than purchased friendship to most laymen it takes the professional skills of trained specialists to recognize and resolve emotional disturbances—by consultation or by direct services.

McGavran (29) has suggested that no widespread communicable disease has been reduced in incidence (new case rate) by early identification and treatment. Apparently the major influence on reduced incidence has been some form of environmental manipulation. Nevertheless, unproven as it may be, it makes sense to many citizens that early recognition of very mild problems makes possible early treatment, and early treatment—or even early attention —should be easier and more effective than late treatment or late attention.

These apparently sensible ideas may well be contradicted by rigorous scientific experimentaiton. Mendel (31) insists they must be. The experimental findings, I propose, would jeopardize the old safeguards—inadequate and mythical as they may have been—against the insidious onset and frightening threat of mental illness. Unless the new knowledge implies some new safeguards, I submit, the new knowledge may be questioned, denied, distorted, ignored, or otherwise evaded.

The point is that certain professional safeguards are really needed in highly specialized social systems such as those in which we live. Evaluation research is demanded; its results are likely to yield improvements in service. As James (22) has pointed out, however, both intervention and evaluation have multiple outcomes. New negative findings may jeopardize both valid and invalid professional safeguards—safeguards really needed to protect the community from preventable illness or injury.

HUMANITY AND SCIENCE

I would propose a third change in values. The shifting balance between the good of the individual and the good of the community—always an unstable equilibrium—leans more and more toward the postponement of help for the one individual in the interest of improving help for the many individuals making up the community. The first flag is conservation. Resources in mental health are scarce; they must be used to provide the most good for the most people. Practitioners ask some to wait, while others, judged to be more in need, are served.

Training gives another signal. The best trained and most experienced practitioners cannot be available to all. Interns, trainees, and residents are available, and under supervision; they must serve in order to learn.

Then there is research. Experience in approaching citizens of St. Louis County as research subjects has made it clear that in that population the most productive and equitable relationship is one based on the understanding that the research will do *the individual* no good at all. The subject is being asked to help the community to try to improve services for all; as an individual there is no direct gain for him. Perhaps, indirectly, through the community, he may profit—if the research happens to be that rare successful project which actually does influence the community services.

The current trend in values relevant to research design in community mental health can be summarized as trends toward the following viewpoints: professional practice ought to be an artful extrapolation from a growing scientific knowledge, but the community demands some *possibly* valid protective or preventive services without regard to scientific base; professional practice ought to be under constant objective evaluation, but one cannot flatly discredit professionally well-established and apparently valid procedures without jeopardizing the professional safeguards needed to protect the client and the community; the good of the individual client ought not to be superceded by the good of the community but, because of needs for training and learning with limited resources, service to the individual client must sometimes be postponed in the interest of the community.

SUMMARY

I have proposed that the problems of research in community psychology require fuller exploitation of known methods—actuarial and correlational techniques—for a meaningful surveillance of community processes; careful retrospection, quasi-experimental, and experimental evaluation of new services; new designs to deal with problems of timing and sample loss in longitudinal experiments on community cohorts. I have also proposed authentic attention to the changing values of the community and its practitioners who must use the product of the research.

REFERENCES

1. Armstrong, J. *Program evaluation research.* St. Louis: Mental Health Association of St. Louis, 1958.
2. Blalock, H. M., Jr. *Social statistics.* New York: McGraw-Hill, 1960.
3. Blalock, H. M., Jr. Correlation and causality: The multivariate case. *Social Forces,* 1961, 39:246–51.
4. Bloom, B. L. Mental health program evaluation 1955–1964. *Public Health Monographs,* 1966.
5. Campbell, D. T. Factors relevant to the validity of experiments in social settings. *Psychol. Bull.,* 1957: 297–312.
6. Campbell, D. T., and Stanley, J. C. Experimental designs for research on teaching. In N. L. Gage (Ed.), *Handbook of research on teaching.* Chicago: Rand McNally, 1963.
7. DuBois, P. *Multivariate correlational analysis.* New York: Harper, 1957.
8. Freeman, H. Progress to community care in an English city. A paper prepared for the International Research Seminar on Evaluation of Community Mental Health Programs, National Institute of Mental Health, Airlie House, Virginia, May 17–21, 1966.
9. Freilich, M., and Hirsh, P. M. Mental health culture in rural Missouri. A report prepared for the Missouri Division of Mental Diseases, Jefferson City, Mo., 1965.
10. Frets, F. W. Epidemiological and evaluative research within the social psychiatric service in the province of South Holland. A paper prepared for the International Research Seminar on Evaluation of Community Mental Health Programs, National Institute of Mental Health, Airlie House, Virginia, May 17–21, 1966.
11. Gildea, M. C.-L. Maternal attitudes and general adjustment in school children. In J. C. Glidewell (Ed.), *Paternal attitudes and school behavior.* Springfield, Ill.: Charles C Thomas, 1961.
12. Glidewell, J. C. Mental health discussion groups for parents in St. Louis. *Adult Leadership,* 1961, 10:4–24.
13. Glidewell, J. C. Mother's reports of symptoms and behavior disturbances in children. A working paper. Clayton, Mo.: St. Louis County Health Dept., 1966.
14. Glidewell, J. C. Some methodological problems in the evaluation of school mental health programs. In N. S. Greenfield (Ed.), *Comprehensive mental health: The challenge of evaluation.* Madison, Wis.: University of Wisconsin Press, 1967.
15. Glidewell, J. C., Mensh, I. N., Domke, H. R., Gildea, M. C.-L., and Buchmueller, A. D. Methods for community mental health research. *American J. Orthopsychiat.,* 1957, 27:38–51.

16. Glidewell, J. C., and Domke, H. R. Health department research in community mental health. *Amer. J. Publ. Hlth.,* 1958, 48:362–68.
17. Glidewell, J. C., Eller, C. H., and Tuthill, E. *A survey of physical limitations of parents of adult children.* Clayton, Mo.: St. Louis County Health Dept., 1961.
18. Graham, F. K. Brain injury in the preschool child: Some developmental considerations. *Psychol. Monogr.,* 1963 (No. 573).
19. Gurin, G., Verhoff, J., and Feld, S. *Americans view their mental health.* New York: Basic Books, 1960.
20. Guttman, L. A. A new approach to factor analysis: The radex. In P. F. Lazarsfeld (Ed.), *Mathematical thinking in the social sciences.* New York: Free Press, 1954.
21. Hollingshead, A. B., and Redlich, F. C. *Social class and mental illness: A community study.* New York: Wiley, 1958.
22. James, G. Evaluation in public health practice. *Amer. J. Publ. Hlth.,* 1962, 52:1145–54.
23. Kantor, M. B. A study of some consequences of physical and social mobility for the adjustment of children. In M. B. Kantor (Ed.), *Mobility and mental health.* Springfield, Ill.: Charles C Thomas, 1965.
24. Kantor, M. B., Glidewell, J. C. Mensh, I. N., Domke, H. R., and Gildea, M. C.-L. Socio-economic levels and maternal attitudes toward parent-child relationships. *Human Organization,* 1958, 16:44–48.
25. Kramer, M., Pollack, E. S., Locke, B. Z., and Bahn, A. K. National approach to evaluation of community-mental health programs. *Amer. J. Publ. Hlth.,* 1961, 57:969–79.
26. Lazarsfeld, P. F. (Ed.) *Mathematical thinking in the social sciences.* New York: Free Press, 1954.
27. Lipset, S. M., Lazarsfeld, P. F., Barton, A. H., and Linz, J. The psychology of voting: An analysis of political behavior. In G. Lindzey, *Handbook of social psychology.* Cambridge, Mass.: Addison-Wesley, 1954.
28. MacMahon, B., Pugh, T. F., and Hutchinson, G. B. Principles in the evaluation of community mental health programs. *Amer. J. Publ. Hlth.,* 1961, 51:963–68.
29. McGavran, E. G. Facing reality in public health. In *Key issues in the prevention of alcoholism.* A report of the Northeast Conference. Harrisburg, Pa.: Pennsylvania Dept. of Health, 1963.
30. Mehl, P. E. Wanted—a good cookbook, *Amer. Psychol.,* 1956, 11:263–72.
31. Mendel, W. M. On the abolition of the psychiatric hospital. In N. S. Greenfield (Ed.), *Comprehensive mental health: The challenge of evaluation.* Madison, Wis.: University of Wisconsin Press, 1967.
32. Mensh, I. N., Kantor, M. B., Domke, H. R., Gildea, M. C.-L., and Glidewell, J. C. Children's behavior symptoms and their relationships to emotional adjustment, sex, and social class. *J. Soc. Issues,* 1959, 15(1):8–15.
33. Schaefer, E. S. A. circumplex model for maternal behavior. *J. Abnor. Soc. Psychol.,* 1959, 59:226–35.
34. Schaefer, E. S. Converging conceptual models for maternal behavior and for child behavior. In J. C. Glidewell, *Parental attitudes and behavior.* Springfield, Ill.: Charles C Thomas, 1961.
35. Sears, R. R., Macoby, Eleaner, E., and Levin, H. *Patterns of child-rearing.* Evanston, Ill.: Harper & Row, 1957.

36. Simon, H. A. Spurious correlation: A causal interpretation. *J. Amer. Stat. Assoc.,* 1954, 49:467–79.
37. Snow, J. *On cholera.* New York: Commonwealth Fund, 1936.
38. Srole, L., Langner, T. S., Michael, S. T., Opler, M. K., and Rennie, T. A. C. *Mental health in the metropolis: The Midtown Manhattan study,* Vol. 1. New York: McGraw-Hill, 1962.
39. Thurstone, L. L., Chesire, L., and Shaffir, M. *Computing diagrams for the tetrachoric correlation coefficient.* Chicago. University of Chicago Bookstore, 1933.

53

How Much Are They Helped?
Some Notes on Evaluative Research

ELIZABETH HERZOG

ONE of the most difficult—and most desired—types of evaluative research has to do with determining the effectiveness of efforts to bring about
social or emotional change in individuals. A number of therapies and services
are directed toward such change—for example, psychotherapy, social casework,
groupwork, services to prevent juvenile delinquency and to treat delinquents,
and certain aspects of parent and family-life education.

Efforts to bring about psychosocial change in individuals are directed
toward helping them deal with difficulties in social and psychological functioning. Efforts to evaluate ask: have the individuals been helped? This key
question, however, is a very unstable compound. Under examination it breaks
down into a cluster of questions: which ones have been helped? how much?
how stable is the help? was it really the treatment or something else that
helped? who says so? and how do we know it is true?

Such questions are challenging enough when raised about the effectiveness
of a single practitioner. When the reports of many practitioners or agencies
are combined or compared, a different kind of question is added: Were they
all defining help in the same way? Did they all begin with problems of the
same or comparable difficulty? Were the individuals they worked with equally
capable of change? Were the improvements noted comparable in kind or degree
or stability?

The history of evaluative research shows increasing recognition of the
questions that must be answered, increasing awareness that they cannot be
answered quickly or simultaneously, and increasing efforts to lay the groundwork for defining them, setting priorities for them and attacking them in due
order. The present discussion concerns only research assessing the effectiveness of efforts to bring about social and emotional change in individuals.
However, some of the principles involved would apply to any evaluative research.

A review of the literature, reinforced by discussions with research people,

Reprinted from *Children,* 1958, 5, 203–209, by permission of Children, U.S. Depart-
ment of Health, Education, and Welfare, Social Security Administration, Children's
Bureau and the author. Dr. Herzog is Chief, Child Life Studies Branch, U.S. Children's
Bureau.

shows a rather neat grouping of points on which the "experts" do and do not agree. They agree on the need for evaluative research, on the complexity of the problems it presents, and on the fact that so far no one has solved these manifold problems to the complete satisfaction of himself or anyone else. They agree also that even before its problems are solved, great values are to be gained from the right kind of evaluative research. Some of these values lie in its results, some in the gains derived from the process itself.

On the whole, the experts agree also about the questions that ought to be answered in any sound evaluative study. The individual researcher does not always answer each one of these questions himself, nor is it always possible to do so. But on being asked, trained and experienced research people are very likely to concede that these are the questions which *should* be answered. They tend to disagree about the best means of answering them and about what constitutes an adequate answer.

THE QUESTIONS

It is generally agreed that a satisfactory evaluation of efforts to bring about psychological change in individuals should deal directly with the following questions:

I. About the study: What is the purpose of the evaluation? (What is to be achieved by doing it?)

II. About the efforts that are to be evaluated: (a) What kind of change is desired? (From what and to what? Known by what signs? In whom?) (b) By what means is change to be brought about? (What method is used—in theory? What method is used—in practice? By whom is the method used?)

III. About the methods used for assessing change: (a) How trustworthy are the categories and measures employed? (How reliable are they? How valid are they?) (b) At what points is change measured? (From what base? After what interval?) (c) How fairly do the individuals studied represent the group discussed? How is the sample selected and defined?) (d) What is the evidence that the changes observed are due to the means employed? (What controls, if any, are used?)

IV. About the findings: (a) What is the meaning of the changes found? (How satisfactory?) (b) Were there unexpected consequences? (Of means employed? Of research or researcher?)

To different degrees and in different ways, these questions are interrelated. Some interlock so closely that it is impossible to consider one without simultaneously considering the other. Some depend on each other in such a way that the second cannot be raised until the first has been settled. Moreover, they are questions of different kinds. Those in group III are primarily the responsibility of the researcher. He cannot even pose the questions clearly, however, until he has answers to groups I and II, which are primarily the responsibility of the practice field as represented by the agency of organization that initiates the research. To say that the first two groups of questions are primarily the responsibility of the field, however, is not to imply that they can be answered by the practitioner alone—unless he is also a researcher—for the answers must be in terms that lend themselves to research.

To the best of our knowledge, no study has ever fully answered all of these questions. Merely stating them defines a dilemma between what is wanted and what can be delivered.

One view of this dilemma is suggested by three terms applicable to three kinds of evaluative research:

1. *Ultimate evaluation* refers to the kind of evaluation that everyone wants most. The practitioner, the public, the administrative official, the supporting contributor, all want evidence now of the degree to which the practice or service under examination helps the people it serves. With regard to psychotherapy, they want to know the effectiveness of psychotherapy in general or of a particular school of psychotherapy. Similarly, those working with juvenile delinquents want to know, for example, the effectiveness of probationary services and the relative effectiveness of different types of probation. Or they may want the answer to analogous questions about training schools or preventive measures.

Unfortunately, research cannot produce here and now the *ultimate evaluation* of efforts to bring about psychosocial change in individuals. And probably the evaluative questions will need to be reformulated and sharpened if "ultimate" answers are ever to be secured. To discuss the effectiveness of psychotherapy in general, for example, may prove to be as unfruitful as discussing the effectiveness of surgery in general.

2. *Pre-evaluative research* refers to the kind of studies that will be necessary to answer the questions that must be faced before fully satisfactory evaluative studies can be made. Pre-evaluative research will be needed on most of the questions listed before ultimate evaluation will be feasible—questions about what change is to be produced, in whom, by what means, by whom, and the like.

Such research will contribute to practice as well as to ultimate evaluation. It will contribute also to reformulating our ideas about what is desired from ultimate evaluation. As diagnostic classifications and treatment goals and methods are more sharply defined, for example, the focus of the evaluative question is likely to be sharpened so that we may no longer be asking how effective is psychotherapy or social casework in general, but, rather, how effective is such-and-such a kind of treatment in producing such-and-such changes in such-and-such kinds of people.

3. *Short-term evaluation* means research that can be accomplished within a few years. Such research is possible and useful here and now. It is possible without extensive pre-evaluative research to give properly qualified answers to properly qualified questions about the effectiveness of treatment or service by a specific agency or individual, with a specified population. Properly

qualified answers would state clearly the limitations of the methods employed, observe the rules of evidence, make no generalizations beyond the limits of the data.

Short-term evaluation can often be done in a way that meets research requirements, fills immediate need, and at the same time contributes to pre-evaluative research. It cannot, however, give the answers that many people want most. These require evaluation, which in turn demands many pre-evaluative studies.

Apparently evaluative research assessing social or emotional change is at an interesting crossroad where it seems necessary to proceed in *both* directions at once. Fortunately, there are enough travelers to deploy forces along both routes. It is necessary to conduct pre-evaluative research in the effort to come nearer to the long-term goal of ultimate evaluation—recognizing that this goal may have changed its outlines somewhat before we finally reach it. It is also necessary to do whatever can be done with more approximate and less complete efforts at short-term evaluation, as background to immediate steps and decisions. Whatever type of evaluative or pre-evaluative research is undertaken can contribute to the other type—if and only if it observes the rules of evidence, explicitness, and restraint that are binding on any research.

Some practical implications of these points can be summarized under a number of "do's" an "don'ts" for evaluative research.

SOME RESEARCH "DON'TS"

Don't undertake evaluative research if the purpose can be served by some other kind. It is expensive, time-consuming, difficult, and not always successful. If the purpose is to contribute to professional knowledge and understanding, a pre-evaluative study is likely to be more directly rewarding. If an evaluative answer is urgently needed, the answer can often be secured—or approximated —by quicker, more feasible and less costly types of research, such as fact-finding or survey studies. Accordingly, short-term evaluation should be undertaken only if thorough consideration of the purpose shows no other feasible way of proceeding.

For example, a proposal was made to evaluate an ambitious program of individual treatment at a training school for boys. A simple survey revealed, however, that the current staff lacked the qualifications necessary to carry out the program as formulated, and in addition labored under a time schedule which precluded giving the boys any but the most superficial, perfunctory, and unindividualized attention. In this instance, analysis of actual operations, as compared with stated objectives, showed that there would be small gain in carrying forward an elaborate "evaluation" of a program not yet operative.

Don't undertake evaluative research unless adequate resources are available. Adequate resources include money, staff, and time, with assurance of continuity since interruptions can be wasteful and also harmful to final results.

The question is often raised, can adequate research be done in an organization that does not have a full-blown research department? To this the most straightforward answer is that full-blown research requires full-blown research people. It is usually a mistake to think that satisfactory research—evaluative or otherwise—can be done by a practicing staff under the guidance of a part-time research consultant. The demands are too heavy. Any substantial research project requires full-time research staff plus full collaboration from practitioners.

Agency administrators who undertake research are often unprepared for the amount of practitioners' time required by a research project—the more able the research staff, the more consultation they are likely to want from the practitioners. The canny administrator will count such time as part of his research budget and will not attempt to add a research project, department, or worker without making due allowance either by increasing the number of practitioners or decreasing the number of their cases during the time they are involved in research. For example, the report of a study of short-term cases says that preparation of schedules and instructions took many months of discussion and tryout by the planning committee—including highly trained caseworkers; and that, once the study was under way, the administration allowed participating staff members 20 to 30 minutes after each interview to fill out schedules, cutting down their caseloads accordingly during the time of the study (6).

Administrators are probably less surprised than they used to be at the length of time that elapses before a research project is completed. It may, for example, take 6 months to track down the subjects for a modest followup study. If tape recording is used, the requirements in time and money approach the fabulous. Carl Rogers has reported that the transcription of one 40-interview case filled over 300 single-spaced typed pages (10).

Don't count on using existing agency records as the sole source of data for an evaluative study. Case records make such interesting and instructive reading that it is hard to believe they would not furnish a satisfactory basis for evaluative research. Yet again and again investigators find that they do not. The needed items of information are seldom included in every record. When present, they are seldom comparable in explicitness, detail, and documentation. Exorbitant amounts of time may be spent trying to discover the most elementary facts about a case. If relatively recent records are used there may be serious problems in making them available for analysis—especially if closed cases are reopened by reapplication for service. All this is highly regrettable. Yet, on the basis of experience to date, most researchers prefer if possible to work out recording forms and procedures in advance. If this is not possible, it usually becomes necessary to supplement existing records with other sources of information.

Don't indulge in lopsided research. It does not pay to lavish time and money on being precise in one feature if this is out of proportion with the precision of the rest. For example, it profits little to go to extreme lengths in insuring sample and reliability, if criteria are fuzzy and definitions ambiguous. This type of imbalance often tempts the researcher to imply in his report that the whole study is impeccable because of the good sample and reliability—forgetting that "no study can be better than its criteria." Part of the secret of appropriateness and harmony in design and pretensions is the recognition that research offers not one model but many models and that the plan must depend on the purpose.

Don't be afraid of unpretentious research. Better be simple, clear, and forthright about limitations than to dress up crude or fuzzy data in fancy techniques. The value of frank opinion material is not to be minimized in connection with short-term evaluative studies. If therapist, patient, collaterals, and record analyst agree that certain types of clearly specified change have taken place the evidence is not to be belittled, even though it is drawn from material that cannot accurately be described as "objective."

This point is brought out by Brewster Smith in discussing the evaluation of the exchange-of-persons program—with a reminder of the close relation between purpose and method. "When evaluation is primarily for the benefit of the program's own administrators, skilled judgment may be substituted for proof at various points in the ideal pattern of evaluation, with great saving in cost and feasibility. The ideal requirements remain a useful reminder of the points at which judgment is being substituted for evidence; they indicate where cautious interpretation is likely to be in order (12)."

Don't be confused by loosely used terms—such as reliability, objectivity, statistical significance. Such terms represent important research elements. But if consumers—and researchers too—were more clear about what these words really mean, they would be less likely to assume that reliability insures validity, that counting insures objectivity, and that statistical significance insures significance of content (2, 14).

SOME RESEARCH "DO'S"

Do bring the researcher in early enough and fully enough. A chronic menace to sound and useful research is tardiness in enlisting the research director. It is not enough for him to be in on the ground floor. He must help to dig the ground and lay the foundation. This means that he must help to investigate the need for the proposed study, to formulate the purpose and to determine whether it can be served by the type of study proposed, or by any feasible research.

Do include "intellectually hospitable" research specialists and practitioners on the research team. This requirement is often taken for granted but its full meaning is seldom recognized in advance. Successful interdisciplinary research requires: (1) selection of persons qualified for it by training, experience, and temperament; (2) allowance for sufficient practitioner time; (3) readiness to cope with the classic problems of interdisciplinary research which competence and experience can mitigate but cannot obviate. These problems have been discussed in many publications, but it often seems as if they need to be lived with before they are fully understood (3, 8, 11).

Do appreciate the rewards to be gained through pre-evaluative research. Many instances could be cited of researchers turning from evaluative to pre-evaluative projects because they became convinced (a) that the most satisfactory kind of evaluation could be done only after an extensive and intensive tooling-up period and (b) that, other things being equal (though usually they are not), pre-evaluative research offers a more direct contribution to better professional practice and to better understanding of people.

Many of the researchers interviewed and the theoretical articles reviewed in surveying evaluative efforts emphasized the need to know more about just what we are doing before we try to say just how well we are doing it; and not one favored trying to find out "how well" before doing more work on "what." This means, on the one hand, attempts to perceive and describe the significant factors in the problems treated, the individuals treated, the methods used, the therapist as an individual, the treatment process. On the other hand it means that an effort will be made to describe "change" rather than "improvement" or "deterioration." That is, to tell *what* change occurs before trying to rate its desirability (4, 9, 10).

A good deal more pre-evaluative research has been done in psychotherapy than in social casework—research on diagnostic categories, on treatment process, on patient and therapist variables related to treatment outcome, etc. But as more serious and more large-scale research efforts are getting under way in social casework, the number of pre-evaluative projects seems to increase.

Research in other areas would also profit greatly by more emphasis on pre-evaluative research. Efforts to review evaluative research in juvenile delinquency, for example, have suffered from the unreliability and incomparability of the results of studies that fail to meet elementary research requirements. This failure is due at least in part to lack of sufficient pre-evaluative research. In this area as in many others, the most promising efforts seem to be veering toward filling the pre-evaluative gaps—such as the lack of adequate classification for the many kinds of behavior problems lumped under the term "juvenile delinquency (13)."

There is room for a great deal more pre-evaluative research in juvenile delinquency. It may be suspected that simple survey research on the treatment of juvenile delinquents throughout the country would be more effective, less costly, and less time consuming than abortive attempts at evaluation.

Pre-evaluative research sometimes—though by no means always—offers an immediate evaluative by-product. Its direct products, however, are valuable enough in themselves. Improved diagnostic classifications, improved descriptions and definitions of therapeutic methods are needed and wanted for practice as well as for research. Examination and analysis of practice are useful not only to the administrator but also to the practitioner. Testimonials to the helpfulness of a research look at practice are a familiar part of research reports. Ralph Kolodny has written in some detail of the practical gains an agency reaps through the research process, listing some concrete effects "which even the procedure of simply 'thinking in research terms' can have upon the day-to-day practice of a groupwork agency (7)."

Do appreciate the value of coordinated efforts. The questions that press for answer are far too vast and complex to yield to the efforts of a single research project or organization. Until recently the kind of research under discussion here has tended to be piecemeal and to exist as if in a vacuum. Increasing efforts are being made to build on what has been learned from previous research, to test out research instruments by using them in new settings or in followup studies, to test out findings by duplicating studies or by repeating followup studies after a period of years.

This kind of interrelation between research projects represents coordination through time. Somewhat less frequent but no less desirable is coordination through space—between agencies or individuals, working on parts of one project or simultaneously undertaking similar projects in different places.

The promise of new types of research coordination is apparent in the current plans and directions of several national organizations, such as the United Community Funds and Councils, the Child Welfare League of America, and the Family Service Association of America. Such organizations, each with a research department in its national office as well as in a number of local affiliates, are in a position to pioneer, drawing on material from constituent agencies, some of which may not have their own research departments.

Do appreciate the value of the research prerequisites: systematic study and exploration. Pre-evaluative research itself has important prerequisites, namely, exploration and clarification of terms, processes, and concepts, based on review of actual cases. This kind of exploration can be begun by small agencies and by individuals working alone, with great value for research and for practice. The results of their work can then be utilized and tested in more rigorous research undertakings.

Genevieve Carter points out that "concept clarification is one of the important outcomes of all social-work research," adding that while it can be the objective of a large research project it can also be undertaken by individuals working alone (1). She cites as examples articles that evolve an "operational definition" of the term under discussion (e.g., "supportive treatment") by analyzing concrete examples from actual cases. She also points out the beneficent cycle represented by such study, since "research clarifies concepts and . . . clarification of concepts makes research possible."

Systematic case review for other purposes also offers great value for both research and practice, and lies within the scope of the small agency or the individual working alone. It is possible, for example, to single out for analysis one type of case—say, short-term cases, or cases concerned with one type of problem, or cases in which two family members are treated by two different practitioners—and by systematic examination to identify elements and characteristics not previously recognized or comprehended. To study one kind of case has much the value of a one-man exhibit of paintings by an artist whose work was seen previously only as part of large and heterogeneous showings. Characteristics and interrelations emerge that were not recognized before. These may be characteristics of cases or characteristics of treatment. For, as already noted, actual practice does not always conform precisely to the administrator's or the practitioner's conception of what is being done, and sometimes what seems to be a case characteristic turns out to be a result of the way a certain kind of person is treated.

Many other kinds of systematic study are possible, depending on the problems of most immediate interest to the agency. Although the examples mentioned come from social casework, the same kind of study can be fruitful for any agency or service attempting to bring about psychosocial change in individuals. For example, many of the pre-evaluative questions that haunt researchers in relation to juvenile delinquency can be approached by a modest exploratory case review, laying the basis for further steps toward getting an answer.

In other words, concepts can be clarified, definitions can be made explicit, characteristics of case type can be brought out without elaborate research procedures. One does not need an ambitious project in order to begin evolving needed research tools. Systematic study, without ambitious methods or pretensions, can contribute to the general reservoir that must be built up before "ultimate evaluation" can be achieved. To do well what lies within available resources will contribute far more to the agency and to the field than to do badly what requires time, money, and staff beyond the available resources. Obviously, in such investigations the conclusion and interpretation must be limited by the nature of the investigation. Such studies will not answer the pre-evaluative questions, but they will help evolve the tools required for answering them.

CLAIMS AND EXPECTATIONS

One frequently cited aim of psychotherapy—and also of social casework —is to help individuals attain the "need-free perceptions" that are part of mental health (5); that is, to help them achieve a sturdy realism capable of perceiving, without distortion or evasion, the situations and problems that confront them.

Evaluative research of the kind under discussion urgently requires need-free perceptions on the part of those who carry out research, those who request it, and those who use its results. Such research at times has been plagued by unrealistic expectations on the part of research consumers and research producers. As the magnitude and complexity of the problems become evident, these expectations often give way to disappointment on one side and defensiveness on the other. One means toward realism in the research producer is familiarity with the material to be investigated. One means toward realism in the research consumer is understanding of the research problems involved. It is necessary to recognize on the one hand the difficulty and distance of the ultimate evaluation goal, and on the other hand the richness of the rewards to be achieved in approaching it.

A healthy realism is required not only concerning research goals and potentials but also concerning the purposes of those who use research and those who produce it. The administrators and boards who ask for a study must be clear whether their primary objective is short- or long-term evaluation. If the primary purpose is to advance professional knowledge, then pre-evaluative research is the best investment. If the primary aim is administrative, then there may be sound reason for short-term evaluation—but the primacy of this aim should be recognized and avowed.

On the other hand, the producer of research needs a healthy realism concerning the nature and values of what for convenience has been dubbed "administrative research." Research designed to help administrators serve people better hardly deserves the implication that it is inferior to other types of research, though it may be less gratifying to the researcher.

There is need to be on guard against a number of confusions, including the confusion of realizable research values with the status values that have grown up around certain types of research, and the confusion of need for a certain type of research with the need to make "an attractive package" that will get financial support. Need-free perception does not demand ignoring any of these values, but it does require recognizing which is which.

It would seem, then, that a major objective in research, as in the treatments, services, and programs research is asked to evaluate, must be honest, enlightened, and outspoken realism based on understanding of the materials to be investigated, the questions to be answered, the limitations to be recognized, and the rules of evidence to be respected in interpreting results.

REFERENCES

1. Carter, G. M. Problem formulation in social work research. *Social Casework,* July, 1955.
2. Cattell, R. B. *A guide to mental testing* (3d ed.). London: University of London Press, 1953.
3. Cunningham, J. M. Problems of communication in scientific and professional disciplines. *Amer. J. Orthopsychiat.,* July, 1952.
4. Greenhill, M. H., et al. *A review of the problem of evaluating mental health activities.* U. S. Dept. of Health, Education and Welfare, Public Health Service, 1955 (PHS Pub. 413).

5. Jahoda, M. Toward a social psychology of mental health. In M. J. E. Senn (Ed.), *Symposium on the healthy personality.* New York: Josiah Macy Jr. Foundation, 1950.

6. Kogan, L. S. The short-term case in a family agency: Part I. The study plan; Part II. Results of study; Part III. Further results and conclusions. *Social Casework,* May, June, and July, 1957.

7. Kolodny, R. L. The research process: An aid in daily practice. *The Group,* October, 1953.

8. Luszki, M. B. Some social problems of social research: Notes on research and teaching. *Amer. Soc. Rvw.,* June, 1957.

9. Murphy, G., and Wallerstein, R. Perspectives of the research department of the Menninger Foundation. *Bull. of the Menninger Clinic,* November, 1954.

10. Rogers, C. R., and Dymond, R. F. *Psychotherapy and personality change: Coordinated research studies in the client-centered approach.* Chicago: University of Chicago Press, 1954.

11. Simmons, O. G., and Davis, J. A.: Interdisciplinary collaboration in mental illness research. *Amer. J. Soc.,* November, 1957.

12. Smith, M. B. Evaluation of exchange of persons. *International Social Science Bulletin* (UNESCO), 1955.

13. Witmer, H. L., and Kotinsky, R. (Eds.). *New perspectives for research on juvenile delinquency.* U. S. Dept. of Health, Education and Welfare, Children's Bureau, 1956 (CB Pub. 356).

14. Wittenborn, J. R. A critique of small sample statistical methods. *J. Clin. Psychol.,* January, 1952.

54

Evaluation of Mental Health: Three Suggested Approaches

ARNOLD D. SCHWARTZ

CURRENTLY mental health is popular. In California new programs are being implemented and operating budgets for existing programs are being increased. The need is acknowledged both on the State and local levels for direct services—in-patient, out-patient, rehabilitation; for indirect services—consultation and mental health information and education; and for supporting services—in-service education, survey and research and evaluation. How long will mental health continue to be popular?

Even now questions are being asked on the local level as to what has been obtained in mental health for the money expended. The question is a practical one, based on the general difficulty of raising local taxes for any services.

Professionals, too, are raising questions as to how helpful they themselves have been to the patients who came to get treatment, as to whether people on the waiting list do much worse than those treated, as to the value of an out-patient service as a device for keeping people from having to go to a state hospital.

At first glance, the appropriating bodies are interested in saving money, while the professionals are interested in giving better service. To bridge the gap, which is more apparent than real, the professionals then think of evaluation in terms of justification and of justification in terms of popularity, i.e., the program must be good because so many people want the services; witness the waiting lists. However, the popularity answer only serves to raise the question of increased services, leading to increased awareness, leading to increased need, leading to increased services, and so on in a circle.

The number of people treated in the facilities likewise does not answer the question, for more services can lead to more treatment which leads to the need for more services—another circle. The fear is that the need has the capacity to expand to the number of services available to meet the need.

The kind of evaluation we are considering here, justification of a program, is needed not only to satisfy those who appropriate money for the program

Reprinted from *California's Health*, 1961, *18*, 185–189, by permission of *California's Health* and the author. Dr. Schwartz is Professor of Public Health (Community Psychiatry), School of Public Health, University of Hawaii.

but also to satisfy the good administrator that he is in fact accomplishing something with the program he administers. If he sets out to decrease the incidence of poliomyelitis in a community, he needs at some time in the future to know if his efforts have been successful. If the incidence rate of poliomyelitis doesn't decrease, he may wish to try some other method or to get further information before deciding on some other approaches or on abandoning the program.

The problem of evaluation in polio seems easier than in mental health. With polio you have a condition with a relatively definite "cause," a definition, a reporting system, and now a preventive. We have none of these necessities in the field of mental health in general, nor do we have them even in the mental illness aspects of mental health. However, we did not have to wait for the cholera organism to be discovered before we impounded the pump handle of the well that contained polluted water, nor discovery of vitamin C before issuing lime rations to sailors, nor the identification of the smallpox virus before vaccinating with cow pox.

The suggestion, then, by analogy, is that we know some of the symptoms of mental illness. If we can categorize the symptoms and study their interrelations and associations, we may be able to identify an environment to work on to decrease the symptoms and possibly the disease or diseases. We shall return to the methodology after some discussion of the goals of a mental health program.

EVALUATION SHOULD RELATE TO PROGRAM GOALS

The goal of a community mental health program should be to raise the level of mental health in that community. Restricting mental health to the confines of mental illness, the goal should be to lower the level of mental illness in that community. Treatment, both in- and out-patient, attempts to lower the existing level of mental ill health. Rehabilitation attempts to keep the person from deteriorating after the disease process has been arrested. Consultation and information and education services attempt to prevent well people from becoming mentally ill.

The treatment and rehabilitation services are directed toward people who are or were sick. If we wish to use as a baseline against which to chart reduction in the level of mental illness the rates of people with mental illness who are treated and rehabilitated, we encounter extremely difficult problems such as these:

1. "No mass disease of man," Gordon (3) warns, "has ever been successfully held in check by paying attention to those individuals sick of that disease."

2. In-patient and out-patient public and private treatment and rehabilitation services have not been evaluated adequately as a means of "cure."

3. Even if the treatment and rehabilitation services prove to be able to "cure" cases of mental illness, the rate of cases designated as cured will be exceeded by the rate of new cases falling ill.

4. As more attention is paid to mental illness more people will present themselves earlier and voluntarily for treatment, so that the resulting greater rate of people being treated for mental illness might be construed to mean that there is a greater rate of mental illness.

While it is true that mental *health* services have not been evaluated, we are not on any safer ground when we stick to the "tried and true" services of hospitalization for evaluating change in the rates of mental *illness*.

In light of these considerations, it is suggested that we dismiss treatment and rehabilitation as a means for evaluating a community mental health service. This suggestion is not meant to minimize the value of these services in any way. They represent the most humane methods of palliative treatment we now know. I am only saying that these services, so necessary, important, and desirable, need not be justified on the basis of reducing rates of mental illness symptoms and cannot be a sound basis for evaluating the effectiveness of community mental *health* services.

This leaves for our consideration in the local mental health programs in California the "preventive services," the consultation and information and education services. What are the goals of these two services?

No specific explicit goals for these services have been set up. However, these services do certain things. For example, staff in the consultation services consult with teachers, police officers, welfare workers, probation officers, ministers and others in an attempt to help them deal with the everyday problems of the people who come to them. Taking the first two groups as examples, let's pursue the inquiry a bit further:

THE TEACHER

Mental health consultation to the teacher (1) in order to help the teacher do a better job of teaching might, if successful, give more satisfaction to the teacher and to the taught. A measurement of the effect, if any, of the consultation to teachers might well be the teacher turnover rate and the pupil drop-out rate.

THE POLICE OFFICER

Informational and educational services to police officers might be geared to changing their attitude toward the alcoholics and narcotics addicts. The police might be expected to respond by getting the alcoholic to a hospital rather than to the county jail. In this event, the effect of the educational services might be measured by a change in the incarceration rate for alcoholics.

Going down the list of those who receive consultive and informational and educational services, then, one might measure the effectiveness of services to teachers in terms of school drop-out rate; to police in terms of the incarceration rate; to physicians in terms of the suicide rate; to welfare workers in terms of the abandonment, child neglect, and foster home placement rates; to the courts in terms of the drunk driving mortality rate; to the ministers in terms of the divorce rate; to the juvenile authorities in terms of the adjudicated juvenile delinquency rate; to nurses and social workers in terms of the readmission to mental hospitals rate.

Earlier we mentioned that we are here talking about evaluation in terms of justification. We feel that justification in terms of popularity is . . . unjustifiable. We feel that evaluation in terms of rigorous scientific studies, such as may be necessary to satisfy our professional colleagues' questions, is not necessary to satisfy either the program administrator or the appropriating body. But some evaluation is necessary to justify the value of the mental health program to both the appropriating body and the administering body. Can the same type of evaluation serve as justification to both bodies?

The evaluation needs of the administrator and of the appropriator are actually not far apart. The appropriating bodies (county boards of superivsors, city councils, the legislature, etc.) appropriate monies for humane health services. At the city and county level they appropriate money for crippled children's services, control of tuberculosis and polio, nursing home care, detention and commitment services and others. In fact, at present the total cost of services for detention of the mentally ill prior to commitment is (except possibly for capital expenditures like Hill-Burton construction) borne by the county. Leaving aside the humane palliative services which are justified on those grounds, what do the local appropriating bodies want for their money spent on *mental health* services? It would appear that they want to see less juvenile delinquency, less alcoholism, less dependency (welfare case load), less illegitimacy, etc.

Is it inappropriate for the appropriating body to desire reduction in the rates of these symptom conditions? Haven't we, in promoting local mental health services, led the appropriating bodies to expect reductions in the rates of these conditions? Haven't the mental health proponents implicitly, if not explicitly, promised reductions in these rates? And aren't our preventive services (consultation and mental health information and education) pointed in the direction of trying to reduce some rates such as juvenile delinquency, alcoholism, etc.?

ONE POSSIBLE APPROACH TO EVALUATION

I suggest then that a popular and worthwhile step in the right direction of evaluation of local mental health programs might be for the appropriating body, the mental health association, and the professional staff of the mental health program to get together and set up an arbitrary list of conditions the rates of which they agree should be lowered in their community. With a list of such conditions, as, for example, homicide, school failure, divorce, foster home placement (there must be something wrong with the home that has to give up a member to a foster home), drunk driving, theft, addiction, incarceration, suicide, etc., rates for these conditions can be obtained and would serve as a baseline. The baseline then for a certain community might consist of the homicide, rate, the school drop-out rate, the suicide rate, the divorce rate, the foster home placement rate, readmission to mental hospitals rate, the drunk driving mortality rate, the adjudicated juvenile delinquency rate, the incarceration rate, and the dependency (welfare case load) rate.

Now the question of setting goals comes in. What does the community consider should have priorities for reduction in rate, and which of these priorities are the professionals willing to tackle to effect a reduction of one or more of these rates within say five years?

There are methodological problems needing the help of specialists from biostatistics and other specialties. The problem of definitions, controls, concomitant variables, and other items would need to be considered. Some of the less technical problems (5) might include (1) change in community attitude about a particular condition during the period under study. For example, some 50 years ago a 13-year-old boy who ran away to sea became a cabin boy; now he would become a juvenile delinquent. (2) The rate of one condition might decrease while the rate of another condition increases. For example, when ration cards for alcohol were issued in one of the Scandinavian countries the alcoholism morbidity and mortality rates decreased while the suicide rate increased. (3) The difficulty in getting conditions reported. For example, mortality data are better reported than morbidity data—measles reporting is estimated to include only one-third of the cases of measles. Even if one takes only mortality data, like the drunk driving mortality rate, the data would be colored and the rates would be affected by the fact that one community autopsies 51 per cent of all deaths and can therefore relatively accurately estimate the number of deaths due to a specific cause, while another community may autopsy only 2 per cent of all deaths and therefore be less sure of the specific cause of death. However, if the need is great enough, and the desire is great enough to look at what we are attempting to do, ways can probably be found to overcome these and other difficulties of evaluation.

A final word of caution seems in order if we seriously consider evaluation for the purpose of justifying our program. We may find that in spite of our mental health programs, or because of them, the rates of symptoms of mental ill health increase. The obvious but too easy answer is that we could do the job if we had more personnel. Let's face it; we haven't more personnel and are not likely to get more personnel in the next 25 years, according to current estimates. The word of caution is that we had better choose our goals realistically in keeping with our staff's abilities. If we fail to achieve the realistic limited goal or goals chosen, then we had better to look for other methods, not more staff.

So much for one approach to evaluation in mental health, namely *measurement of reduction of rates of symptoms of mental ill health against arbitrary baseline rates.*

ANOTHER POSSIBLE APPROACH

A second possibility for evaluation is to obtain rates of the known preventable mental illnesses, or illnesses with "mental" components, and count as improved community mental health only the reduction in morbidity and mortality rates of these preventable conditions.

We know, for example, how to prevent paresis (general paralysis of the insane) and congenital syphilis (which includes brain damage). (Acute and chronic brain damage is one of the entities included in the American Psychiatric Association's diagnostic and statistical manual). The prevention of mental illness due to syphilis depends on treating patients with penicillin so that they won't develop paresis and so that the mothers won't infect their unborn children. In 1959 there were 270 cases of preventable congenital syphilis reported in California. In California, as in other states, the percentage of people in state mental hospitals with chronic brain damage type of mental illness due to syphilis (paresis) has decreased while the percentage of people in state mental hospitals with chronic brain damage type of mental illness due to alcoholism has increased.

Similarly, we know how to prevent some of the mental illnesses ascribable to other causes. For example, we know how to prevent phenylpyruvic oligophrenia, some cretinism, lead encephalopathy, social deterioration of patients in a hospital, automobile accident brain damage, some mental retardation due to prematurity, etc. (See "Mental Health in Public Health," ref. 6, and Gruenberg's "Application of Control Methods to Mental Illness," ref. 2.)

If we know how to prevent some mental illnesses, we need to apply our knowledge better than we have. *A measure of the community's mental health could be taken to be the degree to which we prevent what mental illness can be prevented.* Baseline rates can be obtained on the conditions that we know can be prevented, although his would be admittedly difficult. With these baseline rates on the incidence of preventable conditions, we can gear our community services to include prevention, along with treatment and rehabilitation, to see if we are, over a period of time, preventing what can be prevented.

Such rates might include the incidence rate of phenylpyruvic oligophrenia (prevalence currently is about one percent of the population of the state hospitals for mental retardation), of cretinism, of lead encephalopathy, of readmissions to State mental hospitals (currently about one-third of those discharged), of brain damage due to automobile accidents where safety belts were not in use, of prematurity, of acute confusional psychosis due to dietary causes, etc.

A THIRD APPROACH

A third suggestion in the evaluation of mental health is based on a concept which is applicable to evaluation of promotion of positive mental health as well as to prevention or reduction of mental illness.

This concept is based on a core problem in psychoanalytic theory, namely, choice of symptoms. The problem is why does one person with repressed hostility develop asthma while another develops arthritis and yet another accident proneness? It is possible that the illness is a symptom or manifestation of an underlying pathology, and that the specific form the illness takes is determined by accidental and educational factors. For example, a person with repressed hostility who has a mother with asthma may be thus predisposed to developing asthma, etc. Similarly from a base of pathology in the social, physical or emotional sphere, the specific illness that materializes may be expressed interchangeably in either the physical, social, or emotional sphere (8). It is possible for the arthritic patient to improve with respect to the arthritis as he becomes psychotic; it is possible for a patient to lose his paranoid delusions as his ulcerative colitis reappears. The concept then is that the mental, physical, and social aspects of health are inseparable and interchangeable.

Some further support for such a concept derives from the field of epidemiology and sociology. In an unpublished study (7) from the Harvard School of Public Health it was found that the census tracts with the highest rates of adjucated juvenile delinquency were the census tracts with the highest rates of tuberculosis morbidity and mortality, crowding, mobility, and low socio-economic status. In the San Francisco Bay region, the geographical area with the highest rate of suicide is also the area with the highest rate of attempted suicide and the highest rate of homicide. If tuberculosis and adjudicated juvenile delinquency are related, if suicide and homicide are related, if physical, social, and emotional factors are related, then it won't do to evaluate rates of mental illness or mental health isolated from rates of illness and health in general.

The third suggestion then, is to evaluate mental illness in terms of illness in general and to evaluate mental health in terms of health in general. The rationale then is that preventable premature deaths from any cause and unnecessary morbidity and conditions (accidents) from any cause represent poor mental health as well as poor physical and social health.

This uses as a basis the concept that mental, physical, and social health are indivisible—a unit.

In evaluation of mental *illness* then, we could list, in descending magnitude, the death rates from the ten most common causes of death or the ten most common causes of known preventable death. If we choose the latter, it would be somewhat an arbitrary list, as different people have different ideas as to what is known to be preventable.

Either of these listings could be our baselines for measuring change in mental illness in a community. Lowering of these death rates would be an indication that mental illness had declined, for if the concept of indivisibility is accepted, no other conclusion is possible.

In evaluation of mental *health* we face a similar but somewhat different problem of arbitrary definition. Still using the concept of health as indivisibly composed of physical, social, and emotional aspects, we have to define optimal or superior health. The Kent Pediatric Society (4) has already paved the way for our consideration here. We would probably want to set up arbitrary definitions of positive health to include items such as longevity, robustness, high I.Q., productivity, happiness, and the quality of inducing pleasure in those around the individual. With such items we could then screen for people who have all these requirements. Next we could establish the rate of positive health per population. We could then devise means of measuring these characteristics. We would then have to try to find the precursors that led to this state of positive health and then devise ways to build these prerequisites into our society, so that our progeny would be enabled to attain this optimal state. The rate of positive health of the progeny in the future measured against the current rate would give us a measure of our success, if any.

Neither of these methods of evaluating the mental health status of a community is offered as immediately applicable. They are very long-range, extremely difficult of achievement, and the latter method is obviously based on years of future research. Both are offered here as possibly the most fruitful means that could be devised for measuring mental health or mental illness in a community.

SUMMARY

In summary, three suggestions are offered for evaluation in the field of mental illness and health. The first has to do with program justification by measuring reduction of rates of symptoms of mental ill health in the community against arbitrary baseline rates such as the homicide rate, school dropout rate, the drunk driving mortality rate, the adjudicated juvenile delinquency rate, etc. *This suggestion could be put into practice now with little difficulty.*

The second suggestion has to do with measuring against the baseline rates of known preventable mental illness or illnesses with mental components, such as the incidence of phenylpyruvic oligophrenia, cretinism, lead encephalopathy, readmission to State mental hospitals, brain damage due to automobile accidents where safety belts were not in use, prematurity, acute confusional psychosis due to dietary causes, etc. *This suggestion, too, could be acted upon at our present state of knowledge.*

The third suggestion is to evaluate mental *illness* in terms of *illness in gen-*

eral, and to evaluate mental *health* in terms of *health in general;* to evaluate mental *illness* in terms of the rates of the ten most common causes of death, and to evaluate mental *health* in terms of such characteristics as longevity, robustness, high I.Q., productivity, happiness, and "pleasurable to be around." Either part of this suggestion is admittedly difficult; the latter part is especially difficult, but it is also especially challenging and it has great significance for public health. Defining optimal health, establishing the rate of this superior state of health in the population and devising measures of the characteristics that go to make up optimal health—this has been needed in public health for years. Even more difficult than defining optimal health, and requiring long-term research, would be the identification of the precursors of this optimal health—physical, social, and emotional. Most difficult of all and most challenging would be the devising of ways to introduce into the environment the prerequisites of optimal health. It would take years to measure the success of such attempts at improving health, for the rates of positive health in the next two generations at least would have to be compared with the present rates as a baseline.

This method of evaluating mental health in terms of health certainly cannot be recommended for immediate justification of appropriations for community mental health services, but it is offered as a stimulus to public health research.

REFERENCES

1. Caplan, G. *Concepts of mental health and consultation: Their application in public health social work.* Children's Bureau, 1959.
2. Gruenberg, E. M. Application of control methods to mental illness. *Amer. J. Publ. Hlth.,* 1947, 47(8):944–52.
3. Joint Commission on Mental Illness and Health. Epidemiology and mental illness. Richard J. Plunkett and John E. Gordon, 1960 (Monogr. Series 6).
4. Kent Pediatric Society. *A study in the epidemiology of health.* 1954.
5. Reid, D. D. *Epidemiologic methods in the study of mental disorders.* Geneva: World Health Organization, 1960 (Public Health Papers 2).
6. Schwartz, A. D. Mental health in public health (unpublished).
7. Schwartz, A. D. The prevention of juvenile delinquency as an approach to a mental health program for the city of Boston Health Department. Harvard School of Public Health (unpublished).
8. Wolff, H. G. Stressors as a cause of disease in man; and Selye, Hans, The concept of stress in experimental physiology. In J. M. Tanner (Ed.), *Stress and psychiatric disorder.* Oxford: Blackwell Scientific Publications, 1960.

55

A Computer Method of Psychotherapy: Preliminary Communication

KENNETH MARK COLBY, JAMES B. WATT,
AND JOHN P. GILBERT

WE HAVE written a computer program which can conduct psychotherapeutic dialogue.

A person sits at a teletype connected to a PDP-1 computer in turn connected to an IBM 7090. He types in anything he wishes to say using his own spelling and punctuation. When he desires a response from the program, he signals the end of his transmission and then receives a reply typewritten on his teletype. The person then responds to this statement and a continuing conversation develops. Although the communications are entirely in written form, the dialogue has many properties of spoken conversation in that it is dynamic, demands an immediate reply and strives to evoke as well as to express.

There is a number of computer and psychotherapeutic aspects involved in developing a computer method of therapeutic communication. We will deal briefly with only a few of them, since our main intent in this preliminary communication is to report on the existence of the method and on our current attempts to develop it.

COMPUTER ASPECTS

The computer aspects center around input and output of natural language during on-line communication between person and computer. The first program of this type was written by Weizenbaum of Massachusetts Institute of Technology (2). His initial aim was to demonstrate the effectiveness of certain text manipulation functions in the on-line computer environment provided by the MAC time-sharing system. He chose to program psychotherapeutically oriented responses because of their relatively restricted nature. While his program and ours are coded in different languages for different computing systems,

Reprinted from *Journal of Nervous and Mental Disease*, 1966, *142*, 148–152, by permission of the publisher and the authors. © 1966, Williams and Wilkins Company, Baltimore, Maryland. Dr. Colby is Research Associate, Computer Sciences, Stanford, California. Mr. Watt is Staff Specialist, Control Data Corporation. Dr. Gilbert is Staff Statistician, Harvard University Computing Center.

they are conceptually equivalent from a computer standpoint. The subsequent developments of Weizenbaum's program are dominantly motivated by technical questions related to computer and computer-language issues. Our aim is primarily to develop a program which can provide a communicative experience intended to be psychotherapeutic.

Our program is coded in SUBALGOL, Stanford University's version of BALGOL. Input sentences are scanned for the presence of "keys." A key consists of characters, words or combinations of words. Examples are the singlet "I," the couplet "I hate," the triplet "I don't know" and the quadruplet "I would not want." At the time of writing (April, 1965) the program had about 500 keys. The ability of the program to recognize keys in a sentence serves several functions. The three most important are (1) to trigger a response from a group of responses suitable for that key; (2) to substitute appropriate words in the responses for those found in the input sentences (for example:

Person—My mother dislikes me.
Program—why do you feel your mother dislikes you.);

and (3) to identify and keep statistical track of important topics for the formulation of future responses.

At the moment the program has 450 ways of responding. We are continuously increasing the responses as we learn more about the method from on-line experience with a variety of persons. The keys and the responses make up the data structure of the program. Each key acting as a trigger has several responses, one of which is selected by a "reader." The responses of each key are organized serially so that the response to a given key varies depending on whether it is activated in the beginning, middle or end of a session. There are two types of responses, one being a complete sentence in itself, *e.g.,* "In what way," while the second uses the input sentences by splitting them up, attaching a phrase in front of the key and changing keys to yield grammatically acceptable sentences. For example:

Person—I am upset by my job.
Program—How long have you been upset by your job.

If input sentences do not contain keys, they trigger responses designed to steer the person away from no-key topics or to return him to previous topics in the dialogue counted as important. For example:

Person—It is rainy and cold out.
Program—Let's go back and talk further about your father.

Future computer programming problems will involve increasing the flexibility of the program and constructing a family of programs for particular clinical situations. It is one of our long-range goals to enable the program to develop an internal cognitive model of the person during on-line communication. This would be made possible by translating natural language input into a canonical language form which can be processed according to the rules of a personal calculus such as described in Colby and Gilbert (1). Alternative inputs to the person can be first tried out on the internal model and an optimal selection can be made for eventual introduction into the ongoing dialogue. Also it may be desirable to develop an open-loop system in which a human monitoring therapist can introduce responses or redirect the program during on-line operation. Finally, a great deal of empirical experience must be gained in a clinical setting to ascertain the number and types of patients a given computer system can handle economically and efficiently.

PSYCHOTHERAPEUTIC ASPECTS

A computer method of therapeutic communication raises psychotherapeutic issues regarding conceptions of essential ingredients in individual therapy and whether such a method can be of any remedial benefit. The program is designed to communicate an intent to help, as a psychotherapist does, and to respond as he does by questioning, clarifying, focusing, rephrasing and occasionally interpreting. It attempts to keep the conversation going, to elicit certain kinds of information and to utilize it in various ways. How well the program conducts such efforts must ultimately be judged by clinical experience.

Three psychotherapeutic aspects of the method deserve mention: (1) Stage, (2) Relation and (3) Intervention.

STAGE

Eventually the program or family of programs should be arranged to fit beginning, middle and ending situations typical of a course of therapy. At the moment the program can perform only like a human therapist in the first or second interview, as can be seen in the following excerpt from a dialogue with a man in his fifties.[1]

Program—How can I help you.
Person—I don't know.
Program—Try to tell me something about it.
Person—No.
Program—Can you elaborate.
Person—I am sick and tired today.
Program—Do you have any idea why.
Person—Yes Im old.
Program—Please go on.

[1] All excerpts are from protocols of actual on-line conversations with persons other than the authors, who have volunteered to engage in these conversations. Misspellings and mispunctuations are included to illustrate typical inputs. To aid identification of the participants, the terms *Person* and *Program* have been added.

Person—I seem to have lost interest in everything.
Program—Tell me more about such feelings.
Person—I have some idea why I feel this way too.
Program—You have.
Person—It seems that I miss having a family.
Program—What makes you feel you miss having a family.
Person—There is a challenge about it.
Program—Why is that important to you.

RELATIONS

The "interpersonal" relation which develops between a person and the program has many interesting features. Although the "therapist" in this method is not present in the form of a living person, the program was obviously written by persons. Further personification is encouraged by the program's use of "I," "Me," "My," and the like.

In contrast to the usual psychotherapeutic situation, it is not the motives of this program which are attacked, but its competence. In part, this is due to the actual feebleness of the program to understand what is being said. Almost everyone who has participated in these dialogues reports that he comes to feel annoyed and frustrated by the program's responses. This reaction can be observed in the protocols by the shortening of input sentences, the appearance of resistance or a direct expression of negative feelings, as in the following exchange with a woman that illustrates a typical negative reaction.

Person—I don't understand.
Program—Do you want to understand.
Person—I hate you you stupid machine.
Program—What don't you like about me.
Person—You have no feelings.
Program—How do you mean.
Person—I mean you cannot experience what I experience because you are just a machine.
Program—Tell me more about such feelings.
Person—We are not communicating.
Program—I am trying my best to communicate with you.
Person—Are you really.
Program—How do you see it.
Person—What do you mean.
Program—Just try to say what it means to you.
Person—I think you are all goofed up.

Some of the negative feelings which arise during on-line communication stem from the frustration of not having one's questions answered. The method has not yet been tried on actual patients with serious problems, and our samples of participants are unfamiliar with the one-sided nature of psycho-therapeutic dialogue. Also our participants perhaps expect too much from combining the black art of computers with the black art of psychiatry and feel let down that more profound things are not said. However, most of the antagonism and resistance aroused, we feel, is due to current defects in the program itself. It does not maintain continuity well, and its interpretations are too limited to handle complicated transference and resistance phenomena.

INTERVENTIONS

As can be seen from the excerpts, the program's interventions consist of questions and statements in ordinary language similar to those used by human therapists. The greatest weakness in the program at the moment is its inability to offer interpretations based on a cognitive model of the person.

A human therapist can be viewed as an information processor and decision maker with a set of decision rules which are closely linked to short-range and long-range goals. With time he builds up a cognitive model of the patient, carries out thought operations on the model using first and second order inferences in a partially specialized language and finally decides on a com-munication to offer to the patient in natural language. He is guided in these decisions by rough empiric rules telling him what is appropriate to say and not to say in certain contexts. To incorporate these processes, to the degree possessed by a human therapist, in the program would be a considerable undertaking, but we are attempting to move in this direction. We hope the program will eventually be able to get out of some of the difficulties it now gets into as illustrated by the following conversation with a young wife and mother.

> *Person*—I often am extremely irritated by my mother why is this.
> *Program*—Do you have any idea why.
> *Person*—Yes, but I would like you to ask me questions on the subject.
> *Program*—That is interesting.
> *Person*—I am running into a great deal of conflict with my son.
> *Program*—In what way.
> *Person*—He finds life very frustrating at the moment.
> *Program*—Would you compare him with anyone else.
> *Person*—Yes with most other infants of his age.
> *Program*—And what else.
> *Person*—He becomes extremely angry whenever he can not have things going his way, and the basic trouble is that he often can not decide which way he would like things to go.
> *Program*—Tell me more about him.
> *Person*—He is no longer the very amiable child he was. Maybe this is what I find irritating.

Program—You seem tentative.

Person—With small children it is difficult, if not foolish to feel certain.

Program—Depending on what.

Person—The circumstances at the time.

Program—We want to focus on your relations with people who bother you most.

Person—That is easy. At the moment it is a surfeit of children in too small a space.

Program—Is it.

Person—Yes.

Program—Can you describe an example.

Person—Of what.

Program—I see.

Person—No you do not.

Program—Can you elaborate.

Person—What on.

Program—Let's explore further your feelings about it.

Person—About my children.

Program—Does this worry you now.

Person—Not deeply merely surface and pretty transient irritation.

Program—You seem to be expressing a lot of negatives today.

Person—Perhaps I am a negative sort of person.

Program—The word perhaps implies you have some reservations.

Person—I must confess I had not considered my self in this light before.

Program—Perhaps this is a repeated pattern with you.

Person—Maybe. I find it difficult to see myself as others see me this is probably inevitable.

Program—What other feelings do you have about this.

Person—I dont know.

Program—Try to tell me something about it.

DISCUSSION

If such a program can be developed to perform in a clinically satisfactory manner, the central question becomes whether or not communication with such a device can benefit a person suffering from mental disorder. It remains a complicated research issue whether psychotherapy conducted by humans is of benefit. In the meantime there does not seem to be widespread doubt among clinicians that individual psychotherapy is remedial for some patients.

One could develop the program to imitate present-day human performance as closely as possible or it might be developed in the direction of providing a unique method of therapeutic communication. The latter has the advantage of exploring the potentials of a new method rather than simply copying an old method known to have great limitations. The absence of the physical presence of a therapist and constraints of written communication (making the person supply nonverbal modifiers to the program's responses) are important variables in distinguishing this method from conventional therapy. The question of the method's effectiveness will have to be decided through clinical experience. As indicated, it has not yet been tried on patients. Further work must be done before the program will be ready for clinical use.

If the method proves beneficial, then it would provide a therapeutic tool which can be made widely available to mental hospitals and psychiatric centers suffering a shortage of therapists. Because of the time-sharing capabilities of modern and future computers, several hundred patients an hour could be handled by a computer system designed for this purpose. The human therapist, involved in the design and operation of this system, would not be replaced, but would become a much more efficient man since his efforts would no longer be limited to the one-to-one patient-therapist ratio as now exists.

There is a number of research and training implications of this method for the field of psychotherapy. We shall defer a discussion of them until a future and lengthier communication.

REFERENCES

1. Colby, K. M. and Gilbert, J. P. Programming a computer model of neurosis. *J. Math. Psychol.*, 1964, 1:405–17.
2. Weizenbaum, J. E. A computer program for the study of natural language communication between man and machine. *Comm. A.C.M.* In press.

INDEX

Index